gwriter

ong

D.

E.

c
her

Record
Producer

Record
Company

Record
Company

Ind.
Producer

Publisher

Publisher

Artist

Artist

Artist

Artist

Record
Company

Record
Company

RT 1

1986 Songwriter's Market

1986 SONG WRITER'S MARKET®

WHERE TO SELL YOUR SONGS

Edited by Rand Ruggeberg

Writer's Digest Books

Cincinnati, Ohio

Distributed in Canada by Prentice-Hall of Canada Ltd., 1870 Birchmount Road, Scarborough, Ontario M1P 2J7, and in Australia and New Zealand by Bookwise (Aust.) Pty. Ltd., Box 296, Welland, S.A. 5007 Australia.

Managing Editor, Market Books Department: Constance J. Achabal.

International Standard Serial Number 0161-5971
International Standard Book Number 0-89879-201-0

Contents

Services & Opportunities

Appendix

Glossary

Late Arrivals

Index

Some very important notes:

- Although every listing in *Songwriter's Market* is updated, verified or researched prior to publication, some changes are bound to occur between now and the time you contact any listing.
- Listings are based on editorial interviews and questionnaires. They are *not* advertisements, *nor* are markets reported here necessarily endorsed by the editor.
- Looking for a particular market? Check the Index. If you don't find it there, it is because 1) It's not interested in receiving material at this time. 2) It's no longer in business or has merged with another company. 3) It charges (counter to our criteria for inclusion) for services a songwriter should receive free. 4) It has failed to verify or update its listing annually. 5) It has requested that it not be listed. 6) We have received reports from songwriters about unresolved problems they've had with the company.
- A word of warning. Don't pay to have your song published and/or recorded, or to have your lyrics—or a poem—set to music. Read "The Rip Offs" and "Contracts" (both located in the Appendix to this book) to learn how to recognize and protect yourself from the songshark.
- *Songwriter's Market* reserves the right to exclude any listing which does not meet its requirements.

The Profession

Introduction

Life is full of options. From deciding what clothes to wear in the morning to choosing a career path, we're all presented with a myriad of choices every day of our lives. No matter what the endeavor, often how well we make those choices determines whether or not we succeed.

Songwriting is like that too. Choosing the appropriate lyrics, style, tempo, rhythm, or key can often determine the magnitude of creative success you achieve.

For the songwriter who sees his craft as a vocation rather than a hobby, making the right choices in marketing your music is just as critical. Whether you approach the business through traditional channels such as music publishers, record companies or record producers; or non-traditional ones like advertising agencies, audiovisual firms, managers and booking agents, or musical theatre, the place to start is here, the 1986 *Songwriter's Market*.

Inside this year's edition you'll find 2,000 listings covering those seven crucial markets. In addition, this year's edition includes a greatly expanded number of listings from the international marketplace, an important, but often ignored, option that could enable you to make that first "sale" or help you make the most out of your already proven material. To help you get started, Starborn Records President Brian Ross explains some of the ins and outs of international deal making in his article "Exploring the International Music Marketplace."

To help you explore your creative options, gold record lyricist and author of *The Craft of Lyric Writing* Sheila Davis shows you how to make your lyrics more meaningful and memorable in "Finding Your Lyrical Voice Through Characters." Helping you mold your creative work into salable form is George Williams, author of *The Songwriter's Demo Manual and Success Guide*, with his step-by-step article on the intricacies of demo production entitled "Great Demos: The Secret to Songwriting Success."

Also in this edition, Songwriters Guild Projects Director Bob Leone helps you repel the "songshark" by enlightening you on some of the dark mysteries of contracts in "Answers to Your Contract Questions." Also included in this section are sample publishing and international sub-publishing contracts to aid you in making the correct legal choices *before* you sign on the dotted line.

Rounding out this year's edition are a dozen Close-up interviews wherein recording stars such as Richard Carpenter, Bobby Bare and other music industry professionals tell you what paths to success they chose and why.

Whatever path to songwriting success you decide to follow make sure you take along a trusted friend, the 1986 *Songwriter's Market*. However, as with any trusted friend, *Songwriter's Market* can only point out the options, *you* must make the choices.

—*Rand Ruggeberg*

Using Your Songwriter's Market_____

To most effectively use *Songwriter's Market*, read the section introductions *first*. Each gives a brief overview of the market area and can help you decide if it's a field of songwriting you'd be interested in working with. Any special information and phraseology found within the listings will also be mentioned.

Then, *study* the listings, keeping these facts in mind:

- The information you are reading came directly from representatives of the companies listed. It is reported exactly as they gave it to us.
- All correspondence and submissions should be addressed to the contact person named in the listing.
- All mail should contain a stamped, self-addressed envelope (SASE); submissions to listings in foreign countries should include a self-addressed envelope (SAE) and International Reply Coupons (IRC) available at most major post offices.
- "Does not accept unsolicited material" means you should never submit anything before you query *and* receive permission to submit.
- "Query" means to contact the company by phone or mail *before* submitting anything.
- The types of music, the number of songs you may include in the submission, and the way you should submit your songs are stated in each listing. Failure to follow these instructions could result in your submission being refused or returned. Your close attention to the exact specifications of a particular listing will help assure your success.
- Some markets may indicate in their listing that you may send a videocassette copy of you or your group in performance for evaluation in lieu of a standard cassette or reel-to-reel demo. Pay particular attention to the format (Beta or VHS) required. If no format is stated it is generally safe to assume that either format is acceptable, but it is always a good idea to check with market listed *first*. Always be sure to include a lyric and/or lead sheet with your video submission as you would with any other.
- It's always a good idea to write (or call) first for appropriate video format and television system before sending a videocassette as part of an international submission. Be aware that many foreign countries utilize a different television system than does the United States. For example, a Beta or VHS format tape recorded using the US system (called NTSC) will not playback on a standard English VCR (using the PAL system) even if the recorder formats are identical. It is possible to transfer a video demo from one system to another but the expense in both time and money may outweigh its usefulness as opposed to a standard audio demo. Systems for some countries include: NTSC—United States, Canada, and Japan; PAL—United Kingdom (including England); Australia; and West Germany; and SECAM—France.
- The year the company was established will be given only for companies established in 1984 and after. The risk is sometimes greater when dealing with new companies. So far as we know, all are reputable but some are unable to compete with larger, older companies. Many do survive, however, and become very successful. And most all new companies are wide open to material from new songwriters.
- An asterisk appears before the names of companies new to this edition.
- Figures given (e.g., number of songs published, released or produced per year or number of new songwriters published per year) are approximations to

help you determine a market's activity and its openness to material from new songwriters.

• The length of time markets say that they need to report back to songwriters on submissions is approximate. Publishers especially, go through periods of unbelievably heavy loads of submissions. Allow extra time for international submissions, especially if sent via "surface" mail. If a market doesn't respond within several weeks after the reporting time given in its listing, don't despair. As long as your submission is in the possession of a market there is a chance he or she may eventually find the time to review it a second, or even a third time. Every listening your demo gets represents one more chance for it to be picked up. That opportunity ends when your demo is sent back to you. Not receiving your submission back right away doesn't necessarily mean you've been ripped off. If after a reasonable length of time you still haven't received word on your submission, follow up with a *friendly* letter giving detailed information about your submission. Include your name, address and phone number; titles of songs submitted; type of demo submitted; and the date of submission.

• The Glossary in the back of this book will explain unfamiliar terms you might encounter while reading the listing.

Finding Your Lyrical Voice Through Characters

BY SHEILA DAVIS

From turn-of-the-century hits like "Sweet Rosie O'Grady," "Since Maggie Dooley Learned the Hooley Hooley," and "Bill Bailey, Won't You Please Come Home," to such contemporary successes as "Mrs. Robinson," "Me and Bobby Magee," and "Billie Jean" it seems safe to say that there's never been a time in the history of American popular music in which a song featuring a name in the title hasn't been high on the charts.

Creating "name" lyric titles and story songs with named characters affords a unique means to express ideas in fresh and memorable ways. The aforementioned songs leave lasting impressions because the lyrics particularize, rather than generalize.

In my lyric writing classes at the Songwriters Guild in New York, I have found it productive to give advanced students—those already well grounded in *The Basics*—the kinds of assignments that make them seek the particular by creating characters.

These assignments cover the total spectrum of "name songs": real people—past or present; fictional characters from novels/poetry/film/paintings/comic strips; and invented characters.

The first group includes such songs as "Abraham, Martin and John," Dick Holler's tribute to Lincoln, King and Kennedy; "Vincent," Don McLean's ode to Van Gogh; and Rick Springfield's recent hit "Bruce" in which the writer/performer amusingly bemoaned the trials of his being confused in fans' minds with superstar Bruce Springsteen.

"Mona Lisa" and "Snoopy's Christmas" illustrate the fictional category.

The third and most widely used type of *name song*—the one into which all the examples in my opening fall—is the *invented* character. In addition to the "Sweet Sue" kind of name title, this group includes two subtypes: the labeling of a readily recognizable group, such as "California Girls," "Valley Girls" and "Private Dancer"; and the characterized personality as in "Small Fry," "Hard Hearted Hannah," and "Desperado."

Using some student assignments as examples, let's look at the various ways you can employ imaginary characters and see how the choice of viewpoint and time frame influence the lyric's impact on its audience.

The effect a lyric creates depends to a large degree on whether its action is happening right now (present tense) or is reflecting on a former event (past tense); whether it is *thought* or is *spoken*; and if it addresses a single person, a particular group, or the world at large.

A song can be set in the first, second, or third person; and in the present or in the past—either immediate or remote. Although writers generally make such choices instinctively, there is no question that the more knowledgable you are about the treatment options, the more successful your lyric will be. And successful songs, after all, result from making the right choices.

---

*Lyricist/composer/consultant **Sheila Davis** is author of The Craft of Lyric Writing published by Writer's Digest Books. Davis is currently conducting a series of lyric writing mini-courses around the country which synthesize the theories outlined in her well known course held at the Songwriters Guild headquarters in New York City.*

The First-Person Viewpoint

Writing a lyric in which the singer identifies himself by some qualifying characteristic ("[I'm] Just a Gigolo") seems to be the least favored character—song treatment. I can offer no clearcut reason for the fact that it's seldom used other than to suggest that the first-person voice requires a singer to assume a specific (and possibly unflattering) identity, and is thus potentially a risky way to design a lyric.

When, however, the first-person song resonates with a universal emotion, it can be very effective. For example, in "Good Time Charlie's Got the Blues" (Danny O'Keefe) the singer bemoans the fact that his friends are all moving to LA, and at thirty-three, his life lacks focus—that feeling of uncertainty about the future is common to all of us.

The 1985 hit, "(I'm a) Material Girl," (P. Brown/R. Rang) is an unusual first person song: Not so long ago, a lyric that put the singer in the position of claiming she wanted only monied men would have been considered unrecordable because of making the artist unsympathetic. You may recall that as recently as 1980, Sheena Easton avoided the role of a selfish and unfeeling woman when she sang "(She's a) Modern Girl," rather than "(I'm a) Modern Girl." That we find the expressed values of "Material Girl" acceptable reflects our rapidly changing times: the robotized backup singers chanting "material world . . . material world . . . material world" implies the performer is simply a victim of decadent society, and her materialism is justified.

The Second-Person Viewpoint

Second-person character-songs have three variations.
1. *Singular—where one singee is addressed*:
A character-song set in the second-person singular almost always reflects a personal relationship between the singer and singee.

The singee may be either addressed obliquely in an interior monologue such as "Other Lady" (Gore/Weston) in which a married woman imagines what she would say to her husband's lover, or directly in a conversation as in Gilbert O'Sullivan's "Claire," where the writer-performer assumes the role of a baby-sitting uncle asking his 3-year old niece to behave. In fact, in many second-person singular songs the singer entreats the singee to do (or not to do) something, as in "Young Girl—you better run, girl" (Jerry Fuller) and "Ruby, Don't Take Your Love to Town" (Mel Tillis). In "Desperado" (Glenn Frey/Don Henley) Linda Ronstadt pleads with a singee, who's been out riding fences, to "come down from your fences before it's too late." It's not uncommon for the singer to even berate the singee as in "(You ain't nothin' but a) Hound Dog" (Jerry Leiber/Mike Stoller), "Big Shot" (Billy Joel), and "Gloria" (Umberto Tozzi/Trevor Veitch).

Second-person singular name songs involve the audience by placing it in the position of eavesdropping on a conversation between two people who are emotionally intimate. The following two lyrics by students illustrate the way in which different treatment devices—an interior monologue and the letter device—create a different psychic distance between the audience and the song. The lyrics are presented in ascending order of impact.

The first is the interior monologue in which the singer addresses the singee in her mind. Despite the fact that the verses appear to be written in third person, the overall effect of the lyric is that of second person.

LONG, GONE WILLIE

He was rodeo cowboy with gray in his hair,
Didn't know where he was headin' and didn't really care.
When he came in the diner I knew from the start
That man would be stealin' a piece of my heart.

LONG, GONE WILLIE, oh where have you gone?
Are you still headin' west? Are you still runnin' strong?
LONG, GONE WILLIE, the one love for me,
Who had to go trav'lin', who had to be free.

He said he'd only been plannin' to stay for the night
But he ran into trouble and ended in a fight
So I poured up some coffee and gave him a smile
And he soon began talkin' 'bout stayin' a while.

LONG, GONE WILLIE, Oh, where have you gone?
Are you still headin' West? Are you still runnin' strong?
LONG, GONE WILLIE, the one love for me,
Who had to go trav'lin, who had to be free.

Tho' he was not one for dancin' or sweet talkin' stuff,
And scratching for a living had made him kinda rough,
That man was more tender and had more love to give
Than any I'll know for as long as I love.

LONG, GONE WILLIE, oh, where have you gone?
Are you still headin' West? Are you still running' strong?
LONG, GONE WILLIE, the one love for me,
Why'd you have to trav'lin'—why'd you have to be free?

© 1985 Words and music by Barry Downes
  Used with permission

Through its subtle sound repetitions of consonance (long/gone) and alliteration (long/Willie) the title is made memorable; the compound adjective *long gone* also compounds that longing the singer expresses in the chorus. Yet, a lyric that reflects upon a past event lacks the immediacy generated by one in which the singer is communicating directly with the singee—even if it's by mail.

The second lyric employs the letter technique, and brings us a little closer to the singer's emotional state—even though the singee is still absent:

DEAR RUDY CROCKETT

DEAR RUDY CROCKETT
Remember me?
We were an item
In 1963
At Camp Rikocki
Near Lake Shangri-la
I played girls' hockey
You played twelve-string guitar.

Yes, RUDY CROCKETT
It's me, Charlene
I saw your picture
In *People Magazine*
They loved your record
You're almost a star
I'm playin' house now
You're still playin' guitar

I know it was ages and ages ago
Since we sat in the woods in the rain
You sang me a song you wrote special for me
"Sweet Charlene" still goes around in my brain.

Remember Jeffrey—
Did magic tricks?
We got married
In 1966.
We have two daughters.
He owns a bar.
I'm playin' grownup.
You kept playin' guitar.

    I know it was only a summer romance
    But the only one I can't forget.
    Remember the night we escaped from the dance
    And made out in the head counselor's yellow Corvette?

So RUDY CROCKETT
If you're in town
Here's my number
If you care to write it down
I always knew
That you'd go far.
I'll play your records
You keep playin' guitar.

Sincerely,
    Sweet Charlene.

© 1985 Francesca Blumenthal
    Used with permission

With its early-on Rikocki/hockey rhyme, the lyricist announces a light-hearted song. Yet the lyric is touching as well as amusing because it portrays a suburban housewife comparing her drab life to the glamorous existence she supposes her one-night-stand camp lover now leads. We unquestionably feel more involved here than in the first lyric due to the fact that the singer is in the act of addressing the singee *now*.

The most involving second-person lyric is one that positions the singer and singee in a face-to-face conversation as in Laura Branigan's 1982 hit "Gloria." Nothing beats intimacy for creating emotional impact.

2) Second-person singular—where the singee is sung about:

Less immediate, but equally memorable, are those lyrics in which a particular individual is being sung *about*, rather than sung to. Such songs, addressed either to the world in general or to one person in particular, often take the form of a warning about a "dangerous" singee: "Don't Bring Lulu—she's the kind of smartie that breaks up every party" (Rose/Brown); "Witchy Woman, (she's been sleepin' in the devil's bed)" (Leadon/Henley); "(She's got) Bette Davis Eyes" (DeShannon/Weiss); "(She's a) Maneater" (Hall & Oates). The listener's identification with such songs is usually the "aha" recognition of a clearly defined archetype.

3) Second-person plural in which a group is addressed:

A song constructed to make the singer address a designated group is frequently the result of a lyricist's desire to take a political or moral stand. In "Bad Girls," for example, Donna Summer shook her finger at hookers; since prostitution is still illegal everywhere but Nevada, "Bad Girls" works. But more often than not, lyrics that exude a judgmental attitude, toward either an individual or a group, fail. Nonperforming lyricists must bear in mind a governing principle of songwriting: A song should be designed in such a manner as to make it recordable by a large number of artists who would want to express its central idea as if it were their own.

Songs that take to the pulpit—putting the singer in the "I'm ok, you're not ok" position—are rarities. It's worth noting that "Mr. Businessman," a quasi-judgmental hit of the sixties was recorded by its writer, Ray Parker, Jr. As an illustration of this genre, here's the first draft of a student's lyric that overstates itself out of the running.

BOSS LADY
She goes to work in a high-fashion suit,
She packs a lunch of Granola and fruit,
She grabs a cab and she spends the commute
Looking chic
Reading *Business Week*.
Assistants nod as she walks down the hall,
She hardly looks at their faces at all.
Can't stop to chat with the 9-to-5 crew
She's got much too much to do.

BOSS LADY—BOSS LADY
Got everything under control.
She uses her brain
But she can't explain
The terrible pain in the soul.
BOSS LADY—BOSS LADY
She's hitting the corporate heights
But after each long day she goes home alone
To face even longer nights.

She works a ten- or twelve-hour day,
She tells herself that there's no other way
To get the perks and the pension and pay
That's she got—
But her nerves are shot.
She had a man but she left him behind.
No time for love in the workaday grind.
She wouldn't let anything interfere
With her blossoming career.

[REPEAT CHORUS]

She wanted success
Wouldn't settle for anything less
Success is nice but you pay a price:
They call it loneliness.

[REPEAT CHORUS]

©1984 Marc Miller
  Used with permission

"Boss Lady" has put the audience in the uncomfortable position of making harsh judgments about female executives. The fine second draft excises (most of) the ire, softens the conclusions and puts the lyrics in the (almost) recordable category.

BOSS LADY
(revision)

She goes to work in a high-fashion suit,
She packs a lunch of granola and fruit,
She grabs a cab and she spends the commute
Looking chic
Reading *Business Week*.
Assistants nod as she walks down the hall,
She hardly looks at their faces at all,
Can't stop to chat with the 9-5 crew
She's got much too much to do.

BOSS LADY
How is the view from the 40th floor?
Now that you've got an executive suite
Do you feel complete?
BOSS LADY, BOSS LADY,
Now that you've made it on Madison Ave
Do you ever think about
Things you may never have?

She's written up in career-advice books,
She shops at Bloomie's and Bendel's and Brooks,
Thanks to Elizabeth Arden, she looks
Simply great
But she's cold on a date.
She had a guy but she left him behind
No time for love in the workaday grind,
She wouldn't let anything interfere
With her blossoming career.

BOSS LADY, BOSS LADY
How is the view from the 40th floor?
Now that you've got an executive suite
Do you feel complete?
BOSS LADY, BOSS LADY,
Now that you've made it on Madison Ave
Do you ever think about
Things you may never have?

© 1985 Marc Miller
  Used with permission

    The angry tone of the first draft was moderated considerably by eliminating such biased conclusions as "She goes home alone to face even longer nights" and the melodramatic "She can't explain the terrible pain in her soul." It's also worth pointing out that in the rewrite the lyricist chose to switch from a consistently third-person voice to an alternation between third person in the verses and second person in the chorus (also true of "Long, Gone Willie"). This lyric answers a question I'm often asked: "Can viewpoints within one song be mixed?" The answer is obviously: yes, if it works. And it works when the shift doesn't call attention to itself, but seems natural.

The Third-Person Viewpoint

Third-person songs are generally the choice of sociologically oriented lyricists who, using either a closeup or a long-distance lens, present cameos of individuals or mini-documentaries that comment on the human condition.

In the cameo category we could include: The Doors' profile of a plastic woman in "Twentieth Century Fox"; "Mr. Bojangles," Jerry Jeff Walker's memorable portrait of a dancer; and John Prine's powerful protest song "Sam Stone," about a Vietman veteran who died, not in action, but years later in *reaction* to a drug habit acquired during hospitalization for a battle wound.

The singer of the third-person *name* song usually has no personal relationship to the singee but acts as a kind of Charles Kuralt offering a particular view of the way we live. "Eleanor Rigby," the Beatles' memorable documentary on loneliness, may be the quintessential example of the camera technique—panning from a wedding scene outside the church, to Father Mackenzie's rectory room, to a graveyard. Another more recent instance is John Cougar Mellencamp's number one record—the self-penned "Jack and Diane"—a searing indictment of a society in which teenagers fear the responsibilities of adulthood.

In the following lyric a student, by creating two rather *generic* characters, is able to make a provocative comment on the difficulty of maintaining relationships:

SUE AND JOHN
SUE AND JOHN are busy moving
To a cute and cozy nest
The peeling walls could use improving
And the view is not the best
But she'll sew a flowered curtain,
Have a baby, and John's certain
Sue will be the perfect wife—
There's nothing like the married life.

SUE AND JOHN are busy moving
To a nice suburban home.
His office hours need improving—
They've so little time alone.
But with three young mouths to feed
She doesn't dare bring up her needs;
She tries to be the perfect wife.
There's nothing like the married life.

SUE AND JOHN are busy moving,
Neither one will say quite where.
She says her mind could use improving
He tells her that he doesn't care
With the kids off at college
Sue will go in search of knowledge;
John will seek the perfect wife.
There's nothing like the married life.

© 1985 Marilyn Munder
   Used with permission

"Sue and John" illustrates how content and form are inseparable: The repeated title line and closing ironic refrain framing each verse, and the additional motifs *need improving*, and *perfect wife* solidify the AAA structure while making the passage of time easy to grasp. The standard bland names, Sue and John, help to illustrate the point that this script is being repeated all over the country—only the writer didn't state it, she *showed* it, and let the listener draw the inference.

Unquestionably, the ability to create characters comes more naturally to some lyricists than to others. It is, however, a skill that can be developed, and one well worth acquiring. What it takes is practice. The first step is to begin analyzing both current hits and standards from the standpoint of plot devices. And as you listen, learn to discriminate between the interior monologue and dialogue, and between second person and third person.

The next step is to plan a self-improvement agenda. You could start by designing a one-month program of four character-song assignments chosen from the various categories illustrated above. In each instance identify the singer or singee with either a given name ("Sue and John") or a characterizing label ("Boss Lady"). Here are some possibilities.

1) Write a first-person singular lyric characterizing the singer in a manner that makes him or her likeable.
2) Write a second-person singular using the device of a letter.
3) Write a second-person plural lyric addressed to a readily recognizable group.
4) Using the singer as a commentator on society, create a character(s) through whom to express a particular personal observation about society.

After you've completed the invented character category, challenge yourself to write lyrics using real people and then characters from fiction. Concepts for self-assignments are virtually limitless.

By developing the self-assignment habit you'll not only keep writer's block at bay, but as a bonus, you'll discover a great deal about yourself. W.H. Auden's often quoted question applies as much to lyricists as to poets: "How can I know what I think till I see what I say?"

It is perhaps paradoxical that a songwriter may find his truest voice and express his most personal view of the world by designing a lyric that speaks to, through, or about an invented character.

Exploring the International Music Marketplace

BY BRIAN ROSS

Ten billion dollars! That figure, and more, represents how much the record and music industry earns each year. Songwriters, musicians, singers, producers, record labels, managers, agents, attorneys, recording studios, engineers and talent promoters all make their living with money earned in one form or another in the music industry.

Think about this for a moment, forty million people purchased a copy of Michael Jackson's *Thriller.* The retail list price of an album today is $8.98 and $8.98 times 40 million is roughly 360 million dollars. Imagine having written just one song for that album. Your mechanical income combined with your performance income from radio and television as well as income from sheet music sales could amount to a very substantial figure.

Realistically, not everyone sells 40 million units of an album, but with some strong, well developed international contacts, some marketing expertise and some luck almost any songwriter can increase his or her share of the financial "pie."

International Opportunities

We have already established that the international record and music industry is a ten billion dollar per year business, but what is the American market share as compared to the rest of the world's? The American market accounts for four billion dollars or a 40% share of the worldwide record and tape industry, by far the largest such market in the world. But just because America is the largest single market, we must not overlook the remaining 60%. It is divided among such strong and diverse markets as Japan, United Kingdom, France, Italy, Germany, Australia and Holland, to name a few, and represents a burgeoning, relatively untapped opportunity to increase the songwriter's income.

Consider this, if you sell one million albums in the US ($8,980,000), but have no sales outside the US, you have ignored a potential of increased revenues amounting to approximately thirteen and a half million dollars! This situation offers talented songwriters, singers and acts some very unusual and possibly very lucrative opportunities that are too often overlooked. Remember, songs are needed by artists all over the world, not just here in the US. If you have a publisher in a foreign country plugging one or several of your songs, you might very well earn thousands of dollars in royalties even though your song may never be recorded and released in the US.

Getting Prepared

When submitting a song or group of songs either here or internationally, be sure to conform with the following:

1. Be creative. If you are submitting a number of songs, design your own envelope with your name or the name of your company. This can be done very inexpensively at a local print shop. Label the cassette as well as the envelope. I would like to

---

Brian Ross *is president of Starborn Records which specializes in the representation of music in overseas markets. He has also founded The International Music Commission, a computer based service organization created to promote the exchange of music between the US and other countries around the world.*

have a dime for every tape that was separated from its original envelope with no name on it. This kind of situation represents a lost opportunity for the songwriter.

2. Always include a SASE (self-addressed stamped envelope) with your mailing if you want your tape back. If everybody reading this book sends me just one tape, I could receive as many as 20,000 mailings in a year. Save your potential publisher as much time as possible in reviewing your song material, don't make him sit down, address an envelope or lick a stamp. Submissions to foreign countries should include a self-addressed envelope (SAE) and International Reply Coupons (IRC) available at most major post offices.

3. Make your demo package easy to open. Never use a staple gun on your envelope. There is nothing worse than a package sealed across the opening with about ten or more staples. Many publishers won't even try to open such submissions.

4. Try to *cast* the song if you are submitting to a music publisher. In your cover letter, mention that you think you have a great song for Madonna, David Bowie, Rod Stewart, Michael Jackson, or whomever. Give the person listening to your tape an idea of who you think might be right for the song. That publisher might just have a connection with the producer of that particular artist(s), or know how to get a tape to that individual. If you have no particular artist in mind, state that fact too.

5. Make sure you mention what you are seeking. Do you want a publisher? Have you published your own song and are offering it to an artist? Are you a singer/songwriter looking for both an artist contract as well as a songwriter contract?

6. Make certain to display your notice of copyright (©1986 by *You*) on your tape and lead or lryic sheet. Today there is general paranoia in the music industry regarding the evaluation of unsolicited and/or uncopyrighted submissions. Because of the Bee Gee's litigation and other infringement cases, many A&R executives at record labels and music publishers will not listen to a song unless you display this notice of copyright clearly on your tape and lead or lyric sheet. Do not confuse registering your song for copyright with publishing your own song. Anybody may file a claim to copyright with the Library of Congress in Washington D.C. by filling out a simple form and accompanying this form with a check for ten dollars. You may later *assign* your copyright to a music publisher, but you will be protected in the meantime. There is no substitute for a formal copyright granted by the Library of Congress. Your songs are your annuities and can earn an income for you for the rest of your life—protect them.

Earning Income with Your Songs in the International Market

It is important to know that there is an annual meeting that takes place in Cannes, France, called MIDEM. Here over 7,500 top industry executives representing over 1,700 record and music companies from over 50 countries gather for five days for no purpose other than to strike deals and exchange product. In a sense, this event could be likened to a giant musical "swap meet" where representatives like myself bring songs we have published, or are administering for others, to pitch to other music publishers and record companies from all over the world.

In a massive convention center called the Palais de Congress, there are representatives manning exhibit booths or just roaming the convention floor continually making appointments, playing and listening to each other's tapes and generally exchanging product. This is where the real action is, for with every exchange of product there is a monetary advance for the songwriter or artist. Each advance represents a payment to secure the rights to a particular song on an exclusive basis for a given territory. Advances can range anywhere from $100 for a newly copyrighted song to $100,000 for a group of copyrights for a period of time ranging from three to five years to the life of the copyright.

It doesn't take a mental giant to realize that if somebody thinks enough of your song material to provide you with an advance, that party has a good reason to *work*

The author on the floor of the Palais de Congress exploring the many exhibits from music companies around the world.

Visiting one of the South American booths at MIDEM.

your song(s) very hard. They of course want to recoup that advance, and more, and the only way they can do that is by obtaining activity on your copyright. Only after you and the other party have come to a mutually acceptable agreement on an advance and you assign them your copyright can the promotion needed to get activity on your copyright begin.

Once you have reached such an agreement your foreign representative will present your song to artists, publishers, record companies or producers in the areas or countries where they have secured the rights to represent it. Hopefully your representative can then obtain a cover record or records in English and perhaps, after securing a translation into the applicable language, obtain additional cover records. Once your representative secures such activity on your song, the agreed upon advance—often recoupable against any expenses incurred to promote your song—will be paid to you.

An important adage to remember when negotiating agreements pertaining to your copyright is that "everything is negotiable." At the same time it is always important to be fair and equitable in your requests so that the people interested in your material do not lose interest in representing it. Deal making is an art and for this reason many successful songwriters assign their music to competent publishers or administrators to look out for their interests while they concentrate on being creative.

There are some real benefits to working with a fulltime publisher who has offices and staff in foreign countries to promote your material overseas. If you sign with such a publisher you may only have to deal one time for representation covering the entire world for a given song. A disadvantage to this method is that while some publishers have very strong ties in some countries, I have yet to find one that is universally strong in ALL countries. It is very possible that if you put forth the time and effort to make agreements on a country-by-country basis you could receive far more in aggregate advances than by signing one worldwide representation agreement.

Sub-Publishing

Sub-publishers are professional music publishers located outside the songwriter's home country, whose principal business is the representation of foreign copyrighted works (your songs) in their home country and/or any other countries for which you have given them permission to do so. Sub-publishers will often pay advances to use your song(s) on an exclusive basis in their territory or country. For every publisher here in the US, there is another publisher in a foreign country ready to promote your songs and earn you extra income.

If any of your songs have been, or are about to be published in the US, chances are very good that your publisher already has a working relationship with one or more sub-publishers. That doesn't necessarily mean he is going to send your demo to each one, or for that matter, any at all, but you can at least explore that possibility during your negotiations with him. It is even possible to make your deal contingent on the fact that he "shops" your songs in an agreed upon number of foreign countries and gives you prompt feedback on the results. Some publishers might be willing to give you a list of their sub-publishers abroad and let you contact them yourself or send a demo of your song for their consideration.

Recognizing the Potential

Everybody wants to expand his horizons and open up more income producing opportunities for his music. It only makes sense to market your music in every country possible. Knowing the potential of the international marketplace and how to approach it effectively are the keys to making the best of ALL the opportunities open to you.

Editor's Note: See the author's sub-publishing agreement in the appendix of this book.

The Markets

Music Publishers _____

It is the music publisher who plays the central role in guiding a song from its simple beginning (perhaps as a random melody only in a songwriter's head) through its recording and, hopefully, its appearance on the trade music charts. Music publishers, the largest single market for songwriters, are the music industry's prime source of new music for an increasingly hit-hungry, music-loving public. In a very real sense the publisher is the vital link between creative expression and the hard business realities that make up today's music industry.

The publisher's music industry know-how and network of contacts within the industry make a new songwriter's association with him especially invaluable. He knows which artists, record companies, producers and other publishers are currently looking for new material; what styles of music they most likely need; and how best to approach them. When he's not out pitching new material, he's trying to get cover records for the previously published material in his catalog.

The other side of the publisher's dual role in the music business is just that, *business*. They enable the writer to concentrate on the creative aspects without the distractions inherent in business matters like contract negotiation, copyright or collection of royalties. Music publishers handle all these functions that must be expertly taken care of if the songwriter is to be creatively and financially successful.

In addition, the publisher also serves as the songwriter's confidant, critic and friend. Through his encouragement and direction new songwriters often find that one critical but elusive element that makes an ordinary tune a hit record.

In today's music market many publishers believe that element is originality. One needs only to look at any music trade chart to see that the record buying public demands, and usually gets, a fresh supply of new music on a regular basis. Within the past year previously unknown names such as Madonna, Huey Lewis, Prince, and Cyndi Lauper have become household words. Originality fuels the music business and keeps it moving forward.

In addition to originality the publisher also looks for cross-over potential in a song. Cross-over potential is an element of universal appeal in a piece of music that gives a publisher enough confidence in the material to approach other less obvious or traditional markets with the hopes of broadening the song's appeal and increasing its revenue-generating potential.

Even if a song has both originality and cross-over potential, its future will be limited at best if it is not presented in a professional manner. When presenting a demo to a publisher always keep in mind that you are, in effect, applying for a job, and that your presentation, whether by mail or in person, speaks for the kind of songwriter and business partner you're likely to be. A properly designed and executed demo submission is far more likely to catch a publisher's attention than a sloppy one. (See the article on ''Great Demos: The Secret to Songwriting Success,'' by George Williams in the appendix.)

Before contacting a publisher read his listing carefully. What type of music does he publish most often, what songs has he placed and what artists have recorded

them? Keep in mind that many times the smaller or newer publishers are more receptive to new songs and songwriters. Often the larger, more established publishers, though usually willing to listen to your music, may not have the time or inclina-
tion to help you develop your song into a viable contender. They usually prefer more
established writers who know exactly what kind of music is needed and how to best
present it.

When researching new markets for the music they represent, music publishers
look not only to markets in their own countries, but to the international music marketplace as well. One needs only to consider the world-wide success of groups like
The Beatles and ABBA to realize the potential value of pitching material in foreign
countries. And because the international market has contributed to the popularity
and profitability of more songs and artists than ever, we have increased the number
of listings from important music markets such as Canada, England, Australia, Germany and Japan. Each listee has expressed a willingness to work with songwriters
from other countries; some already have. Others indicate that they have not yet, but
would be willing to listen to material from foreign songwriters. (See "Exploring the
International Music Marketplace," by Brian Ross in the front of this book)

To keep abreast of important events in the music business, both here and
abroad, check *Billboard* and *Cash Box*. The charts in both these publications are invaluable in helping you monitor the activity of songs, artists and publishers both
here and in many foreign countries.

*ABBOTSFORD MUSIC CO., 1221 Hunter Rd., Wilmette IL 60091. President: J. Fay. ASCAP. Mu-
sic publisher. Publishes 4 songs/year; publishes 2 new songwriters/year. Affiliated publishing firm:
Bedford Falls Music Co.
How to Contact: Prefers cassette with 1-10 songs and lyric sheet. "Studio recordings are fine. Home recordings on cheap cassettes are OK too. Just keep the vocals up front." SASE. Reports in 2-3 weeks.
Music: Mostly top 40/pop, rock and folk; also ballads, dance-oriented and country.
Tips: "For our protection, please enclose a signed and dated letter with your submissions stating 'I am
enclosing (title of song #1, title of song #2, etc.) but no other music,' I'm sorry, but all submissions
without this enclosure will not be listened to and will promptly be returned."

ACOUSTIC MUSIC, INC., Box 1546, Nashville TN 37202. (615)242-9198. Affiliates: Lawday Music Corp. (BMI), Daydan Music Corp. (ASCAP), and Allmusic Inc. (ASCAP). Administrator: Nancy
Dunne. Music publisher. BMI. Publishes 35-50 songs/year. Pays standard royalties.
How to Contact: Call or write first. Prefers cassette with 2-3 songs. SASE. Reports in 1 month.
Music: Country, folk, MOR and gospel. Recently published "Come to Me" (by Gene Price), recorded
by Aretha Franklin; "Ready to Take My Chances" (by Dewayne Orender and Helen Cornelius), record-
ed by Oak Ridge Boys/MCA Records; and "Woman, Sensuous Woman," recorded by Ray Charles/
CBS Records.

ACE ADAMS MUSIC/ADAM PUERTAS MUSIC, 100-19 Alcott Pl., Bronx NY 10475. (212)379-
2593. A&R Department: Adam Puertas. Music publisher and record producer (Ra-Jo International).
ASCAP, BMI. Member NMPA. Publishes 50 songs/year; publishes 10 new songwriters/year. Pays stan-
dard royalty.
How to Contact: Call first and obtain permission to submit. Prefers cassette. SASE.
Music: Pop and blues.

ALEXIS, Box 532, Malibu CA 90265. (213)858-7282. Affiliates: Marvelle (BMI), Lou-Lee (BMI)
and D.R. Music (ASCAP). President: Lee Magid. Music publisher, record company, and record and
video producer. ASCAP. Member AIMP. Publishes 40 songs/year; publishes 5 new songwriters/year.
Pays standard royalty.
How to Contact: Prefers cassette with 1-3 songs and lyric sheet. "Try to make demo as clear as possible—guitar or piano should be sufficient. A full rhythm and vocal demo is always better." SASE. Reports in 1 month.
Music: Bluegrass, blues, church/religious, country, dance-oriented, folk, gospel, jazz, Spanish and
R&B. Recently published "Jesus Is Just Alright" (by Art Reynolds), recorded by Doobie Brothers on
WB Records (rock gospel); "Something About the South" (by Al Abajian), recorded by Becky Bishop
on CMI Records (rhythm rock); and "Don't You Know" (by Bobby Worth), recorded by Della Reese
and Jerry Vale.

AL-KRIS MUSIC, 4322 Mahoning Ave., Youngstown OH 44515. (216)793-7295. Professional Manager: Richard Hahn. Music publisher, record company and record producer. BMI. Publishes 8 songs/year; publishes 4 new songwriters/year. Pays standard royalty.
How to Contact: Prefers cassette with 3-5 songs and lyric sheet. SASE. Reports in 3 weeks.
Music: Children's, country, folk, gospel, MOR and top 40/pop. Recently published "Prom Night" (by Don Yalleck), recorded by the B-Minors on Ikon Records; "Teach Me Lovely Lady" (by Hahn); and "Help Me I'm Falling" (by Hahn), recorded by Kirsti Manna on Genuine Records.

ALPHA-ROBINSON MUSIC, 19176 Mitchell, Detroit MI 48234. (313)893-9370. President: Juanita Robinson. Music publisher. ASCAP. Publishes 100 songs/year; publishes 10 new songwriters/year. Works with composers and teams collaborators. Pays standard royalty.
How to Contact: Prefers cassette or videocassette with 2-4 songs and lyric sheet. SASE. Reports in 1 month; "longer if we're out of town."
Music: Mostly top 40/pop and R&B; also MOR. Recently published "Can't Get You Off My Mind," and "Back to Back," recorded by Renee on Ninja; and "Until the Feelin Is Light," recorded by Eric and Alpha on Ninja (R&B single).
Tips: Needs "songs that are complete enough to make you want to dance."

ALTERNATIVE DIRECTION MUSIC PUBLISHERS, Box 3278, Station D, Ottawa, Ontario K1P 6H8 Canada. (613)820-6066. President and Director of Publishing: David Stein. Music publisher. PROCAN. Publishes 7-10 songs/year; publishes 1-3 new songwriters/year. Pays standard royalty.
How to Contact: Prefers cassette or Beta videocassette with 2-4 songs. SASE if sent from within Canada; American songwriters send SAE and $1 for postage and handling. Reports in 6 weeks.
Music: Uptempo rock, uptempo R&B, and ballads (rock, R&B and pop). Recently published "Big Kiss" (by David Ray), recorded by Cindy Valentine/CBS Records (rock).
Tips: "Before sending out your songs ask yourself whether your hooks and lyrics are as strong as what you hear on the radio. If they are not, go back and rewrite or rework the song. Also make certain the song has a contemporary feel and sound."

AMALGAMATED TULIP CORP., 117 W. Rockland Rd., Box 615, Libertyville IL 60048. (312)362-4060. President: Perry Johnson. Music publisher, record company and record producer. BMI. Publishes 12 songs/year; publishes 5 new songwriters/year. Pays standard royalty.
How to Contact: Write about your interest. Prefers cassette with 3-5 songs and lyric sheet. SASE. Prefers studio produced demos. Reports in 1 month.
Music: Mostly rock, top 40 pop and country; also MOR, blues, and easy listening progressive. Recently published "This Feels Like Love to Me," (by Charles Sermay) recorded by Sacha Diskel (pop); "Stop Wastin' Time," (by Tom Gallagher), recorded by Orjan (country); and "In the Middle of the Night," recorded by Oh Boy (pop).
Tips: "We're aggressive and work a song."

AMERICUS MUSIC, Box 314, Hendersonville TN 37075. (615)824-8308. Affiliate: Stars and Stripes Music (BMI). President: D.L. Riis. Music publisher. ASCAP. Publishes 15-20 songs/year; publishes 4 new songwriters/year. Pays standard royalty.
How to Contact: Prefers cassette with 1-5 songs. SASE. Reports in 3 weeks.
Music: Mostly country; also bluegrass, easy listening, gospel, R&B and top 40/pop.

*****AMSE PUBLISHING**, 5415 N. Sheridan, Chicago IL 60640. (312)878-7121. President: Sylvester Ames, Jr. ASCAP. Music publisher and record producer (A/S Productions). Publishes 32 + songs/year. Pays standard royalty.
How to Contact: Prefers cassette. SASE. Reports in 4 weeks.
Music: Mostly contemporary gospel.

*****ANDRADE PUBLISHING COMPANY**, Drawer 520, Stafford TX 77477. Manager: Daniel Andrade. Music publisher. BMI. Member NSAI. Publishes 24 new songwriters/year. Pays standard royalty.
How to Contact: Write first and obtain permission to submit. Prefers cassette with 2-5 songs and lead sheet. "Include return postage." SASE. Reports in 2 months.
Music: Church/religious, country and top 40/pop. Recently published "Cheaters Never Win" (by Daniel Andrade), recorded by Daniel Andrade on New England Records (top 40/pop, country); "Hank Williams Is Singing Again," recorded by "Hank the Drifter" on Cattle Records (country); "A Lonely Stranger," recorded by "Hank the Drifter" on RCA Records (country); and "Hank Williams Ghost," recorded by "Hank the Drifter" on New England Records (country).

*ANGELSONG PUBLISHING CO., 2714 Westwood Dr., Nashville TN 37402. (615)297-2246. President: Mabel Birdsong. BMI, ASCAP. Music publisher and record company. Publishes 2 songs/year; publishes 2 new songwriters/year. Affiliated publishing firm: Birdsong Records.
How to Contact: Prefers cassette with maximum 4 songs and lyric sheet. Does not return unsolicited material. Reports in 2 weeks, "if requested."
Music: Mostly gospel, country and MOR; also pop. Recently published *Easier*, (by Pam Tillis/Jan Buskingham), recorded by Sandy Croft on Angelsong (country).

*ANODE MUSIC, Box 11967, Houston TX 77016. (713)694-2971. President: Freddie Kober. Secretary/Treasurer: Clauda Kober. BMI, ASCAP. Music publisher, record company (Freko Records/Honeybee Records) and record producer (Freddie Kober Productions/Honeybee Recording Studio). Publishes 10-15 songs/year; publishes 5-8 new songwriters/year. Pays standard royalty. Affiliated publishing firm: Clauda B. Music (ASCAP).
How to Contact: Prefers cassette with 2-3 songs and lyric sheet. SASE. Reports in 2 weeks.
Music: Mostly blues, rock and country. Recently published "I Feel You, I Feel Me," (by Freddie Kober and Clauda Kober) and "Life Can Be Beautiful," (by F. Kober), recorded by Rue Davis on Freko (R&B); and "Things Are Going to Get Better," written and recorded by R. Davis on Freko (R&B).

*ANOTHER EAR MUSIC, #V-4, 380 Harding Pl., Nashville TN 37211. (615)834-2682. General Manager: T.J. Kirby. BMI, ASCAP. Music publisher, record company (T.J. Records) and record producer (T.J. Productions). Publishes 6 songs/year; publishes 4 new songwriters/year. Pays standard royalty. Affiliated publishing firm: Pepermint Rainbow Music/ASCAP.
How to Contact: Write or call first to arrange personal interview. Prefers cassette, 7½ ips reel-to-reel or VHS videocassette with 3 songs and lyric sheet. Reports in 2 weeks.
Music: Mostly country/pop, gospel and R&B; also rock and "concept songs." Recently published "You Always Look Me Up on Your Way Down," (by Jesse Turnbow); "Back on My Own Two Feet Again," (by John O. Love); and "Who'll Help Me Get Over You," (by Ray Sanders and Maryanne Ketts) (country).

APPLE-GLASS MUSIC, A division of American Music Company, Box 8604, Madison WI 53708. Professional Manager: Daniel W. Miller. Music publisher and recording studio (Legend). BMI. Publishes 10-25 songs/year. Pays standard royalty.
How to Contact: Prefers "professionally produced" 7½ ips reel-to-reel or cassette with 1-3 songs and lyric sheet. "We suggest songwriter's name, address and song titles be typed on labels affixed to tape reel (or cassette) and box for identification." SASE. Reports in 6 months. "Our contracts do not feature reversion clauses and we do not offer advances on unearned royalties."
Music: Bluegrass, country, polka, gospel and top 40/rock.

APRIL FOOL MUSIC PUBLISHING COMPANY, INC., 7th Floor, 16 E. 41st St., New York NY 10017. (212)822-7769. President: Joe Ferry. Music publisher, record company and record producer. BMI. Publishes 6 songs/year; publishes 3 new songwriters/year. Pays standard royalty. Prefers studio produced demos.
How to Contact: Prefers cassette or VHS videocassette with 2-4 songs and lyric sheet. SASE. "Do not call. We will be in touch with you." Reports in 6-8 weeks.
Music: Mostly dance-oriented and R&B; also jazz-fusion. Recently published "In the Middle of the Room," (by Al Caldwell), recorded by Al Caldwell on SOS; "Love Is Conditional," written and recorded by John Tummolo on SOS; and "Life Still Goes On," (by Warren Michaels), recorded by Tommy Salera on SOS.

ARCADE MUSIC CO., Arzee Recording Co., 3010 N. Front St., Philadelphia PA 19133. (215)426-5682. Affiliates: Valleybrook (ASCAP), Rex Zario Music (BMI) and Seabreeze Music (BMI). President: Rex Zario. Music publisher, booking agency and record company. ASCAP. Publishes 100-150 songs/year. Pays standard royalty.
How to Contact: Prefers 7½ or 15 ips reel-to-reel or cassette with 5-10 songs and lead or lyric sheet. SASE. Reports in 1 month.
Music: Bluegrass, country, easy listening, folk, gospel, rock (fifties style) and top 40/pop. Recently published "Why Do I Cry Over You," (by DeKnight and Keefer), recorded by Bill Haley on Arzee Records (country); "Hand Clap For Jesus," (by Rodney Harris), recorded by Gospel Blenders on Arzee Records (gospel); and "I Couldn't See the Tears," (by Miller and Marcin), recorded by Dee Dee Marcin on Arzee Records (country).

ARISTA MUSIC PUBLISHING GROUP, 8370 Wilshire Blvd., Beverly Hills CA 90211. (213)852-0771. Affiliates: Arista Music, Inc. (ASCAP), Careers Music, Inc. (BMI), and A-Plus Music, Inc. (SE-

SAC). General Professional Manager: Judy Stakee. Music publisher. BMI and ASCAP. Member NM-PA. Hires staff writers. Pays per individual contracts.
How to Contact: Must call before sending tape. Cassette only with 2 songs and "neat" lyric and lead sheets. "SASE imperative." Reports in 1 month, "depending on backlog of submissions."
Music: Rock, R&B and country. Recently published "Heart N' Soul," (by Chapmon-Chinn), recorded by Huey Lewis (rock); "Don't Call It Love," (by Snow/Pitchford), recorded by Dolly Parton (country); and "Rhythm of the Nite," (by D. Wanen), recorded by De Barge (R&B).
Tips: "All material is listened to, so if it's a hit!. . . ."

*ARPELL/PINELLAS MUSIC PUBLISHING**, Box 568, Woodland Hills CA 91365. (818)992-4922. ASCAP, BMI. Music publisher. Pays standard royalty.
How to Contact: Prefers cassette with 3-4 songs and lyric sheet. SASE. Reports in 2 weeks.
Music: Mostly pop, rock and R&B.

ART AUDIO PUBLISHING CO., 9706 Cameron Ave., Detroit MI 48211. (313)893-3406. President: Albert M. Leigh. Professional Manager: Dolores M. Leigh. Music publisher and record producer. BMI. Pays standard royalty.
How to Contact: Prefers cassette with 1-3 songs and lead sheet and lyric sheet. SASE. Reports in 2 weeks.
Music: Disco, easy listening, R&B, soul, rock, country, gospel and top 40/pop. Recently published "The Garden of Eden" and "Biblical History of Moses" (by Willie Ayres), recorded by The Morning Echoes on E-Tone Records (gospel); and "Are You an Angel," recorded by Willie Jennings on Echoic Hi-Fi Records (adult contemporary).
Tips: "Basically we are interested only in a new product with a strong title; a love story expressive of soul, excitement, taste; heavy lead singer delivering emotional sound. All lyrics are up-front, words clearly understandable. Arrange your songs to match a professional recording artist's style and pattern."

*ASTERISK MUSIC**, Box 18F, Chessington, Surrey KT9 1U2, England. (01)397-8957/(01)390-3711. Contact: John Beecher. PRS. Music publisher and record company (Roller Coaster). Pays standard royalty.
How to Contact: Prefers cassette and lyric sheet. SAE and IRC.

ATTIC PUBLISHING GROUP, 624 King St. W., Toronto, Ontario M5V 1M7 Canada. (416)862-0352. Affiliates: Pondwater Music (CAPAC), Abovewater Music (PROCAN) and Downchild Music (CAPAC). President: Al Mair. Professional Manager: Walter Zwol. Music publisher and record company. Publishes 50 songs/year; publishes 15 new songwriters/year. Pays standard royalty.
How to Contact: Call professional manager first about your interest. Prefers cassette with 1-4 songs and lyric sheet. SAE and IRC. Reports in 3 weeks or longer.
Music: Rock and top 40/pop.

ATV MUSIC CORP., 1217 16th Ave. S., Nashville TN 37212. (615)327-2753. Affiliates: Welbeck Music (ASCAP), Venice Music (BMI) and Maclen Music (BMI). General Manager: Gerald E. Teifer. Professional Manager: Barry Sanders. Music publisher. BMI, ASCAP. Member CMA, NARAS and NMPA. Pays standard royalties.
How to Contact: Arrange personal interview *only*; "do not mail tapes." Prefers cassette with 1-3 songs.
Music: Mostly country and pop; also MOR, R&B, rock, soul and gospel. Recently published "Scarlet Fever" (by Dekle), recorded by Kenny Rogers/EMI/Liberty Records; "Touch Me" (by Al Downing), recorded by Tom Jones/Mercury Records; and "Lucille" (by A. Collins and R. Penninan), recorded by Waylon Jennings/RCA Records (all country).
Tips: "Be extremely selective. Submit material with hit single potential. Write strong ideas—be different."

AUDIO MUSIC PUBLISHERS, 449 N. Vista St., Los Angeles CA 90036. (213)658-6417. Contact: Ben Weisman. Music publisher, record company and record producer. ASCAP. Publishes 30 songs/year; publishes 20 new songwriters/year. Pays standard royalty.
How to Contact: Prefers cassette with 3-10 songs and lyric sheet. "We do not return unsolicited material without SASE." Reports in 1 month.
Music: Mostly top 40/pop, R&B and soul; also rock (all types). Recently published "Queen," written and recorded by Hakeem on Parliament (R&B); "Gangbanger," and "Caught Between a Cold Place and a Fire," (by Hakeem), recorded by Princess on Parliament.

*AUTOMATIC MUSIC CO. LTD.**, 5 Avery Row, London W1X 9HA England. (01)493-9744. Director: N.A. Mobbs. PRS, MCPS. Music publisher. Publishes 1 new songwriter/year. Pays negotiable royalty.

How to Contact: Prefers cassette with 4 songs and lyric sheet. SAE and IRC. Reports in 4 weeks. **Music:** Interested in "electric dance music."

AXBAR PRODUCTIONS, Box 12353, San Antonio TX 78212. (512)735-3322. Affiliate: Axbar Productions and Axe Handle Music (ASCAP). Business Manager: Joe Scates. Music publisher, record company, record producer and record distributors. BMI. Member CMA. Publishes 30-40 songs/year; publishes 10 new songwriters/year. Works with composers. Pays standard royalty.
How to Contact: Arrange personal interview. Prefers 7½ ips reel-to-reel or cassette with 1-5 songs and lyric sheet. SASE. Reports as soon as possible, but "we hold the better songs for more detailed study." **Music:** Mostly country, crossover MOR and comedy; also blues, MOR and rock (soft). Recently published "Welcome Fool," (by David Loggins), recorded by Mark Chestnutt on Axbar (country up tempo); "Will You Love Me in the Morning?," written and recorded by Clifton Jansky on Axbar (country ballad); and "Scotty's Blues," (by Clifford Scott), recorded by Jack Wyatt Trio on Prince (jazz single).
Tips: "Polish your material. Don't expect us to rework your lyrics. Bad grammar and poor spelling hurt your chances."

B.C. ENTERPRISES OF MEMPHIS, INC., 726 E. McLemore Ave., Memphis TN 38106. (901)947-2553. Affiliates: Colca Music (BMI), Insight Music (BMI), and Epitome Music (BMI). Administrative Assistant: Nat Engleberg. Music publisher, record company and record producer. BMI. Publishes 10 songs/year; publishes 1 new songwriter/year. Pays standard royalty.
How to Contact: Write first. Prefers cassette with 1-3 songs. SASE. Reports in 1 week.
Music: Blues, black gospel, R&B and soul. Recently published "Elephant Walk," recorded by Don Jenkins; and "Don't Let the Hearse Have to Take You to Church" (by Bob Catron), recorded by the Masonic Spiritualeers.

*BAGATELLE MUSIC PUBLISHING CO., 400 San Jacinto St., Houston TX 77002. (713)225-6654. President: Bryon Benton. BMI. Music publisher, record company and record producer. Publishes 100-200 songs/year, publishes 20 new songwriters/year. Pays standard royalty. Affiliated publishing firm: Floyd Tillman Publishing Co.
How to Contact: Prefers cassette with any number of songs and lyric sheet.
Music: Mostly country, gospel and blues. Recently published "Everyday I Belong to You," written and recorded by Johnny Nelms on Bagatelle (country); "They Took the Stars Out of Heaven," written and recorded by Floyd Tillman on Bagatelle (country); and "Elfie The Christmas Elf," (by Charles Benton), recorded by Marlene and the Cheena Streets Children's Chorus on Bagatelle (country).

BAG LADY MUSIC, Suite 602, 928 Broadway, New York NY 10010. (212)505-7300. Principals: Libby Bush, Ted Lehrman, Alan Zwirn. Music publisher. Works with songwriters on standard contract.
How to Contact: *"Not interested* in album cuts." Prefers cassette with maximum 3 songs and lyric sheets. SASE. Reports in 4 weeks.
Music: Rock ("no heavy metal"), soul/pop, dance and MOR. Recently released "Video! TV-Oh," by Scarlett/Coast-to-Coast Records.

BAL & BAL MUSIC PUBLISHING CO., Box 369, LaCanada CA 91011. (213)952-1242. President: Adrian Bal. Music publisher, record company and record producer. ASCAP. Member AGAC and AIMP. Publishes 2-4 songs/year; publishes 2 new songwriters/year. Pays royalty per AGAC contract.
How to Contact: Prefers cassette with 3 songs and lyric sheet. SASE. Reports in 1 month.
Music: Mostly MOR; also blues, church/religious, country, easy listening, jazz, R&B, rock, soul and top 40/pop. Recently published "Los Angeles" (by Rich Martin), recorded by Bob Ryer/Bal Records (MOR); and "Song of the Pasadena Rose Parade" (by Jack Heinderich), recorded by B. Ryer/Bal Records (swing).
Tips: "Songs should be commercial; purchased by 9- to 18-year-old group."

BANJO MAN MUSIC, INC./SARATOGA TRUNK MUSIC, INC., 3122 Sale St., Dallas TX 75219. (214)522-8900. Vice President Promotion: Ralph Witsell. Music publisher and record company. BMI, ASCAP. Member CMA, TMA. Pays standard royalty.
How to Contact: Prefers cassette with 1-2 songs and lyric sheet. SASE. Reports in 3 weeks.
Music: Strictly country.

BEARSONGS, 190 Monument Rd., Birmingham, B16 8UV, England. 44-021-454-7020. Managing Director: Jim Simpson. Music publisher and record company. MCPS, PRS. Publishes 25 songs/year; publishes 15-20 new songwriters/year.

How to Contact: Prefers reel-to-reel or cassette. SAE and IRC. Reports in 2-3 weeks.
Music: Blues, jazz and soul.

BEAU-JIM MUSIC, INC., Box 84, Hermitage TN 37076. (615)889-3139. Affiliate: Beau-Di Music Inc. President: Buddy Hooper. Music publisher, record company, record producer and management firm. BMI, ASCAP. Member CMA, NSAI, NMA, AGAC. Publishes 10 songs/year; publishes 2 new songwriters/year.
How to Contact: Prefers cassette or videocassete with 3-5 songs and lyric sheet. SASE. Reports in 3 weeks.
Music: Country. Recently published "My Woman," written and recorded by Jimmy Kaye on MCA (country); "Life," written and recorded by Barry Kaye on MCA (country); and "You Do Me," (by Buddy Hooper), recorded by B. Kaye on Beau-Jim (country).

BEAUTIFUL DAY MUSIC, % Omnipop Enterprises, Suite 225, 223 Jericho Turnpike, Mineola NY 11501. (516)248-4019. Branch: 22240 Schoenborn St., Canoga Park CA 91304. (213)883-4865. Contact: Tom Ingegno (New York); Mike Frenchik (California). Music publisher and record producer. BMI. Publishes 10-20 songs/year; publishes 4 new songwriters/year. Pays standard royalty.
How to Contact: Prefers cassette with minimum of 3 songs and lyric sheet. SASE. Reports in 3 weeks.
Music: Rock and top 40/pop. Recently published "Breaking My Heart" (by Ingegno, Monaco and Frenchik); "Tonight" (by Fullerton); and "You Don't Remember Me" (by Ingegno), all recorded by Thrills (all rock).

*BEDFORD FALLS MUSIC CO., 1221 Hunter Rd., Wilmette IL 60091. President: J. Fay. BMI. Music publisher. Estab. 1985. Publishes 4 songs/year; publishes 2 new songwriters/year. Pays standard royalty. Affiliated publishing firm: Abbotsford Music Co.
How to Contact: Prefers cassette with 1-10 songs and lyric sheet. "Studio recordings are fine. Home recordings on cheap cassettes are OK too. Just keep the vocals up front." Reports in 2-3 weeks.
Music: Mostly top 40/pop, rock and folk; also ballads, dance-oriented and country.
Tips: "For our protection, please enclose a signed and dated letter with your submissions stating 'I am enclosing (title of song #1, title of song #2, etc.) but no other music.' I'm sorry, but all submissions without this enclosure will not be listened to and will promptly be returned."

*BEE RAY MUSIC, 7046 Hollywood Blvd., Hollywood CA 90028. (213)462-0502. Contact: Harry Gordon.
How to Contact: Prefers cassette or videocassette. SASE.

BEECHWOOD, 6920 Sunset Blvd., Hollywood CA 90028. (213)469-8371. Affiliates: Screen Gems (BMI) and Col-Gems (ASCAP). President: Fred Willms. Vice President: Jack Rosner. Music publisher. BMI and ASCAP. Member NMPA. Publishes several songs/year. Hires staff writers.
How to Contact: Call first. Prefers cassette and lyric/lead sheet. Refuses unsolicited material. SASE. Reports in 1 month.
Music: MOR, rock and top 40/pop.

*BELIEVE'N PRODUCTIONS, Box 120204, Nashville TN 37212. (615)385-9408. President: Lanny E. Smith. BMI, ASCAP. Music publisher and record producer. Publishes 20 songs/year; publishes 5 new songwriters/year. Pays standard royalty. Affiliated publishing firm: Out of the Heart Music/ASCAP.
How to Contact: Write or call first and obtain permission to submit. Prefers cassette with 3 songs and lyric sheet. SASE. Reports in 3 weeks.
Music: Mostly country, country pop and pop; also R&R and new age. Recently published "Believe in Your Love," (by Lanny Smith), recorded by Christy Lane on LS Records (AC); "Good Morning Love," (by L. Smith), recorded by Jeff Coye (AC); and "Your Love Will Pull Me Thru," written and recorded by L. Smith (AC).

QUINT BENEDETTI MUSIC, Box 2388, Toluca Lake CA 91602. (818)985-8284. Affiliate: Mi-Dav-An-Mark Music (BMI). Contact: Quint Benedetti. Music publisher, record producer and artist manager. Pays standard royalty.
How to Contact: Prefers cassette with 3 songs and lead sheet. Submit Christmas songs no later than July 15. SASE. Reports in 2 months "or sooner."
Music: Christmas songs only. Recently published "Christmas Is for Children," and "Christmas Presents."

BERANDOL MUSIC LTD., 11 Saint Joseph St., Toronto, Ontario, M4Y 1J8 Canada. (416)924-8121. A/R Director: Tony Procewiat. Music publisher, record company, record producer and distributor. BMI. Member CMPA, CIRPA, CRIA. Pays negotiable royalty.
How to Contact: Submit demo tape with 2-5 songs. Reports in 4-6 weeks.
Music: Hip-hop, funk and R&B; also children's, classical, heavy metal and pop.

HAL BERNARD ENTERPRISES, INC., Box 6507, 2181 Victory Pkwy., Cincinnati OH 45206. (513)861-1500. Affiliates: Sunnyslope Music (ASCAP), Bumpershoot Music (BMI), Apple Butter Music (ASCAP), Saiko Music (ASCAP), TYI Music (ASCAP) and Smorgaschord Music (ASCAP). President: Stan Hertzman. Professional Manager: S. Monian. Music publisher, record company and management firm. Pays negotiable royalty.
How to Contact: Prefers cassette with 3 songs and lyric sheet. SASE. Reports in 6 weeks.
Music: Rock, R&B and top 40/pop. Recently published "Twang Bar King" (by Adrian Belew), recorded by Belew/Island Records (progressive); "Fear is Never Boring" (by R. Fetters), recorded by The Raisins/Strugglebaby Records (rock); and "Stupid in Love" (by P. Michael), recorded by The Adults/Strugglebaby Records (rock).
Tips: "Best material should appear first on demo. Cast your demos. If you as the songwriter can't sing it—don't. Get someone who can present your song properly, use a straight rhythm track and keep it as naked as possible. If you think it still needs something else, have a string arranger, etc. help you, but still keep the *voice up* and the *lyrics clear*."

BETH-RIDGE MUSIC PUBLISHING CO., Suite 204, 1508 Harlem, Memphis TN 38114. (901)274-2726. Affiliate: Chartbound Music Ltd. (ASCAP). Professional Manager: Reginald Eskridge. Music publisher, record company, record producer and recording studio. BMI. Publishes 40 songs/year; publishes 4-7 new songwriters/year. Pays standard royalty.
How to Contact: Prefers 15 or 7 1/2 ips reel-to-reel or cassette with 3-5 songs and lyric sheet. SASE. Reports in 1 month.
Music: Mostly R&B, top 40, dance and blues; also soul and gospel. Recently published "Strings of My Heart," (by Adames Govan and Beach), recorded by Eddie Mayberry on Blue Town Records (blues/R&B); "I'm Trying to Make It In," (by Odessa Alexander) on GCS Records (gospel); and "Across the Miles," (by Lee Moss) on GCS Records.
Tips: "Write or call to see what our needs are."

BIG MIKE MUSIC, Big Mike Productions, Suite 2-W, 408 W. 115th St., New York NY 10025. (212)222-8715. Manager: Bill Downs. Music publisher. ASCAP, BMI. Publishes 10 songs/year; publishes 4 new songwriters/year. Pays standard royalty.
How to Contact: . Prefers cassette or videocassette with 2-3 songs on demo and lead sheet. Prefers studio produced demos. "Must have clean lead sheet and good demo with instrumental background. We will not accept tapes with vocal only. Video with a night club setting and the excitement of a live audience would be good." Does not return unsolicited material. Reports in 4 weeks.
Music: Mostly dance/disco and rock/soul; also R&B, rock and soul. Recently published "Check It Out," (by Horace Linsley), recorded by Tim Scarcy (soul); "Rocket Cruiser," recorded by David Lane on RCA-Europe (rock/soul); and "Loneliness Is Driving Me Crazy," (by Horace Linsley), recorded by T. Searcy.
Tips: "Keep trying even after refusals. Most of the time a producer is looking for a song for now without a thought of the future."

*BIL-KAR MUSIC, Box 25066, Nashville TN 37202. (615)269-0593. Assistant Manager: Brenda L. Madden. SESAC, ASCAP, BMI. Music publisher, record company (Mesa Records) and record producer. Publishes 25 songs/year. Pays standard royalty. Affiliated publishing firms: Sparkling Good Music and Sparks Gotta Fly.
How to Contact: Write first and obtain permission to submit. Prefers cassette. SASE.
Music: Mostly country. Recently published "Starlite," (by Karen Taylor-Good and W.E. Taylor), recorded by Taylor-Good on Mesa (country); "Welcome to the World," written and recorded by K. Taylor-Good on Mesa (country); and "Words Are Cheap," (by W.E. Taylor), recorded by K. Taylor-Good on Mesa (country).

BILLETDOUX MUSIC PUBLISHING, Box 11960, Chicago IL 60611. (312)561-0027. Production Manager: Mary Freeman. Music publisher, record company and record producer. BMI. Publishes 10 songs/year; publishes 3 new songwriters/year. Works with lyricists and composers and teams collaborators. Pays standard royalty.

How to Contact: Prefers cassette or videocassette with 3-6 songs and lyric sheet. SASE. Reports in 1 month.
Music: Mostly R&B; also blues, country, gospel, jazz, MOR, rock (pop, country and hard), soul and top 40/pop. Recently published "Crossroads" (by Cliff Rubin), recorded by Randy Terry on Grandville Records (pop/MOR/easy listening); "Made in USA" (by Stutz), recorded by Stutz on Electric Ice Records (rock); and "Journey to Beyond" (by D. Kirk), recorded by Duncan Kirk on GRV Records (crossover rock).

*****BIRCH TREE GROUP, LTD.**, Box 2072, Princeton NJ 08540. (609)683-0090. Contact: Editorial Department. ASCAP, SESAC. Music publisher. Affiliated publishing firms: Summy-Birchard Music, Suzuki Method International.
How to Contact: "We are interested in manuscripts for educational material only." SASE. Reports in 4 weeks.
Music: Mostly educational and school performance.
Tips: "We are interested in Suzuki-related material and early childhood music education."

*****BLACK GOLD RECORD PRODUCTIONS, LTD.**, 73a Glasgow Rd., Blamefield, Glasgow G63 9HY Scotland. (0360)70177/(041)956-4900. A&R Promotions Manager: Alan Morrison. PRS, MCPS. Music publisher and record company (Quicksilver/Quicksilver Country/Rob Roy). Publishes 40 songs/year; publishes 3-4 new songwriters/year. Pays 60% royalty. Affiliated publishing firms: Middle Road Publishing, Ltd., and Black Gold Music.
How to Contact: Prefers cassette with maximum of 4 songs. SAE and IRC.
Music: Mostly commercial pop, current pop and rock; also country, gospel and traditional Scottish/Irish. Recently published "Scotland's Coming Alive Again," (by Rob Smith), recorded by Middle of the Road on Quicksilver (pop); "Let's All Stand Together," written and recorded by Hugh Allan on Old Eagle (pop); and "Italia Mia," written and recorded by Roberto Bernard on Ridolf (ethnic pop).
Tips: "Concentrate on short melodic songs with drive."

BLACK STALLION COUNTRY PUBLISHING, Box 2250, Culver City CA 90230. (213)419-8142. President: Kenn Kingsbury. Music publisher and book publisher (*Who's Who in Country & Western Music*). BMI. Member ACM, CMA, CMF. Publishes 2 songs/year; publishes 1 new songwriter/year. Pays standard royalty.
How to Contact: Prefers 7½ ips reel-to-reel or cassette with 2-4 songs and lyric sheet. SASE. Reports in 1 month.
Music: Bluegrass, country and top 40/pop.
Tips: "Be professional in attitude and presentation. Submit only the material you think is better than anything being played on the radio."

*****BLACKHEART MUSIC**, Box 15856, St. Louis MO 63114. (314)576-1569. Contact: Robert Schoenfeld. Music publisher, record company and record producer. Publishes 20-30 songs/year; publishes 1-2 new songwriters/year. Pays standard royalty.
How to Contact: Prefers cassette with 4-6 songs and lyric sheet. SASE. Reports in 3 weeks.
Music: Mostly reggae, blues and R&B.
Tips: Looking for "gutsy tunes with character and a message."

BLUE ISLAND PUBLISHING, Box 171265, San Diego CA 92117-0975. (619)477-4442. Affiliates: Bob Fleming Music (BMI), Dahlhouse Publishing (ASCAP), and Bob Gilbert Music (BMI). General Manager: Bob Gilbert. Music publisher, record company and record producer. Publishes 50 songs/year. Pays standard royalty.
How to Contact: Prefers cassette with 3-6 songs and lyric sheets. "Submit only your best single-oriented songs to fit top 40 format. Easy to understand songs with strong hooks and good lyrics make it." SASE. Reports in 3 weeks.
Music: Country, MOR, rock, top 40/pop and disco/dance.

BLUE UMBRELLA MUSIC PUBLISHING CO./PARASOL MUSIC PUBLISHING CO., 3011 Beach 40th St., Brooklyn NY 11224. (718)372-6436. Contact: Kadish Millet. Music publisher. ASCAP, BMI. Publishes 10 songs/year; publishes 3 new songwriters/year. Pays standard royalty.
How to Contact: Prefers cassette with 1-10 songs and lead sheet. Prefers studio produced demos. "Wrap cassette well; some cassette boxes have fairly sharp edges and break through envelope. I want a lead sheet (not lyric sheet) and accurate info on who owns the copyright and if it was registered in Washington at the time of submission. Affiliation of writers or non-affiliation needed in order to issue proper contract." SASE "with proper amount of return postage." Reports in 2 weeks.
Music: Country. "I want only country songs with double entendre (sexy, adult type) lyrics such as 'Be-

hind Closed Doors,' 'Almost Persuaded,' 'Here Comes My Weekend Friend,' 'Help Me Make it Through the Night,' 'Sleepin' Single in a Double Bed,' and 'Teach Me to Cheat.' ''

BOGGY DEPOT MUSIC, 10051 Greenleaf, Santa Fe Spring CA 90670. (213)946-3193. President: Overton Lee. Music publisher, record company, record producer and video producer. BMI, ASCAP. Publishes 10 songs/year. Pays standard royalty.
How to Contact: Prefers cassette with 1-3 songs and lyric sheet. Does not return unsolicited material. Reports in 3-4 months.
Music: Mostly country; also bluegrass, blues and gospel. Recently published "It May Be Tonight," recorded by Gene Davis on O.L. Records (country); "Ordinary Hero," recorded by The Bonner Family on O.L. Records (country); and "I Have a Dream," recorded by Darvy Traylor on O.L. Records (gospel).

*BOOGIETUNES MUSIKPRODUKTION GMBH, Grossbeerenstr. 88, 1000 Berlin 61, West Germany. (030)2510601. Managing Director: Timothy E. Green. Music publisher and record company. Publishes 100 songs/year. Pays standard GEMA rate.
How to Contact: Prefers cassette or VHS videocassette. Does not return unsolicited material.
Music: Mostly dance and electronic. Recently published "Hold On," (by Wobker/Sawatzki), recorded by Boytronic on Mercury (dance); and "The Killer," (by Schoppner), recorded by Electric Theatre on Mercury (dance).
Tips: "Write good commercial pop."

BOOTCHUTE MUSIC CO., Box 12025, Memphis TN 38112. (901)458-4496. Affiliate: Fallin' Arches Music (ASCAP). General Manager: Jerry Thompson. Music Publisher. BMI. Publishes 5-10 songs/year; publishes 1 new songwriter/year. Pays standard royalty.
How to Contact: Prefers cassette with 1-4 songs and lyric sheet. SASE. Reports in 1-2 months.
Music: Mostly pop; also bluegrass, blues, classical, country, easy listening, gospel, R&B, rock and soul. Recently published "I Don't Need You" (by R. Christian), recorded by Kenny Rogers/EMI Records (pop/country).

BOP TALK MUSIC, Box 566, Massena NY 13662. (315)769-2448. Affiliate: Tom Tom Publishing Co. Vice President: Thomas Gramuglia. Music publisher and record company. Pays standard royalty.
How to Contact: Prefers 7¹/₂ ips reel with 1-12 songs. SASE. Reports in 1 month.
Music: Jazz and folk.

BO-RICH PUBLISHING CO., Box 1128, College Branch, Madison TN 37116-1128. (615)868-0559. Contact: Bobby Rich. Music publisher and record producer. BMI, ASCAP. Publishes 4 new songwriters/year. Pays standard royalty.
How to Contact: Prefers cassette or videocassette with 4-6 songs and lyric sheet. SASE. Reports in 1 month.
Music: Bluegrass, country, gospel, MOR, rock (hard and country) and top 40/pop. Recently published "Work on It Baby," "Good Times Come Easy," and "Take Another Look" (by Bob Money), all recorded by B. Money (country).

BOSS APPLE TUNES, 1517 W. Lake St., Minneapolis MN 55408. (612)825-0766. President: Charles Campbell. Music publisher and record company. BMI. Publishes 10 songs/year. Pays standard royalty.
How to Contact: Call first. Prefers cassette.
Music: Blues, jazz, R&B, reggae and calypso.

BOSTON'S FINEST MUSIC, 334 Marlborough St., Boston MA 02115. (617)536-5464. Contact: Kevin Dixon, David Wetherell. Music publisher and record company. ASCAP. Publishes 50-80 songs/year; publishes 10 new songwriters/year. Pays standard royalty.
How to Contact: Prefers cassette with 1-4 songs and lyric sheet. Reports in 2 months. "Writers outside Greater Boston area must be previously published to be considered. No tapes returned."
Music: Mostly MOR, pop, rock and R&B; also all other types except choral and church/religious.

TOMMY BOYCE & MELVIN POWERS MUSIC ENTERPRISES, 12015 Sherman Rd., North Hollywood CA 91605. (213)875-1711. President: Melvin Powers. Music publisher and record company. ASCAP.
How to Contact: Prefers cassette with 3 songs and lyric sheet. SASE. Reports in 1 month.
Music: Country and MOR. Recently published "Willie Burgundy" (by Tommy Boyce and Melvin Powers), recorded by Teresa Brewer (MOR); "Mr. Songwriter" (by T. Boyce and M. Powers), recorded

by Sunday Sharpe (country); and "Who Wants a Slightly Used Woman?" (by T. Boyce and M. Powers), recorded by Connie Cato (country).
Tips: "Before you send your songs to a publisher, have a *professional* (musician, singer) listen to them. Get their professional critique. New songwriters waste a lot of time and money which they should be using on courses in song and lyric writing and workshops. Then test your songs against those on the radio. Do they measure up? I'd recommend collaboration as the best source of instant feedback and critique."

BRANCH INTERNATIONAL MUSIC, Box 31819, Dallas TX 75231. (214)750-0720. A&R Director: Mike Anthony. Music publisher. BMI. Publishes 20 songs/year. Pays standard maximum royalty.
How to Contact: Submit demo tape and lead or lyric sheet. Prefers cassette with 1-4 songs on demo. SASE. Reports in 1 month.
Music: C&W and gospel. Recently published "Too Many Ladies" (by David Denman, Kevin Clark and Bart Barton), recorded by D. Denman/Yatahey Records (C&W); and "Hide Me" (by Jess Hudson and Kenny Serrat), recorded by D. Denman/Yatahey Records (uptempo country).

BRANDWOOD MUSIC, INC., Suite 305, 1300 Division St. Nashville TN 37202. (615)292-3593 or 242-2980. President: Ansley R. Fleetwood. Music publisher. BMI. Publishes 30 songs/year; publishes 4 new songwriters/year. Pays standard royalty.
How to Contact: Prefers cassette with 2-5 songs and lyric sheet. "Demo songs with voice and one instrument, preferably not a full band. Use high-quality tape; make sure all lyrics can be understood." SASE. Reports in 6 weeks.
Music: Country, MOR and top 40/pop. Recently published "Just Good Ol' Boys" (by A. Fleetwood), recorded by Moe Bandy and Joe Stampley/Columbia Records (country); "Finding You" (by A. Fleetwood and J. Dickens), recorded by Joe Stampley/Epic Records (top 20 country); and "I've Aged Twenty Years in Five" (by C. Gordon), recorded by George Jones/Epic Records (country).

BRENTWOOD PUBLISHING, Box 1028, Brentwood TN 37027. (615)373-3950. Affiliates: New Spring (ASCAP), Designer (SESAC) and Bridge Building (BMI). Contact: Music Editor. Music publisher and record company. BMI, ASCAP, SESAC. Member CBA and GMA. Publishes 75 songs/year; publishes 15 new songwriters/year. Pays standard royalty.
How to Contact: Prefers cassette with 2-3 songs and lyric sheet. SASE. Reports in 1 month.
Music: Gospel.

BROADMAN PRESS, 127 9th Ave. N., Nashville TN 37234. (615)251-2533. Music Editor: Mark Blankenship. Music publisher. SESAC, ASCAP and BMI. Publishes 200 songs/year.
How to Contact: Prefers reel-to-reel or cassette with 1-10 songs and lead sheet. SASE. Reports in 6 weeks.
Music: Choral, church/religious and gospel. "We publish all forms of sacred music including solo/choral for all ages, and instrumental for handbell, organ, piano, recorder and orchestra."

ALBERT E. BRUMLEY & SONS, Powell MO 65730. (417)435-2225. Affiliate: Hartford Music (SESAC). President: Bob Brumley. Music publisher. SESAC. Publishes 25-50 songs/year; publishes 5-10 new songwriters/year. Pays standard royalties.
How to Contact: Prefers cassette with 3-4 songs and lead sheet. SASE. Reports in 3 weeks.
Music: Choral, church/religious, country and gospel.

BUG MUSIC, 9th Floor, 6777 Hollywood Blvd., Hollywood CA 90028. Contact: Fred Bourgoise. Music publisher. Represents songwriters from anywhere; currently publishes and administers over 400 publishers and artists. "Sometimes" reviews material for acts.
How to Contact: Prefers cassette with 2 songs. SASE. Reports as soon as possible.
Music: All types, including country, easy listening, R&B, rock (all), soul and top 40/pop. Current acts include Blasters, Iggy Pop, Del Shannon, Moon Martin, John Hiatt, T. Bone Burnett, Tom Kelly, Jack Nitzsche, Shoes, Commander Cody, Asleep at the Wheel, Stooges, Richie Cole, Dwight Twilley, Los Lobos, Surf Punks, Nicky Hopkins, Mose Allison, Willie Dixon, Muddy Waters, Dream Syndicate and Romeo Void.

BUSH/LEHRMAN PRODUCTIONS, 928 Broadway, New York NY 10010. (212)505-7300. Professional Managers: Ted Lehrman, Libby Bush. Music publisher and record producer. ASCAP. Publishes 5 songs/year. Pays standard royalty.
How to Contact: Prefers 7¹/₂ ips reel-to-reel, cassette or videocasssette with 2-4 songs and lyric sheet. Reports in 4 weeks. "Please enclose self-addressed stamped envelope."
Music: Mostly MOR, rock, R&B and country/pop; also soul/pop, dance and adult contemporary. Recently published "The Bed's Too Big Without You" (by Ed Chalfin), recorded by Carol Hahn/Nickel

Records (MOR); "Lorelei" (by P. Lieberman), recorded by Peter Lieberman/Laurie Records (rock); and "Video TV-OH!" (by Gent and Woode), recorded by Scarlett/Coast to Coast Records (rock).
Tips: "Send us potential hit singles material only, no album cuts. Strong hooks; positive lyrics; medium and up-tempo songs; clean, listenable demo. Doesn't have to be complicated."

*BUTTON MUSIC, 322 Whitchurch Lane, Edgware, Middlesex HA8 6QX, England. (01)952-3551. Director: Helen Holt. PRS. Music publisher and record company. Publishes 50 songs/year; publishes 5 new songwriters/year. Pays 60% royalty. Affiliated publishing firm: Dingle's Music.
How to Contact: Prefers cassette. Reports in 4-6 weeks.
Music: Mostly folk, pop and novelty; also country, gospel and MOR. Recently published "Sun," (by M. White), recorded by Charm School on Button Records (pop); "Silent Sleep," written and recorded by D. Wins on Button Records (MOR); and "Bluebell Polka," (traditional arrangement by Holt), recorded by Tied Logs on Button Records (folk).

C. A. MUSIC/NEW BRANCH MUSIC, Box 1990, Thousand Oaks CA 91360. (805)499-4306. Director of Publishing: Barb Voorhees. Music publisher. BMI, ASCAP. Member GMA, AIMP, AGM. "We sign 50-75 songs per year. We do have some exclusive writers with monthly advances." Pays standard royalty.
How to Contact: Prefers cassette with 1-3 songs and lyric sheet. SASE. Reports in 1 month.
Music: Mostly MOR, inspirational and worship; also choral, church/religious and gospel. "Country, easy listening, jazz, progressive, R&B, rock, soul and top 40/pop are suitable styles, but they must have Christian lyrics." Recently published "Within His Joy" (by Tim Hosman), recorded by Scott Wesley Brown/Sparrow Records (pop/Christian); " 'Til You Hear the Music" (by Jeff Kennedy/Claire Cloninger), recorded by Joyce Landorf/Word Records (MOR ballad/gospel); and "He Opens a Window" (by Ronna Jordan), recorded by Continental Singers/C.A. Records-Sparrow Records (pop/inspirational).
Tips: "Songwriters must be aware that we are a contemporary Christian publishing company. I don't care what musical style they write in, I look for anything from traditional to new wave, but it must have a Christian lyric, with some real freshness and uniqueness to it."

CACTUS MUSIC AND GIDGET PUBLISHING, 5 Aldom Circle, West Caldwell NJ 07006. (201)226-0035. Contact: Jim Hall or Gidget Starr. Music publisher, record company and record producer. ASCAP. Publishes 10 songs/year; publishes 15 new songwriters. Pays standard royalty.
How to Contact: Write or call first about your interest, or arrange personal interview. Prefers 7½ ips reel-to-reel or cassette with 4 songs minimum and lyric sheet. Does not return unsolicited material. Reports in 1 month.
Music: Mostly country, rock and gospel; also bluegrass, blues, easy listening, R&B and top 40/pop. Recently published "Truck Drivin' Man" (by Clevenger and Hall) and "I Found My Love" (by Sal Franco), recorded by S. Franco/Deadwood Records; "I'm Still in Love With You" (by Rucki-Hall), "Game of Love" (by Starr-Hall), "Why Don't You Write" (by Bailey-Hall), and "You're My Used To Be" (by Bailey-Hall), recorded by Charlie Bailey/Tar Heel Records.

*CALIFORNIA BLUE ROSE, 629 W. Milwaukee St., Jefferson WI 53549. (414)674-5199. Professional Manager: Felix Kubik, Sr. Music publisher. Publishes 3 songs/year; publishes 1 new songwriter/year.
How to Contact: Call first and obtain permission to submit. Prefers cassette. SASE. Reports in 6 weeks.
Music: Mostly country.

CALVARY MUSIC GROUP, INC., 142 8th Ave. N., Nashville TN 37203. (615)244-8800. Affiliates: Songs of Calvary, Music of Calvary and LifeStream Music, Soldier of the Light, Torchbearer Music. President: Dr. Nelson S. Parkerson. Music publisher (ASCAP, BMI, SESAC) and record company. Publishes 30-40 songs/year; publishes 2-3 new songwriters/year. Pays standard royalty.
How to Contact: Prefers cassette with 1 song and lyric sheet. SASE. Reports in 6 weeks.
Music: Church/religious, contemporary Christian, gospel and wedding music.

CAMERICA MUSIC, 489 5th Ave., New York NY 10017. (212)682-8400. Affiliate: Camex Music. Contact: A&R Dept. Music publisher and production firm. ASCAP, BMI. Publishes 50 songs/year; publishes 10 new songwriters/year. Works with lyricists and composers and teams collaborators. Pays standard royalty.
How to Contact: Prefers cassette with 1-2 songs on demo and lyric sheet. "Songs should have great hooks, interesting chord changes, classic melodies and conversational lyrics." SASE. Reports in 8 weeks.

Music: Mostly dance-oriented rock; also easy listening, folk, jazz, MOR, R&B, rock, soul and top 40/pop. Recently published "Wish We Were Heroes" (by Austin Gravelding), recorded by Kenny Dale on Capitol Records (country/pop); and "Change of Heart" (by Eric Carmen), recorded by Donna Fargo on Warner Bros. Records (pop rock).

GLEN CAMPBELL MUSIC, 1710 Roy Acuff Place, Nashville TN 37203. (615)244-5044. Publishing company. BMI, ASCAP. Publishes 25 songs/year; publishes 2 new songwriters/year. Pays standard royalty.
How to Contact: Prefers cassette with 1-2 songs and lead sheet. SASE, but accepts no responsibility for materials.
Music: Mostly contemporary country, country pop and traditional country. Recently published "Letter to Home," (by Carl Jackson), recorded by Glen Campbell on Atlantic (country); "You Showed Me Something About Lovin'," (by Phil Redrow), recorded by Waylon Jennings on RCA (country); and "I'm Beside Myself," (by Carl Jackson/Ethan Reilly), recorded by Keith Stegall on Epic (country).
Tips: "Looking for positive lyrics (no cheating, hurting, drinking) and moderate to uptempo songs for female artists. Ballads submitted need powerful, rangy song."

CANDLESTICK PUBLISHING CO., 582 Armour Circle NE, Atlanta GA 30324. (404)875-8272. Affiliate: Dream Merchant Music (BMI). Partners: Larry King, R.B. Hudmon, Gwen Kesler. Music publisher. BMI. Pays standard royalty.
How to Contact: Prefers cassette with 1-6 songs and lead sheet. SASE. Reports in 1-2 months.
Music: Rock, R&B, soul, country and top 40/pop. Recently published "How Can I Be a Witness?," "If You Don't Cheat on Me;" "Holdin' On;" and "Searching For Your Love" recorded by R.B. Hudmon (soul).

*CAPITOL STAR ARTIST ENTS., INC., 301 W. Ridge Rd., Rochester NY 14615. (716)266-3252. Director: Don Redanz. Associate Director: Tony Powlowski. Music publisher, record company and record producer. BMI. Publishes 4 songs/year; publishes 6-7 new songwriters/year. Pays standard royalty.
Music: Bluegrass, church/religious, country and gospel. Recently published "Dust on Mother's Bible," and "Away from Home," (by Anthony Powlowski), recorded by Tony Starr on Capitol Star (country); and "It's You Not Me," (by Jane Hathoway).
Tips: "We like country songs with a heartwarming story."

GRAHAM CARLTON MUSIC CO., Box 333, Evanston IL 60204. (312)274-9126. Affiliates: S. Pie Music Co., Buddy Ghouly Music, Innocent Lust Music. President: Graham Carlton. Music publisher, record company and record producer. BMI. Publishes 300 songs/year; publishes 15 new songwriters/year. Pays standard royalty.
How to Contact: Prefers cassette or videocassette with 1-5 songs and lyric sheet. SASE. "Demo doesn't have to be fancy but it has to be clean." Reports as soon as possible.
Music: Mostly country and soul; also bluegrass, blues, dance-oriented, easy listening, folk, jazz, MOR, progressive, R&B, rock (all types), top 40/pop and humorous. Recently published "Al Capone Clone" (by Carlton and Diamond), recorded by Hustlers, Inc./Riot Records (dance); and "More & More" (by Carlton and Diamond), recorded by Annie Wynne/Hybrid Records (country).
Tips: "Put art first, don't worry about sales potential or what's on radio. Be unique but don't send garbage. Something good transcends all barriers."

*DAVID CASE ARTIST PRODUCTIONS, INC., Box 132, Station B, Sudbury, Ontario P3E 2MS Canada. Producer/President: David Case. CAPAC. Music publisher, record company (Case of Gold Music) and record producer. Publishes 10-20 songs/year; publishes 4-5 new songwriters/year. Pays standard royalty.
How to Contact: Prefers cassette with 4 songs and lyric sheet and lead sheets. SAE and IRC "only." Reports in 2 weeks.
Music: Mostly pop, R&B and rock; also country. Recently published "Don't Stop Me," and "Thing Called Love," (by Rob Brennan), recorded by Mainstreet on Mainstreet (MOR); and "Technicolor," written and recorded by David Case on Case of Gold Records (R&B).
Tips: "Take your time and put your heart into your music."

CASTELAR PUBLISHING, INC., 2322 S. 64th Ave., Omaha NE 68106. (402)554-0123. President: Nils Anders Erickson. Music publisher, record company, record producer, sound and light company. BMI. Publishes 20-30 songs/year; publishes 3 new songwriters/year. Pays standard royalty.
How to Contact: Write first about your interest. Prefers cassette with 1-3 songs. SASE. Reports in 1 month.
Music: Mostly rock; also bluegrass, children's, choral, church/religious, classical, country, dance-ori-

ented, easy listening, folk, gospel, jazz, MOR, progressive, Spanish, R&B, soul and top 40/pop. Recently published "Hit & Run," "Dark Nights," and "Tom Ware" (European distribution)

CATALPA PUBLISHING CO., 2609 NW 36th St., Oklahoma City OK 73112. (405)942-0462. Professional Manager: Bobby Boyd. Music publisher, record company and record producer. BMI. Publishes 100 songs/year; publishes 6 new songwriters/year. Pays standard royalty.
How to Contact: Write first and obtain permission to submit, then submit demo tape and lyric sheet. Prefers 7½ ips reel-to-reel with 3-12 songs. Does not return unsolicited material. Reports in 2 weeks.
Music: Country, R&B, rock, soul and top 40/pop.

*CATERO RECORDS CO., 1301 Chestnut St., San Carlos CA 94070. (415)593-6720. President: Fred Catero. Record company and record producer. Publishes 45 songs/year; publishes 5 new songwriters/year. Pays legal mechanical rate.
How to Contact: Call first and obtain permission to submit. Prefers cassette. "Keep demos short—we'll ask for more if we're interested." Does not return unsolicited material.
Music: Mostly jazz, new age and contemporary "pop"; also R&B and classical. Recently published "Moving Day," written and recorded by T. Garthwaite on Catero (vocal/pop); "Special to You," written and recorded by R. Vandervort on Catero (pop vocal); and "I Like You, You're Nice," (by B. Dearie), recorded by T. Garthwaite on Catero (jazz vocal).
Tips: "Say something listeners can relate to in a way they wish they had. Target songs to the baby boomer—the 30-40-year-old crowd."

*CEDAR VALLEY PUBLISHING, Rt. 3, Box 243-B, Stephenville TX 76401. (817)965-4132. Contact: Carroll Parham. Music publisher and record company (Scotty Records). Publishes 12 songs/year; publishes 15 new songwriters/year. Pays standard royalty. Affiliated publishing firm: Dusty Rose Music.
How to Contact: Prefers cassette. Does not return unsolicited material. Reports in 8 weeks.
Music: Mostly country, gospel and light progressive. Recently published "Tucumcari," (by Stan Knowles), recorded by Charlotte Brown on Scotty (country); "Growing Older," written and recorded by J.W. Seals on Scotty (gospel); and "Past Is Past," (by Martin/Parham), recorded by C.C. Martin on Cedar Valley (country).
Tips: "Make sure all material has a good hook and strong lyrics."

*CENTERSTREAM PUBLISHING, Box 5052, Fullerton CA 92635. (714)738-6332. Contact: Ron Middlebrook. BMI. Music publisher.
How to Contact: Prefers cassette or videocassette.
Music: Mostly country, rock and blues; also gospel.

*FRANK CHACKSFIELD MUSIC/EROS MUSIC, Allegro, Elm Walk, Farnborough Park, Orpington, Kent BR6 8LX England. Farnborough 55509. Contact: Frank Chacksfield. PRS, MCPS, BASCA. Music publisher.
How to Contact: Prefers cassette. SAE and IRC.
Music: Mostly instrumental.

CHAPIE MUSIC, Chapman Recording Studios, 228 W. 5th St., Kansas City MO 64105. (816)842-6854. Owner: Chuck Chapman. Music publisher and record company. BMI. Publishes 25 songs/year; publishes 12 new songwriters/year. Pays standard royalty.
How to Contact: Prefers cassette with minimum 3 songs. Prefers studio produced demos. SASE. Reports in 1 month.
Music: Mostly country; also bluegrass, choral, church/religious, classical, disco, easy listening, folk, gospel, jazz, MOR, progressive, rock, soul, and top 40/pop. Recently published "Roll Me Up," written and recorded by Greg Camp on Fifth Street (country); "She's Tellin' Me Lies," (by Gary Pardes), recorded by G. Camp on Fifth Street (country); and "I'm So Glad," written and recorded by Ira Wilkes on Fifth Street (R&B).
Tips: Be "short and to the point."

CHAPPELL & CO. (AUST.) PTY LTD., 99 Forbes St., Woolloomooloo, Box KX250 Kings Cross, Sydney, NSW 2011, Australia. 61-02-356-3322. International Manager: Jennifer Wright. Professional Manager: Robert DuRose. Music publisher. Member AMCOS, APRA and Australian Music Publishers Association Pty, Ltd. Pays negotiable royalty; royalties paid directly to US songwriters or paid to US songwriters through US publishing affiliate.
How to Contact: Write first. Prefers cassette with 1-5 songs and lyric sheet. SAE and IRC. Reports in approximately 2 weeks.

Close-up

Richard Carpenter
Songwriter/Performer
Los Angeles, California

As a songwriter, Richard Carpenter knows the importance of keeping up with the times. Although most of the gold records he and his sister Karen had in the late sixties and early seventies were recorded before the advent of today's high tech, computer-based synthesizers and musical instruments, Carpenter isn't afraid to experiment with them and capitalize on the benefits they can provide him as a songwriter. At the same time he realizes there can also be a danger in becoming too dependent on these modern wonders.

"Certain records of late are more productions than they are songs," explains Carpenter, "to gauge the merit of a song, songwriters and artists should ask themselves 'How would this song sound if it didn't have this full-blown production? Is it a great song all by itself or does it need the production to make it viable?' I'm a firm believer in a song standing on its own."

Even though he feels technology can be a friend of the songwriter, Carpenter also feels it has been turned against them to some degree, citing the home taping controversy as a prime example. Carpenter says, "So many people really don't know how the music business works and I think quite a few don't even think they're causing any trouble by taping albums at home. The average person looks only at the most successful artists who are getting all the media attention. They hear how certain artists made tens of millions of dollars last year, buy homes all over the world, and drive Rolls Royces; while the rest of us come along with the record companies and say we're not getting our fair share. It's a sticky situation and the problem's being made even worse by record rental stores. There you can rent a record, copy it, and you have maybe two or three dollars in the whole thing. Something definitely needs to be done and I think an important part of the solution is in educating the public."

On the subject of music video, an area he'll be getting into upon the completion of his solo album project for A&M Records, Carpenter sees this innovation as positive. "I think music video has been a major shot in the arm for the music business and I think it's an especially important factor in a new artist's career."

To help aspiring songwriters avoid some of the pitfalls in the business, Carpenter gives this advice, "Look out for those offers saying 'Writers we need your songs!' If it comes down to a songwriter or artist paying someone to get something recorded, that's obviously the reverse of the way it's supposed to be. Additionally, I feel the songwriter, or artist for that matter, needs to write about what they believe in and not sell out for the sake of success. You need a great deal of tenacity to make it in this business.

"As far as my future career is concerned, in addition to recording and performing I definitely have my eyes on scoring for motion pictures. Either a love story or something with a romantic side to it. With the way I write, and being an incurable romantic, it would have to be something along those lines."

Music: Blues, children's, country, dance-oriented, easy listening, folk, jazz, MOR, R&B, rock, soul and top 40/pop.
Tips: "Submit good commercial, clear demos."

*CHARGO MUSIC, 98-40 64th Ave., Forest Hills NY 11375. (516)783-8800. Director of A&R: Chuck Mymit. BMI. Music publisher and record producer (Chuck Mymit Productions). Publishes 3-5 songs/year; publishes 3-5 new songwriters/year. Pays standard royalty.
How to Contact: Prefers cassette with 3-5 songs and lyric sheet or lead sheet. "Send short bio of artist/songwriter with picture if possible." Reports in 2-4 weeks.
Music: Mostly MOR, rock and country; also jazz, instrumentals and ballads. Recently published "Here I Go Again," (by C. Mymit), recorded by We Three on Roma (pop ballad); "Sad Eyes," (by B. Epstein), recorded by Laurie Skye on Geller International (pop ballad); and "Alone," (by A. Eng/C. Ballany), recorded by Top Notes on Denon (rock).

CHARTBOUND MUSIC PUBLICATIONS, LTD., Suite 204, 1508 Harlem, Memphis TN 38114. (901)274-2726. Executive Director: Reginald Eskridge. Music publisher and recording studio. ASCAP. Member NMPA (pending), BMA, NARAS, MSMA and The Blues Foundation. Publishes 2-4 songs/year; publishes 3 new songwriters/year. "We plan to employ songwriters on salary to exclusively write for our company within the next 12-18 months." Pays standard royalty.
How to Contact: Call or write first. Prefers 15 and 7½ ips reel-to-reel or cassette with 1-5 songs and lyric sheet. "Submit only unpublished songs for our consideration. Submit only your best. Big demo production is not necessary, but it helps." SASE. Reports in 3 weeks.
Music: Dance-oriented, MOR, R&B, soul and top 40/pop. Recently published "Am I Gonna be the One?" (by Thomas, Wade and E.R. Thomas), recorded by Colors/First Take Records (R&B/dance); "Steep Is the Stairway to Heaven" (by Gloria Suggs), CGS Records/gospel; and "Early Morning Man (by Weinfeld, Medlock and Easley), recorded by Sheryl Fox/GCS Records (top 40).

*CHASCOT MUSIC PUBLISHING, Box 3161, Atlanta GA 30302. President: Charles E. Scott. Music publisher, record company and record producer. BMI. Publishes 25 songs/year. Pays standard royalty.
How to Contact: Prefers cassette and lead sheet. SASE. Reports in 3 weeks.
Music: Blues, disco, gospel, R&B, soul and top 40/pop. Recently published "Do It Again," by John Weber (blues); "Come On, Try It," by Bobby Lewis (R&B); and "Pay My Bills," by Janet Steinberg (pop).

C. CHASE MUSIC PRODUCTIONS, Division of Chase Dominion Limited. 83 Kneeland Ave., Binghamton NY 13905. (607)797-1190. Director: Dr. Clarence W. Chase. Music publisher and music engraver specializing in hymns; gospel, popular and vocal music; children's songs and lead sheets. ASCAP. Publishes 8 songs/year; publishes 1 new songwriter/year. Works with lyricists. Pays minimum standard royalty.
How to Contact: Write first about your interest. Prefers cassette with 1-3 songs and lead sheet. Does not return unsolicited material. Reports "as time allows."
Music: Children's, traditional hymns and country. Recently published "Florida, I Love You," by J. Hevener (ballad); "Greenman Center Greeting Song," by C. Chase; and "Tombstones by the Highways," by W. Berry, K. Berry, C. Chase (country).
Tips: "Hymns must be a marriage of words and music—use words embodying ideas that will stimulate the imagination. Don't just write poetry—make your hymns 'sing.' "

CHEAVORIA MUSIC CO., 1219 Kerlin Ave., Brewton AL 36426. (205)867-2228. Affiliate: Bait String Music (ASCAP). Songwriter: Roy Edwards. Producer: Shannon Edwards. Music publisher, record producer and management firm. BMI. Publishes 15 songs/year; publishes 10 new songwriters/year. Pays standard royalty.
How to Contact: Query. Prefers cassette with 2-5 songs and lead sheet. SASE. Reports in 3 weeks.
Music: Mostly country, R&B, MOR; also disco, easy listening, progressive, soul and top 40/pop. Recently published "I've Changed to Your Kind of Life" (by Ruby Wilson); "Empty Promises" (by Bobbie Roberson); and "Let Me Go" (by B. Roberson), all recorded by B. Roberson/Bolivia Records (country); "Always and Forever" (by Jim Portwood), recorded by J. Portwood (country); and "Make Me Forget" (by Horace Linsley), recorded by B. Roberson.

CHIP 'N' DALE MUSIC PUBLISHERS, INC., 2125 8th Ave. S, Nashville TN 37204. (615)383-6002. Affiliates: Door Knob Music (BMI) and Lodestar Music (SESAC). President: Gene Kennedy. Vice President: Karen Jeglum. Music publisher. ASCAP. Member NSAI, CMA, NMPA, and ACM. Publishes 200 songs/year; publishes 100 new songwriters/year. Pays standard royalty.

How to Contact: Arrange personal interview. Prefers 7½ ips reel-to-reel or cassette with 1-4 songs and lyric sheet. SASE. Reports in 1-3 weeks.
Music: Country, MOR and gospel. Recently published "New Tradition," (by Steve Chiasson), recorded by Bobby G. Rice on Door Knob Records.

THE CHU YEKO MUSICAL FOUNDATION, Box 10051, Beverly Hills CA 90213. (818)761-2646. Branch: Box 1314, Englewood Cliffs NJ 07632. Affiliates: Broadway/Hollywood International Music Publishers. Producer: Doris Chu. Music publisher, record company, record producer, video and film producer. ASCAP, BMI. Publishes 10-20 songs/year; publishes 2-7 new songwriters/year. Pays negotiable royalty (up to 10% of profits).
How to Contact: Prefers cassette with any number songs and lyric sheet. SASE. Reports in 1 month.
Music: Mostly musicals; also pop/rock, R&B, C&W and rock. "Complete musicals already produced in Los Angeles preferred." Recently published "81 Proof," recorded on CYM Foundation Records; "Here's to L.A." (by Samovitz, Everest, Skyer, etc.), recorded by Paul Wong/The CYM Foundation Records (MOR); and "The Gun Control Tango" (by John Everest), recorded by various artists/The CYM Foundation Records (satire).
Tips: Interested in complete musicals, and top 40/pop, rock, R&B, country, MOR, religious-oriented songs. "Co-publishers welcome."

CIANO PUBLISHING, Box 263, Hasbrouck Heights NJ 07604. (201)288-8935. Branch: Ciano Publishing (South), Box 263, Brigantine NJ 08203. (609)266-2623. President: Ron Luciano. Music publisher, record company and record producer. BMI. Publishes 12 songs/year. Pays standard royalty.
How to Contact: Query. Prefers 7½ ips reel-to-reel, cassette or acetate with 2-6 songs and lead sheet. SASE. Reports in 1 month.
Music: Disco, easy listening, MOR, R&B, rock, soul and top 40/pop. Recently published "Lucky" (by T. Galloway), recorded by Lucifer/Legz Records (rock); "Fly Away" (by Philip Mitchell and Barron and Susan Sillars), recorded by Lucifer/Tiara Records (folk); and "Love's a Crazy Game" (by Joseph M. Leo and Paul Cannarella), recorded by Lucifer (top 40/disco).

CLARUS MUSIC, LTD., 340 Bellevue Ave., Yonkers NY 10703. (914)591-7715. President: Mrs. S. Fass. Music publisher, record company and record producer. ASCAP. Member MENC, NYSSMA, RIAA. "We publish children's records and material." Publishes 2 new songwriters/year. "Royalties paid are based on various reasons (plays, songs, etc.)."
How to Contact: Prefers cassette with 4-10 songs and lyric sheet. SASE. Reports in 1-3 months.
Music: Children's.

*R.D. CLEVERE MUSIKVERLAG, Postfach 2145, D-6078 Neu-Isenburg, West Germany. (6102)52696. Professional Manager: Tony Hermonez. GEMA. Music publisher. Publishes 700-900 songs/year; publishes 40 new songwriters/year. Pays standard royalty. Affiliated publishing firms: Big Sound Music, Hot Night Music, Lizzy's Blues Music, Max Banana Music, R.D. Clevére-Cocabana-Music, R.D. Clevére-Far East & Orient-Music, and R.D. Clevére-America-Today-Music.
How to Contact: Prefers cassette, reel-to-reel or U-matic or VHS (PAL) videocassette with "no limit" on songs and lyric sheet. SAE and IRC. Reports in 3 weeks.
Music: Mostly pop, disco, rock, R&B, country and folk; also musicals.

BRUCE COHN MUSIC, Box 359, Sonoma CA 95476. (707)938-4060. Affiliates: Flat Lizard Music, Maybe Music, Quark Music, Skunkster Publishing, Snug Music, Noodle Tunes, Pants Down Music, Spikes Music, Soquel Songs, Tauripin Tunes, Windecor Music and R.P. Winkelman Tunes. Manager/Owner: Bruce Cohn. Music publisher (ASCAP, BMI, SESAC) and management firm. Publishes 10-20 songs/year.
How to Contact: Prefers cassette. SASE. Reports in 2-3 weeks.
Music: MOR, rock, soul, and top 40/pop.

COMPLETE MUSIC LIMITED, 53 Kensington Gardens Square, London W2 4BA, England. 44-01-8854. Joint Managing Directors: Theo Chalmers and Martin Costello. Chairman: Iain McNay. Music publisher. MCPS, PRS. Publishes 500 songs/year. Pays negotiable royalty to songwriters; royalties paid directly to US songwriters.
How to Contact: Prefers cassette with 2 songs and lyric sheet. Does not return unsolicited material. Reports in 1 month.
Music: Mostly electronic pop, dance-oriented, and punk; also classical. Recently published "Don't Tell Me," (by Arthur/Luscombe), recorded by Blanchmange (dance-oriented); "Each and Everyone," (by Watt/Thorn), recorded by Everything But the Girl (ballad); and "I Survive," (by Luke Morley), recorded by Terraplane (melodic rock).
Tips: "Be non-derivative."

CONYPOL MUSIC, INC., C Modestino, 66, Paternopoli, AV. Italy 83052. (082)7-71073. Telex: 722136. President: Sal Barbieri. Music publisher, record company and record producer. BMI. Publishes 8-10 songs/year; publishes 4 new songwriters/year. Pays standard royalty.
How to Contact: Prefers cassette with 1-15 songs and lyric sheet. SASE. Reports in 1 month.
Music: Mostly dance and top 40; also country, easy listening, MOR, progressive, R&B, rock and soul. Recently published "In the Name of Love" (by S. Barbieri), recorded by S. Barbieri on BSO Europe Records (dance); "Coming Up" (by S. Barbieri and G. Lion), recorded by Sigfrida on BSO Europe Records (top 40); and "Heavy Stuff" (by S. Barbieri and R. Leweun), recorded by S. Barbieri on BSO Records (top 40).

***COOL CAT MUSIC**, Heinrich-Hertz Str. 106, 2 Hamburg 76, West Germany. (040)2270903. A&R Manager: Nina Martin. GVL, GEMA. Music pubisher and record producer. Publishes 50 songs/year; publishes 20 new songwriters/year. Pays standard royalty.
How to Contact: Prefers cassette or VHS videocassette. SAE and IRC. Reports in 6 weeks.
Music: Mostly pop, rock and ballads; also hard rock. Recently published: "Final Call," (by Viva Vergo), recorded by Martinque on Teldec (pop); and "Do It Yourself," (by Speer) and "Nice Girls," (by Gerlach), both recorded by C'est La Vie on Teldec (pop).
Tips: "Any good song stands a chance. Quality of tape is unimportant."

***COPYRIGHT SERVICE BUREAU LTD.**, 221 W. 57th St., New York NY 10019. (212)582-5030. President: Gitte Hofer. Music publisher. BMI, ASCAP, SESAC.
How to Contact: Prefers cassette with 5 songs and lyric sheet. "Include a note in your submission and follow up with a letter." Does not return unsolicited material. Reports in 6 weeks.
Music: All types.

COUNTERPOP MUSIC GROUP, Suite 8, 3121 Maple Drive, Atlanta GA 30305. (404)231-9888. Affiliates: O.A.S. Music Publishing (ASCAP) and Andgold Music Publishing (BMI). Catalog Administrator: Vicki Tunstall. Music publisher. Publishes 15 songs/year; publishes 3 new songwriters/year. Pays standard royalty.
How to Contact: Cassette only with 1-3 songs and lyric sheet. SASE. Reports as soon as possible.
Music: Mostly country, pop and rock; also MOR, R&B and top 40. Recently published "The Woman in Me" (by Susan Thomas), recorded by Crystal Gayle on CBS Records (MOR).

COUNTRY CLASSICS MUSIC PUBLISHING CO., Box 15222, Oklahoma City OK 73115. (405)677-6448. General Manager: Sonny Lane. Music publisher and record company. BMI. Publishes 6-12 songs/year; publishes 2 new songwriters/year. Pays standard royalty.
How to Contact: Prefers cassette with 4 songs and lyric sheet. SASE. Reports in 3 weeks.
Music: Country/western, gospel and MOR. Recently published "How Many Times Jesus," (by Yvonne DeVaney), recorded by Wanda Jackson on Vine (gospel); and "Tell Me a Lie," and "Forever and One Day," (by Y. DeVaney), both recorded by Ragnhild on Tab (country).

COUNTRY STAR MUSIC, 439 Wiley Ave., Franklin PA 16323. (814)432-4633. Affiliates: Kelly Music Publications (BMI) and Process Music Publications (BMI). President: Norman Kelly. Music publisher and record company. ASCAP. Publishes 10-15 songs/year; publishes 3-4 new songwriters/year. Pays standard royalty.
How to Contact: Prefers 7½ ips reel-to-reel or cassette with 1-4 songs and lyric sheet. SASE. Reports in 2 weeks.
Music: Mostly country; also bluegrass, easy listening, folk, rock, gospel, MOR and top 40/pop. Recently published "Porch Light," (by McHan/Goff/Moon), recorded by J.C. Young on Country Star (country); "Wings (Guarding America)," (by Wright/Struckburg/Hill), recorded by Sal Rainone on Process (MOR); and "Knock It Off," written and recorded by Dave Drayer on Mersey (rock).
Tips: "Send only your best songs—ones you feel are equal to or better than current hits."

COUSINS MUSIC, 211 Birchwood Ave., Upper Nyack NY 10960. (914)358-0861. Affiliate: Neems (ASCAP). President: Lou Cicchetti. Music publisher and record producer. BMI. Publishes 6-8 songs/year; publishes 3-4 new songwriters/year. Pays standard royalty.
How to Contact: Prefers 7½ or 15 ips reel-to-reel or cassette with any number of songs and lyric sheet. SASE. Reports in 2 weeks.
Music: Mostly country; also rock. Recently published "I Wish You Had Lied," (by Jacklyn Hopwood), recorded by Co Co (country); and "Runaway," (by Jerman Hall), recorded by Apostle (rock).

COVERED BRIDGE MUSIC, Box 110829, Nashville TN 37222. (615)776-2060. Affiliates: Town Square and Iron Skillet. General Manager: Bill Wence. Music publisher. ASCAP, BMI, SESAC.

How to Contact: Submit cassette only with maximum 2 songs and lyric sheet. SASE. Reports in 4 weeks.
Music: Country. Recently published "Marriage on the Rocks" (by Carl Struck), recorded by C. Struck/Rustic Records (country); "Quicksand" and "I Wanna Do It Again" (by Bill Wence), recorded by B. Wence (country).

COWBOY JUNCTION PUB. CO., Highway 44 West, Lecanto FL 32661. (904)746-4754. President: Elizabeth Thompson. Music publisher and record producer. BMI. Publishes 28 songs/year.
How to Contact: SASE. Reports as soon as possible.
Music: Mostly country; also bluegrass and gospel. Recently published "You May Take Possession Darling," (by Boris Max Pastuch), recorded by Buddy Max on Cowboy Junction (country); "The Gift," written and recorded by Ruth Hansan on Cowboy Junction (country); and "Second Wedding Nights," written and recorded by Charlie Floyd on Cowboy Junction (country).

CREATIVE ENTERTAINMENT CORPORATION, Suite 1700, 6290 Sunset Blvd., Los Angeles CA 90028. Affiliates: Creative Entertainment Music (BMI), Weezy Music (ASCAP). Professional Manager: Mark Savage. Music publisher and management firm. BMI, ASCAP. Member NMPA. Publishes 25 songs/year; publishes 8 new songwriters/year. Pays standard royalty.
How to Contact: Prefers cassette or videocassette with 1-5 songs and lyric sheet. SASE. Reports in 1 month. "No telephone calls please!"
Music: Mostly R&B, dance, and rock; also pop, and soul. Recently published "Shattered Glass," recorded by Krystol on CBS-Epic (R&B); "If Looks Could Kill," recorded by Heart on Capitol (rock); and "I Just Want You To Love Me," recorded by Reena Scott on MCA (R&B/dance).

CREOLE MUSIC LTD., 91-93 High St., Harlesden, London, England. 44-01-965-9223. Publishing Manager: Bruce White. Music publisher, record company and record producer. MCPS, PRS, Phonographic Performance Ltd. Member MPA, IFPI. Publishes 100 songs/year; publishes 3-5 new songwriters/year. Pays standard royalty; royalties paid directly to US songwriters.
How to Contact: Prefers cassette or VHS videocassette with 2-6 songs and lyric sheet. SAE and IRC. Reports in 3 weeks.
Music: Mostly pop, rock, dance and ballads; also country, easy listening, R&B, disco and soul. Recently published "Single Handed" (by Bob Puzey), recorded by Haywoode/CBS Records (dance); "Cherry O'Baby" (by Eric Donaldson), recorded by UB40/DEP/Virgin Records (MOR); and "Lady of Mine" (by Pete McDonald), recorded by McDonald/Creole Records (MOR/ballad).
Tips: "It must be brilliant."

*****CRYSTAL IMAGE MUSIC**, 6239 Herndon Place, Stockton CA 95209. (209)957-5044. Contact: John Covert. BMI. Music publisher, record company (Berberian/Dream Records Tokay Records, Aroma Records) and record producer. Publishes 5-10 songs/year; publishes 5 new songwriters/year. Pays standard royalty. Affiliated publishing firm: Richard Berberian Music/BMI.
How to Contact: Prefers cassette with 2 songs and lyric sheet. "We can generally tell from a lyric whether a song will interest us. In fact, we encourage writers to send lyrics with SASE first—it saves them money. If we love the lyric and think it may fit a contact, then we ask to hear tape." SASE. Reports in 8-10 weeks.
Music: Mostly country pop, MOR and easy listening. Recently published "The Ballad of Willis & Jud," (by Hank Healy), recorded by Crystal Image on Tokay (country); "Time for Another Broken Heart," (by Frank Ahl), recorded by Crystal Image on Tokay (country); and "You Don't Have to Be from Texas," (by Rod Washburn), recorded by Crystal Image on Berberian (country).

*****CSB KAMINSKY GMBH**, Wilhelmstrasse 10, 2407 Bad Schwartau, West Germany. (0451)21530. General Manager: Pia Kaminsky. GEMA, PRS. Music publisher and collecting agency. Pays 85% royalty. Affiliated publishing firms: Copyright Service Bureau, Ltd. and Leosong Copyright Service, Ltd.
How to Contact: Write first and obtain permission to submit. Prefers cassette. Does not return unsolicited material. Reports in 4 weeks.
Music: Mostly rock, country and reggae.

CYHOEDDIADAU SAIN, Llandwrog, Caernarfon, Gwynedd, LL54 5TG, United Kingdom. 44-0286-831-111. Directors: Dafydd Iwan and O.P. Huws. Music publisher, record company, record producer and record distributors. MCPS, PRS, Phonographic Performance Ltd., BPI, IFPI. Member APRS. Publishes 150 songs/year; publishes 10 new songwriters/year. Has not yet, but would listen to songs from US songwriters. Pays 6¼% of retail price of album to songwriters, prorated per number of songs.
How to Contact: Prefers cassette with 1-5 songs and lyric sheet. SAE and IRC. Reports in 1 month.

Music: Mostly MOR and choral (Welsh language); also children's, church/religious, classical, country and folk. Recently published "Mi Glywaf Y Llais," (by Dafydd Iwan), recorded by Trebor Edwards on Sain (MOR); "Madras," written and recorded by Geraint Griffiths on Sain (funk); and "Da Ni'm Yn Rhan O'th Gem Fach Di," recorded by Maffia Mr. Huws on Sain (rock).
Tips: "Songs should be relevant to the scene in Wales."

DANA PUBLISHING CO., 824 83rd St., Miami Beach FL 33141. (305)865-8960. President: Walter Dana. Music publisher, record company and record producer. BMI. Pays standard royalty.
How to Contact: Write first. Prefers 7½ or 15 ips reel-to-reel or cassette. SASE.
Music: Classical and ethnic (Polish).

*DARK CLOUD MUSIC, 373 Walnut St., Englewood NJ 07631. (201)567-6855. Vice President: Vincent Castellano. BMI, ASCAP, SESAC. Music publisher and record producer (Silverlining Productions). Publishes 20-30 songs/year; publishes 5-10 new songwriters/year. Pays standard royalty. Affiliated publishing firms: We Got Music and D.A.M. Music.
How to Contact: Prefers cassette, 7½ or 15 ips reel-to-reel or VHS videocassette with 3 songs and lyric sheet. SASE. Reports in 3- weeks.
Music: Mostly rock (commercial), R&B (contemporary) and AOR; also heavy metal and pop. Recently published "Who'll Be the 1st One," and "Breakfast in Bed," written and recorded by Ray Goodman and Brown on Panaramic (R&B).

DARK HEART MUSIC, 1236 S. Staples, Corpus Christi TX 78404. (512)882-7066. A/R: Arnold Garcia. BMI. Music publisher, record company (Hacienda Records) and record producer. Publishes 50-100 songs/year; publishes varying number of new songwriters/year. Pays standard royalty. Affiliated publishing firms: Roland Garcia Music, El Palacio Music, Dillettante Music.
How to Contact: Prefers cassette. Submissions must include complete name, address and phone number. Does not return unsolicited material. Reporting time varies.
Music: Mostly rock, Spanish and country; also gospel. Recently published "Ready as Hell," (by Jim Dandy), recorded by Black Oak Arkansas on Hacienda (rock); "Tiz Magic," (by Pio Trevino), recorded by Magic on Hacienda (Spanish); and "Tomame," (by David Hernandez), recorded by Cielo on Hacienda (Spanish).

DAVID MUSIC, 1650 Broadway, New York NY 11021. (212)247-2159. Affiliates: Felicia Wynne Music (BMI), Sarah Music (ASCAP). President: Morton Wax. Music publisher and record company. BMI. Pays standard royalty.
How to Contact: Prefers cassette and lyric sheet. Does not return unsolicited material. Reports as soon as possible.
Music: All kinds, with strong interest in country/pop.

DAWN PRODUCTIONS LTD., Cloud 300, Mt. Gretna PA 17064. Affiliates: Ursula Music, Welz Music, Comet-tale Music and Wynwood Music. President: Joey Welz. Music publisher, record company and record producer. BMI and ASCAP. Member AFM. Publishes 15-20 songs/year; publishes 4 new songwriters/year. Pays standard royalty.
How to Contact: Prefers cassette with 4-6 songs and lyric sheet—"not returnable, we hold in files." Does not return unsolicited material. Reports "when we place a song with an artist."
Music: Mostly rock, country, dance-oriented, easy listening, folk, MOR, R&B, and top 40/pop. Recently published "I'm A Head," and "Heavy Metal Kids," (by Bob McCormic), recorded by Joel Welz on Caprice Records; and "Love Is Forever," by Doug Clifton.

DE WALDEN MUSIC INTERNATIONAL, INC., #1911, 6255 Sunset Blvd., Hollywood CA 90028. (213)462-1922. Affiliates: Chriswald Music, Inc., Father Music, Hopi Sound Music and TSOM Music. Managing Director: Christian de Walden. Music publisher and record producer. ASCAP, BMI. Publishes 100-150 songs/year; publishes 1-2 new songwriters/year. Works with lyricists and composers and teams collaborators. Pays standard royalty.
How to Contact: Arrange personal interview if in the area or submit demo tape. Prefers cassette with 1-3 songs and lyric sheet. SASE. Reports in 6-8 weeks.
Music: Pop, R&B and dance. Recently published "House Bound" (by A. Roberts, C. Black and T. Rocco), recorded by E.T. Conley on RCA Records (country/pop); "Read All About It" (by T. Cerhey and K. Robbins), recorded by Sylvia on RCA Records (country/pop); and "100% Chance of Rain," (by A. Roberts and C. Black), recorded by Gary Morris on WB (pop/crossover).
Tips: "Please do not submit country songs."

DELEV MUSIC COMPANY, 7231 Mansfield Ave., Philadelphia PA 19138. (215)276-8861. Affiliate: Sign of the Ram Music (ASCAP). President: W. Lloyd Lucas. Music publisher, record company, re-

cord producer and management firm. BMI, ASCAP. Member AGAC, Black Music Assoc. and Country Music Assoc. Publishes 10-15 new songwriters/year; publishes 6-10 new songwriters. Pays standard royalty.
How to Contact: Write first about your interest. Prefers cassette with 1-5 songs and lyric sheet. SASE. "We will not accept certified mail." Reports in 3 weeks.
Music: R&B, dance-oriented, crossover and country pop. Recently published "Send It In," (by Paul Hotchkiss), recorded by Bill Lucas on Surprize (pop uptempo); "This Love's For You," (by Raymond Delisio), recorded by Original Pleasure on Surprize (pop ballad); and "Better Beware," written and recorded by Bill Lucas on Surprize (pop uptempo).
Tips: "Songs submitted must be lyrically and melodically strong with good strong hook lines, and tell a story that will appeal to and be related to by the radio-listening and record-buying public. Most important is that the demo be a clear quality product with understandable vocal and lyrics out front."

*DENNY MUSIC GROUP, 39 Music Sq. E., Nashville TN 37203. (615)256-3558. Chief Executive Officer: John E. Denny. ASCAP, BMI. Music publisher, record company (Dollie Record Co., Jed Record Production) and record producer. Employs songwriters on a salary basis. Pays standard royalty.
How to Contact: Write or call first and obtain permission to submit. Prefers cassette with 4 songs and lyric sheet. Reports in 6 weeks.
Music: Mostly country and gospel.

DESERT BREEZE PUBLISHING CO., 40655 Jefferson, Bermuda Dune CA 92201. (619)345-2851. President: Rick Lewis. Music publisher and record company. Estab. 1983. Pays standard royalty.
How to Contact: Prefers cassette with 4-10 songs and lyric sheet. SASE. Reports in 1 month.
Music: Mostly country, dance-oriented, R&B and rock (country).
Tips: Need "good lyrics that tell a story."

DO SOL PUBLISHING, Box 2262, Dorval, Quebec, H9S 5J4 Canada. (514)692-1036. Professional Manager: Robert Salagan. Music publisher and cassette producer. PROCAN. Publishes 40 songs/year; publishes 10 new songwriters/year. Pays standard royalty.
How to Contact: Prefers 7½ ips reel-to-reel with 3-7 songs and lyric sheet. "Make purpose of communication clear and fog-free." SAE and IRC. Reports in 1 month.
Music: Country, easy listening, folk, MOR and top 40/pop. Recently published "Hey Lord!" (by Richards and Tyler), recorded by Bonny Richards on A&M Records (MOR); "One Day" (by A. DeSouza), recorded by Alan Jones on George Records (top 40/pop); and "Come Forth" (by J. Clement), recorded by Please on George Records (folk).

DON-DEL MUSIC/DON-DE MUSIC, 15041 Wabash Ave., South Holland IL 60473. (312)339-0307. President: Donald De Lucia. Music publisher, record producer and record company. BMI and ASCAP. Pays standard royalty.
How to Contact: Prefers 7½ ips reel-to-reel with 4-6 songs and lyric sheet. SASE. Reports in 1 week.
Music: Country, rock and top 40/pop.

DONNA MARIE MUSIC, c/o International Entertainment Associates, Suite 818, 1616 Pacific Ave., Atlantic City NJ 08401. (609)347-0484. President: Danny Luciano. Associate Producer: Armand Cucinotti. Music publisher, record company and record producer. ASCAP. Publishes 6 songs/year; publishes 3 new songwriters/year. Pays standard royalty.
How to Contact: Prefers 7½ ips reel-to-reel or cassette with 4-8 songs and lyric sheet. "No 8-tracks." SASE. Reports in 6 weeks.
Music: MOR, R&B, rock, soul and top 40/pop.

DONNA MUSIC PUBLISHING CO., Box 113, Woburn MA 01801. (617)933-1474. General Manager: Frank Paul. Music publisher, record company, record producer, management firm and booking agency. BMI. Publishes 50-75 songs/year. Pays standard royalty.
How to Contact: Prefers cassette with 3-6 songs and lead sheet. "We will listen to tapes but will not return material. If we believe a song has potential, we will contact the songwriter." Reports in 1 month.
Music: Country, easy listening, gospel, MOR, R&B, rock, soul and top 40/pop. Recently published "Happy Happy Birthday Baby," recorded by Mango Sylvia and Gilbert Lopez/Casa Grande Records (R&B).

DOOMS MUSIC PUBLISHING CO., Box 2072, Waynesboro VA 22980. (703)949-0106. Contact: John Major. Music publisher and record company. BMI. Pays on royalty basis.
How to Contact: Prefers cassette. SASE. Reports in 3 weeks.
Music: Bluegrass, country, easy listening, gospel and MOR. Recently published "Honky Tonk Angel on the Road," recorded by Joey Davis.

DOOR KNOB MUSIC PUBLISHING, INC., 2125 8th Ave. S., Nashville TN 37204. (615)383-6002. Affiliates: Chip 'N' Dale Music Publishers, Inc (ASCAP); and Lodestar Music (SESAC). President: Gene Kennedy. Vice President: Karen Jeglum. Music publisher. BMI. Member NMPA, NSAI, CMA and ACM. Publishes 200 songs/year; publishes 100 new songwriters/year. Pays standard royalty.
How to Contact: Arrange personal interview. Prefers 7½ ips reel-to-reel or cassette with 1-4 songs and lyric sheet. SASE. Reports in 1-3 weeks.
Music: Country, MOR and gospel. Recently published "Those Words I Never Heard," (by Buffalo T. Jones/Don Casale), recorded by Bobby G. Rice/Door Knob Records.

*DOWN TO EARTH, Box H, Harvard MA 01451. (617)456-8111. Licensing Manager: Joshua Green. ASCAP. Music publisher, record company (Wouldn Shoe) and record producer (It's a Hit Productions). Publishes 3-5 songs/year; publishes 1-2 new songwriters/year. Pays standard royalty.
How to Contact: Prefers cassette. SASE.
Music: Mostly rock, pop and country. Recently published "Hearts Overflowing," recorded by Anne Marie Alden on Wouldn Shoe (pop); "Into Another Life," written and recorded by Dean Adrien on Wouldn Shoe (pop); and "Once They're Gone," (by Allen Estes), recorded by Allen Estes Band on Greenpeace (pop/rock).

*DRAGON INTERNATIONAL, Box 8263, Haledon NJ 07522. (201)942-6810. BMI. Music publisher and record company. Publishes 3 songs/year. Pays standard royalty.
How to Contact: Prefers cassette or reel-to-reel and lyric sheet or lead sheet. SASE. Reports in 5 weeks.
Music: Mostly gospel.

THE DRAKE MUSIC GROUP, 809 18th Ave. S., Nashville TN 37203. (615)327-3211. Affiliates: Petewood Music (ASCAP) and Window Music Pub. Co. Inc. (BMI). Professional Manager: Rose Drake. Music publisher. BMI, ASCAP, SESAC. Member NMA, CMA, GMA. Publishes 100 songs/year; publishes 6 new songwriters/year. Hires staff writers. Pays standard royalty.
How to Contact: Write or call about your interest. Prefers cassette with 2-4 songs on demo. SASE. Reports in 3 weeks.
Music: Mostly country and gospel; also church/religious, country, easy listening, MOR and top 40/pop. Recently published "Dixie Road," (by Kennedy/Rose/Goodman), recorded by Lee Greenwood on MCA (country); "It'll Be Love By Morning," (by Frizzell/Roberts), recorded by Allen Frizzell on CBS (country); and "If Drinkin' Don't Kill Me," recorded by George Jones (country).

*DREAM CITY MUSIC, 827 Meridian, Nashville TN 37207. (615)227-0920. Professional Manager: Donna Bridges. BMI. Music publisher. Publishes 20+ songs/year; publishes 20+ new songwriters/year. Pays standard royalty. Affiliated publishing firms: Charlie Parker Music, Streets of Gold Music, Vanjo Music, and Janon Music.
How to Contact: Prefers cassette or ¾" videocassette and lyric sheet. SASE. Reports in 1-6 weeks.
Music: Mostly country, gospel and soft rock; also progressive jazz.

DUANE MUSIC, INC., 382 Clarence Ave., Sunnyvale CA 94086. (408)739-6133. Affiliate: Morhits Publishing (BMI). President: Garrie Thompson. Music publisher. BMI. Publishes 10-20 songs/year; publishes 1 new songwriter/year. Pays standard royalty.
How to Contact: Prefers cassette with 1-4 songs and lead sheet. SASE. Reports in 1 month.
Music: Blues, country, disco, easy listening, rock, soul and top 40/pop. Recently published "Little Girl," recorded by Ban (rock); "Warm Tender Love," recorded by Percy Sledge (soul); and "My Adorable One," recorded by Joe Simon (blues).

DUPUY RECORDS/PRODUCTIONS/PUBLISHING, INC., Suite 200, 10960 Ventura Blvd., Studio City CA 91604. (818)980-6412). President: Pedro Dupuy. Music publisher, record company and record producer. ASCAP. Member AGAC. Publishes 50 songs/year; publishes 4 new songwriters/year. Hires staff writers. Pays standard royalty.
How to Contact: Write or call first about your interest or arrange personal interview. Prefers cassette with 2-4 songs and lyric sheet. SASE. Reports in 1 month.
Music: Mostly R&B and pop; also easy listening, jazz, MOR, soul and top 40. Recently published "Find a Way," "I Don't Wanna Know," and "Precious Love," written and recorded by Gordon Gilman.
Tips: "Songs should have very definitive lyrics with hook."

DUSTY ROSE MUSIC, 6505 Sheridan Rd., Fort Worth TX 76134. (817)293-5561; 737-4012, ext. 261. Affiliate: Cedar Valley Music (BMI). Contact: Stan Knowles. Music publisher, record producer and syndicated radio program producer. Estab. 1984. BMI. Pays standard royalty.

How to Contact: Write first. Prefers 7^1/$_2$ ips reel-to-reel or cassette with 3-4 songs. SASE. Reports in 3 weeks.
Music: Country.
Tips: "Submit tapes that are 'clean.' In other words, what we will be influenced most by are the things we hear. Many times tapes come in that sound like they've been cut in a sewer pipe, hard to hear and all. Better with just a guitar and one voice clean than with an orchestra."

DYNAMO PUBLISHING CO., 484 Lake Park Ave., Box 6, Oakland CA 94610. (415)482-4854. A&R Director: Dan Orth. Music publisher, record company and record producer. BMI. Member SRS. Publishes 1 song/year, pays 10-50% royalty.
How to Contact: Write or call first. Prefers cassette with 1-3 songs and lyric sheet. SASE. Reports in 1 month.
Music: Mostly pop rock and new wave; also country, easy listening, folk, MOR and R&B. Recently published "Cruisin' the Strip" and "Hard-Boiled" (by Dan Orth and Phil Phillips), recorded by P. Phillips (hard rock); and "It Takes More" written and recorded by P. Phillips (pop rock).

E.L.J. RECORD CO., 1344 Waldron, St. Louis MO 63130. (314)803-3605. President: Eddie Johnson. Vice President: William Johnson. Music publisher and record company. BMI. Publishes 8-10 songs/year; publishes 2 new songwriters/year. Pays 5-10% royalty.
How to Contact: Prefers 7^1/$_2$ ips reel-to-reel or cassette with 4 songs and lead sheet. SASE. Reports in 2 weeks.
Music: Mostly top 40; also blues, easy listening, soul and pop. Recently published "Strange Feeling" (by Tab Smith), recorded by Eddie Johnson on E.L.J. Records (top 40); "Tables are Turned" (by Bobby Scott), recorded by Scott on E.L.J. Records (top 40); and "Hold Me" (by Ann Richardson), recorded by Richardson on E.L.J. Records (soul).

EAGLE ROCK MUSIC CO., 5414 Radford Ave., North Hollywood CA 91607. (213)760-8771. President: Mort Katz. Music publisher. ASCAP. Member AGAC, ACM, CMA. Publishes 12 songs/year; publishes 3 new songwriters/year. Pays standard royalty.
How to Contact: Prefers cassette with 2-3 songs and lyric sheet. SASE. Reports in 3 weeks.
Music: Country, gospel and MOR. Recently published "Love Your Pet," (by Mort Katz and Reuben Katz), recorded by Bob Caldwell (country); "Chutzpah," (by Dorothy LaPell and Robbie Gillman), recorded by Frolic Taylor (MOR); and "No Matter How You Slice It," (by Jacklyn Hopwood and Mort Katz), recorded by J. Hopwood (country).
Tips: "Have a professional attitude and appreciate constructive criticism."

EARL MUSIC CO., 111 East 88th St., New York NY 10128. (212)289-9036. Affiliates: Peg Music (BMI). President and General Manager: Earl Shuman. Music publisher. ASCAP, BMI. Member NMPA. Publishes 10 songs/year; publishes 2 new songwriters/year. Pays standard royalty.
How to Contact: Prefers cassette with 1-3 songs and lyric sheet. SASE. "Writer should inquire about submitted material in 2 weeks."
Music: Rock, heavy metal and top 40. Recently published "Read 'Em and Weep," recorded by Barry Manilow; and "Two Out of Three Ain't Bad" (by Jim Steinman), recorded by Meatloaf/Epic Records (rock ballad).
Tips: "You must have a great song—it helps if it is presented on a strong demo."

EARLY BIRD MUSIC, Waltner Enterprises, 14702 Canterbury, Tustin CA 92680. (714)731-2981. President: Steve Waltner. Music publisher and record company. BMI. Publishes 12 songs/year; publishes 3 new songwriters/year. Works with lyricists. Pays standard royalty on mechanicals.
How to Contact: Prefers cassette with 2-4 songs and lead sheet. SASE. Reports in 3 weeks.
Music: Country, easy listening, MOR and top 40/pop.

EARTHSCREAM MUSIC PUBLISHING CO., Suite A, 2036 Pasket, Houston TX 77092. (713)688-8067. Contact: Jeff Johnson. Music publisher, record company and record producer. BMI. Publishes 10-20 songs/year. Pays standard royalty.
How to Contact: Prefers cassette with 2-5 songs and lyric sheet. SASE. Reports in 1 month.
Music: New rock and top 40/pop. Recently published "Don't Take My Heart" (by Pennington-Wells-Deluxe), recorded by Barbara Pennington Band on Earth Records (new-rock); and "I Think It's Better" (by Jim Travis), recorded by The Switch on Earth Records (new-rock).

*EDITIONS NAHEJ, 5514 Isabella, Montreal, Quebec H3X 1R6 Canada. (514)487-0859. Affiliates: Valcor, Yiddish, Zapiti, Nahej, Kif-Kif and Shoubidouwa. President: Jehan V. Valiquet. Music Publisher and record company. CAPAC, PROCAN. Publishes 25 songs/year; publishes 10 new songwriters/

year. Pays standard royalty.
How to Contact: Prefers cassette with mimimum 3 songs and lyric sheet. SAE and IRC.
Music: Children's (French), MOR and top 40/pop.

EMANDELL TUNES, 10220 Glade Ave., Chatsworth CA 91311. (818)341-2264. Affiliates: Ben-Lee Music (BMI), Adarom Music (ASCAP), Northworth Songs (SESAC), Roymar Music (BMI), Gertrude Music (SESAC), LMS Print/Publishing Co. and Clara Ward Music Group. President/Administrator: Leroy C. Lovett Jr. Publishes 60 songs/year; publishes 2-3 new songwriters/year. Pays standard royalty "twice a year."
How to Contact: Prefers cassette with 4-5 songs and lead sheet or lyric sheet. Include information about writer, singer or group. SASE. Reports in 3-4 weeks.
Music: Mostly inspirational, contemporary and traditional gospel, chorals and general church music; also top 40 and R&B. Recently published "Wonderful," by Steve Hunt on Columbia; "I Love You," (by Ricky Tomack), recorded by James Cleveland Mass Choir; and "Look Where God Has Brought Us," on Birthright.

EPOCH UNIVERSAL PUBLICATIONS, INC., 10802 N. 23rd Ave., Phoenix AZ 85029. (602)864-1980. Affiliates: NALR (BMI), Epoch Music Corp. (ASCAP), Epoch Universal Publications, Ltd. (Canada). Executive Vice President: David Serey. Music publisher, record company and record producer. BMI. Publishes 100-300 songs/year; publishes 20 new songwriters/year. Hires staff writers. "Position filled at this time, but resumes may be sent to be kept on file." Pays standard royalty.
How to Contact: Prefers 7½ ips reel-to-reel or cassette with minimum 3 songs and lyric sheet. SASE. Reports in 1 month.
Music: Children's, choral, church/religious, classical, gospel and liturgical. Recently published "Here I Am, Lord" (by Dan Schutte), recorded by St. Louis Jesuits/NALR Records (liturgical); "Land of Love" (by Marcy Tigner), recorded by Little Marcy/Sounds of Hope Records (children's); and "The Ones I Love" (by Carey Landry), recorded by C. Landry/NALR Records (liturgical).
Tips: "Songs should be strong but simple enough for congregational singing, preferably in a liturgical setting."

EQUA MUSIC, 1800 Mowry Ave., Fremont CA 94538. (415)794-6637. Affiliate: Mepro Music (BMI). President: Warren M. Johnson. Music publisher and record company. ASCAP. Member CMA. Publishes 10-15 songs/year; publishes 5 new songwriters/year. Pays standard royalty.
How to Contact: Prefers cassette with 3-6 songs and lyric sheet. SASE. Reports in 3 weeks.
Music: C&W. Recently published "No Place to Hide" (by Kay Savage), and "Goin' Home Alone" (by Gail Zeiler), recorded by G. Zeiler/Equa Records (C&W ballad); and "It Ain't My Concern" (by G. Zeiler) recorded by G. Zeiler/Equa Records (C&W uptempo).

EQUINOX MUSIC (AVI Music Publishing Group), Suite 1212, 7060 Hollywood Blvd., Hollywood CA 90028. (213)462-7151. Affiliates: Bel-Canto Music (ASCAP), Forsythe Music (ASCAP), and Norfolk Music (BMI). Contact: A&R Director. Music publisher, record company, record producer, and artist management. BMI, SESAC. Publishes 90 songs/year; publishes 15 new songwriters/year. Pays standard royalty or as specified in individual contracts.
How to Contact: Prefers cassette with any 1-4 songs and lyric sheet. SASE. Reports in 2 weeks.
Music: Mostly jazz and gospel. Recently published "Tainted Love" (by Ed Cobb), recorded by Soft Cell/Sire Records (rock/pop); "Take A Look Inside My Heart" (by David Benoit), recorded by D. Benoit/AVI Records (jazz fusion).

*EXPRESS MUSIC (LONDON) LTD., Yew Tree Studio, Charing Heath, Kent TN27 OAU England. (02337)3361. President: Siggy Jackson. PRS, MRS, MCPS. Music publisher, record company (Spectrum Records) and record producer (Siggy Jackson Productions, Ltd.). Publishes 15 songs/year; publishes 10 new songwriters/year. Pays standard royalty. Affiliated publishing firm: Tempo Music Ltd.
How to Contact: Prefers cassette or videocassette and lyric and lead sheet. SAE and IRC.
Music: Mostly country, rock, pop; also jazz. Recently published "Lets Have a Good Time," (by Jackson/Mallot), recorded by Sugarstick on Spectrum (pop).

FAIRCHILD MUSIC PUBLISHING, 13112 N. Halcourt, Norwalk CA 90650. (714)554-0851. Contact: Jerry Wood. Music publisher. BMI. Publishes 10 songs/year; publishes 6-8 new songwriters/year. Pays standard royalty.
How to Contact: Prefers 7½ ips reel-to-reel or cassette with 1-4 songs and lyric sheet. SASE. Reports in 2 weeks.
Music: Country, easy listening and MOR. Recently published "Many Are the Colors" and "I Won't Be

There" (by Roy Dee), recorded by R. Dee on Tribal Records (country); "99 Years" (by Ron Hayden), recorded by R. Hayden on Tribal Records (country); "Mine Is Yours to Share" and "Put Back the Pieces of My Heart" (by Wanda Davis), recorded by W. Davis on Tribal Records (country).

FAME PUBLISHING CO., INC., Box 2527, Muscle Shoals AL 35660. Affiliate: Rick Hall Music, Inc. (ASCAP). Publishing Manager: Walt Aldridge. Music publisher and record producer. BMI. Publishes 100 songs/year; publishes 5 new songwriters/year. Pays standard royalty.
How to Contact: Prefers cassette with 1-3 songs. "Please include legible lyrics." No tapes returned. Reports in 6 weeks. "No phone calls."
Music: Mostly country/pop and MOR; also R&B and top 40/pop. Recently published "She Sure Got Away with My Heart," (by Aldridge/Brasfield), recorded by John Anderson on Warner Bros. (country); "One Owner Heart," (by Aldridge/Brasfield/McAulley), recorded by T.G. Sheppard on Warner Bros. (country); and "They Never Had to Get Over You," (by McGuare-McGuare) recorded by Johnny Lee on Warner Bros. (country).

FAMOUS DOOR PUBLISHING CO., Box 16608, Milwaukee WI 53216. (414)461-0602. Representative: Odell Tillman. Music publisher, record company and record producer. BMI. Publishes 10 songs/year; publishes 4 new songwriters/year. Hires staff writers. Pays standard royalty.
How to Contact: Prefers cassette with 4-6 songs and lyric sheet. SASE. Reports in 3 weeks.
Music: Bluegrass, blues, jazz, R&B, rock and soul.

FESTIVE MUSIC, 2305 Hungary Rd., Richmond VA 23228. (804)264-0539. Contact: W.H. Smith. Music publisher, record company and record producer. BMI. Pays standard royalty.
How to Contact: Prefers cassette and lyric sheet. SASE. Reports in 1 month.
Music: Country, R&B, rock and top 40/pop.

FIESTA CITY PUBLISHERS, Box 5861, Santa Barbara CA 93150. (805)969-2891. President: Frank E. Cooke. ASCAP. Member AGAC, SBSA, SBSG. Publishes 4 songs/year; publishes 2 new songwriters/year. Pays standard royalty.
How to Contact: Query first. Prefers cassette with 1-3 songs and lead sheet. "Looking for tight, concise lyrics; memorable melodies; good prosody." SASE.
Music: Mostly MOR and country; also easy listening and gospel. Recently published "Clearly" (by Eddie Frank), recorded by J. Harris on Homegrown Records (adult contemporary); "My Favorite Dish Is You," "Motherhood, the Flag and Apple Pie" and "Cooking With Music," (by F. Cooke), recorded by J. Harris on Homegrown Records (adult contemporary).
Tips: "Submit (after query) clean typewritten double-spaced lyric sheet with lead sheet if available and simple cassette with clearly enunciated lyrics."

BOBBY FISCHER MUSIC, Suite 902, 50 Music Square W., Box 2333, Nashville TN 37203. (615)329-2278. Affiliates: Tessie's Tunes (BMI), Nashcal Music (BMI), Bobby's Beat (SESAC). General Manager: Bobby Fischer. Music publisher, record company and record producer, promoter and distributor. ASCAP. Member CMA, NSAI and FICAP. Publishes 50 songs/year; publishes 2 new songwriters/year. Pays standard royalty.
How to Contact: Prefers cassette with 2-3 songs and lyric sheet. "We review material as time permits and return (with SASE) *if* time permits." Reports as soon as possible.
Music: Country (modern) and MOR. Recently published "Breaking Even, (by Bobby Fischer), recorded by Lee Greenwood on MCA; and "The Eyes Have It," (by Bobby Fischer/Rick Giles), recorded by Lee Wright on Prairie Dust.

FOCAL POINT MUSIC PUBLISHERS, 922 McArthur Blvd., Warner Robins GA 31093. (912)923-6533. Manager: Ray Melton. Music publisher and record company. BMI. Publishes 8 songs/year; publishes 1 new songwriter/year. Pays standard royalty.
How to Contact: Prefers cassette with 2-4 songs and lead sheet. Prefers studio produced demos. SASE.
Music: Country, gospel and "old-style pop". Recently published "Tribute to George Jones" (by Wayne Holcomb/Steve Jacobs), and "My Family Reunion" (by W. Holcomb/Steve Jacobs), recorded by W. Holcomb on R-M Records (country); and "He's Big Enough" (by Charles Dennis), recorded by C. Dennis on Gospel Voice Records (gospel).
Tips: "Let the publisher know you're in the business as an entertainer or serious songwriter."

*FOLKTRACKS, 16 Brunswick Sq., Gloucester, GL1 1VG England. (0452)415110. Contact: Mr. Kennedy. PRS, MCPS. Music publisher, record company, record producer and music library. Publishes 100 songs/year; publishes 5 new songwriters/year. Pays standard royalty.
How to Contact: Write first and obtain permission to submit. Prefers cassette, 7½ ips reel-to-reel or

VHS (PAL) videocassette with 1-20 songs and lyric sheet or lead sheet. "Songs must be in the traditional or folk idiom." SAE and IRC. Reports in 2-3 weeks.
Music: Mostly traditional, folk and blues; also topical and protest. Recently published "Ring of Iron," (by Graeme Miles), recorded by Ewan MacColl on EMI (protest); "Peter's Private Army," (by Martin Graebe), recorded by Johnny Collins on SFA (historical); and "Purdue Heather," (by Frank McPeake), recorded by Chieftains on Clad (Irish folk).
Tips: "Make use of the most powerful techniques of your own tradition."

*FREE & SHOW MUSIC, Suite #398, 2554 Lincoln Blvd., Marina del Rey CA 90292. (213)822-7629. President: Ron Patton. Professional Manager: Laurie Roberts. ASCAP, BMI. Music publisher, record company (Baywest Records) and record producer (Baywest Productions). Publishes 10 songs/year; publishes 3 new songwriters/year. Pays standard royalty. Affiliated publishing firm: Honeymaker Music.
How to Contact: Prefers cassette with 2-4 songs and lyric sheet. SASE. Reports in 3 weeks.
Music: Mostly R&B, soul, dance-oriented and top 40/pop; rock (all types), easy listening and gospel. Recently published "Your Key Fits," (by L. Roberts/R. Patton/T. Elliot/M. Peyser), recorded by Laurie Roberts on Baywest (R&B dance/pop); "Don't Blame Me," (by Laurie Roberts and Ron Patton), recorded by Michael Peyser on Baywest (top 40/pop/rock); and "Midnight Fantasies," (by Betsy Fiedorczyk), recorded by Lizz Fiedora on Satin Sounds (top 40/pop).
Tips: "No home tapes. Be prepare to rewrite if required."

FRICK MUSIC PUBLISHING CO., 404 Bluegrass Ave., Madison TN 37115. (615)865-6380. Contact: Bob Frick. Music publisher, record company and record producer. BMI. Publishes 50 songs/year; publishes 2 new songwriters/year. Pays standard royalty.
How to Contact: Call first. Prefers 7½ ips reel-to-reel or cassette with 2-10 songs and lyric sheet. SASE. Reports in 1 month.
Music: Mostly gospel; also country, rock and top 40/pop. Recently published "I Love You in Jesus," (by Bob Frick); "Here I Am," (by Marlitta Boyce); and "I Got It Together," (by Jan Kelley), all recorded by B. Frick on R.E.F. (gospel).

*THE FRICON ENTERTAINMENT CO., INC., 1048 S. Ogden Dr., Los Angeles CA 90019. (213)931-7323. Professional Manager: John McCullough. BMI, ASCAP. Music publisher. Publishes 50 songs/year; publishes 25 new songwriters/year. Employs songwriters on a salary basis. Pays standard royalty.
How to Contact: Write first and obtain permission to submit. Prefers cassette with 2 songs and lyric sheet. Does not return unsolicited material. Reports in 4-6 weeks.
Music: Mostly pop/rock, R&B/pop, dance, and country crossover.

FROZEN INCA MUSIC, Suite 201, 450 14th St., Atlanta GA 30318. (404)873-3918. President: Michael Rothschild. Music publisher and record company. BMI. Publishes 10 songs/year; publishes 3 new songwriters/year. Pays standard royalty.
How to Contact: Write or call first. Prefers cassette with 4-10 songs and lyric sheet. SASE. Reports in 1 month.
Music: Mostly blues, dance-oriented and progressive; also jazz, MOR, R&B, rock, soul and top 40/pop. Recently published "Red Dress" (by Tinsley Ellis), recorded by The Heartfixers (blues); "Forever More" (by Ricky Keller), recorded by Keller (pop); and "Mr. Bad" (by Peckham, Cancro and Smith), recorded by It (dance).

*FUNKTURM-VERLAGE MUSIKPRODUKTION/FUNKY RECORDS PRODUKTION, Postfach 0267, Liebenowzeile 3, 1000 West Berlin 41, West Germany. (030)796 17 69. GEMA, GVL. Music publisher, record company and record producer. Publishes 15-20 songs/year; publishes 2-3 new songwriters/year. Pays standard royalty. Affiliated publishing firms: Edition Vansche/Edition Munich GmbH, Edition BEGA/Edition Bifu.
How to Contact: Prefers cassette, reel-to-reel or videocassette. SAE and IRC. Reports in 1 month.
Music: Mostly folk and pop; also big band songs, film music and musicals/TV music. Recently published "Flip Side," (Dixie Jo), on Teldec (instrumental pop); "Ein Boy," (by J. Schentai/F. Huppermans), on Decca/PA (slow); and "Souviens Toi," (by J. Schentai/Huppermans), on Decca/PA (pop).

Market conditions are constantly changing! If this is 1987 or later, buy the newest edition of *Songwriter's Market* at your favorite bookstore or order directly from Writer's Digest Books.

FUTURE STEP SIRKLE, Box 2095, Philadelphia PA 19103. (215)844-8736. President: Krun Vallatine. Vice President: S. Deane Henderson. Music publisher, record company and management firm.
ASCAP. Publishes 10-15 songs/year; publishes 6 new songwriters/year. Pays standard royalty.
How to Contact: Prefers cassette or VHS videocassette with 4-8 songs and lyric sheets. Does not return
unsolicited material. Reports in 2 weeks.
Music: Dance-oriented, easy listening, gospel, MOR, R&B, rock, soul, top 40/pop, funk and heavy
metal. Recently published "Hot Number" (by John Fitch), recorded by The Racers on Future Step
Sirkle Records (heavy rock); "Delirious" recorded by Molecules of Force on Future Step Sirkle Re-
cords (new wave); "Save Me Jesus" and "In God's Hand" (by Verdell Colbert), recorded by V. Colbert
& Off Spring Gospel Singers/Future Step Sirkle Records (gospel).

FYDAQ MUSIC, 240 E. Radcliffe Dr., Claremont CA 91711. (714)624-0677. Affiliate: Jubilation
Music (BMI). President: Gary Buckley. Music publisher and production company. BMI. Member
ACM, CMA, GMA, NARAS, Audio Engineering. Publishes 30-40 songs/year.
How to Contact: Prefers 7½ ips reel-to-reel or cassette with 1-4 songs and lead or lyric sheet. SASE.
Reports in 3 weeks.
Music: Country, easy listening, gospel, MOR, progressive, rock (country), soul and top 40/pop. Re-
cently published "She Comes to Me Softly" recorded by Borderline on Quikstar Records (top 40/pop);
"Still in the Game" recorded by Michael Noll on Gottabehit Records (top 40/pop); and "It's A Long
Lonesome Walk," recorded by Finley Duke on Majega Records.

G.G. MUSIC, INC., Box 374, Fairview NJ 07022. (201)941-3987. Affiliate: Wazuri Music. President: Linwood Simon. Music publisher and artist management company. BMI. Pays standard royalty.
How to Contact: Prefers cassette with 1-2 songs and lyric sheet. SASE. Reports in 3 weeks.
Music: Dance-oriented, R&B, rock (light), soul and melodies. Recently published "Strive" (by Linwood Simon), recorded by Gloria Gaynor/CBS Records (disco rock); "Mack Side" (by L. Simon), recorded by G. Gaynor/Atlantic Records (R&B); and "More Than Enough" (by G. Gaynor), recorded by
G. Gaynor/CBS Records (love ballad).
Tips: "The writer should understand that he must recognize all the elements needed to make a hit record:
strong lyrics, good hook and an overall progressive and commercial sound the buying public can relate
to. Love songs are 90% of records sold."

AL GALLICO MUSIC CORP., Suite 606, 9301 Wilshire Blvd., Beverly Hills CA 90210. (213)274-
0165. Affiliates: Algee (BMI), Altam (BMI), Galleon (ASCAP) and Easy Listening (ASCAP). Contact: Publishing Director/A&R. Music publisher. BMI, ASCAP. Member NMPA. Payment differs from
song to song.
How to Contact: Prefers cassette with 2-4 songs and lead sheet. SASE. Reports in 3 weeks.
Music: Country, easy listening and top 40/pop. "We're very strong in contemporary country and crossover material." Recently published "Swingin' " (by John Anderson and Lionel Delmore), recorded by
J. Anderson on Warner Bros. Records (country crossover); "Jose Cuervo" (by Cindy Jordan), recorded
by Shelly West on Riva-Warner Bros. Records (country); and "Black Sheep" (by Daniel D. Darst), recorded by Robert Altman and John Anderson on Warner Bros. Records.
Tips: "Be aware of the artists we work with and the artists who record outside material. Study their
styles. Study the songs being played on the radio; they're being played because a number of people believed in them and said yes. Come up with fresh ideas and titles; vivid, sincere, relationship-oriented lyrics; catchy melodies; tight structures and contemporary chords and feel. Remember the music industry
is based on, and needs, great songs."

AL GALLICO MUSIC CORP., Suite 201, 47 Music Square E., Nashville TN 37203. (615)327-2773.
Music publisher. BMI and ASCAP. Pays standard royalty.
How to Contact: "Send SASE for a copy of our review policy."
Music: Country and country cross-over. Recently published "Didn't See a Thing," recorded by George
Jones and Ray Charles; "The Ride," recorded by David Allan Coe; and "Winding Down," recorded by
Lacy J. Dalton.

GAMMILL-MURPHY MUSIC, 2913 95th St., Lubbock TX 79423. (806)745-5992. A&R Director:
Bill Gammill. Music publisher and record producer. BMI. Publishes 8 songs/year; publishes 1 new
songwriter/year. Pays standard royalty.
How to Contact: Prefers cassette with 1-3 songs and lyric sheet. SASE. Reports in 4 weeks.
Music: Mostly Christian pop and contemporary Christian; also church/religious and gospel. Recently
published "Square Circles," written and recorded by Gammill and Murphy; "Beauty for Ashes," (by
Russ Murphy) and "A Way for You," (by Bill Gammill), both recorded by Gammill and Murphy (all
Christian).
Tips: "We are looking for material that is original, fresh and theologically sound."

GARRON MUSIC, Newtown St., Kilsyth, Glasgow G65 0JX Scotland. 44-0236-821081. Director: Bill Garden. Music publisher and record producer. PRS, Phonographic Performance Ltd. Publishes 5 songs/year; publishes 3 new songwriters/year. Pays standard royalty.
How to Contact: Prefers cassette with 3-6 songs and lyric sheet. SAE and IRC. Reports in 1 month.
Music: Mostly country, MOR and folk; also dance-oriented, easy listening, gospel, jazz, R&B and top 40/pop. Recently published "Key to My Heart," (by K.S. Mouland); "Love on Cat Wal," and "Rich Mean Bitch," (by Gino Ciancio and Marie Martalo).

*GATOR TRACKS & SOUND, 104 E. Main, Houma LA 70360. (504)851-4602. Contact: Engineer/ Manager. BMI. Music publisher (Nawlins Publishing) and record producer (Charlie Positerry). Publishes 5 songs/year; publishes 2 new songwriters/year. Pays standard royalty. Affiliated publishing firms: A-Rose Publishing, Gris-Gris Publishing.
How to Contact: Prefers cassette or 7½ or 15 ips reel-to-reel with 4 songs and lyric sheet. Does not return unsolicited material. Reports in 4 weeks.
Music: Mostly pop/rock, rock (heavy) and pop/country; also blues, gospel and funk. Recently published "Glory Bound," (by Glen Beregron), "Voyager," (by Gerrard Melancon), and "Carol Berzas," (by Carol Berzas), all recorded by Gator Tracks on Gator Records.

GERVASI PUBLISHING CO., Box 4547, Redding CA 96099. (916)222-1401. President: James A. Gervasi. Music publisher, record company, and management and distribution firm. BMI. Publishes 4 songs/year; publishes 2 new songwriters/year. Pays standard royalty.
How to Contact: Prefers cassette with 3-5 songs and lyric sheet. SASE. Reports in 2 weeks.
Music: Mostly country; also country rock. Recently published "Midnight Cabaret" (by Jody Peterson); "Alice in Dallas" (by Merle Haggard and Dave Kirby); and "Don't Lead Me On" (by Wyvon Alexander); recorded by W. Alexander/Gervasi Records (country).

*GIBSON DAVIDSONG PUBLISHING, Box K-1150, Buna TX 77612. (409)423-2521. General Manager: James Gibson. Acting A&R Director: Aline Gibson. Music publisher. ASCAP. Publishes 10-15 songs/year; publishes 3-4 new songwriters/year. Pays standard royalty.
How to Contact: Prefers cassette with 1-4 songs and lyric and/or lead sheet. SASE. Reports ASAP.
Music: Christian/gospel, all styles. Recently published "Running Back to You," (by Eva Bonn/Nancy Cyril), recorded by The Harbingers.

*DON GILBERT MUSIC, 1450 Terrell, Beaumont TX 77701. (713)832-0748. President: Don Gilbert. Music publisher, record company and record producer. BMI. Publishes 10 songs/year; publishes 4 new songwriters/year. Pays standard royalty.
How to Contact: Prefers 7½ ips reel-to-reel or cassette with 2-10 songs and lyric sheet. SASE. Reports in 1 month.
Music: Religious only. Recently published "Five Rooms of Memories" and "The Other One" (by Don Gilbert), recorded by D. Gilbert/Gold Guitar Records (country); and "Souvenirs of My Mind" (By D. Gilbert), recorded by D. Gilbert/Rosco Records (country).

*GIL-GAD MUSIC, 5500 Troost, Kansas MO 64110. (816)361-8455. General Manager/Publisher: Eugene Gold. ASCAP, BMI. Music publisher and record producer. Publishes 30 or more songs/year; publishes 10 or more new songwriters/year. Pays standard royalty. Affiliates: 3G's Music Co., Eugene Gold Music.
How to Contact: Prefers cassette or videocassette with 4-6 songs and lyric sheet. SASE. Reports in 8 weeks.
Music: Mostly R&B, rock and top 40 pop; also disco/dance, gospel and jazz. Recently pubished "Magic," (by Cal-Green, Ronnie & Vicky), recorded by Suspension on 3G's (R&B/top pop); "Bootie Cutie," written and recorded by Robert Newsome on 3G's (R&B); and "Diamond Feather," (by M. Murf), recorded by Bad News Band on NMI (R&B).

GOD'S WORLD, 27335 Penn St., Inkster MI 48141. Affiliates: Manfield Music (BMI), Stephen Enoch Johnson Music (ASCAP). President: Elder Otis G. Johnson. Music publisher, record company and record producer. SESAC. Member American Mechanical Rights Association, GMA, BMA, NARAS. Publishes 10 songs/year; publishes 5 new songwriters/year. Works with lyricists and composers and teams collaborators. Pays standard royalty.
How to Contact: Write or call first or arrange personal interview. Prefers 7½ ips reel-to-reel or cassette with 3 songs. SASE. Reports in 1 month.
Music: Country, easy listening, gospel, church/religious, and jazz. Recently published "More Sad Good-byes" and "You Take Me High" (by Diana Warden), recorded by D. Warden/ASPRO Records (country).

EUGENE GOLD MUSIC, 5500 Troost, Kansas City MO 64110. (816)361-8455. President: Eugene Gold. Music publisher, record company and record producer. BMI, ASCAP. Publishes 24 songs/year; publishes 4 new songwriters/year. Pays standard royalty.
How to Contact: Prefers cassette or videocassette with 4-8 songs and lyric sheet. SASE. Reports in 1 month.
Music: Mostly R&B and gospel; also church/religious, jazz and soul. Recently published "Diamond Feather" (by M. Murf), recorded by Bad News Band/NMI Records (R&B); "You Left Me At A Bad Bad Time" (by R. Sanders), recorded by Ronnie & Vicky/3G's Records (R&B); and "Baby We Can Make It" (by V. Barbour), recorded by Ronnie & Vicky/3G's Records (R&B).
Tips: "Submit a good demo tape that includes songs with a good R&B beat."

*GOLD HILL MUSIC, INC., 5032 Lankershim Blvd., North Hollywood CA 91601. (818)766-7142. Managing Director: Ken Weiss. ASCAP, BMI. Music publisher. Publishes 20-25 songs/year; publishes 2 new songwriters/year. Pays standard and varying royalties. Affiliated publishing firms: Kenwon Music, Catpatch Music, and Stephen Stills Music.
How to Contact: Call first and obtain permission to submit. Prefers cassette with 3 songs and lyric sheet. SASE. Reports in 4 weeks.
Music: Mostly rock. Recently published "Southern Cross," (by M. Curtis), recorded by Crosby, Stills & Nash on Atlantic (rock); "Step On Out," (by C. Hillman), recorded by Oak Ridge Boys on MCA (country); and "Stranger," written and recorded by Stephen Stills on Atlantic (rock).
Tips: Looking for "well constructed, commercial songs with original ideas."

*GOLDEN ARROW RECORDS, 11 Ruston Mews, London W11 1RB, England. Chairman: John Spiers. Music publisher and record company. Estab. 1985. Pays 60% royalty.
How to Contact: Prefers cassette or videocassette with 3 songs. "Background of songwriter is invaluable." SAE and IRC. Reports in 4 weeks.
Music: Mostly rock and blues.

GOLDEN DAWN MUSIC, 26177 Kinyon Dr., Taylor MI 48180. (313)292-5281. President: Peggy La Sorda. Music publisher and record company. BMI. Publishes 10 songs/year; publishes 2 new songwriters/year. Works with composers. Pays standard royalty.
How to Contact: Write first with SASE. Original unpublished material only. Prefers cassette with 1-4 songs and lyric sheet. Reports in 3 weeks.
Music: Mostly country, pop and top 40; also dance-oriented, easy listening, folk, gospel, MOR, top 40/pop and gospel.
Tips: "Material should reflect today's market."

GOLDEN GUITAR MUSIC, Box 40602, Tucson AZ 85717. President: Jeff Johnson. Music publisher. BMI. Publishes 10-15 songs/year. Pays standard royalty.
How to Contact: Prefers 7½ or 15 ips reel-to-reel or cassette with 2-6 songs and lyric sheet. SASE. Reports in 1 month.
Music: Mostly country; also bluegrass, church/religious, gospel and light rock. Recently published "Willy's Boy" (by Jeff Johnson), recorded by Brenda D./Half Moon Records (country); "Wearing a Smile of a Clown" (by Jerry Haymes), recorded by J. Haymes/Umpire Records (country); and "What's This World Coming To?" (by J. Johnson), recorded by Jeff Johnson/Dewl Records (country/religious).
Tips: "Make an effort to submit a good quality demo—not necessarily complicated but clear and clean."

*GORILLA MUSIK-VERLAG GMBH, Hallerstr. 72, D-2000 Hamburg 13, West Germany. (40)4102161. Contact: Mary Dostal. GEMA. Music publisher, record company and record producer. Publishes 50 songs/year; publishes 10 new songwriters/year. Pays 60% royalty.
How to Contact: Prefers cassette or videocassette and lyric sheet. SAE and IRC. Reports in 2 weeks.
Music: Mostly rock, MOR and blues. Recently published "Der Spieler," written and recorded by Achim Reichel on Ahorn (rock); "No Go," (by Sippie Wallace), recorded by Axel Swingenberger on Vagabond (boogie); and "Volle Segel," written and recorded by Klaus Weiland on Ahorn (instrumental).
Tips: "Send everything. Your worst may be our best."

THE GRAND PASHA PUBLISHER, 5615 Melrose Ave., Hollywood CA 90038. (213)466-3507. Affiliate: The Pasha Music Co. (ASCAP). President: Spencer Proffer. General Manager: Carol Peters. A&R Director: Gail Lee. Music publisher, record company and record producer. Publishes 100 songs/year; publishes 4 new songwriters/year. Pays standard royalty.
How to Contact: Call first. Prefers cassette with 2-4 songs. SASE. Reports in 6 weeks.
Music: Rock and top 40/pop.

GRAVENHURST MUSIC, 1469 3rd Ave., New Brighton PA 15066. (412)847-0111. President: Jerry Reed. Music publisher and record company. BMI. Publishes 30-50 songs/year; publishes 35 new songwriters/year. Pays standard royalty.
How to Contact: Prefers 7½ ips reel-to-reel or cassette with 1-3 songs and lead and lyric sheets. SASE. Reports in 3 weeks.
Music: Mostly pop, country and gospel; also blues, country, disco, easy listening, MOR, rock and soul. Recently published "Warm Eyes," written and recorded by Chris Denem on Jeree (country); "Love, I Know Your Name," written and recorded by Kenny Blake/Green Dolphin (jazz); and "I Can't Wait Anymore," (by Joe Baugher), recorded by Dakota/Jeree (country).

*BILL GREEN MUSIC, 10452 Sentinel, San Antonio TX 78217. (512)654-8773. Contact: Bill Green. BMI. Music publisher, record company (BGM Records) and record producer. Publishes 5 new songwriters/year. Pays standard royalty.
How to Contact: Prefers cassette with 3 songs and lyric sheet. SASE.
Music: Mostly contemporary country and traditional country. Recently published "A Texas Songwriter," written and recorded by David Price on BGM (country); "Louisiana Heatwave," written and recorded by Bobby Jenkins on Zone 7 (country); and "Tell Me How," (by Allen Greene), recorded by Jack Young on BGM (country).

GROOVESVILLE PRODUCTIONS, 15855 Wyoming, Detroit MI 48238. (313)861-2363. Affiliates: Groovesville Music (BMI), Conquistador (ASCAP), Double Sharp (ASCAP) and Sugar Happy Music (SESAC). Director: Will Davis. Music publisher, record company and record producer. BMI. Member NMPA. Publishes 50 songs/year; publishes 10 new songwriters/year. Teams collaborators. Pays standard royalty.
How to Contact: Query. Prefers cassette with 2-3 songs and lyric sheet. SASE. Reports in 4 weeks.
Music: Disco, easy listening, MOR, progressive, R&B, rock, urban contemporary, soul and top 40/pop. Recently published "In the Rain" (by Tony Hester), recorded by Blue Magic/Atlantic Recording; "I've Been Born Again" (by D. Davis and J. Dean), recorded by Glenn Frey/Elektra/Aslyum/Nonesuch Records; "You've Got It" (by L.J. Reynolds), "You & Me" (by William Brown), "Special Effects" (by Calhoun and Stegall), and *Travelin*, all recorded by L.J. Reynolds/Capitol Records.

FRANK GUBALA MUSIC, Hillside Rd., Cumberland RI 02864. (401)333-6097. Contact: Frank Gubala. Music publisher and booking agency.
How to Contact: Prefers cassette and lead sheet. Does not return unsolicited material. Reports in 1 month.
Music: Blues, disco, easy listening, MOR, top 40/pop, rock and country.

*GWYNN PUBLISHING CO., Penygroes, Caernarfon, Gwynedd, Wales. 44-0286-881-797. Leading publishers of Welsh folk songs and dances in printed form. "We specialize in songs and arrangements for choirs (male, female and SATB) as well as Welsh classical solos and children's songs."
How to Contact: "Send for more information to John Roberts at the above address."

HALBEN MUSIC PUBLISHING INC., Suite 38, 4824 Cote des Neiges Rd., Montreal, Quebec H3V 1G4, Canada. (514)739-4774. Affiliates: Rainy River Music Ltd. (PROCAN), Tranzit Music (CAPAC), In-Tranzit Music (PROCAN), Lilbec Music (CAPAC), Angebec Music (PROCAN), Betanne Music (CAPAC), Lapapala Music (PROCAN), Earth Born Music (PROCAN), Eastend Music (CAPAC) and Westend Music (PROCAN). Professional Manager: Ben Kaye. Music publisher and record producer. CAPAC. Publishes approximately 100 songs/year; publishes 6 new songwriters/year. Pays standard royalty.
How to Contact: Prefers cassette with 2-3 songs and lyric or lead sheet. SAE and IRC. Reports in approximately 1 month.
Music: Blues, easy listening, MOR, R&B, rock (hard, country), soul and top 40/pop. Recently published "Lean on Me," written and recorded by Missing In Action/QMS (contemporary rock); "Elle Est Belle" (by Eddy Marnay and Patrick Lemaitre) recorded by Peter Pringle/A&M (ballad); and "Une Columbe," (by Marcel Lefebvre and Paul Baillargeon), recorded by Celine Dion/TBS (ballad).
Tips: "Songs should have an interesting story line (or catch phrases), and a strong hook in chorus or bridge. Keep song within 2½-3½ minute range and don't over-arrange the idea. Simple guitar/vocal or piano/vocal is acceptable."

HALNAT MUSIC PUBLISHING CO., Box 37156, Cincinnati OH 45222. (513)531-7605. Affiliate: Saul Avenue Publishing (BMI). President: Saul Halper. Music publisher. ASCAP. Member NMPA. Publishes 6 songs/year; publishes 3 new songwriters/year. Pays standard royalty.
How to Contact: Prefers cassette with 2-4 songs and lyric sheet. SASE. Reports in 2 weeks.

Music: Bluegrass, blues, country, gospel, R&B and soul. Recently published "Kansas City," recorded by the Beatles (rock); "Ain't Never Seen So Much Rain Before," recorded by Christine Kittrell (soul); and "Meet Me at the Station" (by R. Davis, J. Railey and G. Redd), recorded by Freddy King (rock).

*HAMMER MUSIK GMBH, Esslinger Strasse 42, 7000 Stuttgart, West Germany. (0711)247 5530. Manager: Ingo Kleinhammer. GEMA. Music publisher and record company (Avenue). Publishes 100 songs/year; publishes 10 new songwriters/year. Pays standard royalty. Affiliated publishing firms: Belmont, Vertex, Kraut, and Hor & Lies.
How to Contact: Prefers cassette. SAE and IRC.
Music: Mostly rock and pop; also jazz.

HANNAN-PHILLIPS MUSIC, 1819 W. Thome St., Chicago IL 60660. President: Stoney Phillips. Music publisher, record company and record producer. BMI. Publishes 2 songs/year; publishes 1 new songwriter/year. Pays standard royalty.
How to Contact: Prefers cassette with 1-3 songs on demo and lyric sheet. SASE. Reports in 3 weeks.
Music: Mostly country/crossover and MOR; also easy listening, rock and top 40/pop. Recently published "Baby Please Stay" (by R. Rice), recorded by R. Rice/Stonedog Records (pop); "I Don't Need You" (by A. Dawson), (MOR); and "Forgive a Fool" (by R. Mann), (country).

*GEOFFREY HANSEN ENTS., LTD., Box 63, Orinda CA 94563. (415)937-6469. A&R Representative: J. Malcom Baird. BMI. Music publisher, record company (World Artist), record producer and personal management production of TV, concerts and sporting events. Publishes 20 songs/year; publishes varying number of new songwriters/year. Pays standard or negotiable royalty.
How to Contact: Prefers cassette or ¾ Umatic or ½ VHS videocassette with lyric sheet and lead sheets. SASE. Reports in 4-6 weeks.
Music: Mostly top 40, MOR, rock-a-billy, and country-rock; also TV, motion picture and theatrical music, blues, French and Spanish. Recently published "Dragon's Breath," and "Bloody Battle," (by A. Swan), recorded by Tokyo Explosion on CBS/Sony (soundtrack); and "Lotus Flower," (by L. Starkey), recorded by London West End Show Cast on Columbia (show tune).
Tips: "Send a neat and clear package. We are not interested in form letters or material that is sent to other companies."

HANSEN-O'BRIEN MUSIC, Suite 1, 3120 Casa de Campo, San Mateo CA 94403. President: E.J. O'Brien. Music publisher, record company and record producer. BMI. Publishes 10 songs/year; publishes 10 new songwriters/year. Pays standard royalty.
How to Contact: Prefers cassette with 3-6 songs and lyric sheet. Prefers studio produced demos. Does not return unsolicited material. Reports in 2 weeks.
Music: Mostly country crossover, easy rock, pop, MOR and AOR; also oldies and top 40. Recently published "That's Wrong," (by Paul Hansen and Dale Hansen), recorded by the Hansen Brothers (country); "Let's Forget the Overtures" written and recorded by P. Hansen; and "Enough Is Enough," (by P. Hansen and E.J. O'Brien), recorded by the Hansen Brothers.

*HARLANDALE MUSIC, 705 E. Pioneer Dr., Irving TX 75061. (214)438-8248. Contact: Phil York. ASCAP, BMI. Music publisher and record producer. Publishes 12 songs/year; publishes 8 new songwriters/year. Pays standard royalty of copyright value.
How to Contact: Prefers cassette only with maximum 4 songs and lyric sheet or lead sheet. Reports in 4 weeks.
Music: Mostly rock/pop, country and blues. Recently published: "That Flame Keeps Burning," (by Greene/Roth), recorded by Annie Rowe (country); "Twelve Pound Perch," written and recorded by Ricky Joe Payne on Planet Earth (country); and "Terminal Loneliness," (by A. Greene), recorded by Jill Bradley on Planet Earth (hard rock).
Tips: Looking for "clean, clear demos, with vocals prominent (not excessive intros or solo instrumentals), strong hooks, and developed story ideas. Eliminate long, boring introverted themes. The song will always be the root of the industry. Write songs on the front lines of what interests people in society, but do it differently and you'll have hits."

*HARMONY STREET MUSIC, Box 4107, Kansas City KS 66104. (913)299-2881. President: Charlie Beth. ASCAP, BMI. Music publisher. Estab. 1984. Pays standard royalty. Affiliated publishing firm: Harmony Lane Music.
How to Contact: Prefers cassette with 1-3 songs and lyric sheet or lead sheet. SASE. Reports in 1-3 weeks.
Music: Country (all types). "We publish any and all types of country music." Recently published "To Be Worthy," (by Steven J. Hale), recorded by Rod Hopkins on DMI Records (gospel); and "You'll Be

Better Off Tommorrow," (by Ed Morgan, Charlie Beth and Rod Hopkins), recorded by R. Hopkins on DMI Records (country gospel).

Tips: "Lyrics and melody must be strong and demo must be clear and clean with voice out front."

JOHN HARVEY PUBLISHING CO., Box 245, Encinal TX 78019. President: John Harvey. Music publisher and record producer. BMI. Member Harry Fox Agency. Publishes 24 songs/year; publishes 2 new songwriters/year. Pays standard royalty.
How to Contact: Prefers cassette with 3-6 songs and lyric sheet. Will accept 7½ reel-to-reel. Will return material with return postage. Include brief resume. No query necessary. Reports as soon as possible.
Music: Country, Latin, polkas and waltzes. Recently published "La Untouchable," written and recorded by John Harvey/Mundial (polka); "El Pato," (by Jesus Garza), recorded by "El Chivo"/Mundial (Latin); and "Muchachita Linda," written and recorded by Oscar Gonzalez/Sol 5 (Latin).
Tips: "Make demo as clear-sounding as possible, even if simple. Make all other enclosed material, such as lyric sheets, bios, etc., neat. Send the best material you have. Buy bulk cassettes at low price for demos, and let publishers keep your tape for future reference. This increases chances of your song being reviewed more than once. Needs are changing constantly."

HE ROSE PUBLISHING, 1098 Rose Ave., El Centro CA 92243. (619)352-5774. Contact: Danny Berg. Music publisher and record company. BMI. Member Gospel Music Association. Publishes 20 songs/year; publishes 9 new songwriters/year. Pays standard royalty.
How to Contact: Prefers cassette with 1-3 songs and lyric sheet. SASE. Reports in 6 months.
Music: Contemporary/Christian, church and gospel. Recently published "He Died That We Might Live" (by Bruce Craw and Tom Horne), recorded by Jonah and the Whalers/He Rose Records (contemporary Christian); and "Day by Day" (by Domingo Ulloa, Sam Cannon and B. Craw), recorded by Jonah and the Whalers/He Rose Records (contemporary Christian).
Tips: Looking for "inspirational message lyrics and good melodic structure."

HEAVEN SONGS, 14116 E. Whittier Blvd., Whittier CA 90605. (213)945-5449. Contact: Dave Paton. Music publisher, record company and record producer. BMI. Publishes 30-50 songs/year; publishes 10 new songwriters/year. Pays standard royalty.
How to Contact: Prefers 7½ ips reel-to-reel or cassette with 3-6 songs and lyric sheet. SASE. Reports in 2 weeks.
Music: Country, dance-oriented, easy listening, folk, jazz, MOR, progressive, R&B, rock, soul and top 40/pop.
Tips: Looking for "better quality demos."

HEAVY JAMIN' MUSIC, Box 4740, Nashville TN 37216. (615)865-4740. Affiliates: Sus-Den (ASCAP) and Valynn (BMI). Manager: S.D. Neal. Music publisher. BMI, ASCAP. Publishes 20 songs/year; publishes 6 new songwriters/year. Pays standard royalty.
How to Contact: Prefers 7½ ips reel-to-reel or cassette with 2-6 songs and lyric sheet. SASE. Reports in 3 weeks.
Music: Mostly rock and country; also bluegrass, blues, easy listening, folk, gospel, jazz, MOR, progressive, Spanish, R&B, soul, top 40/pop and rock-a-billy. Recently published "Bright Lights" (by D. Derwald), recorded by Dixie Dee/Terock Records (rock-a-billy); "Home Again" (by L. Lynde), recorded by Linda Lynn/Terock Records (country); and "Lonesome and Blue" (by W. Curtiss), recorded by Wade Curtiss/Lee Records (R&B).

HEDLEY MUSIC GROUP, 71 Rutland Rd., Chesterfield, Derbyshire S40 1ND England. 44-0246-79976. Affiliates: Michael James Music, Hardwick Music, March Music, Hedley Songs and Vehicle Music. Director: Tony Hedley. Music publisher, record company and record producer. MCPS. Member MPA. Publishes 2 new songwriters/year. Has not yet, but would listen to songs from US songwriters. Pays negotiable royalty; royalties paid directly to US songwriters or through US publishing affiliate.
How to Contact: Write first. Prefers cassette with 1-4 songs and lyric sheet. Tapes should be clearly labeled. SAE and IRC. Reports in 2 weeks.
Music: Mostly pop and folk; also country, rock (all types) and soul. Recently published "Fiddlers Green" (by John Conolly), recorded by over forty acts including George Hamilton IV, the Dubliners, Max Boyce, the Yetties, De Hofner (top German band).
Tips: "We are looking for country/pop crossover and rock material for existing artists. We also would like to acquire masters."

JAMES HENDRIX, COMPOSER AND PUBLISHER, (formerly Grawick Music), Box 90639, Nashville TN 37209. (615)321-3319. Affiliates: Mester Music (BMI), Twelve Robes Music (ASCAP), Jimerlean Music (BMI), Carrie Records Co. and Disciple Records. Music publisher and record compa-

ny. Publishes 20 songs/year; publishes 6 new songwriters/year. Pays standard royalty.
How to Contact: Prefers cassette with 3-4 songs and lyric sheet. SASE. Reports in one month.
Music: Church/religious, gospel, hymns and anthems. Recently published "Song Of The Oppressed Christians" (by Daniel G. Zimmerman and James Hendrix); "Pieces Scattered In The Wind" and "My Shakey Castle" (by Lyle T. Carlson); and "Rings and Promises" (by Albert Chew).

HIGH POCKETS PUBLISHING, 527 Meadow Dr., West Seneca NY 14224. (716)675-3974. President: Nicholas Gugliuzza. Music publisher and record company. BMI and ASCAP. Publishes 40 songs/year; publishes 19 new songwriters/year. Pays standard royalty.
How to Contact: Prefers cassette with 1-3 songs and lyric sheet. SASE. Reports in 1 month.
Music: Mostly rock; also bluegrass and blues. Recently published "Undeniable," "Don't Shoot My Dog" and "Down in the Valley" (by Paul Benhatzel), recorded by P. Benhatzel/High Pockets Records (rock).

HIGHEST PRAISE PUBLISHING, Box 1869, Hollywood CA 90078. (213)564-1008. Contact: Kent Washburn or Philip Nicholas. Music publisher, record company and record producer. BMI. Member NARAS, GMA. Publishes 30 songs/year; publishes 1-2 new songwriters/year. Pays standard royalty.
How to Contact: Prefers cassette with 2-4 songs and lyric sheet. Prefers studio produced demos. SASE. Reports in 1 month.
Music: Gospel. Recently published "Dedicated," (by P. Nicholas, K. Washburn, B. Bickelhaupt), recorded by Nicholas (gospel); "Worthy," written and recorded by Rodney Friend (gospel); and "We Can Do It," written and recorded by Vernessa Mitchell (gospel).

HITSBURGH MUSIC CO., Box 195, 157 Ford Ave., Gallatin TN 37066. (615)452-1479. Affiliate: 7th Day Music (BMI). President/General Manager: Harold Gilbert. Music publisher. BMI. Publishes 25 songs/year; publishes 10 new songwriters/year. Pays standard royalty.
How to Contact: Prefers cassette with 2-4 songs and lead sheet. Prefers studio produced demos. Does not return unsolicited material. Reports in 3 weeks.
Music: Country and MOR. Recently published "Don't Let Me Down," (by Gilbert and Brinkley), recorded by Cissy Gilbert (MOR); and "Take the Key," (by Gilbert and Brinkley), recorded by Damon King (MOR).

*HOLLYWOOD MUSIC/HOLLYWOOD RECORDS, 38-40 Upper Clapton Rd., London E5 8BQ, England. (01)806 0071. Managing Director: John Edward. PRS, MCPS. Music publisher, record company and record producer (John Edward Music, Ltd.). Publishes 100 songs/year; publishes 6 new songwriters/year. Employs songwriters on a salary basis. Pays standard royalty.
How to Contact: Prefers cassette or VHS videocassette. SAE and IRC. Reports in 1 week.
Music: Mostly top 40; also rock and country.
Tips: "The material should have as its subject 'love,' 'you-me,' or variations on it, should have a strong hook, and concentrate on simplicity of lyrical and musical style to suit typical top 40 hit songs."

HOLY SPIRIT MUSIC, Box 31, Edmonton KY 42129. (502)432-3183. President: W. Junior Lawson. Music publisher and record company. BMI. Member GMA, International Association of Gospel Music Publishers. Publishes 10 songs/year; publishes 2 new songwriters/year. Pays standard royalty.
How to Contact: Call first. Prefers 7½ ips reel-to-reel or cassette with any number of songs and lyric sheet. SASE. Reports in 3 weeks.
Music: Mostly Southern gospel; also MOR, progressive and top 40/pop. Recently published "I Went to Jesus," recorded by The Servants; "Excuses," recorded by The Kingsmen; and "Canaanland Is Just in Sight" (by Jeff Gibson), recorded by The Florida Boys (Southern gospel).
Tips: Send "good clear cut tape with typed or printed copy of lyrics."

*HORIZON RECORDING STUDIOS LTD., Horizon House, Warwick Rd., Coventry, W. Mid. CV3 6QS England. (0203)21000. Marketing Director: Paul Craddock. PRS, MCPS, PPL. Music publisher and record company (Horizon Records) and record producer. Publishes 20 songs/year; publishes 20 new songwriters/year. Pays standard royalty.
How to Contact: Prefers cassette, 15 ips reel-to-reel or Beta videocassette. SAE and IRC. Reports in 4 weeks.
Music: Mostly rock, electronic and folk; also modern. Recently published *Hard Lines*, written and recorded by Hard Lines (rock); "Don't Go," and "Long Ago," written and recorded by Series Red (rock).

HOT GOLD MUSIC PUBLISHING CO., Box 25654, Richmond VA 23260. (804)225-7810. President: Joseph J. Carter Jr. Music publisher, booking agency and record company. BMI. Publishes 10

songs/year; publishes 2 new songwriters/year. Pays standard royalty.
How to Contact: Prefers cassette with 1-3 songs. SASE. Reports in 60 days.
Music: Mostly pop and R&B; also rock, soul and top 40. Recently published "How Long Will I Be a Fool," (by Willis L. Barnet), recorded by the Waller Family/Dynamic Artists Records (pop/soul); "Get Up Everybody," (by Ronnie R. Cokes), recorded by Starfire/Dynamic Artists Records (funk/soul); and "I Believe in You," (by Joseph J. Carter Jr.), recorded by Waller Family/MCA Records (pop/R&B).

*HOT KNOBS MUSIC, 607 Piney Point Rd., Yorktown VA 23692. (804)898-8155/595-4191. Professional Manager: Lana Puckett or Kim Person. BMI. Music publisher, record company (Cimirron/Rainbird Records), record producer (Humdinger Productions) and Wistaria Recording Studio. Estab. 1984. Publishes 20 songs/year; publishes 5 new songwriters/year. Pays standard royalty.
How to Contact: Write or call first and obtain permission to submit. Prefers cassette or videocassette with 1-5 songs and lyric sheet. SASE. Reports in 3 weeks.
Music: Mostly country, easy listening, pop, bluegrass and traditional; also rock, gospel and children's music. Recently published "Love Ain't What It Seems," (by L. Puckett & K. Person), recorded by L. Puckett on Cimirron/Rainbird (top 40); and "Hard Habit," written and recorded by L. Puckett on Cimirron/Rainbird (country).
Tips: "Have good commercially written and well structured lyrics."

*HOUSE OF PLATINUM MUSIC, Box 381495, Germantown TN 38183-1495. (901)393-8222. Senior Vice President and General Manager: Margie Shaffer. Executive Vice President and Operations Manager: Keith K. Shaffer. BMI. Music publisher and recording studio. Publishes 5 songs/year; publishes 5 new songwriters/year. Pays standard royalty.
How to Contact: Write first and obtain permission to submit. Prefers cassette or 7½ or 15 ips reel-to-reel with 5 songs and lyric sheet. Submit copyrighted material only. Does not return unsolicited material. Reports in 6 weeks.
Music: Mostly country, R&B and blues; also contemporary Christian and pop. Recently published "When You Say No, Does That Mean Yes," (by K. Shaffer) and "My World's So Alone Without You," (by J. Hardy), both recorded by Gene Carithers on IMS (country); and "Let's Put An Outlaw in the White House," (by K. Shaffer), recorded by Steve Butler on IMS (novelty).
Tips: 'We are very selective—songs must have strong hook, be very tight, and very commercial."

*HRS PUBLISHING, 1119 W. Garland Ave., Garland TX 75040. (214)487-8120. Contact: Gene Huddleston. ASCAP. Music publisher. Publishes 20 songs/year; publishes 5 new songwriters/year. Pays standard royalty. Affiliated publishing firm: Sultan Music Publishing (BMI).
How to Contact: Prefers cassette. SASE. Reports in 2 weeks.
Music: Mostly country, Christian and pop. Recently published "Tend to the Mendin'," (by Maggie Fox and G. Huddleston), recorded by Gene Huddleston on Puzzle (country); "Nashville Star," written and recorded by Don Ferguson on Puzzle (country); and "Slow Song," (by Paul Hotchkiss), recorded by Mary Craig on Puzzle (country).
Tips: "Write new material and submit on regular basis."

HUMAN SOUND MUSIC, Box 499, Queens NY 11365. (212)969-2418. Affiliate: Sounds Ambient Music (ASCAP). President: Marty Pekar. Music publisher. BMI. Publishes 10-30 songs/year. Pays standard royalty.
How to Contact: Prefers cassette and lyric sheet. SASE. Reports in 1 month.
Music: "We only publish authentic 50s style rock 'n' roll/doo wop."
Tips: "We publish songs that sound like they could have been hits in the 50s. These songs are submitted to artists on our Ambient Sound Record Label (all from the 50s and 60s, such as Randy & The Rainbows, the Mystics, the Jive Five). We record about 50% of the songs we decide to publish, but they must be pure, authentic 50s rock or don't even bother."

*HUMANFORM PUBLISHING COMPANY, Box 158486, Nashville TN 37215. (615)373-9312. President: M.K. Nairon. BMI. Music publisher. Estab. 1984. Pays standard royalty.
How to Contact: Prefers cassette with 4 songs and lyric and lead sheets. Reports in 4 weeks.
Music: Mostly country, rock and gospel; also jazz, blues and progressive rock.

*HUSTLER'S INC., 548 Broadway, Macon GA 31210. (912)742-1049. Contact: Alan Walden. Music publisher and record producer. Publishes varying number of songs/year; publishes 50-300 new songwriters/year. Pays standard royalty.
How to Contact: Write to obtain permission to submit or to arrange personal interview. Prefers demos with "only one song at a time." Does not return unsolicited material.
Music: Mostly rock; also gospel.

*HUTCHINSON PRODUCTIONS, INC., 56-44 142nd Street, Flushing NY 11355. (718)762-2295. Producer: Clay Hutchinson. Music publisher and record producer. Estab. 1984. Pays standard royalty. **How to Contact:** Call first and obtain permission to submit. Prefers cassette and lyric sheet. SASE. Reports in 4-6 weeks.
Music: Mostly pop/rock and pop/R&B.

*IDEE MUSIK VERLAG, 39 A Boernickerst R., 1000 Berlin 20, West Germany. (030)3619019. Manager: Horst Fuchs. GEMA. Music publisher, record company (Allstar Records) and record producer (Allstar). Publishes 50 songs/year; publishes 5 new songwriters/year. Pays standard royalty.
How to Contact: Prefers cassette. Does not return unsolicited material. Reports in 4 weeks.
Music: Recently published "Heut ist der 1.," (by H. Blum), recorded by Camillo on Allstar (MOR); "Das Schachspiel," (by Nicolas), recorded by Petra Pascal on Allstar (MOR); and "Good Night," written and recorded by Ronny on K-tel (MOR).

IFFIN PUBLISHING CO., Suite #215, 38 Music Square E., Nashville TN 37203. (615)254-0825. Professional Manager: Charlie Bragg. Music publisher. BMI. Publishes 25 songs/year; publishes 10 new songwriters/year. Pays standard royalty.
How to Contact: Prefers cassette with 1-3 songs and lyric sheet. Prefers studio produced demos. SASE. Reports in 1 month.
Music: Country, MOR and pop. Recently published "Promised Land," (by Mari Earl), recorded by Christian Grant/Washville American (MOR); "God and a Country Song," (by Lisa Wilkinson and Andy Wilson), recorded by May Van/Circa (country); and "In Mountain Rain," (by Wayne Carter), recorded by Ray Patrick/Pat Records (country).

*IGUANA MUSIC, INC., 500 West End Ave., New York NY 10024. (212)874-6440. President: Toby Byron. ASCAP, BMI. Music publisher. Affiliated pubishing firms: Hot Transistor Tunes, Inc., Dawg Music.
How to Contact: Write or call first and obtain permission to submit. Prefers cassette. Does not return unsolicited material.
Music: Mostly rock, pop and R&B.

IMAGE MUSIC PTY., LTD., 137 Moray St., South Melbourne, Victoria, 3205, Australia. 61-3-699-9999. US: Mason & Sloane, 1299 Ocean Ave., Santa Monica CA 90401. Affiliates/Australia: Rainbird Music (APRA) and Haven Music (APRA). Affiliates/US: American Image Music (BMI) and American Rainbird Music (ASCAP). Director: John McDonald. Music publisher, record company and record producer. APRA, AMCOS, Phonographic Performance Co. of Australia Ltd. Member AMPAL. Publishes 30-40 songs/year; publishes 8 new songwriters/year. Pays standard royalty; royalties paid directly to US songwriters ("if signed to our Australian company"), or through US publishing affliate ("if songwriter is signed to our US company").
How to Contact: Prefers cassette with 3-6 songs and lyric sheet. Submit directly to Australian office. "Concentrate on quality rather than quantity: strong melodic hooks (choruses), and meaningful lyrics that tell a story. Forget obvious rhymes. Make good demos—pay attention to playing and singing. We will not return material unless instructed to do so. Foreign submissions will not be returned unless postage is paid in advance." SAE and IRC. Reports in 1 week.
Music: Dance-oriented, MOR, rock (all kinds) and top 40/pop. Recently published "Oh How She Loves Me" (by Richard Bennett & Larry Williams), recorded by Bluestone/Avenue Records, Australia (top 40/pop); "Thinking of You" (by Lee Conway), recorded by Gary Holton & Casino Steel/Polygram Records, Europe (top 40/pop); and "Coleraine" (by David Hampson), recorded by the Cobbers/Festival Records, Australia and New Zealand (country).

*IMAGINARY MUSIC, 239-A E. Thach Ave., Auburn AL 36830. (205)821-JASS. Publisher: Lloyd Townsend, Jr. ASCAP. Music publisher, record company and record producer (Almost Audible Audio). Estab. 1984. Publishes 5 songs/year; publishes 1 new songwriter/year. Pays standard royalty.
How to Contact: Prefers cassette or 7½ ips reel-to-reel with 4 songs and lyric and lead sheets. Reports in 4 weeks.
Music: Mostly jazz, blues and rock.

INSTANT REPLAY MUSIC CO., 1409 Harris Ct., Antioch CA 94509. General Manager of Publishing: Betty Jean Waldrup Smith. Vice President/A&R: Michael Edward Waldrup. Music publisher. ASCAP. Publishes 35-50 songs/year; publishes 3-5 new songwriters/year. Pays standard royalty.
How to Contact: Prefers cassette with 2-4 songs and lead sheet. "Use piano and vocal; or bass drums, piano and vocal. Guitar can also be used." SASE. Reports in 3 weeks.
Music: Disco, jazz, soul, and gospel. Recently published "Are You Alone" (by B. Waldrup); "Your

Kind of Guy" recorded by Scotty Wright; and "Trade" recorded by The Seville Band.
Tips: "Keep demos simple."

I'VE GOT THE MUSIC COMPANY, Box 2631, Muscle Shoals AL 35662-2631. (205)381-1455.
Affiliates: Song Tailors Music Co. (BMI), Terry Woodford Music (ASCAP) and Creative Source Music
(BMI). Professional Manager: Richard Butler. Music publisher, record producer and video production
company (Flying Colors Video). BMI, ASCAP. Publishes 100 songs/year; publishes 1-2 new songwriters/year. Hires staff writers. Pays standard royalty.
How to Contact: Submit demo tape to the attention of Richard Butler. Prefers cassette with 2 songs and
lyric sheet. SASE. Reports ASAP.
Music: Mostly top 40/pop and country; also dance-oriented, easy listening, MOR, progressive, R&B,
rock and soul. Recently published "One More Try for Love," (by Robert Byrne/Brandon Barnes), recorded by Ronnie Milsap/RCA (MOR); "I Want to Go Somewhere," (by Mac McAnally/Donny Lowery), recorded by Keith Stegall/Epic (country); and "Let Your Heart Do the Talking," (by Robert
Byrne/Alan Schulman), recorded by Anne Murray/Capitol (country/pop).
Tips: "Be up-to-date on various artists' styles."

IZA MUSIC CORP., Box 325, Englewood NJ 07631. (201)567-7538. Affiliates: Eden Music Corp
(BMI) and Vanessa Music Corp. (ASCAP). Contact: Professional Dept. Music publisher. BMI, ASCAP. Publishes 200+ songs/year; publishes "at least" 4 new songwriters/year. Pays standard royalty.
How to Contact: Prefers cassette with maximum 2 songs and lyric sheet. Prefers studio produced demos. Does not return unsolicited material. Reports "if time permits."
Music: All kinds. "We have many standards."

J.D. MUSIC/FRANKLY MUSIC, Box 8958, Arlington Station, Jacksonville FL 32239. (904)744-
7779. Contact: Fred Frank. Music publisher. BMI, ASCAP.
How to Contact: Prefers cassette with 3 songs and lyric sheet. SASE. Reports in 3 weeks.
Music: Mostly R&B and pop; also country, dance-oriented, gospel, rock (country) and top 40/pop.

JACKPOT MUSIC, 133 Walton Ferry, Hendersonville TN 37075. (615)824-2820. Affiliates: Eager
Beaver Music and His Word Music. President: Clyde Beavers. Music publisher, record producer, record
company (Cash Records, JCL Records, New Star Records) and studio. BMI, ASCAP, SESAC. Pays
standard royalty.
How to Contact: Call first. Prefers 7½ ips reel-to-reel or cassette with 1-3 songs and lyric sheet. SASE.
Reports as soon as possible.
Music: Bluegrass, children's, church/religious, country, folk and gospel.

JACLYN MUSIC, 369 Millwood Dr., Nashville TN 37217. (615)366-9999. Affiliates: Nashville Music Sales, Jaclyn Recording Co. and Nashville Bluegrass Recording Co. President: Jack Lynch. Music
publisher and record company. BMI. Publishes 1-100 songs/year; publishes 10 new songwriters/year.
Works with lyricists and teams collaborators. Pays standard royalty.
How to Contact: Query. Prefers cassette with 1-3 songs and lyric sheet. SASE. Reports in 1 week.
Music: Mostly MOR, bluegrass and country; also gospel. Recently published "Blackheaded Woman,"
written and recorded by Eddy Howard; "Road to Nowhere," written and recorded by Trimble White
(country); and "Just One in a Crowd," (by Ona Meyer), recorded by Patsy Cline Osborne (country).
Tips: "Make good demo cassette tape and send good typed lyric sheet."

DICK JAMES ORGANIZATION, 24 Music Square E., Nashville TN 37203. (615)242-0600. West
Coast Office: 1040 N. Las Palmas Ave., Building 3, Los Angeles CA 90038. (213)469-1940. General
Manager (U.S. Operation): Arthur Braun. Affiliates: Dejamus Music and Dick James Music, Inc. General Manager (U.S. Operation): Arthur Braun. Professional Manager, Mike Hollandsworth. Music publisher. ASCAP, BMI. Member NMPA, NMA and CMA. Publishes 40 songs/year; publishes 3 new songwriters/year. Works with lyricists and composers and teams collaborators. Pays standard royalty.
How to Contact: Prefers cassette with 1-3 songs and lead sheet. SASE. Reports ASAP.
Music: Mostly rock, R&B and country; also easy listening, MOR, soul and top 40/pop. Recently
published "Two Car Garage," recorded by B.J. Thomas; "Ev'ry Heart Should Have One," recorded by
Charley Pride; and "Just a Little Love," recorded by Reba McEntire.

*JAMMY MUSIC PUBLISHERS LTD., Inchbank House, 957 Dumbarton Rd., Glasgow G14 9UF
Scotland. (041)339 5337. Managing Director: John D. R. MacCalman. PRS. Music publisher and record company. Publishes 40 songs/year; publishes 2 new songwriters/year. Royalty "negotiable in excess of 50%."

How to Contact: Prefers cassette with 4 songs and lyric sheet. SAE and IRC. Reports in 6 weeks.
Music: Mostly rock, pop and country; also Scottish. Recently published "Always Argyll," (by Duncan McCrowe), recorded by Valerie Dunbar on Igus (Scottish); "Takes Two," (by Smithy Tollan); recorded by Dance Trance on Rollerball (pop); and "What We Say with Our Eyes," written and recorded by James Oliver on Ritz (ballad).

JANELL MUSIC PUBLISHING/TIKI ENTERPRISES, INC., 792 E. Julian St., San Jose CA 95112. (408)286-9840 or (408)286-9845. Affiliates: Janell (BMI) and Tooter Scooter Music (BMI). President: Gradie O'Neal. Secretary: Jeannine O'Neal. Music publisher and record company. BMI. Publishes 75 songs/year; publishes 50 new songwriters/year. Pays standard royalty.
How to Contact: Prefers cassette with 3 songs and lyric or lead sheet. SASE. Reports in 2 weeks.
Music: Mostly country, rock, and gospel; also easy listening, MOR, soul and top 40/pop. Recently published "Daddy's Song," (by John Brett), recorded by Gypsy Lu/Rowena (country); "Brand New Song," (by Cal and Joyce Hyden), recorded by Sharon (country); and "Caught On the Tracks," (by Hayden and Hayden), recorded by Ulzhua/Rowena (rock).

JASON MUSIC/MOORESIDE MUSIC, 14 Soho St., London, W1 V6HR, England. 44-01-437-2245. Managing Director: David Marcus. Music publisher, record company and record producer. BMI, MCPS, PRS, PPL. Publishes 10 songs/year. Has not yet, but would listen to songs from US songwriters. Pays standard royalty; royalties paid directly to US songwriters.
How to Contact: Write first and obtain permission to submit. Prefers cassette with 2-4 songs. SAE and IRC. Reports in 1 month.
Music: Mostly MOR and dance-oriented; also blues, country, easy listening and R&B.

JAY JAY PUBLISHING, 35 NE 62nd St., Miami FL 33138. (305)758-0000. Contact: Walter Jagiello. Music publisher, record company and record producer. BMI. Member NARAS. Publishes 15-25 songs/year. Pays standard royalty.
How to Contact: Prefers 15 ips reel-to-reel with 2-6 songs and lyric sheet. SASE. Reports in 1 month.
Music: Mostly polkas and waltzes; also country and easy listening.

JEMIAH PUBLISHING, Box 2501, Columbia SC 29202. (803)754-3556. Professional Manager: Myron Alford. Music publisher, record producer and artist management firm. BMI. Publishes 5-10 songs/year; publishes 4 new songwriters/year. Pays standard royalty.
How to Contact: Prefers 7¹/₂ ips reel-to-reel or cassette with 1-4 songs and lyric sheet. SASE. Reports in 1 month.
Music: Mostly R&B; also gospel, MOR, country, rock (top 40), soul and top 40/pop. Recently published "Enjoy with Me" (by E. Jackson, M. Alford and R. Hoefer, Jr.), recorded by Midnight Blue/Enjoy Records (R&B); "Wishing" (by M. Alford, D. Bailey, E. Jackson, R. Hoefer, Jr. and D. Hodge, Jr.), and "Feel It and Groove Together" (by D. Hodge, Jr., E. Jackson and M. Alford), both recorded by Midnight Blue/Samarah Records (R&B); and "Reaching Out" and "Filth" (by J. Campbell, G. Parsons, E. Robinson, Jr., J. Duffir, K. Brown, G. Hackett, K. Hubbert), recorded by Private Stash.

*JENEANE & JUDE MUSIC, #404, 150 Fifth Ave., New York NY 10011. (212)691-5630. General Manager: Jude St. George. ASCAP. Music publisher. Publishes 15 songs/year. Pays standard royalty.
How to Contact: Write first and obtain permission to submit. Prefers cassette with 4 songs and lyric sheet. "Typewritten letters preferred." Does not return unsolicited material. Reports in 3-4 weeks.
Music: Mostly progressive, jazz and blues. Recently published: "The Street Musicians," "Carry On," and "Simple Life," (all by Jeneane Claps), all recorded by Freeway Fusion on J&J Musical Enterprises (progressive).

JERJOY MUSIC, Box 3615, Peoria IL 61604. (309)673-5755. Professional Manager: Jerry Hanlon. Music publisher. BMI. Publishes 4 songs/year; publishes 3 new songwriters/year. Pays standard royalty.
How to Contact: Prefers cassette with 4-8 songs and lyric sheet. SASE. Reports in 2 weeks.
Music: Country. Recently published "Love Has Gone Away" (by D. Moody), recorded by Jerry Hanlon (country ballad); "Hey, Little Dan" (by A. Simmons), recorded by J. Hanlon (country); and "Scarlet Woman" (by J. Hanlon and J. Schneider), recorded by J. Hanlon (country).

JERO MUSIC LTD., Suite 11, 2309 N. 36th St., Milwaukee WI 53210. (414)445-4872. President: Marvell Love. Music publisher, record company and record producer. BMI. Publishes 6-7 songs/year; publishes 5 new songwriters/year. Works with lyricists and composers and teams collaborators. Pays standard royalty.
How to Contact: Prefers cassette with 3-5 songs and lyric sheet. SASE. Reports in 1 month.
Music: Mostly soul; also gospel, raggae, R&B and top 40/pop. Recently published "Trust in God" (by

Darrell Hines), recorded by Phebe Hines/New World Records (gospel); *Don't Play Games* (by Lemanuel Hightire and Jim Bush), recorded by Hightire/New World Records (pop); and "A Brand New Thing" (by James Alkins), recorded by Action/New World Records (R&B).
Tips: "Need songs that carry a message."

JIBARO MUSIC CO., INC., Box 424, Mount Clemens MI 48043. (313)791-2678. President/Professional Manager: Jim Roach. General Manager: Ann Roach. Music publisher and production company. BMI. Pays standard royalty.
How to Contact: Prefers cassette with 1-4 songs and lead sheet. SASE. Reports in 2 weeks.
Music: Jazz, MOR and soul. Recently published "Casanova Brown," recorded by Gloria Gaynor (disco/soul); "Thank God You're My Lady," recorded by the Dells (ballad); "I Dig Your Music," recorded by the Dramatics (disco/soul); and "You're My Super Hero" and "Super Heros Theme" (both by Jim Roach), both recorded by Everlife/CRC Records (pop).

*JMC MUSIC GROUP, 2700 Champa, Denver CO 80205. (303)297-3131. Creative Director: Jon Chandler. BMI, ASCAP. Music publisher, record company (Roundtree) and record producer. Publishes 10-15 songs/year; publishes 1-2 new songwriters/year. Pays standard royalty. Affiliated publishing firms: Western Dog/BMI, Modern Art/ASCAP.
How to Contact: Write or call first and obtain permission to submit. Prefers cassette with 3-4 songs and lyric sheet. Does not return unsolicited material. Reports in 3-5 weeks.
Music: Mostly country, pop and dance; also jazz. Recently published "Moonlight Marvel," (by C. Donaldson), recorded by Wickety Wac on EMI (pop); "Stealin'," (by John Cable); recorded by Gidget Baird on PVR (country); and "151," written and recorded by Jon Chandler on Roundtree (country).

JOHNNY ANGEL MUSIC, Box 295, Riverdale NY 10463. (212)549-0502. President: John Clark. Music publisher, record company, record producer and artist booking firm. BMI. Publishes 2 songs/year. Pays standard royalty.
How to Contact: Submit demo tape. Prefers studio produced demos. Does not return unsolicited materials.
Music: Mostly top 40; also dance-oriented and hard rock. Recently published "New Girl on My Block," and "Angel Maureen," (by J. Clark/A. Browne), recorded by Jimmy and Crestones/Avenue D (top 40/50s oldie).

LITTLE RICHIE JOHNSON MUSIC, 913 S. Main St., Belen NM 87002. (505)864-7441. Manager: Curt Huckabone. Music publisher, record company and record producer. BMI. Publishes 25 songs/year; publishes 15-20 new songwriters/year. Pays standard royalty.
How to Contact: Prefers 7½ ips reel-to-reel or cassette with 6-8 songs and lyric sheet. SASE. Reports in 2 weeks.
Music: Country, gospel and Spanish. Recently published "Sweet Freedom" and "Let It Be" (by Nadine Moore), recorded by C. Roman on LRJ Records (country); and "I Just Want to Be Free," written and recorded by Carol Roman on LRJ Records (country).

*JONDI MUSIC, #1106, 130 W. 42nd St., New York NY 10036. (212)819-0920. President: Dick Charles. BMI. Music publisher, record company and record producer. Estab. 1984. Pays standard royalty.
How to Contact: Prefers cassette or VHS or ¾" U-matic videocassette with 3 songs and lyric sheet. Reports in 2 weeks.
Music: Mostly country, top 40/pop, and gospel.

JO-WEE PUBLISHING HOUSE, Box 4029, Winston-Salem NC 27105. (919)723-1822. General Manager: Jo Daniels. Music publisher, record producer and management firm. ASCAP. Publishes 3 songs/year.
How to Contact: Prefers cassette or ¾" videocassette with 3-8 songs and lyric sheet. SASE. Reports in 1 month.
Music: Mostly reggae; also jazz, R&B and soul. Recently published "I Like Reggae," (by Givens, Robinson, Pauling), recorded by Cinnamon Reggae/Cinnamon Records (Reggae); and "Searching," (by Daniels), recorded by Jo Dread/Cinnamon Records (Reggae).
Tips: "Have a plan or proposal."

*JUBO MUSIC, Box 4924, Union City NJ 07087. (201)471-3464. Representative: Julian Hernandez. ASCAP. Publishes 10-15 songs/year; publishes 3-6 new songwriters/year. Pays standard royalty.
How to Contact: Write first and obtain permission to submit. Prefers cassette with 2-4 songs and lyric sheet. Demos must be professional. SASE. Reports in 8 weeks.

Music: Mostly pop/R&B dance, top 40 pop/rock and rap; also R&B ballads. Recently published "Prophecy," (by Mike Roman/Julian Hernandez), recorded by Diamond Z Crew on A.S.D. Records (rap); "Can't Get Enough of You," (by Bob Allecca/Jullian Hernandez), recorded by Wickket on Street Wave Records (dance/R&B); and "In Need of Love," (by J. Hernandez), recorded by Herns & Ray on Big Time/CBS Songs (R&B/dance).

*JUICY PEEPLE, Anklamer Ring 18, 2000 Hamburg 73, West Germany. (040)647 6280. Contact: Jimmy Pratt. GEMA. Music publisher and record company (Jax Pax). Publishes 100 songs/year; publishes varying number of new songwriters/year. Pays standard royalty.
How to Contact: Prefers cassette with 2-12 songs. "Send cassette air parcel post with no value on declaration." Does not return unsolicited material. Reports in 2 weeks.
Music: Mostly hard metal, rock/pop and electronic; also jazz. Recently published "Don't It Make You Feel," (by R. Harper), recorded by The Breathers on Jax Pax (rock/pop); "Doktor! Help Me," (by R&J Zohn), recorded by The Breathers on Jax Pax (rock); and "Red House," (by P. Gillan), recorded by Pauline Gillan & Northern Dancer on Bullet (heavy metal).

KACK KLICK, INC., Mirror Records, Inc., 645 Titus Ave., Rochester NY 14617. (716)544-3500. Vice President: Armand Schaubroeck. Manager: Kim Simons. Music publisher and record company. BMI. Publishes 20 songs/year; publishes 4-12 new songwriters/year. Pays standard royalty.
How to Contact: Prefers cassette. Include photo. SASE. Reports in 2 months.
Music: MOR, progressive, rock, top 40/pop and new wave. Recently published "I Cannot Find Her," recorded by Chesterfield Kings; and "I Shot My Guardian Angel," recorded by Armand Schaubroeck Steals.

KARJAN MUSIC PUBLISHING CO., Box 205, White Lake NY 12786. (914)583-4471. President: Mickey Barnett. Music publisher, record company and record producer. SESAC. Member CMA. Publishes 25 songs/year; publishes 4 new songwriters/year. Pays standard royalty.
How to Contact: Prefers cassette with 1-3 songs and lyric sheet. SASE. Reports in 3 weeks.
Music: Blues, country, easy listening, MOR, R&B and top 40/pop.

KATCH NAZAR MUSIC, Rose Hill Group, 1326 Midland Ave., Syracuse NY 13205. (315)475-2936. Affiliate: Bleecker Street Music. A&R Director: Vincent Taft. Music publisher. ASCAP, BMI. Publishes 6-15 songs/year; publishes 2 new songwriters/year. Pays standard royalty.
How to Contact: Prefers cassette with 1-4 songs and lyric sheet. "Please be selective. Songs should be melodic and have 'un-busy' music; strong, realistic lyrics; a beginning, middle and end." SASE. Reports in 2 weeks.
Music: Mostly rock and top 40/pop; also country, dance-oriented, jazz and R&B. Recently published "She's the One" (by Mike Crissan), recorded by Tickets (rock); "Ocean Algae" (by Sudan Baronian), recorded by Taksim (jazz); and "Skytrain" (by Zarm), recorded by Zarm (dance).

KEENY-YORK PUBLISHING, 29 S. Erie, Toledo OH 43602. (419)244-8599. Affiliate: Park J. Tunes (ASCAP). Contact: Doug Larue. Music publisher, record company, record producer and film producer. BMI. Publishes 50 songs/year; publishes 4 new songwriters/year. Pays standard royalty.
How to Contact: Prefers cassette with 5-10 songs and lyric sheet. Include photo and one-page resume. SASE. Reports in 1 month.
Music: Mostly top 40/pop; also country, easy listening and MOR. Recently published "Where Do We Go From Here" (by J. Petrone), recorded by Kathy White/Jamestune Records (pop); "Wintersong" (by M. Shaw), recorded by Nevada Flatts (country); "Pigskin Blues" (by M. Shaw), recorded by MDS (country); "Theme from Limelight (by Dan Faehnle); and "Oh Them Hens," recorded by Hotlix/MDS Entertainment Records (song and video about the Toledo Mud Hens).

*KEEP CALM MUSIC LIMITED, 65 Bedford Hill, London SW12 9HA England. (01)675-5584. Professional Manager: Paul Oakenfold. PRS, MCPS. Music publisher. Pays varying royalty. Affiliated publishing firm: Titch Tunes Ltd.
How to Contact: Prefers cassette or VHS (Pal) videocassette. Submissions should be "clearly labeled and marked if they are to be returned." Reports in 2 weeks.
Music: Mostly black dance, soul/funk and AOR/rock; also pop and all dance oriented material. Recently published "Give It Up," (by Klein/Walsh), recorded by Divine on Proto (disco); "Show Me Around," (by Walsh), recorded by Divine on Proto (disco); and "Street People," (by Titchener); recorded by Triple Beat Alliance on Fresh 'N Bad (hip/hop).

KELLIJAI MUSIC LIMITED/JA'NIKKI SONGS, Suite 202, 217 W. Alameda, Burbank CA 91502. (818)842-8900. Director of A&R: Steve Dancz. Music publisher. BMI, ASCAP. Publishes 100

songs/year; publishes 10 new songwriters/year. Employs songwriters on salary basis. Pays standard royalty. Affiliated publishing firms: Mindes Music, Pisces Music.
How to Contact: Prefers cassette with 1-5 songs and lyric sheet. SASE. Reports in 1-4 weeks.
Music: Mostly rock, R&B and pop. Recently published "Joy" (by J. Jarrett), recorded by The Band AKA/Epic-Eur./UK (R&B/Pop); "Suspicious," (by E. Strickland/D. Barnes/M. Carpenter/J. Jarrett), recorded by Lejenz on Bouvier (R&B); and "Still the Sun Rises," (by G. O'Brien), recorded by Glorya on Credence (rock).

KENCO PUBLISHING CO., 3784 Realty, Dallas TX 75234. (214)241-7854. Affiliate: Luvco Music (BMI). President: K.J. Hughes. Music publisher, record company (Luv Records), record producer and 24 track recording studio. ASCAP. Publishes 25 songs/year; publishes 15 new songwriters/year.
How to Contact: Prefers cassette with 3 songs and lyric sheet. SASE. Reports in 5 weeks.
Music: Mostly country, gospel and novelty; also MOR. Recently published "Dallas Does It," written and recorded by Nancy Parrish on Luv Records (MOR); "Dolly Parton for President," (by Johnny Hughes), recorded by Roger Howell on Merit Records (country); and "One Heart," (by Larry Fargo), recorded by Hollie Hughes on Oak Records (country).

GENE KENNEDY ENTERPRISES, INC., 2125 8th Ave. S., Nashville TN 37204. (615)383-6002. Affiliates: Chip 'n Dale (ASCAP), Door Knob Music (BMI), Lodestar (SESAC), Bekson (BMI) and Kenwall (ASCAP). President: Gene Kennedy. Vice President: Karen Jeglum. Music publisher, independent producer, distributor and promoter.
How to Contact: Query or arrange personal interview. Prefers cassette or 7½ ips reel-to-reel with 1-3 songs. "Tape should be accompanied by lyrics." SASE. Reports in 2-5 weeks.
Music: Bluegrass, country, gospel and MOR.

KENWON MUSIC, Suite #2, 5032 Lankershim Blvd., North Hollywood CA 91601. (818)766-7142. Contact: Ken Weiss or Michael Schneider. Music publisher. BMI, ASCAP. Member Harry Fox Agency, NMPA. Publishes 20 songs/year; publishes 3 new songwriters/year. Hires staff writers. Pays standard royalty.
How to Contact: Prefers cassette with 1-3 songs and lyric sheet. SASE. Reports in 3 weeks.
Music: Mostly rock; also bluegrass and R&B. Recently published "Southern Cross" (by Stephen Stills, Michael Curtis and Richard Curtis), recorded by Crosby, Stills & Nash/ Atlantic Records (pop/easy listening); "You Are the Woman" (by Rick Roberts), recorded by Firefall/Atlantic Records (easy listening); and "Blue Letter" (by R. and M. Curtis), recorded by Fleetwood Mac/Warner Bros. Records (rock).
Tips: "Songs that lend themselves to visuals are often given extra consideration."

*KERISTENE MUSIC, LTD., #21,1605 N. Martel, Hollywood CA 90046-3515. (213)851-9418. Affiliates: Faax Music Publishing, Coleman, Kestin & Smith, Ltd. President: Kenneth H. Smith. BMI, ASCAP. Music publisher, record company (D-Town Records, Inc.) and record producer (Platinum Sound Productions). Publishes 6-8 songs/year; publishes 3 new songwriters/year. Pays standard royalty.
How to Contact: Write or call first and obtain permission to submit. Prefers cassette or VHS videocassette with maximum 3 songs and lyric sheet. "Please include SASE for response." Does not return unsolicited material. Reports in 6-8 weeks.
Music: Mostly gospel, rock and heavy metal; also country, R&B and dance. Recently published "Sweet Tonight," written and recorded by Cindy Bandes on D-Town (country); "Midnight Fantasy," written and recorded by Debby Winton on Platinum Sound (rock); and "Hard Handed Heart," and "Make-Up Your Mind," written and recorded by William Dean on D-Town (gospel).

KICKING MULE PUBLISHING/DESK DRAWER PUBLISHING, Box 158, Alderpoint CA 95411. (707)926-5312. Manager: Ed Denson. Music publisher and record company. BMI and ASCAP. Member NAIRD. Publishes 120 songs/year; publishes 7 new songwriters/year. Pays standard royalties.
How to Contact: Write first. Prefers cassette with 1-3 songs. Does not return unsolicited material. Reports "as soon as possible."
Music: Blues (fingerpicking); and folk (guitar/banjo only). "We publish only material released on our albums. Since we record virtuoso guitar and banjo players, virtually the only way to get a tune published with us is to be such a player, or to have such a player record your song. We don't publish many 'songs' per se, our entire catalog is devoted 95% to instrumentals and 5% to songs with lyrics. As publishers we are not in the market for new songs. This listing is more of a hope that people will not waste their time and ours sending us blue-sky demos of material that does not relate to our very specialized business." Recently published "The Sweeper" (by George Gritzbach), recorded by Gritzbach/KM Records (folk); "Thunder On The Run" (by Stefan Grossman), recorded by Grossman/KM Records (guitar instrumental); and "Pokerface Smile" (by Robert Force), recorded by Force & D'Ossche (country).

*KIMTRA MUSIC/HATBAND MUSIC, Sound 70 Suite N-101, 210 25th Ave. N, Nashville TN 37203. Contact: Douglas Casmus. Music publisher.
How to Contact: Query by mail. "Submissions *must* include SASE if you expect a reply or tape returned." Cassettes only with 1-2 songs and "typed lyric sheet."
Music: Country, rock and top 40/pop. Current acts include Charlie Daniels Band (country rock); Dobie Gray (country); David Murphy (country); and Johnny Cobb (rock).

*KINGSPORT CREEK MUSIC PUBLISHING, Box 6085, Burbank CA 91510. Contact: Vice President. BMI. Music publisher and record company (Cowgirl Records). Employs songwriters on a salary basis.
How to Contact: Write or call first to obtain permission to submit or arrange personal interview. Prefers cassette or videocassette with any number of songs and lyric sheet. Does not return unsolicited material.
Music: Mostly country and gospel. Recently published "Tennessee Cowgirl," and "Only Life I Know," (country), and "Wash Your Hands," (gospel), written and recorded by Melvene Kaye.
Tips: "Videocassettes are advantageous."

*JIMMY KISH MUSIC PUBLISHING CO., Box 140316, Nashville TN 37214. (615)889-6675. Contact: Jimmy Kish. BMI. Music publisher and record company (Pyramid).
How to Contact: Prefers cassette "with words or music." SASE. Reports in 2 weeks.
Music: Mostly country, western and gospel; also Christmas and square dance. Recently published "Christmastime in Heaven," and "Goldenrod Calgary Stampede," (by Bob Pauley), recorded by Jimmy Kish on Pyramid (country); and "Wolf Girl, Devil's River," (by Red River Dave McEnery), recorded by J. Kish on Kess (country).

NEIL A. KJOS MUSIC COMPANY, 4382 Jutland Dr., San Diego CA 92117. (619)483-0501. Affiliates: Kjos West (SESAC), General Words and Music Company (ASCAP), Andrews Publications (SESAC), La Jolla Music (BMI), Loop Music Company (ASCAP), Pallma Music Company (SESAC), Parks Music Corp. (SESAC), Tuskegee Music Press (SESAC), Curtis Music Press (SESAC) and Curtis House of Music (ASCAP). Editorial Secretary: Lela Prewitt. Educational music publisher. SESAC. Member MPA, NAMM, RSMDA, ACDA, MENC, MTNA. Publishes 55 choral octavos/year; publishes 3 new composers/year. Pays "standard royalty of 10%."
How to Contact: Write first. Prefers cassette. SASE. "We are an educational publisher, publishing choral music for schools and churches. We do not publish vocal solos. We acknowledge receipt of manuscript in 1 week, make decision in 4 months."
Music: Sacred, secular and choral.
Tips: "We do not publish 'pop' songs."

KLICKITAT MUSIC, 1931 SE. Morrison, Portland OR 97214. (800)547-5547. Professional Manager: Gary Perman. Music publisher and record producer. BMI. Member NARAS. Publishes 10 songs/year; publishes 3 new songwriters/year. Pays standard royalty.
How to Contact: Prefers cassette with 2-4 songs and lyric sheet. SASE. Reports in 1 month.
Music: Mostly top 40/pop; also dance-oriented, MOR and pop/rock. Recently published "Shining Star" (by D. O'Brian/G. Michaels), recorded by Pamela Cansler/New Day Records; and "Alone in the City" (by David O'Brian), recorded by P. Cansler/Cricket Records.
Tips: "Strong lyrics are a must. We want bright, uptempo songs with a strong melody, catchy hook and good, strong lyrics."

KROEPCKE MUSIKVERLAGE, Goethestr. 16, 3000 Hannover-1, West Germany. 0511/15553. Managing Director: Michael Mellenthin. Music publisher. GEMA. Publishes 160 songs/year; publishes 10 new songwriters/year. Pays royalty of 60% to songwriters and 40% to publishers.
How to Contact: Arrange personal interview to play demo tape. Prefers cassette and lyric sheet. SAE and IRC. Reports in 3 weeks.
Music: Jazz, blues, rock (heavy metal/hard rock/country rock/pop songs), and new wave. Recently published *Lady Macbeth* (by Jon Symon), recorded on Lava Records (rock); *Warlock* and *Look*, (by Matthices Horndarch) recorded on Blind Man Records (jazz-piano-solo); and *Cadenance Wildgeese* (by K.P. Matziol, H. Folberth, H. Arkana and J. Nemec), recorded by Milan Disques (pop).

KRPCO MUSIC, 4926 W. Gunnison, Chicago IL 60630. (312)399-5535. President: Ray Peck. Music publisher, record company, record producer and record distributor. BMI, ASCAP. Publishes 12-16 songs/year; publishes 5 new songwriters/year. Pays standard royalty.
How to Contact: Prefers cassette with 4-6 songs and lyric sheet. SASE. Reports in 1 month.
Music: All types. Recently published "Oh That Man" (by Nadine Herman), recorded on Stang Records; "John Lennon," recorded by Torn Orphans/Kiderian Records; "Hard for the Money," recorded by Alicja Adur/Kiderian Records; and "Could Be You," recorded by Destiny/Kiderian Records.

*L E MUSIC, 93 Castle Hill Rd., Hindley, Wigan, Lancs., WN2 4BH England. (942)58555. Studio Manager: David Fillingham. Music publisher and record company (Castle Records). Publishes 9 songs/year; publishes 2 new songwriters/year. Pays standard royalty.
How to Contact: Prefers cassette with 1 or more songs and lyric sheet. Does not return unsolicited material. Reports in 4 weeks.
Music: Mostly MOR pop "only." Recently published "Bambinos," (by Steve Clay), recorded by Samda on Castle (pop); "Walk Thru Impinana," (by Leyland), recorded by Rainbow Cottage on Page One (country); and "Watch That Girl," (by S. Clay), on Castle (pop).

LA LOU MUSIC, 711 Stevenson St., Lafayette LA 70501. (318)234-5577. President: Carol J. Rachou, Sr. Music publisher, record company (La Louisianne), record producer, recording studio and distributing company. BMI. Publishes 45 songs/year. Pays standard royalty.
How to Contact: Prefers 7½ ips reel-to-reel or cassette with 1-6 songs and lyric sheet. "If possible, we would like variations of each song (tempos, styles, keys, etc.)." SASE.
Music: "We are primarily interested in Cajun French songs." Also bluegrass, blues, church/religious, country, folk, gospel, jazz, MOR, progressive, R&B, top 40/pop, comedy and French comedy. Published "Lache Pas La Patate" (by C.J. Trahan), recorded by Jimmy C. Newman/La Louisianne Records (Canjun/French); "When the Saints Go Marching In" (in Cajun French and English by Jimmy C. Newman/La Louisianne Records); and "Sweet Cajun Love Song" (by Eddy Raven), recorded by Eddy Raven/La Louisianne Records (Cajun French/English).

LADD MUSIC CO., 401 Wintermantle Ave., Scranton PA 18505. (717)343-6718. President: Phil Ladd. Music publisher, record company and record producer. BMI. Publishes 4 songs/year. Pays standard royalty.
How to Contact: Query. Prefers cassette with minimum 2 songs and lead sheet. SASE. Reports in 3 weeks.
Music: Children's, country, easy listening, R&B, rock and top 40/pop. Recently published "Piano Nelly," (by Bobby Poe), recorded by Bobby Brant/Whiterock Records (rock); and "Miss Lucy" (by Poe), recorded by Big Al Downing/Whiterock Records (rock).

LANCE JAY MUSIC, Box 62, Shiloh TN 38376. (901)632-1289. Contact: C.M. Meadows. Music publisher. ASCAP. Affiliate: Carol Faye Music. BMI and ASCAP. Works with songwriters on contract.
How to Contact: Prefers cassette with 2-4 songs and lead sheet. SASE. Reports in 1 month.
Music: Bluegrass, country and gospel. Recently published "Young Sheriff," "Big Tracks," and "Farewell."

STUART LANIS MUSIC, INC., 1273½ N. Crescent Hts. Blvd., Los Angeles CA 90046. (213)650-6500. Affiliate: Peter Piper Publishing. A&R: Stuart Lanis. Music publisher, record producer and record company. ASCAP, BMI. Publishes 15-20 songs/year. Pays standard royalty.
How to Contact: Prefers cassette with 3-6 songs and lyric sheet. SASE. Reports in 4 weeks.
Music: Children's, church/religious, classical, easy listening, gospel, MOR and top 40/pop.

*LANTERN MUSIC PUBLISHING, Box 121135, Nashville TN 37212. (615)327-3110. Professional Manager: Willi Pack. BMI, ASCAP. Music publisher. Employs songwriters on a salary basis. Pays standard royalty. Affiliated publishing firms: Lantern Light Music, Mulberry Street Music.
How to Contact: Prefers cassette with 3 songs and lyric sheet. SASE. Reports ASAP.
Music: Country, MOR, R&B and top 40. Recently published "He Won't Give In," (by J. Pierce), recorded by Kathy Matteay on Mercury (country); *South Bound All the Way*, written and recorded by South Bound on New Colony (country crossover); and *Harvest Moon* written and recorded by J. Waters on New Colony (country).

*LAPELLE MUSIC PUBLISHING, 1221 11th Ave. SW, Calgary, Alberta T3C 0M5 Canada. (403)228-0440. Contact: Bruce Thompson. Music publisher. PROCAN. Publishes 10-20 songs/year.
How to Contact: Prefers reel-to-reel or cassette and lead sheet. SAE and IRC.
Music: Country and gospel (contemporary and "Jesus" music). Recently published "What's The Use," recorded by May Van and Kenny Payne; "Play Me A Country Song," recorded by Kenny Payne; and "Video-Mania Blues," recorded by Hod Pharis.

LARGO MUSIC, INC., 425 Park Ave., New York NY 10022. (212)371-9400. Los Angeles: 606 N. Larchmont Blvd., Los Angeles CA 90004. Vice President/General Manager: Norman Weiser. East Creative Director: John Murro. Affiliates: Minstrel Music (ASCAP), Chilly Wind Music (BMI), and Twelve O'Clock Music (SESAC). Music publisher. ASCAP. Member NMPA. Publishes 500 songs/

year; publishes 30 new songwriters/year. Pays standard royalty.
How to Contact: Write or call first or arrange personal interview. "Any submissions by mail must include SASE or it will not be returned." Prefers cassette or videocassette with 2-5 songs and lyric sheet. Reports ASAP.
Music: Mostly pop, country and jazz; also blues, country, dance-oriented, easy listening, gospel, MOR, progressive, rock, soul and top 40. Recently published "Can It Be Done" (by Willie T), recorded by Weather Report/Columbia Records (pop); "Jesus," (by Shirley Caesar), recorded by S. Caesar/Word Records (gospel); and "Your Eyes," (by Bill Anderson), recorded by B. Anderson/Southern Tracks Records (country).
Tips: "Initial contact is most important."

*LARKSPUR MUSIC PUBLISHING, Box 1001, Soquel CA 95073. General Manager: Jon Hutchings. Music publisher, record company, record producer and sound reinforcement company. BMI. Member Billboard's Association of Publishers/Producers. Pays standard royalty.
How to Contact: Prefers cassette with 3-5 songs and lyric sheet. "Include 8x10 photo and bio." SASE. Reports "after material is reviewed; time varies."
Music: R&B, rock and top 40/pop.

*LAURIE PUBLISHING GROUP, 20F Robert Pitt Dr., Monsey NY 10952. (914)425-7000. Vice President: Eliot Greenberg. ASCAP, BMI. Music publisher. Pays standard royalty. Affiliated publishing firms: Schwartz Music Co., Inc., Roznique Music, Inc., 3 Seas Music and Northvale Music.
How to Contact: Prefers cassette. SASE.
Music: Mostly rock.

LE MATT MUSIC, LTD., c/o Stewart House, Hillbottom Rd., Highwycombe, Bucks. England. 44-0491-36301 or 44-0525-220400. Affiliate: Lee Music, Ltd. Contact: Ron or Cathrine Lee. Music publisher, record company and record producer. MCPS, PRS. Member MPA, PPL. Publishes 50 songs/year; publishes 15 new songwriters/year. Works with lyricists and composers and teams collaborators. Pays standard royalty; royalties paid directly to US songwriters or through US publishing affiliate.
How to Contact: Prefers 7½ or 15 ips reel-to-reel, cassette or VHS/Beta 625/PAL system videocassette with 1-3 songs and lyric sheet. "Make sure name and address are on reel or cassette." SAE and IRC. Reports in 3 weeks.
Music: Mostly pop/rock and rock; also bluegrass, blues, country, dance-oriented, easy listening, MOR, progressive, R&B, soul, disco, new wave and top 40/pop. Recently published "Total Reaction," (by Daniel Boone), recorded by D. Boone/Swoop Records (rock); "I Wanna Be Shot," (by D. Boone), recorded by Nightmare/Swoop Records (rock); and "Hot Stuff," (by R.C. Bowman), recorded by The Chromatics/Grenoville Records (rock).

LEMON SQUARE MUSIC, Box 31819, Dallas TX 75231. (214)750-0720. A&R Director: Mike Anthony. BMI, ASCAP. Music publisher, record company (Yatahey Records) and record producer. Publishes 20 songs/year; publishes 5 new songwriters/year. Pays standard royalty. Affiliated publishing firms: Branch International Music, Friends of the General Music, Forest Creek Music, Eagle Nest Music.
How to Contact: Write first and obtain permission to submit. Prefers cassette and lyric sheet or lead sheet. "Send only to Mike Anthony." Does not return unsolicited material. Reports in 6-8 weeks.
Music: Mostly country and gospel. Recently pubished "You'll Never Find a Good Man," and "All I Really Need," (by Stan Ratcliff), recorded by Audie Henry on CCR Canyon Creek (country); and "Tennessee Moon," (by Glen Bailey), recorded by Show Down on Yatahey (country).

ALFRED LENGNICK & CO. LTD., Purley Oaks Studios, 421A Brighton Rd., South Croydon, Surrey, CR2 6YR, England. Music publisher. MCPS, PRS, MRS. Pays standard royalty; royalties paid directly to US songwriters.
Music: Choral, church/religious, classical, folk and MOR.

*LEOSONG COPYRIGHT SERVICE PTY. LTD., GPO Box 2089, Sydney, 2001 Australia. (2)233-5577. Contact: Manager. Music publisher.
How to Contact: Prefers cassette or PAL-VHS videocassette. Does not return unsolicited material. Reports in 6 weeks.
Music: Mostly contemporary pop/rock, film soundtracks and country.

*LIFT HIM UP MUSIC, 9 Halstead Place, Elmwood Park NJ 07407. (201)791-9425. President: Paul Ferrar. ASCAP. Music publisher. Publishes 10 songs/year; publishes 3 new songwriters/year. Pays standard royalty.

How to Contact: Prefers cassette with 3 songs "only" and lyric sheet or lead sheet. Prefers studio produced demos. Does not return unsolicited material.

Music: Mostly pop-inspirational-gospel, rock-inspirational-gospel and jazz-inspirational-gospel; also pop, rock and jazz. Recently published: "Let Him Love You Tonight," "Breakout," and "Destiny," (by Paul Ferrar), all recorded by Praise (inspirational).

Tips: Looking for "strong lyrics with pop music and crossover material for both inspirational and pop markets." Needs "a simple approach to songwriting with good production possibilities."

LINEAGE PUBLISHING CO., Box 211, East Prairie MO 63845. (314)649-2211. Professional Manager: Tommy Loomas. Music publisher, record producer and record company. BMI. Pays standard royalty.

How to Contact: Query first. Prefers cassette with 2-4 songs and lyric sheet. SASE. Reports in 1 month.

Music: Country, easy listening, MOR, country rock, and top 40/pop. Recently published "Yesterdays Teardrops," and "Round & Round," (by Phil and Larry Burchett), recorded by the Burchetts/Capstan Records (country).

LISAS THEME MUSIC, INC., Drawer 20146, St. Petersburg FL 33742. (813)321-8649. Affiliate: First Dynasty Records, Inc. President: Mike Douglas. A&R: Lee C. Bevilacqua/Larry Lyman. Music publisher, record company, record producer and marketing company. BMI. Publishes 50 songs/year. Pays standard royalty.

How to Contact: Prefers cassette with 1-4 songs and lyric sheet. "Use clean tapes." SASE. Reports ASAP.

Music: Christian comtemporary and gospel. Recently published "Life Without You" and "Neath the Shadow of His Wings," (by Mike Rudasill), recorded by M. Rudasill (country gospel); and "Operator," and "Born to Be With You," by The Joint Heirs/First Dynasty Records (gospel).

LITTLE JOE MUSIC CO., 604 Broad St., Johnstown PA 15906. (814)539-8117. Owner: Al Page. Music publisher. BMI. Publishes 12-24 songs/year; publishes 2 new songwriters/year. Pays standard royalty.

How to Contact: Prefers 3¾ ips reel-to-reel with 2-4 songs and lead sheet. SASE. Reports in 2 weeks.

Music: Bluegrass, church/religious, country, folk and polkas. Recently published *Orthodox Catholic Choir*; *Catholic Church Choir* (Roman Catholic music); *Orthodox Greek Catholic Choir* (religious); and *Organ* (instrumental).

LITTLE WIZARD MUSIC PUBLISHER, 116 Wendy Dr., Box 384, Holtsville NY 11742. (516)654-8459. A&R Director: Arthur Christopher. Music publisher, record company and record producer. BMI. Publishes 10-50 songs/year; publishes 4 new songwriters/year. Pays standard royalty.

How to Contact: Write first and obtain permission to submit. Prefers cassette or videocassette with 1-3 songs. SASE. Reports in 3 weeks.

Music: Country, dance-oriented, easy listening, MOR, R&B, rock, soul and top 40/pop.

*LO PINE MUSIC, Box 444, Taylor MI 48180. (313)782-4973. President: John D. Lollio. BMI. Music publisher. Publishes 10 songs/year; publishes 2 new songwriters/year. Pays standard royalty. Affiliated publishing firm: Carrie-Lynn.

How to Contact: Prefers cassette and lyric sheet or lead sheet. SASE. Reports in 2 weeks.

Music: Mostly country and gospel. Recently published "Sweetest Worlds," written and recorded by Johni Dee on Ace (country); "If That's What Makes You Crazy," written and recorded by Marty Parker on Mystery Train (country); and "After the Pain," (by Jim W. Rice), recorded by Johni Dee on Ace (country).

LODESTAR MUSIC, (Division of Gene Kennedy Enterprises, Inc.), 2125 8th Ave., S., Nashville TN 37204. (615)383-6002. Affiliates: Chip 'N' Dale Music Publishers, Inc. (ASCAP) and Door Knob Music Publishing, Inc. (BMI). President: Gene Kennedy. Vice President: Karen Jeglum. Music publisher. SESAC. Member NSAI, CMA and ACM. Publishes 20 songs/year; publishes 10 new songwriters/year. Pays standard royalty.

How to Contact: Arrange personal interview. Prefers 7½ ips reel-to-reel or cassette with 1-4 songs and lyric sheet. SASE. Reports in 1-3 weeks.

Music: Country, MOR and gospel. Recently published "Nightrider," by Grace Paul Dierks.

THE LORENZ CORPORATION, 501 E. 3rd St., Dayton OH 45401. Affiliates: Lorenz Publishing Company and Sonshine Productions (publishes monthly sacred music periodicals for youth and adult choirs as well as piano and organ periodicals); Sacred Music Press (publishes in octavo form "a more

Close-up

Bill Lowery
Music publisher
Atlanta, Georgia

People sometimes tell Atlanta music publisher Bill Lowery "they don't write songs like they used to." But Lowery, president of The Lowery Group of Music Publishing Companies for 33 years and recipient of more than 20 Gold Records, doesn't agree.

"Some of our (company's) songs today are as great as what we had early on." It's those early songs, Lowery's "golden oldies," which people remember so well today. Gene Vincent's "Be-Bop-a-Lula," which sold a million copies and "Young Love," a hit record in 1957 for both Sonny James and Tab Hunter, are just two examples.

Other hits from the more than 5,000 titles in the Lowery catalogs include "Down in the Boondocks," "Games People Play," "I Never Promised You a Rose Garden," "Traces (of Love)," "Dizzy," "Imaginary Lover" and "I Love the Nightlife."

Lowery says he tries to "reach out and find a song with universal appeal." And he's been thrilled to learn of the international popularity of his hits. He cites an example from a recent trip to Rio de Janeiro.

"This place had a troubadour," recalls Lowery, "who was singing in Portuguese. I asked him if he would sing 'Traces,' and son of a gun if he didn't start singing it in Portuguese! And I said, 'My God, isn't this wonderful?' "

Lowery feels "Traces" is a good song because it offers the listener "a glimmer of hope." He likes to publish songs which are upbeat. "What I've always said is try to appeal to the masses, rather than think about the downers. Generally, people want to hope, dream and aspire. Sometimes it's difficult to get songwriters to see that philosophy."

"Today, more than ever before, it's hard to get recording contracts for new artists," Lowery says. "There aren't many independent record companies anymore," he says, "and if *they* don't like your song, you're rejected." To help combat the problem, Lowery releases and promotes records on his own and works hard to develop such groups as Nuts and Bolts and local talent, The Atlanta Rhythm Section and Joe South. He thinks the growth of the music industry in Atlanta has been good, but his dream has always been to see Atlanta become a major music capital.

"We'd like very much to see a CBS move here," he said. "Atlanta's airport is accessible, and you can ship overnight from here. But I've not been able to convince anybody of that so far; we're considered to be in the hinterlands."

Hinterlands or not, Lowery is committed to expanding Atlanta's musical influence. In fact, he recently spent $1 million on a new recording studio located behind his Atlanta offices.

"The studio is a very fine facility," he says. "We're making some product and we're determined to try."

—*Tyler Cox*

stylized type of sacred music for church and school choirs''); Laurel Press; Triune Music/Triangle Records Cantus (Trigon); Lorenz Creative Services; Heritage Music Press and Roger Dean (the exclusive distributor for American Guild of English Handbell Ringers and Chorister's Guild). Music Editor: Gene McClusky. Music publisher. ASCAP, BMI and SESAC. Member NMPA, MPA and CMPA. Publishes 200 songs/year; publishes 10 new songwriters/year. Pays standard royalty.
How to Contact: Send manuscripts and demo tapes. SASE. Reports in 1 month.

*LORING MUSIC CO., 1048 N. Carol Dr., Los Angeles CA 90069. (213)276-7103. Professional Manager: Ms. Ginger Blake. BMI, ASCAP. Music publisher. Publishes 30 songs/year, publishes 5 new songwriters/year. Pays standard royalty. Affiliates: Loring Music, Chandler Music.
How to Contact: Prefers cassette with up to 10 songs and lyric sheet and/or lead sheet. "Please send a short biography (paragraph or so) about yourself." SASE. Reports in 3 weeks.
Music: Mostly rock/pop, R&B and country; also creative novelty.
Tips: "Send quality cassette with some musical arrangements and clear vocals."

LOS ANGELES INTERNATIONAL MUSIC, Box 209, 102 Burbank Dr., Toledo OH 43695. President: Florence Lloyd. Music publisher. ASCAP. Member NMPA. Publishes 20 songs/year; publishes 5-8 new songwriters/year. Hires staff writers; pays negotiable salary "depending on expectations and music of songwriter." Works with lyricists and composers and teams collaborators. Pays standard royalty.
How to Contact: Prefers 7½ ips reel-to-reel, cassette or demo records with 3-6 songs and lyric sheet. "Send only best songs with as much attention to music as to lyrics. Include lead sheets and/or arrangements. Sound and creativity are very important." Does not return unsolicited material. Reports in 3 weeks.
Music: Pop, R&B, country and gospel. Recently published "Baby You Got My Lovin'," and "Live People," recorded by Unique Pleasure (pop); and "This Time We Won't Fail" (by Snodgrass-Lloyd), (R&B).
Tips: "Have a good knowledge of music and what sounds are becoming hit records. We prefer songwriters who are dedicated to the belief that songs are salable in today's market."

*LOUIE B. PUBLISHING, Box 15117, Kansas City MO 64106. (816)931-5866. General Manager: Marion Brown. BMI. Music publisher, record company (Quinton Productions) and record producer. Publishes varying number of songs and new songwriters/year. Pays standard royalty.
How to Contact: Prefers cassette with maximum 3 songs and lyric sheet or lead sheet. SASE. Reports 1-8 weeks.
Music: Mostly rock, gospel and country; also blues and R&B. Recently published "Christmas Came Too Soon," (by L. Brown), recorded by Marion Duke on QP (R&B).
Tips: "Enclosed lead sheets listened to first. Vocal should be intelligible."

LOWERY MUSIC CO., INC., 3051 Clairmont Rd. NE, Atlanta GA 30329. (404)325-0832. Affiliates: Brother Bill's Music, Low-Sal Inc. and Low-Twi Inc. Member CMA, NARAS and NMPA. Contact: Professional Director. Music publisher and record producer. ASCAP, BMI. Publishes 100 songs/year; publishes 10-15 new songwriters/year. Works with lyricists and composers and teams collaborators. Pays standard royalty.
How to Contact: Prefers cassette with 1-4 songs and lyric sheet. Does not return unsolicited material.
Music: Contemporary Christian, top 40, rock and country. Recently published "I Knew You When" (by South), recorded by Linda Ronstadt (pop rock); "Common Man" (by Sammy Johns), recorded by John Conlee; and "America," (by Sammy Johns), recorded by Waylon Jennings.

HAROLD LUICK & ASSOCIATES MUSIC PUBLISHER, Box B, Carlisle IA 50047. (515)989-3679. President: Harold L. Luick. Music publisher, record company, record producer and music industry consultant. BMI. Publishes 20-25 songs/year; publishes 10 new songwriters/year. Pays standard royalty.
How to Contact: Write or call first about your interest or arrange personal interview. Prefers cassette with 3-5 songs and lyric sheet. SASE. Reports in 3 weeks.
Music: Bluegrass, country, dance-oriented, easy listening, gospel, MOR, R&B, country rock-a-billy and top 40/pop. Recently published "For a Little While" (by T. Neil Smith), recorded by Blue Sky Band/Studio 2000 Records (country); "Pop Corn Song" (by Kenny Hofer), recorded by Kenny Hofer/4 Leaf Records (dance-oriented); and "Yankee Duke" (by Darrell C. Thomas), recorded by D.C. Thomas/DTC Records (country).
Tips: "Know the difference between a *tune* and a *song*. Submit only songs. Make decent 'dubs.' It is not a matter of *luck*, but a matter of being prepared when *luck* comes along. If you are unlucky then you have been unprepared. Submit only your *best* works."

JIM McCOY MUSIC/ALEAR MUSIC, Box 574, Sounds of Winchester, Winchester VA 22601. (703)667-9379. Affiliate: New Edition Publishing. Contact: Jim McCoy. Music publisher, record company, record producer and management firm. BMI. Publishes 50 songs/year; publishes 25 new songwriters/year. Pays standard royalty.
How to Contact: Prefers 7½ ips reel-to-reel or cassette with 5-10 songs and lead sheet. SASE. Reports in 1 month.
Music: Bluegrass, church/religious, country, folk, gospel, progressive and rock. Recently published "Going with Jesus," (by Fred Fox), recorded by Middleburg Harmonizers (gospel); "Lost in Austin," (by Panama Red), recorded by Del Davidson (country); and *Jim McCoy Sings*, recorded by Jim McCoy (country).

LEE MACE'S OZARK OPRY MUSIC PUBLISHING, Box 242, Osage Beach MO 65065. (314)348-2702. Affiliates: Tall Corn Publishing and Mid America Music Publishing. General Manager: Lee Mace. Music publisher, record company and record producer. ASCAP, BMI. Publishes 12 songs/year. Pays standard royalty.
How to Contact: Arrange personal interview. Prefers 7½ ips reel-to-reel or cassette with 2-4 songs and lead sheet. SASE. Reports in 2 weeks.
Music: Bluegrass, blues, church/religious, country, gospel, and R&B. Recently published "Younger Than Tomorrow," (by M. Sexton), recorded by Mark Sexton (pop/country); "I Can't Sell My Self," (by D. Thomas), recorded by Darrel Thomas (country); and "Don't Say No to Me Tonight," (by Don and Dick Addrisi), recorded by M. Sexton/Sun De Mar Records (pop/country).

*MAGIC MESSAGE MUSIC, Box 2236, Largo FL 33540. (813)595-5115. Contact: Alan Redstone. ASCAP. Music publisher and record company (Sureshot Records). Publishes 3 songs/year. Pays standard royalty.
How to Contact: Prefers cassette. SASE.
Music: Mostly pop, country and rock; also adult contemporary. Recently published: "Cold Hands & Wet Feet," (country/rock); and "Magic Message," (adult contemporary), both written and recorded by Alan Redstone on Sureshot.

*MAIN TRIPP PUBLISHING INC., 2804 Beechtree Dr., Sanford NC 27330. (919)774-8926. Vice President/General Manager: John Edwards. BMI. Music publisher and record company. Publishes 50 songs/year; publishes varying number of new songwriters/year. Pays standard royalty.
How to Contact: Prefers cassette or 7½ ips reel-to-reel with any number of songs and lyric sheet. "We will also accept the following: 8-track, record, or just a lead sheet." SASE. Reports in 2 weeks.
Music: Mostly country, country rock or country comedy; also gospel, and bluegrass. Recently published "What the Lonely Can Do," (by John Edwards), recorded by Bill Tripp/Atteram (country); and "Love Is," and "Put Me Down Easy," written and recorded by B. Tripp/Atteram (country).
Tips: "We are songwriter owned and operated, and will be aggressive in searching for good songwriters. Elaborate demos are unnecessary. We don't have to be hit over the head to know when it's a good song. A clean home demo with one voice out front and one instrument is fine. Reversion clause is one year. Returned material includes constructive criticism checklist."

MANFIELD MUSIC, Holy Spirit Records, 27335 Penn St., Inkster MI 48141. (313)862-8220. President: Elder Otis G. Johnson. Music publisher, record producer and record company. BMI. Publishes 10 songs/year; publishes 5 new songwriters/year. Works with lyricists and composers and teams collaborators. Pays standard royalty.
How to Contact: Query. Prefers 3¾ or 7½ ips reel-to-reel or cassette with minimum 3 songs and lyric sheet. Include phone number. SASE. Reports in 1 month.
Music: Church/religious, easy listening and gospel. Recently published "And to Be With You," by Otis G. Johnson and Valorie Jean Rena/Aspro; "I Found You," written and recorded by V.J. Rena; and "That Feeling Called Love," by Annexus/Aspro.

*CHARLES MANNA PUBLISHING, 128 Colonial Pkwy., Yonkers NY 10710. (914)337-4462. President: Charles Manna. BMI. Music publisher. Publishes 5 songs/year; publishes 2 new songwriters/year. Pays standard royalty.
How to Contact: Prefers cassette. Does not return unsolicited material.
Music: Mostly rock, dance and jazz. Recently published "Trying," "Falling," and "Time," written and recorded by L. Frisaura, on Apple Pye Records.

MARK OF ARIES MUSIC, Suite 9G, 579 W. 215th St., New York NY 10034. (212)942-5004. President: Dennis L. Bell. Music publisher and record producer. BMI. Publishes 2 songs/year. Pays standard royalty.

How to Contact: Prefers cassette with 1-2 songs and lyric sheet. Prefers studio produced demos. Does not return material.
Music: Mostly R&B/dance; also dance-oriented, gospel, soul and top 40/pop. Recently published "Wrap It Up," (by D. Bell et al.), recorded by Touché on Emergency Records (dance); and "Just Like A Doorknob," (by D. Bell et al.), recorded by Touché on NRPQ Records/Italy (dance).

MARMIK MUSIC, INC., 135 E. Muller Rd., East Peoria IL 61611. (309)699-4000. President: Martin Mitchell. Music publisher and record company. BMI. Publishes 40-60 songs/year; publishes 10-15 new songwriters/year. Works with lyricists and composers and teams collaborators. Pays negotiable royalty.
How to Contact: Query. Prefers reel-to-reel or cassette with 2-10 songs and lead sheet. "With first submission, include an affidavit of ownership of the material." SASE. Reports in 2 weeks.
Music: Mostly MOR, Christian and country; also church/religious, blues, easy listening and gospel. Recently published "Gloomy Days," by Wade Ray (novelty); "Standing Tall," by Pete Nuchin (country); and "Blue," by Ray Block (country single).
Tips: "Need songs that are topical and upbeat—too many slow songs on the market."

MARSAINT MUSIC, INC., 3809 Clematis Ave., New Orleans LA 70122. (504)949-8386. A&R Director: M.E. Sehorn. Music publisher. BMI. Pays standard royalty.
How to Contact: Prefers cassette with 3-5 songs and lyric sheet. SASE. Reports in 6 weeks.
Music: Blues, gospel, jazz, R&B and soul. Recently published "Released" (by Allen R. Toussaint), recorded by Patti Labelle/CBS Records (soul); "Southern Nights" (by A.R. Toussaint), recorded by Glen Campbell (country); "Hot Shot," recorded by Carla Baker; songs recorded by Ramsey Lewis/CBS Records (progressive jazz) and Eric Gale/CBS Records (progressive jazz).

MARSHALL STREET MELODIES, 8102 Polk St. NE, Minneapolis MN 55432. (612)784-7458. President/General Manager: Michael S.J. Gapinski. Music publisher and record company. BMI. Member MSA. Publishes 10-20 songs/year; publishes 4-6 new songwriters/year. Works with lyricists and composers and teams collaborators. Pays standard royalty.
How to Contact: Write first. Prefers cassette with 1-3 songs. "Include clear and concise sheet music and/or *separate* lyric sheets." Does not return unsolicited material. Reports in 2 weeks.
Music: Mostly funk; also slow dance and country crossover. Recently published "Find New Love," "Nothing Else," and "Turn Up the Fire," (by Michael Gapinski), recorded by Michael Sylvester/Marshall Street Melodies.
Tips: "The song is most important, not the quality of recording or arrangement—don't over produce."

***MARULLO MUSIC PUBLISHERS**, 1121 Market St., Galveston TX 77550. (713)762-4590. President: A.W. Marullo, Sr. Music publisher, record company and record producer. BMI. Publishes 24 songs/year; publishes 8 new songwriters/year. Pays standard royalty.
How to Contact: Prefers cassette "only" with 4-6 songs and lyric sheet. SASE. Reports in 6 weeks.
Music: Country, soul and top 40/pop. Recently published "Girl I Never Had," (by Bobbe Brown), recorded by Brown Bros./Paid Records (country); "Alimony Blues" (by Michael Claughton), recorded by Michael John/Red Dot Records (country); and "We'll Make Believe Again," written and recorded by Kemberly and Michael John/Red Dot Records (country).

***MARYLEBONE MUSIC**, Box 212, London SW1W 9HA England. (01)730-7291. A&R Director: Sam Edwards. PRS. Music publisher, record company (G.C. Recordings/K.R. Recordings) and record producer. Pays negotiable royalty.
How to Contact: Prefers cassette and lyric sheet. SAE and IRC.
Music: Mostly melodic pop, dance and funk; also soul. Recently published "Sticking to My Guns," (by M. Dunne), recorded by T.D.T. on G.C./M.C.A. (pop); "Love Dance," (by Hood/Ryda/Jackson), recorded by Heat on G.C./M.C.A. (dance); and "Transdance," by Nightmoves on G.C./M.C.A. (hi energy).

MASTERLEASE MUSIC PUBLICATIONS, Box 234, St. Louis MO 63166. (314)296-9526. President: Bob Bax. Music publisher and record company. BMI. Publishes 3 songs/year. Pays standard royalty.
How to Contact: Write first about your interest. Prefers cassette with 2-6 songs and lyric sheet. Does not return unsolicited material. Reports in 1 month.
Music: Bluegrass, blues, church/religious, country, gospel, Spanish and R&B.

MASTER'S COLLECTION PUBLISHING & T.M.C. PUBLISHING, Box 189, Station W, Toronto, Ontario M6M 4Z2 Canada. (416)746-1991. President: Paul J. Young. Music publisher and record

company. PROCAN, CAPAC. Member CIRPA. Publishes 50 songs/year; publishes 12 new songwriters/year. Pays standard royalty.
How to Contact: Write first. Prefers cassette with 3-6 songs. Does not return unsolicited material. Reports in 1 month.
Music: Christian/religious. Recently published "Crown of Glory," (by Ruth Fazal) and "One City Stands," (by Andrew Donaldson), on The Master's Collection Records; and "Christmas Is," (by Frank Hargreaves), recorded by His Ambassadors/The Master's Collection Records (Christmas).

*MAWSON AND WAREHAM (MUSIC), LTD., Midgy Ha, Sharperton, Morpeth, Northumberland NE65 7AS, England. PRS. Music publisher, record company and record producer. Publishes 10 songs/year; publishes 1 new songwriter/year. Pays standard royalty.
How to Contact: Prefers cassette with 4 songs. SAE and IRC. Reports in 4 weeks.
Music: Mostly folk, blues and country. Recently published "Under the Rain," (by Rab Noakes) and "On the Other Side," (by Alan Hull), on Black Crow (contemporary); and "At Last It's," (by Mike Elliott), on Rubber (humor).

*MCA MUSIC JAPAN, Akasaka Makabe Bldg. 4-3, 3-chome Minato-ku, Tokyo 107 Japan. A&R: Mark Suzuki. Music publisher. Publishes 500 songs/year; publishes 20 new songwriters/year. Pays 60% royalty. Affiliated pulbishing firms: Mind Music Publisher, Kitty Music, Uni Japan Music, Standard Music.
How to Contact: Prefers cassette and lyric sheet and lead sheet. "Please send the writer's bio." Does not return unsolicited material. Reports in 2-3 weeks.
Music: Mostly pop and rock. Recently published "Romantic Ga Tomaranai," (by Kyohei Tsutsumi and Takashi Matsumoto), recorded by CCB on Polydor (pop); "Mienai Tsubasa," (by Masao Urino and Kisaburo Suzuki), recorded on Maiko Itoh on CBS Sony (pop); and "Koishite Carribean," (by Kyohei Tsutsumi and T. Matsumoto), recorded by Oginome on Victor (pop).
Tips: "Light pop suitable for the Japanese would be most appreciated."

*MCJAMES MUSIC, Box 34, East Irvine CA 92650. (714)891-0868. President: Tim James. BMI. Music publisher and record company (37 Records). Publishes 5 songs/year; publishes 2 new songwriters/year. Pays standard royalty. Affiliated publishing firms: Gopher Baroque Music, More Baroque Music.
How to Contact: Prefers cassette with "3 songs only." SASE. Reports in 4 weeks.
Music: Mostly top 40 pop (uptempo), top 40 pop (ballads) and country; also rock. Recently published "Waiting for the Sun," (by Otha Young and Tim James), recorded by Juice Newton on RCA (country pop); "One More Night," (by Steve McClintock & T. James), recorded by Jay Kaye on CBS (pop); and "Talk to Me," (by Gam Beall and Bob Lawrence), recorded by Private I on 37 Records (pop rock).
Tips: "Be realistic about your competition—listen to the radio."

MEDIA INTERSTELLAR MUSIC, Box 20346, Chicago IL 60620. (312)778-8760. Professional Manager: V. Beleska. Music publisher. BMI. Publishes 20-40 songs/year. Also *"joint ownership plans, where a songwriter becomes co-publisher. Expenses and profits are shared. We don't charge the songwriter for our services as publisher. We cannot consider any material, however, without first receiving a written query (don't phone) describing yourself and your songs in some depth. The letter should explain your background, type of songs written and why songs are unique enough to be listened to."*
How to Contact: "Inquire first, describing yourself and songs available." Prefers 7½ ips reel-to-reel, cassette or disc with 1-5 songs. SASE. Reports in 2-8 weeks.
Music: Avant-garde, country, disco, easy listening, MOR, progressive, rock, soul, and top 40/pop. Recently published "All for You," and "The Show Never Ends," recorded by Christopher (MOR/rock); and "Tricentennial 2076," recorded by Vyto B (avant-garde).

*MENTO MUSIC GROUP KG, Box 7718, D-2000 Hamburg 20, West Germany. (040) 43.00.339. General Manager: Arno H. v. Vught Jr. GEMA. Music publisher, record company (Playbones Records) and record producer (Arteg Productions). Publishes 200 songs/year; publishes 5-7 new songwriters/year. Pays standard royalty. Affiliated publishing firms: Edition RCP Music, Auteursunie, Edition Kunst and Risiko.
How to Contact: Write or call first to arrange personal interview. Prefers cassette or VHS videocassette and lyric sheet or lead sheet. SAE and IRC. Reports in 2 weeks.
Music: Mostly MOR, jazz and country; also background music and film music. Recently published "Hey Hey Marlene," (by Martin), recorded by High Life on Jupiter (MOR); "Memories," (by Kniphals), recorded by Jack Hals on Playbones (MOR); and "Waltz for Berlin," written and recorded by Lackerschmid on Sandra (jazz).

MERCANTILE MUSIC, Box 2271, Palm Springs CA 92263. (619)320-4848. Affiliate: Blueford Music (ASCAP). President: Kent Fox. Music publisher and record producer. Publishes 12 new songwriters/year. Pays standard royalty.
How to Contact: Prefers cassette with 3-12 songs and lyric sheet. SASE. Reports in 1 month.
Music: Country, easy listening, rock, MOR, and top 40/pop.

MERTIS MUSIC CO., 8130 Northlawn, Detroit MI 48204. (313)934-0106. Vice President: Olivia John. Music publisher and record company. BMI. Publishes 40 songs/year; publishes 2-3 new songwriters/year. Works with lyricists and composers and teams collaborators. Pays standard royalty.
How to Contact: Prefers cassette with 4-8 songs and lead sheet. SASE. Reports in 1 month or ASAP.
Music: Mostly gospel, pop and R&B; also country. Recently published "Xmas Comes But Once a Year" and "Why Did You Leave Me" (by Mertis John), recorded by Ray Charles/Columbia Records (Christmas/R&B).
Tips: "We need good black gospel tunes. Send cassettes and lead sheets together."

MID AMERICA MUSIC, (a division of Ozark Opry Records, Inc.), Box 242, Osage Beach MO 65065. (314)348-3383. Affiliate: Tall Corn Publishing. General Manager: Lee Mace. Music publisher. ASCAP, BMI. Publishes 25 songs/year. Pays standard royalty.
How to Contact: Arrange personal interview. Prefers 7½ ips reel-to-reel or cassette with 1-3 songs and lead sheet. "Tape should be of good quality, and the voice should be louder than the music." SASE. Reports in 3 weeks.
Music: Bluegrass, children's, church/religious, country, disco, easy listening, gospel, MOR and rock. Recently published "Never Asking for More," (by Rod Johnson), recorded by Graham Fee/Fee-Line Records (MOR); "Losing the Blues" (by Steve and Juli Ann Whiting), recorded by S. Whiting/KRC Records (MOR); and "Iowa a Place to Grow" (by S. Whiting), recorded by S. Whiting/KRC Records (MOR).

THE MIGHTY THREE MUSIC GROUP, 309 S. Broad St., Philadelphia PA 19107. (215)546-3510. Affiliates: Assorted Music (BMI), Bell Boy Music (BMI), Downstairs Music (BMI), Razor Sharp Music (BMI), Rose Tree Music (ASCAP) and World War Three Music (BMI). President: Earl Shelton. Vice President of Publishing Administration: Constance Heigler. Professional Manager: William Lacy. Music publisher. BMI, ASCAP. Member NMPA. Publishes 100 songs/year; publishes 6 new songwriters/year. Pays standard royalty. Sometimes offers advance: "If a writer is signed to us exclusively, we offer him advances recoupable against writer royalties after songs have been recorded and released."
How to Contact: Prefers cassette with 1-3 songs and lyric sheet. "Must provide large SASE for return." Reports in 8 weeks.
Music: Country, disco, easy listening, folk, gospel, jazz, MOR, progressive, rock (hard, country), soul and top 40/pop. Recently published "Swing That Sexy Thing," by Carl Carlton/International Records; and "Your Body's Here with Me" (by Gilbert, Sigler and Sigler), recorded by The O'Jays/Philadelphia International Records (gospel); and "God Said It" (by Gamble and Womack), recorded by The 5 Blind Boys of Alabama/Peace International Records.

MIGHTY TWINNS MUSIC, 9134 S. Indiana Ave., Chicago IL 60619. (312)493-0441. General Manager: Ron Scott. Music publisher and record producer. BMI. Member NMPA. Publishes 2-8 songs/year; publishes 3 new songwriters/year. Works with lyricists and composers. Pays standard royalty.
How to Contact: Prefers cassette or videocassette with 2-4 songs and lyric sheet. SASE "only if you want material returned." Reports in 1 month.
Music: Mostly top 40 and gospel; also children's, church/religious and R&B. Recently published "The Right Man" (by Keithen Carter and Ron Scot), recorded by K. Carter and R. Scott/Unison Records (top 40/pop).
Tips: Looking for "good hot songs with hot hooks."

MIMIC MUSIC, Box 201, Smyrna GA 30081. (404)432-2454. Affiliates: Skip Jack Music and Stepping Stone. Manager: Tom Hodges. Music publisher, record producer, record company and management company. BMI. Publishes 20 songs/year. Pays standard royalty.
How to Contact: Prefers cassette with 3-10 songs and lyric sheet. SASE. Reports in 2 weeks.
Music: Bluegrass, blues, church/religious, country, easy listening, gospel, MOR, R&B, rock, soul and top 40/pop. Recently published "Please Tell Her to Wait" (by Norman Skipper), recorded on Capitol Records (country); "Good Ole Country Music" (by Helen Humphries), recorded on British Overseas Records (country); and "Take Away the Roses" (by Burke-Bailey), recorded on British Overseas Records (country).

MIND TO SOUND MUSIC PUBLISHING, Box 229, Planetarium Station, New York NY 10024. Contact: Margaret Gresh. Music publisher. BMI. Publishes 10 songs/year; publishes 2 new songwriters/year. Pays standard royalty.
How to Contact: Prefers cassette with 3-5 songs and lyric sheet. SASE. Reports in 1 month.
Music: Church/religious, gospel, MOR, R&B, rock (soft), soul and top 40/pop.

MIRACLE-JOY PUBLICATIONS, Box 711, Hackensack NJ 07601. (201)488-5211. President: Johnny Miracle. Vice President: Aileen Joy. Music publisher and record company. BMI.
How to Contact: Prefers 7½ ips reel-to-reel or cassette with 2-6 songs and lead sheet. SASE. Reports in 2 weeks.
Music: Children's, church/religious, country, easy listening, folk and gospel. Recently published *The Way It Might Have Been*, recorded by Mike Galo; and *Sound Hut*, recorded by Donna Winters.

MR. MORT MUSIC, 44 Music Square E., Nashville TN 37203. (615)255-2175. Affiliate: Jason Dee Music (BMI). President: Charles Fields. Music publisher, record company and record producer. ASCAP. Publishes 50 songs/year; publishes 8 new songwriters/year. Pays standard royalty.
How to Contact: Prefers 7½ ips reel-to-reel or cassette with 1-4 songs and lead sheet. SASE. Reports in 2 weeks.
Music: Mostly MOR, easy listening and country; also blues and top 40/pop. Recently published "Country Man/Country Lady," (by Steve Brown), recorded by Steve and Debby Brown/Charta (MOR); "You Touched Me," (by Roni Futoran/David Gelman), recorded by Sun Rize Jim/Passion (country); and "Did She Tell You Daddy Loves You," written and recorded by David Walsh/Charta (MOR).

MISTER SUNSHINE MUSIC, INC., Box 7877, College Park Station, Orlando FL 32854. (305)299-0077. Professional Manager: Kelly McKenna. BMI, ASCAP. Music publisher, record company (Parc Records/CBS) and record producer (Pat Armstrong & Assoc. Inc.). Publishes 40 songs/year; pubishes 5 new songwriters/year. Pays standard royalty. Affiliated publishing firms: Armco Music, Martik Music, Les Etoiles De La Musique.
How to Contact: Prefers cassette or VHS videocassette with lyric sheet. SASE. Reports in 4 weeks.
Music: Mostly rock/heavy metal and top 40/pop. Recently published "Flirtin With Disaster," (by D. Hlubek, D. Brown and B. Thomas), recorded by Molly Hatchet on Epic (rock); "Party in My Pants," (by J. Campanello, J. Luis and J. Vols), recorded by Four-In-Legion on CBS Assoc., (rock); and "Good, Smoke & Whiskey," (by D.J. Brown, B. Crump, J. Calvin, D. Hlubek, D. Roland, R. West), recorded by Molly Hatchet on Epic (rock).
Tips: "Listen to AOR, CHR (contemporary hit radio), top 40 and adult contemporary radio and emulate the structure and subject matter."

IVAN MOGULL MUSIC CORP., 625 Madison Ave., New York NY 10022. (212)355-5636. President: Ivan Mogull. Music publisher. ASCAP, BMI and SESAC. Member NMPA. Publishes 10-30 songs/year. Pays standard royalty.
How to Contact: Prefers 7½ ips reel-to-reel or cassette and lyric sheet. SASE. Reports in 2 weeks.
Music: Rock and top 40/pop. Publisher of all Abba hits.

***MONARD MUSIC**, 10622 Commerce Ave., Tujunga CA 91042. (818)352-7155. Affiliate: Pencott Publishing. Contact: Kent Washburn. Music publisher, record company and record producer. ASCAP, BMI. Member NARAS, GMA. Publishes 15 songs/year; publishes 1 new songwriter/year. Pays standard royalty.
How to Contact: Prefers cassette with 2-4 songs and lyric sheet. SASE. Reports in 1 month.
Music: Mostly R&B; also gospel, jazz, soul and top 40/pop. Recently published "Resurrection," (by Terry Lupton), recorded by Paul Davis/Spirit Records (gospel); "Don't Burn No Bridges," (by R. Anderson), recorded by Hypnotics/Emkay Records (R&B); and "Ain't No Flys," (by R. Matthews), recorded by R. Matthews/Spirit Records (gospel).

MONTINA MUSIC, Box 702, Snowdon Station, Montreal, Quebec H3X 3X8 Canada. Affiliate: Sabre Music (CAPAC). Professional General Manager: David P. Leonard. Music publisher. PROCAN. Member MIEA. Pays standard royalty.
How to Contact: Prefers 15 or 7½ ips reel-to-reel, cassette, phonograph record or videocasette and lyric sheet. Does not return unsolicited material.
Music: Mostly top 40; also bluegrass, blues, country, dance-oriented, easy listening, folk, gospel, jazz, MOR, progressive, R&B, rock and soul.

DOUG MOODY MUSIC, Mystic Records Inc., 6277 Selma Ave., Hollywood CA 90028. President: Doug Moody. Music publisher, record company and record producer (music library for TV, film, etc.).

BMI. Publishes 200 songs/year; publishes 100 new songwriters/year. Pays standard royalty.
How to Contact: Prefers cassette with 1-2 songs and lyric sheet. SASE. Reports as soon as possible.
Music: "We are now looking for punk, hardcore and heavy metal—we need an aggressive young sound."

MOON RIDGE MUSIC, 2940 E. Miraloma, Anaheim CA 92806. (714)992-6820. President: Chuck Whittington. ASCAP. Publishes 30 songs/year; publishes 1 new songwriter/year. Pays standard royalty.
How to Contact: Prefers cassette with 2-4 songs and lyric sheet. Does not return unsolicited material. Reports in 1 month.
Music: Country, gospel and top 40/pop. Recently published *Waltzes & Western Swing* and "Big Tulsa Tillie" (by Donnie Rohrs); and "Building Up to a Letdown" (by Robert Lee Smith), all recorded by Donnie Rohrs/Pacific Challenger Records.

MORRISON HILL MUSIC, C-1, 227 Union St., Lodi NJ 07644. (201)471-2770. Manager: Joseph A. Sterner. Music publisher. ASCAP. Pays standard royalty; uses AGAC contract. Affiliate: Monja-Hearn Music (BMI).
How to Contact: Write or call first about your interest. "We prefer to discuss how-to-submit with prospective writers by mail or phone." SASE. Reports in 2 weeks.
Music: Country (all types), folk, gospel (contemporary), and easy listening. Recently published "Do You Love Him," (by K.W. Gazzillo), recorded by The Edwards/Private (religious); "Home Where I Belong," written and recorded by Laurie Reed/PJS Records (country); and "Countin' Down To Love," (by A. Stanten), recorded by Sylvia Kaye/Yellow Jacket (country).
Tips: "We are looking for talented songwriters, not 'one-song' writers. We will inform those who inquire, and are accepted, what we want and how we want it. We are publishers and song-pluggers. We also manage professional groups. Be professional and businesslike in your dealings with publishers and it will carry over into your writing. A writer, who is a professional craftsperson, is always rewarded."

*MOTORCOACH PUBLISHING, 630 West Adler Rd., Marshfield WI 54449. (715)832-4812. President: Daniel Korn. BMI. Music publisher and record producer. Publishes 2 songs/year; publishes 1 new songwriter/year. Employs songwriters on a salary basis. Pays standard royalty.
How to Contact: Write first and obtain permission to submit or to arrange personal interview. Prefers cassette and lyric and lead sheets. Submit nothing until given permission to do so. Reports in 1 week.
Music: Mostly blues, jazz and rock; also country, classical, gospel and short stories. Recently published "Sha Boogie," (blues), "Mary (Show Me Again)," (classical), and "Though You Can't See," (classical), all written and recorded by Dan Korn/Sojourn.
Tips: "Works with chord block notation written above are good enough. Include key signature."

MULTIMEDIA MUSIC GROUP, #260, 3401 West End, Nashville TN 37203. (615)327-2532. Affiliate: Songmedia, Multimuse. General Manager: Cliff Williamson. Music publisher. BMI, ASCAP. Publishes 122 songs/year. Hires staff writers. Pays standard royalty.
How to Contact: Prefers cassette with 3 songs and lyric sheet. SASE. Reports in 2 weeks.
Music: Country, top 40/pop and R&B. Recently published "Staying Afloat," (by King and Martin), recorded by Sawyer Brown/EMI-CURB and Oak Ridge Boys/MCA; and "How Blue," (by John Moffat), recorded by Reba McEntire/MCA (all country).

MURIOS PUBLISHING, INC., 2140 Hamilton Ave., Cleveland OH 44114. (216)241-0892. Affiliate: Mirus Publishing Corp. (BMI). General Manager: Gary Doberstyn. Music publisher and record company. BMI and ASCAP. Publishes 50 songs/year; publishes 4 new songwriters/year. Pays standard royalty.
How to Contact: Prefers cassette with 2-5 songs and lead or lyric sheet. SASE. Reports in 2-3 weeks.
Music: Mostly rock, R&B, and top 40/pop; also dance, easy listening, jazz, and heavy metal.

MUSEDCO PUBLISHING CO., Box 5916, Richardson TX 75080. (214)783-9925. Contact: Dick A. Shuff. Music publisher. BMI. Member GMA and AFM. Publishes 8-10 songs/year; publishes 1-2 new songwriters/year. Pays standard royalty.
How to Contact: Query by phone or letter giving background. Prefers cassette with 1-2 songs and lyric sheet. SASE. Does not return unsolicited material. Reports in 1 month.

 The asterisk before a listing indicates that the listing is new in this edition. New markets are often the most receptive to freelance contributions.

Music: Choral, church/religious, country, and gospel. Recently published "Sing Praise to God" and "Rejoice," by Fargason and Shuff (choral-religious).
Tips: "Send positive, one-topic songs, songs that are uninvolved and easy to sing."

MUSIC FOR PERCUSSION, INC., 170 NE 33rd St., Fort Lauderdale FL 33334. (305)563-1844. Affiliate: Plymouth Music (ASCAP). Contact: Bernard Fisher. Music publisher. BMI.
How to Contact: Prefers 7½ ips reel-to-reel and lead sheet. "Be sure that many tapes submitted are carefully labeled with title, name and address of composer." SASE. Reports in 1 month.
Music: "We are interested primarily in percussion music for solo or ensemble."

MUSIC PUBLISHERS OF HAWAII, Box 25141, Honolulu HI 96825. (808)737-7059. President: Gil M. Tanaka. Music publisher, record company and record producer. BMI. Publishes 24 songs/year; publishes 3 new songwriters/year. Pays standard royalty.
How to Contact: Prefers cassette with 1-6 songs and lyric sheet. SASE. Reports in 1 month.
Music: Mostly top 40/pop; also country, easy listening, jazz and rock. Recently published *Kevin I.* (by Kevin I.), recorded by Kevin I./GMT Records (top 40/pop); *Paul Flynn* (by various artists), recorded by Paul Flynn/GMT Records (top 40/pop); and *Music Magic* (by Al Pascua/Fred Schrenders), recorded by Music Magic/GMI Records (jazz).

MUSICANZA CORP., 2878 Bayview Ave., Wantagh NY 11793. Music publisher. ASCAP. Publishes "several" songs/year; publishes 2 new songwriters/year. Pays standard royalty.
How to Contact: Submit lead sheet and SASE. Reports in 1 month.
Music: Children's. Recently published "A Friend Like You" (by Dorothy Mesney); and "I Can Draw Pictures" (by Ray Gill), both to be recorded.

MUSICRAFTERS, Box 1301 Doylestown PA 18901. (215)345-TUNE. Affiliate: Lou DeLise Productions, Bocagé Music. Professional Manager: Elena C. Marino. Music publisher, record producer and producer/distributor of music for advertising, television, radio, films and other audiovisual applications. BMI, ASCAP. Member AFM, AGAC. Publishes 150 songs/year. Payment per sale for production music library.
How to Contact: Prefers cassette with maximum 2 songs and lyric sheet. SASE. Reports in 1 month.
Music: Instrumental only; bluegrass, classical, country, dance-oriented, easy listening, jazz, MOR, progressive, rock and top 40/pop.

*MUSICWORKS PUBLISHING COMPANY, Box 88, Station 'H,' Montreal, Quebec H3G 2K5 Canada. (514)489-2705. Affiliate: Urban-Contempo (ASCAP). President: Paul Klein. Music publisher, record company and record producer. BMI. Publishes 20 songs/year; publishes 5-10 new songwriters/year. Hires staff writers; pays $100/week advance against royalties. Pays standard royalty.
How to Contact: Prefers cassette with 1-4 songs and lyric sheet. Does not return unsolicited material. Reports in 1 month.
Music: Mostly dance, soul/R&B and pop; also soul. Recently published "Thunder in Your Love," (by Phil Valentine), recorded by Lemukia/Street-Level (R&B); "Give It Up Turn It Loose," (by Larry Davis), recorded by Tony & The Night Runners/Musicworks (R&B); and "How I Wish You Knew I Cared," written and recorded by Leslie Ming/AM-FM (ballad).

MUSINFO PUBLISHING GROUP, INC., 5514 Isabella St., Montreal, Quebec, H3X 1R6 Canada. (514)484-5419. General Manager: Jehan V. Valiquet. Music publisher, record company, record producer, promotion and marketing consultants. PROCAN, CAPAC. Publishes 150 songs/year; publishes 10 new songwriters/year. Works with lyricists and composers and teams collaborators. Pays standard royalty.
How to Contact: Prefers cassette or videocassette and lyric sheet. SAE and IRC. Reports in 1 month.
Music: Mostly dance-oriented and top 40/pop in French; also children's, folk, MOR and Spanish. Recently published "Kanzai," (by Paul Sabu), recorded by Isa Minoke/Impression Records (pop); "Danse de Canards," (by Thomas T. Rendall), recorded by Nathalie Simard/T. Canada Records (novelty); and "Comment Ca Va" (by E. de Heer), recorded by the Shorts/Capitol Records (pop).

MUSTEVIC SOUND PUBLISHING, 115-18 222nd St., New York NY 11411. (212)276-2078. President: Beverly Robinson. Music publisher, record producer and record company. BMI. Publishes 3-4 songs/year; publishes 2 new songwriters/year. Pays standard royalty.
How to Contact: Write first about your interest. Prefers cassette with maximim 3 songs. "Send copyrighted material only!" SASE. Reports in 1 month.
Music: Jazz fusion and ethnic. Recently published "One Hard Fall," (by Mike Singer), recorded by Hot Ice/Mustevic (rock); and "Space Place," (by Steve Reid), recorded by Beverly Reid/Mustevic (fusion).

MY DEE DEE MUSIC, Box 1010, Hendersonville TN 37077. (615)451-3920. Affiliate: Mel-Dee Music (BMI). General Manager: Dee Mullins. Music publisher, record company (Melodee) and record producer (Melodee Ent.). ASCAP. Member AFM, AFTRA. Publishes 30-40 songs/year; publishes 4-5 new songwriters/year. Pays standard royalty.
How to Contact: Write or call first or arrange personal interview. Prefers cassette or videocassette with 1-4 songs and lyric sheet. SASE. Reports in 1 month.
Music: Mostly country and crossover country; also bluegrass, folk, gospel, MOR, rock (country) and top 40/pop.

MY! MY! MUSIC PUBLISHING INC., Suite 12A, 211 West 56th St., New York NY 10019. (212)246-5520. Affiliates: Victor Music-Japan, Personal Music Publishing, G.Ricordi & C. S.P.A.-Italy and Chrysalis-U.K. Director: Susan Feilich. Music publisher and record company. BMI, ASCAP. Publishes 12 songs/year; publishes 4 new songwriters/year. Hires staff writers. Pays standard royalty.
How to Contact: Contact Judy Hicks, % Arista Music Publishing, 8370 Wilshire Blvd., Beverly Hills CA 90211. Prefers reel-to-reel, cassette or videocassette with 3-5 songs and lyric sheet. SASE. Reports in 2 weeks.
Music: Mostly dance and R&B; also MOR, rock (high energy), soul and top 40/pop. Recently published "Trommel Tanz" (by George Kranz), recorded by G. Kranz (dance & R&B); "No Way" (by Leroy Burgess and Sonny Davenport), recorded by Inner Life (R&B) and "I'm Not Your Doormat" (by Psychodrama), recorded by Psychodrama (rock).

NANCY JANE PUBLISHING CO., 1102 Virginia St. SW, Lenoir NC 28645. (704)758-4170. President: Mike McCoy. Music publisher, record company and record producer. BMI. Publishes 3 songs/year; publishes 2 new songwriters/year. Works with lyricists and composers. Pays standard royalty.
How to Contact: Prefers cassette with 1-4 songs and lyric sheet. SASE. Reports in 1 month.
Music: Mostly country rock, rock and rockabilly; also religious, gospel, R&B, outlaw country and bluegrass. Recently published "My Baby Loves Old Rock and Roll," "From My Land to Graceland," (country crossover), and "Rock and Roll Outlaw," (rockabilly), all recorded by Mike McCoy/Legend records.

NASHCAL MUSIC, Suite 902, 50 Music Square W., Nashville TN 37203. (615)329-2278. Affiliates: Bobby Fischer Music (ASCAP) and Bobby's Beat (SESAC). Contact: Bobby Fischer. Music publisher, record company, record producer and promotion firm. BMI. Member CMA, NSAI and FICAP. Publishes 25 songs/year; publishes 5 new songwriters/year. Pays standard royalty.
How to Contact: Prefers cassette with 2-3 songs and lyric sheet. "We review material as time permits and return with SASE *if* time permits." Reports as soon as possible.
Music: Modern country. Recently published "City Boy" (by Bob Rodin and C. Blake), recorded by Moe Bandy/Columbia Records; "The Right Stuff," by Mickey Gilley and Charlie McClain/Epic Records (country); and "Girl Don't Ever Get Lonely" (by C. Blake and B. Fischer), recorded by Moe and Joe/Columbia Records (all country).

NATASHA DAWN MUSIC PUBLISHING CO., 1½ W. National Ave., Brazil IN 47834. (812)448-3013. Professional Manager: Laura Allen. Music publisher, record company, record producer and studio. BMI. Member CMA. Publishes 50 songs/year; publishes 14 new songwriters/year. Pays standard royalty.
How to Contact: "Call if you need additional information or guidance." Prefers cassette with 1-3 songs and lyric sheet. SASE. Reports in 3 weeks.
Music: Mostly country; also gospel, country rock and country crossover. Recently published "Fire & the Wine" (by Charlie Quinton/Flavy LeSell), recorded by Loretta Pierce/Natasha Dawn Records (country); "Country Fever" (by Carol Ann Bibb/Gary Wayne Bibb), recorded by Kimberly Dawn/Natasha Dawn (country); and "Let's all Get Crazy Tonight" (by Kevin McCrea), recorded by Kevin McCrea/Natasha Dawn Records (crossover country).

NAUTICAL MUSIC CO., Box 120675, Nashville TN 37212. (615)255-1068. President: Ray McGinnis. Music publisher, record company and record producer. BMI. Publishes 30 songs/year; publishes 2 new songwriters/year. Pays standard royalty.
How to Contact: Prefers cassette with 4-6 songs and lyric sheet. SASE. Reports in 1 month.
Music: Mostly country; also country rock and top 40/pop. Recently published "Finger Pickin Good" and "Long Gone By" (by Teddy Hale), recorded by Teddy Hale/Orbit Records (country); and "Strangers with the Same Last Name" (by Dorval Smith), recorded by Wayne Pierce/Orbit Records (country).

NEWCREATURE MUSIC, 1106 18th Ave. S., Nashville TN 37212. (615)868-3407. President: Bill Anderson Jr. Music publisher, record company, record producer and radio and TV syndicator. BMI.

Publishes 25 songs/year; publishes 1 new songwriter/year. Pays standard royalty.
How to Contact: Prefers 7½ ips reel-to-reel or cassette with 4-10 songs and lyric sheet. SASE. Reports in 1 month.
Music: Country, gospel, jazz, R&B, rock and top 40/pop. Recently published "Fear Not" (by J.C. Yates), recorded by Joanne Cash/Kola Records (gospel); and "Praises Unto the Lord" (by B. Anderson, Jr. and D.D. Morris), gospel theme song for syndicated radio program.

NEWWRITERS MUSIC, 43 Music Square E., Nashville TN 37203. (615)244-1025. Affiliate: Timestar Music (ASCAP). National Promotion Director: Barbara Brown. Music publisher, record company and record producer. BMI. Publishes 150 songs/year; publishes 30 new songwriters/year. Pays standard royalty.
How to Contact: Write first. Prefers cassette with 1-4 songs and lyric sheet. "Please nice *clean clear* production." SASE. Reports in 1 week.

*NICHION, INC., Akasaka Makabe Bldg. 4-3, 3-chome Minato-ku, Tokyo 107 Japan. (03)584-4711. A&R: Mark Suzuki. Music publisher. Publishes 500 songs/year; publishes 20 new songwriters/year. Pays 60% royalty. Affiliates: Mind Music Publisher, Kitty Music, Uni Japan Music, Standard Music.
How to Contact: Prefers cassette and lyric sheet or lead sheet. "Please send the writer's bio." Does not return unsolicited material. Reports in 2-3 weeks.
Music: Mostly pop and rock. Recently published "Romantic Ga Tomaranai," (by Kyohei Tsutsumi and Takashi Matsumoto), recorded by CCB on Polydor (pop); "Mienai Tsubasa," (by Masao Urino and Kisaburo Suzuki), recorded by Maiko Itoh on CBS Sony (pop); and "Koishite Carribean," (by K. Tsutsumi and T. Matsumoto), recorded by Yoko Oginome on Victor (pop).
Tips: "Light pop suitable for the Japanese would be most appreciated."

JOSEPH NICOLETTI MUSIC, Box 2818, Newport Beach CA 92663. California International Records & Video. Vice President: Cheryl Nicoletti. Music publisher, record company and record producer. ASCAP. Member NARAS, AFTRA and SAG (Harry Fox Agency/ASCAP). Publishes 2-3 songs/year. Pays standard royalty.
How to Contact: Prefers "high-quality" cassette with 1-4 songs and lyric sheet. SASE. Reports in 1 month.
Music: MOR, rock (new wave, pop, classical), ballads, top 40/pop, gospel rock and R&B. Recently published "Streetwise," and "Child of Technology," (by Joseph Nicoletti), recorded by J. Nicoletti/California International Records (rock ballad/pop rock).
Tips: "Publishing should be open, demo should be of good quality and the writer should have a strong belief in the material he sends."

NISE PRODUCTIONS INC., Suite 101, 413 Cooper St., Camden NJ 08102. (609)963-3190. Affiliates: Logo III Records, Power Up Records and Wordan Records. President: Michael Nise. Music publisher, record company, recording studio (Power House) and production company. BMI. Publishes 10 songs/year; publishes 5 new songwriters/year. Pays standard royalty.
How to Contact: Prefers cassette or videocassette with 3 songs. SASE. Reports in 1 month.
Music: Mostly dance-oriented, R&B, country and pop, all with pop crossover potential; also children's, church/religious, easy listening, folk, gospel, jazz, rock, soul and top 40. Now recording Production Band (R&B), Nise (R&B/pop), Terry Dan (country).
Tips: "Submit only well-produced demos."

*NOCHISTLAN PUBLISHING CO., 5772 Broadway, Sacramento CA 95820. (916)455-5278. Contact: Pedro V. Reynoso, Jr. ASCAP. Music publisher. Publishes 5 songs/year; publishes 1 new songwriter/year. Pays standard royalty.
How to Contact: Prefers cassette with maximum 4 songs, lyric sheet and brief resume or fact sheet. SASE. Reports in 4-6 weeks.
Music: Mostly Latin international sound, rock and country; also gospel. Recently published "Yo Soy," (by P. Reynoso/F. Lizarraga), recorded by Suenos on Israfel (rock); "Todavia," (by F. Lizarraga/P. Reynoso), recorded by Fernando Quiroz on Israfel (ballad); and "No Puedo ser tu Amigo," (by F. Lizarraga/P. Reynoso), recorded by F. Quiroz on Israfel (rock).

NONPAREIL MUSIC, 9th Floor, 11 W. 17th St., New York NY 10011. (212)924-9338. President: Andy Goldmark. Music publisher. ASCAP. Publishes 20 songs/year; publishes 1-2 new songwriters/year. Works with lyricists and composers and teams collaborators. Pays standard royalty.
How to Contact: Prefers cassette or VHS videocassette with 3-5 songs and lyric sheet. SASE. Reports in 2 months.
Music: Mostly black/pop; also pop, pop/R&B, new dance and country. Recently published "Telegraph

Your Love'' (by Andy Goldmark), recorded by the Pointer Sisters/Planet Records (black/pop); ''That's Not the Way (It's S'posed to Be)'' (by A. Goldmark and Phil Goldston), recorded by Anne Murray/Capitol Records (pop); and ''Dynamite'' (by A. Goldmark and Bruce Roberts), recorded by Jermaine Jackson/Arista Records (R&B/pop).

Tips: ''Take your best shot only with songs you feel are great for today's top artists.''

NORTHERN COMFORT MUSIC, 10 Erica Ave., Toronto, Ontario M3H 3H2 Canada. (416)923-5717. Affiliate: Sacro-Iliac Music (PROCAN). President: J. Allan Vogel. Music publisher and record producer. CAPAC. Member LMPA. Publishes 10-12 songs/year; publishes 1 new songwriter/year. Works with lyricists and composers and teams collaborators. Pays standard royalty.
How to Contact: Prefers 7½ ips reel-to-reel or cassette with 3-5 songs and lyric sheet. SAE and IRC. Reports in 3 weeks.
Music: Mostly contemporary pop/rock (uptempo and/or ballads); also jazz, MOR, progressive, R&B and soul. Recently published ''On the Run,'' ''Beverly,'' and ''Urban Gypsy'' (by J. Vogel), recorded by D. Stokaluck (rock, ballad and country).
Tips: ''Be honest. Write contemporary hit material. Write about city life and make it danceable. Send me hits.''

NOTABLE MUSIC CO. INC., 161 W. 54th St., New York NY 10019. (212)757-9547. Affiliate: Portable Music Co., Inc. (BMI). General Manager: Eric Colodne. Music publisher. ASCAP. Member NMPA. Publishes 50-75 songs/year. Pays standard royalty.
How to Contact: Call first. Prefers cassette with 3-5 songs. SASE. Reports in 1 month.
Music: R&B, rock, soul and top 40/pop.

NOTEWORTHY PUBLISHING CO., 7802 Express St., Burnaby, British Columbia V5A 1T4 Canada. (604)421-3441. Manager: Paul Yaroshuk. Music publisher, record company, record producer and record manufacturer. BMI, PROCAN. Publishes 250 songs/year; publishes 25 new songwriters/year. Pays standard royalty.
How to Contact: Prefers cassette with 10-12 songs and lyric sheet. SAE and IRC. Reports in 1 week.
Music: Church/religious, gospel and gospel rock. Recently published ''I'm Gonna Live'' (by Bruce Wright), recorded by Tunesmith/Servant Records; ''In the Spirit of the King'' (by Hank Laake), recorded by Tunesmith/Hank Laake Records; and ''Find Your Heart a Home'' (by N. Mann), recorded by Tunesmith/Barnabas Records (all gospel rock songs).
Tips: ''We look for people who can sing their own songs.''

NRP MUSIC GROUP, 11th Floor, 160 E. 56th St., New York NY 10022. (212)758-3267. A&R Director: Fred Balin. Music publisher and record company. BMI, ASCAP. Publishes 10-12 songs/year; publishes 2 new songwriters/year. Works with composers and teams collaborators. Pays standard royalty.
How to Contact: Prefers cassette with 3-5 songs and lyric sheet. SASE. Reports in 1 week.
Music: Pop, dance-oriented, R&B, soul and top 40. Recently published ''Come Dance with Me,'' (by J.A. Pimtor), recorded by Bad Street Boys (dance-oriented).
Tips: ''Make it the best it can be!''

NUMBER 9 MUSICAL ENTERPRISES, INC., 498 West End Ave., New York NY 10024. (212)580-6569. Affiliates: Real Zeal Music (ASCAP) and Zoon Tunes Music (BMI). Contact: Vicky Germaise. Music publisher and record producer. BMI and ASCAP. Publishes 5 songs/year; publishes 3 new songwriters/year. Pays standard royalty or ''we co-publish many tunes, allowing writer to retain publishing or income.''
How to Contact: Prefers cassette with 1-4 songs and lyric sheet. ''No tapes returned.'' Reports in 1 month.
Music: Mostly pop, R&B and rock; also salsa, soul and top 40. Recently published ''Tough But Tender,'' (by V. Germaise/R. Klein), recorded by David Broza/CBS International (ballad); ''When Bad Things Happen,'' (by R. Klein/R. Rodriquez), recorded by IRT/RCA (R&B); and ''A Few Good Men,'' (by Carole Blake/M. Chase), recorded by Tara Jans/Select (dance).
Tips: ''Be specific in style and production. Be interesting lyrically, putting a different slant on the same old emotion. We are looking for melodic, emotional, vocal performance on demo. The performance is the key element of the demo.''

*NUNLEY PUBLISHING CO., Rt. 7, Box 683W, Canyon Lake, TX 78130. (512)899-7474. Contact: Donald L. Nunley. BMI. Music publisher, record producer and management company (Prelude). Publishes 20-30 songs/year; publishes 2-3 new songwriters/year. Pays standard royalty.
How to Contact: Write or call first and obtain permission to submit. Prefers cassette and lyric sheet or

lead sheet. "Make sure cassette is labeled with name, address, phone number and song title." Reports in 10 weeks.
Music: Mostly country, blues and rock.

NU-TRAYL PUBLISHING CO., 10015 W. 8 Mile Rd., Franksville WI 53126. (414)835-4622. Contact: Tommy O'Day. Music publisher, record company and record producer. ASCAP. Publishes 10 songs/year; publishes 3 new songwriters/year. Pays standard royalty.
How to Contact: Prefers 7½ ips reel-to-reel or cassette with 1-3 songs and lyric sheet. SASE. Reports in 1 month.
Music: Country, MOR, rock & top 40/pop. Recently published "I Heard a Song Today," (by T. O'Day and J. Marvel), "Kiss Your Past Goodbye," (by Peter Richerson), and "Todays Woman," (by T. O'Day and B. Perice), all recorded by T. O'Day/Nu-trayl Records (country).

*OCEANS-WIDE MUSIC, Box 20115, Philadelphia PA 19145. (215)467-6617. President: John Potere. Professional Manager/A&R: Nick Travis. ASCAP, BMI, SESAC. Music publisher. Affiliate publishing firms: Elk Music Publishing, Sandy World.
How to Contact: Prefers cassette with 1-5 songs and lyric sheet. SASE. Reports in 2-3 weeks.
Music: Mostly R&B, dance-oriented and rock; also soul, country and top 40.

MICHAEL O'CONNOR MUSIC, Box 1869, Studio City CA 91604. (818)762-7551. Affiliate: O'Connor Songs (ASCAP). Contact: Michael O'Connor. Music publisher. BMI. Member NMPA, AIMP. Publishes 25 songs/year; publishes 5 new songwriters/year. Hires staff writers; pays $175-325/week. Pays standard royalty.
How to Contact: Prefers cassette with 1-6 songs and lyric sheet. SASE. Reports in 1 month.
Music: Country, easy listening, R&B, rock, soul and top 40/pop. Recently published "If the Love Fits Wear It," (by Leslie Pearl and Phil Redrow), recorded by L. Pearl/RCA Records (pop); "When Love Goes Right," (by Diane Warren), recorded by Stevie Woods/Atlantic Records (R&B); and "I Found in You (Something I Lost in Me)," recorded by Charlene/Motown Records.
Tips: "We are looking for songs that have a clever title, hopefully revolving around the subject of love; great lyric images—the kind of lyric you find on a greeting card; and have unique ways of expressing ideas that would strike a responsive chord in the public."

OKOBOJI MUSIC, Box 100, Spirit Lake IA 51360. (712)336-2859. President: John Senn. Music publisher, record company and record producer. BMI. Publishes 15 songs/year. Pays standard royalty.
How to Contact: Prefers 7½ or 15 ips reel-to-reel or cassette with 1-5 songs and lyric sheet. SASE. Reports in 1 month.
Music: Mostly country; also church/religious, gospel and top 40/pop.

OLD BOSTON PUBLISHING, 180 Pond St., Cohasset MA 02025. (617)383-9494. Artist Relations: Richard Tinory Jr. Writer Relations: Claire Babcock. Music publisher, record company and record producer. BMI. Publishes 10 songs/year; publishes 2 new songwriters/year. Pays standard royalty.
How to Contact: Call first. Prefers cassette with 1-3 songs. Does not return unsolicited material.
Music: Recently published "Scollay Square," (by Rik Tinory), recorded on Old Boston Records (dixie/nostalgia).

OLD GUIDE PUBLISHING INC., Suite 215, 38 Music Square E., Nashville TN 37203. (615)254-0825. Professional Manager: Charlie Bragg. Music publisher. BMI. Publishes 25 songs/year; publishes 10 new songwriters/year. Pays standard royalty.
How to Contact: Prefers cassette with 1-3 songs and lyric sheet. Prefers studio produced demos. SASE. Reports in 1 month.
Music: Country, pop and MOR. Recently published "The Gift," (by Rodney Owens), recorded by Kathy Kane/G.B.S. (country ballad); "Memory of You," (by Paul Hotchkiss/Mike Terry) (country ballad); and "Texas Honky Tonkin'," (by P. Hotchkiss/M. Terry), recorded by K. Kane/G.B.S. (western swing).

OLD HOME PLACE MUSIC, 8705 Deanna Dr., Gaithersburg MD 20879. (301)253-5962. President: Wayne Busbice. Music publisher, record company and record producer. BMI. Member CMA. Publishes 20-30 songs/year; publishes 6 new songwriters/year. Pays standard royalty.
How to Contact: Write first. Prefers cassette with 3-5 songs. "We prefer songwriters to have recommendation of an established artist." SASE. Reports in 1 month.
Music: Mostly bluegrass; also country. Recently published "I Wish I Was a Bird," "Pretty Blue Eyes," and "Call Out to Jesus," recorded by Jim Eanes/Webco Records; and "Last Call," by The Overland Express.

O'LYRIC MUSIC, Suite 8, 11833 Laurelwood Dr., Studio City CA 91604. (213)506-5473. Affiliate: O'Lyrical Music (ASCAP). President: Jim O'Loughlin. Music publisher and record producer. BMI. Member California Copyright Conference. Publishes 75-100 songs/year; publishes 5-10 new songwriters/year. Hires staff writers; pays $20,000/year—"only duty expected is songwriting. Writers paid by royalties earned and by advances."
How to Contact: Prefers cassette with 1-3 songs and lyric sheet. Tapes can no longer be returned. Reports as soon as possible.
Music: Mostly pop, R&B and country crossover; also country, dance-oriented, easy listening, MOR, progressive, rock, soul and top 40/pop. Recently published "Your Heart's Not in It," recorded by Janie Fricke (country crossover); "Do You Love Like You Dance," (by Tom Shapiro/M. Garvin), recorded by R.O.A.R./Tabu CBS (R&B/pop); and "Never Give Up on a Good Thing," (by T. Shapiro/M. Garvin), recorded by George Benson (R&B/jazz).

*ON RECORD MUSIC, 41 Harvie Ave., Toronto, Ontario M6E 4K2 Canada. President: S. Smeall. PROCAN. Music publisher. Publishes 6 songs/year; publishes 1 new songwriter/year. Pays standard royalty.
How to Contact: Prefers cassette with 3 songs. "Send bio and photo and properly labeled (name, address, phone) demos." SAE and IRC. Reports in 6-8 weeks.
Music: Mostly rock, new music and top 40. Recently published "Cover Girl," and "American Boy," (by Rita Johns), recorded by Veronique Beliveau on A&M (top 40).

ON THE WING MUSIC PUBLISHING CO., 939 Felix Ave. Lwr., Windsor, Ontario N9C 3L2 Canada. (519)256-6604. President: Jim Thomson II. Music publisher, record company and record producer. PROCAN. Publishes 25-30 songs/year; publishes 7 new songwriter/year. Works with composers. Pays standard royalty.
How to Contact: Prefers cassette, ½" VHS or ¾" U-matic videocassette ("no Beta") with minimum 4 songs and lyric sheet. Include bio. "If you are submitting more than 1 style, submit at least 2, preferably 3, songs in each style. I want to know something about the songwriters and artists with whom I work. Send a short bio; include memberships in professional organizations, outside interests and things about which you have strong convictions." Does not return unsolicited material. Reports in 3 weeks "but only if interested, due to volume. Most gospel published comes from winners of the Skylight Records Songwriting Contest."
Music: Mostly rock and MOR; also blues, children's, church/religious, classical, country, easy listening, gospel, jazz, progressive, Spanish, R&B, soul and top 40/pop. Recently published "Baby I'm Gone," "Eden," and "Old Gypsy Moon," recorded by Jim Thomson/JLT (top 40/pop).

ONE HUNDRED GRAND MUSIC, 11 Norton St., Newburgh NY 12550. (914)561-4483. President: Gregg Bauer. Music publisher, record company and record producer. Publishes 10 songs/year; publishes 2 new songwriters/year. Pays standard royalty.
How to Contact: Call first. Prefers cassette with 3-5 songs and lyric sheet. SASE. Reports in 1 month.
Music: Mostly rock, dance and R&B; also choral, dance-oriented, easy listening, folk, jazz, MOR, progressive and soul. Recently published "My Fantasy Girl," and "High Time," (by P. Otero and G. Bauer), and "One of the Girls," (by P. Otero/G. Bauer/D. Baker), all recorded by Art Nouveau/100 Grand (rock).

*OPAL RECORDS/MATRIX MUSIC, Box W41, W. Tamworth 2340 Australia. (067)659290. Contact: Ross Murphy. Music publisher and record company. Pays standard royalty.
How to Contact: Write first to arrange personal interview. Prefers cassette or phonograph record or lyric sheet and lead sheet. Does not return unsolicited material. Reports in 3 weeks.
Music: Mostly country and gospel. Recently published "Tamworth Guitar," written and recorded by L. Butler on Opal (country instrumental); "Wobbly Boot Hotel," (by Stan Coster), recorded by Brian Young on Opal (vocal); and "Broken Down Cowboy," (by Vicki Lawrence), recorded by Michael Cooke on Opal (vocal).

ORCHID PUBLISHING, Bouquet-Orchid Enterprises, Box 18284, Shreveport LA 71138. (318)686-7362. President: Bill Bohannon. Music publisher and record company. BMI. Member CMA. Publishes 8-10 songs/year; publishes 3 new songwriters/year. Pays standard royalty.
How to Contact: Prefers cassette with 3-5 songs and lead sheet. SASE. Reports in 1 month.
Music: Religious ("Dallas Holm, etc.," contemporary gospel"); country ("Barbara Mandrell/Kenny Rogers type material"); and top 40/pop ("Oak Ridge Boys/Hall & Oates type material"). Recently published "A Little More Like You," (by Bill Bohannon); "The South Will Never Fall," (by Daniel Liles); and "A Day To Fall In Love," (by Adam Day) (all country).

OTTO PUBLISHING CO., 7766 NW 44th St., Sunrise FL 33321. (305)741-7766. President: Frank X. Loconto. Music publisher. ASCAP. Publishes 100 songs/year; publishes 10 new songwriters/year. Pays standard royalty.
How to Contact: Prefers cassette with 1-4 songs and lyric sheet. SASE. Reports in 1 month.
Music: Mostly country, MOR and religious. Recently published "Gotta Get Back To You, Baby," (by Frank X. Loconto), recorded by J.J. Brotherton (MOR); "All The Way To Tampa Bay," (by F. Loconto), recorded by The Bruise Brothers (novelty); and "Believe In America," (by F. Loconto), recorded by The Lane Brothers (country).

RAY OVERHOLT MUSIC, 112 S. 26th St., Battle Creek MI 49015. (616)963-0554. A&R Director: Mildred Overholt. Manager: Ray Overholt. Music publisher. BMI. Publishes 25 songs/year; publishes 10 new songwriters/year. Pays 10-25% royalty. "We also use the standard songwriter's contract at the going rate."
How to Contact: Prefers cassette with 1-3 songs and lead sheet. SASE. Reports in 3 weeks.
Music: Church/religious and gospel. Recently published "Tell My Daddy" (by R. Overholt), recorded by Becky Overholt/Artists Records (ballad hymn); "Another Day's Gone By" (by R. Overholt), recorded by Dodson Family/Crusade Records (country gospel); and "Lord, How Long" (by R. Overholt), recorded by Cathedrals/Word Records (country gospel).
Tips: "We desire songs with a country gospel touch—songs that tell a story with a Biblical message or theme."

PACIFIC CHALLENGER MUSIC, 2940 E. Miraloma, Anaheim CA 92806. (714)992-6820. President: Chuck Whittington. Music publisher, record company and record producer. BMI. Publishes 80 songs/year; publishes 2 new songwriters/year. Pays standard royalty.
How to Contact: Prefers cassette with 2-4 songs and lyric sheet. Does not return unsolicited material. Reports in 1 month.
Music: Mostly country; also gospel and top 40/pop. Recently published "Someone's Discovery" (by L.B. Garland), recorded by Lula Belle/Pacific Challenger Records; "Legend of Harry and the Mountain" (by L.B. Garland), recorded by Ron Shaw/Pacific Challenger Records; and "Hurtin' Kind of Love" (by R. Shaw), recorded by R. Shaw/Pacific Challenger Records.

*PALO ALTO RECORDS/TBA RECORDS, Suite A-280A, 755 Page Mill Rd., Palo Alto CA 94304. (415)856-4355. Contacts: Al Evers or Jean Catino. ASCAP, BMI. Music publisher and record company. Affiliated publishing firms: Palo Publishing, Page Mill Publishing. Pays 15% royalty (wholesale).
How to Contact: Write or call first and obtain permission to submit. Prefers cassette with lead sheet. SASE.
Music: Mostly black contemporary pop and jazz-flavored material. Recently published *Don't Be So Shy*, recorded by D. Diggs (blue-eyed soul); "Storm," recorded by Rare Silk (jazz vocal); and "Love Will Find a Way," recorded by G. Howard (pop jazz).

*PANCHO'S MUSIC CO., 3121 29th Ave., Sacramento CA 95820. (916)444-0158. Contact: Frank Lizarraga. BMI. Music publisher. Publishes 5 songs/year; publishes 1 new songwriter/year. Pays standard royalty.
How to Contact: Prefers cassette and lyric sheet and brief resume/fact sheet. SASE. Reports in 4-6 weeks.
Music: Mostly Latin, rock and country; also gospel. Recently published "Crazy for You," (by F. Lizarraga), recorded by Suenos on Israfel (rock); "Vivire Con Tus Recuerdos," (by F. Lizarraga/Perez), recorded by Fernando Quneoz on Israfel (Latin); and "Yo Soy," (by F. Lizarraga/Reynoso), recorded by Suenos on Israfel (Latin).
Tips: "We specialize in Latin music and prefer bilingual songwriters."

PARK J. TUNES, 29 S. Erie, Toledo OH 43602. (419)244-8599. Affiliate: Keeny/York (BMI). A&R Director: Doug Larue. Music publisher, record company and record producer. ASCAP. Publishes 20 songs/year; publishes 2 new songwriters/year. Pays standard royalty.
How to Contact: Prefers cassette with 3-5 songs and lyric sheet. SASE. Reports in 1 month.
Music: Country and top 40/pop. Recently published "Theme from Limelight," (by Dan Faehnle), recorded by Nevada Flatts/MDS Records (instrumental); "Oh Them Hens," (by Michael Shaw), recorded by Hotlix/Jamestune Records (novelty); and "Pigskin Blues," (by M. Shaw), recorded by Mary Bansen/92.5 Records (novelty).

PAVILLION PRODUCTIONS/PROMOTION, INC., Suite 44F, 322 W. 57th St., New York NY 10019. (212)247-6854. President: John Luongo. Music publisher, record promotion, record producer and management office.

How to Contact: Prefers cassette and lyric sheet. Include bio. Does not return unsolicited material. Reports in 4 weeks.
Music: Recently published "I Want a New Drug," recorded by Huey Lewis/Chrysalis; "Burning Flame," recorded by Vitamin Z/Geffen; and "All She Wants to Do Is Dance," recorded by Don Henley/Geffen.

PAYTON PLACE PUBLISHING, Suite 803, 7302 Mullins, Houston TX 77081. (713)776-9219. Affiliate: Clarity Publishing. Contact: President. Music publisher and record producer. Publishes 10 songs/year; publishes 3 new songwriters/year. BMI.
How to Contact: Prefers cassette with 1-2 songs and lyric sheet. SASE.
Music: Mostly country, heavy metal and AOR; also bluegrass, blues and dance. Recently published "Texas Moon," (by Dawson), recorded by Monkeys Meek/AVI (country); "Time & Place," (by Smith); recorded by Hot Mopper/Goldspur (AOR); and "Everybody Loves You," (by Delacy), recorded by Slim Beaumont/Custo (rock).
Tips: "Include return address and phone number on cassette."

PEER-SOUTHERN ORGANIZATION, 6777 Hollywood Blvd., Hollywood CA 90028. Affiliates: Charles K. Harris Music Publishing, La Salle Music, Melody Lane, Panther Music, Peer International, Pera Music, RFD Music and Southern Music. Professional Manager: Roy Kohn. Music publisher and production company. ASCAP, BMI. Member NMPA. Pays standard royalty; 5¢/sheet on sheet music.
How to Contact: Write first. "Unsolicited demo tapes are not accepted."
Music: Country, disco, easy listening, MOR, rock, and top 40/pop.

PEER-SOUTHERN ORGANIZATION, 1740 Broadway, New York NY 10019. (212)265-3910. L.A. Branch: 6777 Hollywood Blvd., Hollywood CA 90028; Nashville branch: 2 Music Circle S., Nashville TN 37203. Affiliates: Peer International Corporation (BMI) and Southern Music Publishing Co., Inc. (ASCAP). Ch. of Board: Monique I. Peer. President: Ralph Peer II. Vice President: Mario Conti. General Repertoire Manager: Kathy Spanberger. Creative Director/East Coast: Holly Green. Music publisher. Member NMPA. Publishes 500 songs/year. Pays standard royalty.
How to Contact: "Due to recent industry complications we no longer review unsolicited material."
Music: Bluegrass, choral, classical, C&W, disco, easy listening, MOR, progressive, R&B, rock, soul and top 40/pop. Recently published "Whenever Hearts Collide," (by Matthew Gang), recorded by Jack Wagner/Quest (pop ballad); "Sharpshooter," (by Marc Bluth/Larry Gottlieb), recorded by Laura Branigan/EMI (pop/rock); and "Cherry Bomb," (by Joan Jett/Kim Fowley), recorded by J. Jett/MCA (rock).

PEER-TALBOT MUSIC GROUP, 2 Music Circle S, Nashville TN 37203. (615)244-6200. Affiliates: Charles K. Harris Music (ASCAP), Jojan Music Publishing Inc. (ASCAP), La Salle Music (ASCAP), Melody Lane (BMI), Panther Music (ASCAP), Peer International (BMI), Pera Music (BMI), RFD Music (ASCAP), Southern Music (ASCAP), Talbot Music Publishing Inc. BMI, ASCAP. Director of Nashville Operations: Jana Talbot. Member NMPA. Pays standard royalty.
How to Contact: Query. Prefers 7½ ips reel-to-reel or cassette wth 1-3 songs and lead sheet. SASE. Reports in 1 month.
Music: Mostly country and pop; also contemporary gospel, MOR, R&B, rock and top 40/pop. Recently published "Georgia On My Mind," (by H. Carmichael), recorded by Willie Nelson; ""I Wouldn't Change You If I Could," (by A. Smith and P. Jones), recorded by Ricky Skaggs and "If You've Got the Money I've Got the Time," (by L. Frizzell and J. Beck), recorded by Willie Nelson.
Tips: "We do not accept material through the mail but will review songs by anyone who comes to Nashville."

PEGASUS MUSIC, 27 Bayside Ave., Te Atatu, Auckland 8, New Zealand. Professional Manager: Ginny Peters. Music publisher and record company. Member APRA. Publishes 8-10 songs/year; publishes 1 new songwriter/year. Has not yet, but would listen to songs from US songwriters. Works with lyricists and composers and temas collaborators. Pays 3-5% to artists on contract and standard royalty to songwriters; royalties paid directly to US songwriters.
How to Contact: Prefers cassette with 3-5 songs and lyric sheet. SAE and IRC. Reports in 1 month.
Music: Mostly country; also bluegrass, easy listening and top 40/pop. Recently published "You Make It Easy," and "Crazy Diamond," written and recorded by Ginny Peters; and "Thanks for Nothing," (by G. Peters), recorded by Fancy Question/Pegasus (all country).
Tips: "Must be fresh and original."

PENNY THOUGHTS MUSIC, 259A Beech St., Belmont MA 02178. (617)489-4510. President: John Penny. Music publisher, record company and record producer. Publishes 20-30 songs/year; publishes 6 new songwriters/year. Pays standard royalty.

How to Contact: Write first about your interest. Prefers cassette. SASE. Reports in 2 weeks.
Music: Mostly country and contemporary; also rock (country). Recently published "Celia Black," and "You'll Be In My Dreams," (by Rich Sliter), recorded by Sliter Bros./Belmont (country); and "Time on the Road," (by Tom Madugno), recorded by 4th Street Station (country).

PEOPLE CITY MUSIC PUBLISHING INC., Suite 600, 1055 Wilson Ave., Toronto, Ontario M3K 1Y9 Canada. (416)630-2973. Affiliate: Lonsong Music Inc. President: Frank Longo. Music publisher, record company and record producer. CAPAC, PROCAN. Member CARAS. Publishes 5 songs/year; publishes 1 new songwriter/year. Pays standard royalty.
How to Contact: Prefers cassette with 1-3 songs and lyric sheet. "Enclose SASE." Reports in 2 weeks.
Music: Mostly R&B and pop; also dance-oriented and easy listening. Recently published "You've Got No-One," recorded by Patti Jannetta/Janta Records (pop/rock); "Coast to Coast," recorded by The Longo Brothers; and "The Nightlife" (by D. Longo, L. Longo, F. Longo), recorded by Wayne St. John/People City Music Records (R&B).

PERLA MUSIC, 20 Martha St., Woodcliff Lake NJ 07675. (201)391-2486. President: Gene A. Perla. Music publisher, record producer and record company. ASCAP. Publishes 12 songs/year; publishes 2 new songwriters/year. Works with lyricists. Pays 75%/25% split.
How to Contact: Call first. Prefers cassette or videocassette and lead sheet. SASE.
Music: Recently published "Korinna" (by Gene Perla), recorded by Elvin Jones/McCoy Tyner Records (ballad); "Bunny Honey" (by G. Perla), recorded by E. Jones/Trio Records (50's rock); and "Bahama Mama" (by G. Perla), recorded by G. Perla/P.M. Records (reggae).

PERSONAL MUSIC PUBLISHING INC., Suite 12A, 211 West 56th St., New York NY 10019. (212)246-5520. Affiliates: My! My! Music, (BMI) Chrysalis-U.K. and Victor Music-Japan. Music publisher and record company. BMI, ASCAP. Publishes 12 songs/year; publishes 4 new songwriters/year. Hires staff writers. Pays standard royalty.
How to Contact: Contact: Judy Hicks, % Arista Music Publishing, 8370 Wilshire Blvd., Beverly Hills CA 90211. Prefers reel-to-reel, cassette or videocassette with 5 songs and lyric sheet. SASE. Reports in 2 weeks.
Music: Mostly dance and R&B; also MOR, rock (high energy), soul and top 40/pop. Recently published "Trommel Tanz" (by George Kranz), recorded by G. Kranz (dance & R&B); "No Way" (by Leroy Burgess and Sonny Davenport), recorded by Inner Life (R&B) and "I'm Not Your Doormat (by Psychodrama), recorded by Psychodrama (rock).

*PAUL PETERSON CREATIVE MANAGEMENT, 6335 W. 50th St., Mission KS 66202. (913)362-4804. Contact: Paul Peterson. BMI, ASCAP. Music publisher and personal management firm. Estab. 1984.
How to Contact: Prefers cassette and lyric sheet. SASE. Reports in 4 weeks.
Music: Mostly rock and jazz; also pop and country.

*PHAB MUSIC, 3 Acacia Dr., Woodham, Weybridge, Surrey KT15 3SH England. (09323)48174. Director: P.H.A. Bailey. PRS, MCPS. Record company. Publishes 15 songs/year; publishes 5 new songwriters/year. Pays standard royalty.
How to Contact: Prefers cassette or 7½ ips reel-to-reel and lyric sheet. Does not return unsolicited material.
Music: Rock (50s), rockabilly and doowop; also country and "crazy/gimmick." Recently published "Girl in Red," written and recorded by Shakin' Stevens on RCA Records (rock); "If I Ain't Home," (by Steve Wooltorston), recorded by Rock Island Line on RCA Records (rockabilly); and "Crazy Little Teddy Girl," (by Cavan Grogam), recorded by Crazy Cavan on Poly Dor Records (rockabilly).

PHILIPPOPOLIS MUSIC, 12027 Califa St., North Hollywood CA 91607. President: Milcho Leviev. Music publisher and record company. BMI. Member GEMA, NARAS. Publishes 5-6 songs/year. Pays standard royalty.
How to Contact: Query. Prefers cassette with 1-3 songs. Prefers studio produced demos. SASE. Reports in 1 month.
Music: Jazz and classical fusion. Recently published "Sboguvane," ("Farewell"), (classical); "Pavane for a True Musical Prince," (classical); and "For Frederic and Bill," (jazz) (all by Milcho Leviev), all recorded by LA Jazz Choir-St 3.
Tips: "Treat music as an art form."

PINE ISLAND MUSIC, #308, 9430 Live Oak Place, Ft. Lauderdale FL 33324. (305)472-7757. Affiliates: Lantana Music (ASCAP) and Twister Music (ASCAP). President: Jack P. Bluestein. Music pub-

lisher, record company and record producer. BMI, ASCAP. Publishes 10-20 songs/year; publishes 3-4 new songwriters/year. Pays standard royalty.
How to Contact: Prefers cassette, 7½ ips reel-to-reel or VHS videocassette with 3 songs and lyric sheet. SASE. Reports in 2-4 months.
Music: Mostly country and pop; also gospel, soft rock and contemporary. Recently published "The Painted Pony" and "Everybody Listens to the Music" (by Ann Leysten), recorded by Gary Oakes and Lou Garcia on Twister (country/pop); and "Please Forgive Me," (by Ronnie Lynn), recorded by Julie Lendon on Twister (country).

*PLAYERS PRESS INC., Box 1132, Studio City CA 91604. (818)789-4980. Vice President Editorial: Robert W. Gordon. Music publisher, record company and record producer. Publishes 10 songs/year; publishes 1-2 new songwriters/year. "Contracts are negotiable."
How to Contact: Prefers cassette or ½" VHS or ¾" U-matic videocassette and lyric sheet. SASE. Reports in 6 weeks.
Music: Mostly musical theater. Recently published "Tune-Line," (by William Lentes); "Machine," (by Jeff Rizzo); and "Wall," (by Joe Sporaco); all recorded by Players Press Inc. on Players Press Records (theatrical).

POLKA TOWNE MUSIC, 211 Post Ave., Westbury NY 11590. President: Teresa Zapolska. Music publisher, record company, record producer and booking agency. BMI. "We review all music once a month."
How to Contact: Prefers cassette with 1-3 songs and lead sheet. "Absolutely must send SASE for return of material and/or reply." Reports within 6 weeks.
Music: Polkas and "some" waltzes.

POSITIVE PRODUCTIONS, Box 1405, Highland Park NJ 08904. (201)463-8147. President: J. Vincenzo. Music publisher and record producer. BMI. Publishes 5 songs/year. Works with composers and teams collaborators. Payment negotiable.
How to Contact: Prefers 7½ ips reel-to-reel with 2-4 songs and lyric sheet. SASE. Reports in 1 month.
Music: Children's, easy listening, and MOR. Recently published "Waiting for the Sunshine," and "Think of Me," written and recorded by J. Remington (MOR).

POWER-PLAY PUBLISHING, 1900 Elm Hill Pike, Nashville TN 37210. (615)889-8000. Contact: Julie Bunt. Music publisher and record company. BMI. Pays standard royalty.
How to Contact: Arrange personal interview. Prefers 7½ ips reel-to-reel with 2 songs. SASE. Reports in 1 month.
Music: Bluegrass, blues, country, disco, easy listening, folk, gospel, R&B, rock, soul and top 40/pop.

*PRAISE INDUSTRIES CORP., 7802 Express St., Burnaby, British Columbia V5J 4V6 Canada. (604)421-3441. Manager: Paul Yaroshuk. PROCAN, CAPAC. Music publisher, record company and record producer. Publishes 400 songs/year; publishes 100 new songwriters/year. Affiliated publishing firms: Noteworth Publishing Co., Innovative Publishing Co.
How to Contact: Prefers cassette. SAE and IRC.
Music: Mostly gospel.

PRESCRIPTION COMPANY, 70 Murray Ave., Port Washington NY 11050. (516)767-1929. President: David F. Gasman. Music publisher, record company and record producer. BMI. Pays standard royalty.
How to Contact: Call or write first about your interest. Prefers cassette with any number songs and lyric sheet. "Send all submissions %Mitch Vidor (general manager) with SASE (or no returns)." Reports in 1 month.
Music: Bluegrass, blues, children's, country, dance-oriented, easy listening, folk, jazz, MOR, progressive, R&B, rock, soul and top 40/pop. Recently published "You Came In," "Rock 'n' Roll Blues," and "Seasons," (by D.F. Gasman), all recorded by Medicine Mike/Prescription Records.
Tips: "Songs should be good and written to last. Forget fads—we want songs that'll sound as good in 10 years as they do today. Organization, communication, and exploration of form is as essential as message (and sincerity matters, too)."

THEODORE PRESSER COMPANY, Presser Place, Bryn Mawr PA 19010. (215)525-3636. Affiliates: Elkan-Vogel, Inc., Merion Music, Inc.; and Mercury Music, Inc. Publications Manager: Laurence Broido. Music publisher. ASCAP, BMI and SESAC. Member MPA. Publishes 50 "mostly choral" songs/year. Payment by contracted royalty.
How to Contact: Prefers cassette and lyric sheet. Reports as soon as possible.

Music: Mostly choral; also children's, church/religious, classical and gospel. "No popular songs."
Tips: "We primarily publish serious music by emerging and established composers, and vocal/choral music which is likely to be accepted in the church and educational markets, as well as gospel chorals of high musical quality. We are *not* primarily a publisher of song sheets or pop songs."

PRETTY GIRL MUSIC COMPANY INC., Box 11547, East Station, Memphis TN 38111. (901)525-5414. Professional Manager: Style Wooten. Music publisher. BMI. Publishes 12-24 songs/year; publishes 4 new songwriters/year. Pays standard royalty.
How to Contact: Write or call first. Prefers 7½ ips reel-to-reel with 2-4 songs. SASE. "Send clean tape and typewritten words." Reports in 1 month.
Music: Mostly country; also bluegrass and gospel.

JIMMY PRICE MUSIC PUBLISHING, 1662 Wyatt Parkway, Lexington KY 40505. (606)254-7474. President: James T. Price. Music publisher, record company, record producer and music printer. BMI. Publishes 7 new songwriters/year. Pays standard royalty.
How to Contact: Prefers 7½ ips reel-to-reel with 1-6 songs and lyric sheet. SASE. Reports in 1 month.
Music: Bluegrass, blues, church/religious, country, gospel and rock. Recently published "Country Waltz" (by James T. Price), recorded by K. Wade/Sun-Ray Records (waltz); "Where the Music Plays Sweetly" (by Charles Stephens), and "Beautiful Love" (by J.T. Price), both recorded by C. Stephens/Sun-Ray Records (country).

PROPHECY PUBLISHING, INC., Box 4945, Austin TX 78765. (512)452-9412. Affiliate: Black Coffee Music (BMI). Administrates Chicken Fried Music, Floating Tones, and Steven Fromholz Publishing. President: T. White. Music publisher. ASCAP. Member NMPA. Publishes 200-300 songs/year. Pays standard royalty, less expenses; "expenses such as tape duplicating, photocopying and long distance phone calls are recouped from the writer's earnings."
How to Contact: Prefers cassette with 1-3 songs and lyric sheet. Does not return unsolicited material. "No reply can be expected, unless we're interested in the material."
Music: Bluegrass, blues, classical, country, disco, easy listening, folk, gospel, jazz, MOR, progressive, rock, soul and top 40/pop. Recently published "No More Weekends in Warsaw," recorded by Jesse Sublett (pop); and "Cheryl Doreen Rodeo Queen," recorded by Rusty Wier (country).

PUBLISHING VENTURES, 201 E. 61st St., New York NY 10021. (212)832-2980. Affiliates: King Kong Music, Gary Bonds Music, Son of Kong Music. Managing Director: Andrea Starr. Music publisher. ASCAP, BMI. Publishes 15 songs/year; publishes 4 new songwriters/year. Pays standard royalty.
How to Contact: Prefers cassette with 1-3 songs and lyric sheet. Does not return unsolicited material. Reports in 3-8 weeks.
Music: Rock, top 40/pop and R&B; also ballads, country and MOR. Recently published "Turn the Music Down" and "Bring Her Back" (by Gary Bonds and Laurie Anderson), recorded by Gary U.S. Bonds/EMI Records (pop/rock).
Tips: Looking for "radio-oriented hit singles with strong hooks and interesting lyrics and titles."

GERALD W. PURCELL ASSOCIATES, 964 Second Ave., New York NY 10022. (212)421-2670, 2674, 2675 and 2676. President: Gerald Purcell. Music publisher. BMI, ASCAP. Member CPM, CMA, NARM. Publishes 50 songs/year; publishes 4 new songwriters/year. Pays standard royalty.
How to Contact: Prefers cassette with maximum 3 songs, lyric sheet and clear lead sheet. SASE. Reports as soon as possible.
Music: Country and MOR.

PYRAMID RECORDS, Box 140316, Nashville TN 37214. (615)889-6675. Music publisher (Jimmy Kish Music Publishing) and record company. BMI.
How to Contact: Prefers 7½ ips reel-to-reel or cassette and lead sheet. SASE. Reports in 4 weeks.
Music: Country and gospel. Recently released "Christmas Time in Heaven" (by Bob Pauley), recorded by Jimmy Kish; and "Life's Railway to Heaven" (by C.D. Tillman), recorded by Jimmy Kish.

QL MUSIC, INC., 314 Romano Ave., Coral Gables FL 33134. (305)446-2477. Executive Director: Robin Burr. Music publisher, record company and record producer. BMI. Member NARAS. Publishes 30 songs/year; publishes 3 new songwriters/year. Pays standard royalty.
How to Contact: Prefers cassette (metal bias) with 2-10 songs and lyric sheet. Reports in 2 months.
Music: Mostly progressive, new wave rock; also classical, dance-oriented, folk, jazz and reggae. Recently published *The Sleep of Reason*, and "Shelters Are Melting," (by O. Herrera), recorded by The Sleep of Reason/QL Records (new wave); and "Stranger In My Room," (by T. Rusch), recorded by Einstein's Riceboys/QL Records (new wave).

QUINONES MUSIC CO., 1344 Waldron, St. Louis MO 63130. President: Eddie Johnson. Music publisher. BMI. Publishes 8-12 songs/year; publishes 2-4 new songwriters/year. Pays standard royalty.
How to Contact: Prefers cassette with 3 songs and lyric sheet. SASE. Reports in 2 weeks.
Music: Mostly blues and top 40; also church/religious, gospel, R&B, soul and pop. Recently published "Strange Feeling," (by Tab Smith), recorded by Eddie Johnson/E.L.J. Records (top 40); "Tables Are Turned," (by Bobby Scott), recorded by B. Scott/E.L.J. Records (top 40); and "Hold Me," (by Ann Richardson), recorded by A. Richardson/E.L.J. Records (soul).

*R. J. MUSIC, 10A Margaret Rd., Barnet, Herts. EN4 9NP England. (01)440-9788. Managing Director: Roger James. PRS. Music publisher.
How to Contact: Prefers cassette and lyric sheet or lead sheet. SAE and IRC.
Music: Mostly blues, country and rock; also disco and chart material.

*RAINBARREL MUSIC COMPANY, 7020 Baldwin, Lawton OK 73505. (405)536-6463. Director: Teresa Parks. BMI. Music publisher, record company (Paragold Records) and record producer. Publishes 2 songs/year; publishes 1 new songwriter/year. Pays standard royalty.
How to Contact: Prefers cassette with 2 songs and lyric and lead sheets. SASE. Reports in 6 weeks.
Music: Mostly country. Recently published "Ghost of Grand Ol Opry," written and recorded by J. Bernard/Paragold (country); "Daddy's Last Letter," (by J. Bernard), recorded by JLyne/Paragold (country); and "Please Don't Turn Me On," (by Ray Davis), recorded by J. Bernard & Julie Jones/Paragold (country).

*THE RAINBOW COLLECTION LTD., Box 300, Solebury PA 18963. (215)297-8437. President: Herb Gart. BMI, ASCAP. Music publisher, record company and record producer. Publishes 50-200 songs/year; publishes 10 new songwriters/year. Occasionally employs songwriters on a salary basis. Pays standard royalty. Affiliated publishing firm: Herbert S. Gart Management Inc.
How to Contact: Prefers cassette or VHS or Beta videocassette with 1-6 songs. Does not return unsolicited material. Reports in 6-8 weeks.
Music: Most rock, pop and country; also blues, new wave, reggae and jazz. Recently published "Wanna Make Love," written and recorded by Jack Bruce on Epic (rock); "Six-Pack Susie," written and recorded by The Pliars on Montage (rock); and "Wasn't It Supposed to Be Me," by J. Wallace, recorded by Judi Kellar on Airborne (country).
Tips: "Send me your finest work. If you are original and great and know it—if you believe in yourself and your artistry and are looking for a believer, contact me."

RAINFIRE MUSIC, 15217 Otsego, Sherman Oaks CA 91430. (805)658-2991. Contact: Professional Manager. Music publisher, record company and record producer. BMI. Member of NARAS, ACM. Publishes 20-40 songs/year; publishes 15 new songwriters/year. Pays standard royalty.
How to Contact: Prefers cassette with 2-3 songs and lyric sheet. SASE. Reports in 2 weeks.
Music: Country, easy listening, MOR, progressive, R&B, rock, soul, top 40/pop and disco. Recently published "Lovers and Losers" (by Penta & Noshkin), recorded by Katie Phillips (country); "In the Beginning" (by Silver & Greenspan), recorded by Karen Silver (disco) and "Love Diet" (by Joe Cannon), recorded by Rita Jenrette (pop).
Tips: "We look for songs with a catchy hook and at least 4 progressions within the body."

RAYBIRD MUSIC, Suite 303, 457 W. 57th St., New York NY 10019. (212)245-2299. Affiliates: Kips Bay Music (ASCAP), TaJah Music (BMI). President: Ray Passman. General Manager: Teddy Charles. Professional Manager: Harold Danko. Music publisher. BMI. Publishes 4-6 songs/year; publishes 2 new songwriters/year. Pays standard royalty.
How to Contact: Write first. Prefers cassette with 3-5 songs. SASE. Reports in 2 weeks.
Music: Jazz. Recently published "Miss Harper Goes Bizarre," (by M. D'Ambrosia /R. Passman), recorded by M. D'Ambrosio/Sunnyside; and "Once Upon a Tempo," and "August Moon," written and recorded by M. D'Ambrosio/Sunnyside.
Tips: "Study new, important writers like Dave Frishberg."

RCS PUBLISHING CO., 5220 Essen Lane, Baton Rouge LA 70808. (504)766-3233. Affiliates: Layback Music and Implusivo. President: Cyril E. Vetter. Music publisher, record company and record producer. ASCAP and BMI. Pays standard royalty.
Music: Country, MOR, R&B, rock, soul and top 40/pop.

*RED COW MUSIC, 1775 Broadway, New York NY 10019. (212)975-0200. Professional Manager: James Dayley. Music publisher and record company (RSO Records). Publishes 40 songs/year. Pays standard royalty.

How to Contact: Prefers cassette or VHS videocassette with 3-4 songs. SASE. Reports in 4 weeks.
Music: Mostly rock, pop and movie scores.

JACK REDICK MUSIC PUBLISHING CO., Rt. 1, Box 85, Georgetown SC 29440. Affiliate: Wagon Wheel Records. Manager: Jack Redick. Music publisher. BMI.
How to Contact: Prefers cassette with 1-6 songs, plus typed lyrics; also reviews records. SASE. "Never send your original master tape of anything, make copies to mail out. Mostly interested in unpublished, uncopyrighted material. Also willing to co-write with lyricists or composers with 50-50, collaboration contract. On lyrics for co-write, send only material that's clear (not tied up with anyone) and that you're the sole writer on. Not reviewing videocassettes."
Music: Mostly country; also rockabilly and gospel. Recently published "Jesus Is More Precious Than Gold," "Talk of the Town," "Pushin' Out One and Pullin' Two Back," and "Please Mr. D.J."
Tips: "Keep lyrics over music, clean and clear to understand. Try to write what is playing today, but be original. Don't be let down when a publisher doesn't take your material, there is a reason, it doesn't always mean your material is bad. Keep trying. A quitter never wins, and a winner never quits."

REN MAUR MUSIC CORP., 521 5th Ave., New York NY 10175. (212)757-3638. Affiliate: R.R. Music (ASCAP). President: Rena L. Feeney. Music publisher and record company. BMI. Member AGAC and NARAS. Publishes 6-8 songs/year. Pays 4-8% royalty.
How to Contact: Prefers cassette with 2-4 songs and lead sheet. SASE. Reports in 1 month.
Music: R&B, rock, soul and top 40/pop. Recently published "Do It to Me and I'll Do It to You," and "Once You Fall in Love," (by Billy Nichols), recorded by Rena/Factory Beat Records; and "Lead Me to Love," (by Brad Smiley), recorded by Carmen John/Factory Beat Records (ballad/dance).
Tips: "Send lead sheets and a good, almost finished cassette ready for producing or remixing."

GARY REVEL MUSIC/JONGLEUR MUSIC, 1551 N. Western Ave., Los Angeles CA 90027. (213)467-6647 (Go-Songs). President: Linda Revel. Music publisher. ASCAP. Publishes 20 songs/year; publishes 4 new songwriters/year. Works with lyricists and composers and teams collaborators. Pays standard royalty.
How to Contact: Write or call first. Prefers cassette or videocassette with 1-12 songs and lyric sheet. SASE. Reports in 1 month.
Music: Mostly pop/rock; also blues, children's, church/religious, country, rock, rockabilly and top 40. Recently published "Bound to Lose" (by Gary Revel), on Plain Wrap Records (country); "Have a Nice Day" (by Robert Arnold), recorded by Barney Spencer/Phoenix Bird Records (pop); "Blue Love" (by R. Arnold), recorded by Rebecca Ryza/Phoenix Bird Records (pop); and "Umbrella Girl" (by G. Revel, Mary Head and Vernon Leftwich), recorded by G. Revel/Top's Records (soft rock).
Tips: "Don't predict future song trends; but express true inner feelings."

WM. REZEY MUSIC CO., Box 833, Albany NY 12201. (518)753-7772. President: Wm. Rezey. Music publisher and record producer. BMI. Publishes 15 songs/year; publishes 2 new songwriters/year. Pays standard royalty.
How to Contact: Prefers cassette with 3 songs and lyric sheet. SASE. Reports in 3 weeks.
Music: Mostly rock and top 40; also church/religious and R&B. Recently published "Gotta Find a Job" (by Gary Tash), "That Girl Is Leaving You" (by Daley and Tash), and "No Place to Go" (by Sagendorf, Rivera and Tash), all recorded by Emerald City Band.

RHYTHMS PRODUCTIONS, Whitney Bldg., Box 34485, Los Angeles CA 90034. Affiliate: Tom Thumb Music. President: Ruth White. Music publisher and record company. ASCAP. Member NARAS. Publishes 3-4 LPs/year. Pays negotiable royalty.
How to Contact: Submit lead sheet with letter outlining background in educational children's music. Prefers cassette. SASE. Reports in 1 month.
Music: "We're only interested in children's songs for the education market. Our materials are sold in schools, so artists/writers with a teaching background would be most likely to understand our requirements." Recently published "Sing Along with Mother Goose," "Singing Games," and "Animals are Wonderful," all on Tom Thumb Records.

*RIC RAC MUSIC, Ric Rac Inc., Box 712, Nashville IN 47448. (812)837-9569. Professional Manager: Sue Hanson. Music publisher. Publishes 5-10 songs/year; publishes 2 songwriters/year. Pays standard royalty. Affiliated pubishing firm: Rick Hanson Music.
How to Contact: Write first and obtain permission to submit. Prefers cassette with 1-4 songs and lyric sheet. SASE. Reports in 6-8 weeks.
Music: Mostly country, rock and gospel; also folk and easy listening. Recently published "Bring Me Another Double," (by Don Coghill), recorded by Rick Hanson on Ric Rac (country); "A Toast to Lov-

ing You Again," (by Woody Hueston), recorded by R. Hanson on Country Bump (country); and "Sara," written and recorded by Barry Johnson on Ric Rac (MOR).
Tips: "Be as professional as possible."

RIDGE MUSIC CORP., Suite 1100, 1650 Broadway, New York NY 10019. (212)582-1667. Affiliates: Natson Music Corp. and Tannen Music Inc. President/General Manager: Paul Tannen. Music publisher and manager. BMI, ASCAP. Member CMA. Pays standard royalty.
How to Contact: Prefers cassette with 3-5 songs and lyric sheet. SASE. Reports in 1 month.
Music: Country, dance-oriented, rock and top 40/pop.

*****RIO HARD LUCK MUSIC**, Box 198, Grain Valley MO 64029. (816)229-7780. President: Dave Freeman. BMI, ASCAP. Music publisher, record company (DMI Records), record producer (Associated Music Productions), recording studio and songwriters' organization. Publishes 200 songs/year; publishes 70 new songwriters/year. Pays standard royalty. Affiliates: Sharamie Music, Bramble Bush Music.
How to Contact: Prefers cassette or 7½/15 ips ½ track reel-to-reel or 7½ ips ¼ track reel-to-reel with 3-4 songs and lyric sheet and lead sheet. SASE. Reports in 1-6 weeks.
Music: Mostly country, pop and country rock ("all with crossover potential"); also R&B, rock and gospel. Recently published "The Door," (by Gary James), recorded by Freewind on DMI Records (pop); "Stairs to Heaven," (by Lavern Walker), recorded by Rod Hopkins on DMI Records (gospel); and "Lady in Sunglasses," (by Josh Garrett), recorded by Steve Hedrick on DMI Records (R&B/pop).
Tips: "Hit single material is high on the list. Use of the music standards in writing highly affects the initial chance of song acceptance."

RMS TRIAD PUBLISHING, 6267 Potomac Circle, West Bloomfield MI 48033. (313)661-5167. Contact: Bob Szajner. Music publisher, record company and record producer. ASCAP. Publishes 9 songs/year; publishes 1 new songwriter/year. Pays negotiable royalty.
How to Contact: Write first about your interest. Prefers cassette with 3 songs and lead sheet. Does not return unsolicited material. Reports in 3 weeks.
Music: Jazz. Recently published "Meeting Competition," "That's Pretty," and "Royal Outhouse Blues," (all by Bob Szajner), recorded by Triad/RMS Records (jazz).

*****ROBA MUSIC**, Feldbrunnenstr. 50, 2 Hamburg 13 West Germany. (40)445086. General Manager: Rolf Baierle. GEMA. Music publisher and record company. Employs songwriters on a salary basis. Pays standard royalty.
How to Contact: Prefers cassette. Reports in 2 weeks.
Music: Mostly rock, disco and ballads. Recently published "Born to Be Alive," recorded by P. Hernander (disco); and "Cold Days," recorded by Moti Special.

FREDDIE ROBERTS MUSIC, Box 99, Rougemont NC 27572. (919)477-4077. Manager: Freddie Roberts. Music publisher, record company and record producer, and management and booking agency. BMI. Publishes 25 songs/year; publishes 7 new songwriters/year. Pays standard royalty.
How to Contact: Write first about your interest or arrange personal interview. Prefers 7½ ips reel-to-reel or cassette with 1-5 songs and lyric sheet. SASE.
Music: Mostly country, MOR and top 40/pop; also bluegrass, church/religious, gospel and rock (country). Recently published "If I Did" written and recorded by Rodney Hutchins (southern rock); "We'll Sing in the Sunshine," written and recorded by Freddie Roberts (C&W); and "Forget It," written and recorded by Brenda Roberts (country rock).
Tips: "Write songs, whatever type, to fit today's market. Send good, clear demos, no matter how simple."

ROCKEN RYTHMN PUBLISHING, Box 12752, Memphis TN 38182-0752. (901)725-5387. A&R Director: Bill Lusk. Music publisher, record company and record producer. BMI. Member Memphis Music Association, Blues Foundation. Publishes varied number of songs/year; publishes 2 new songwriters/year. Pays standard royalty.
How to Contact: Prefers cassette with 1-4 songs and lyric sheet. "Specify number of songs on the tape." SASE, but "we keep tape on file." Reports if interested.
Music: Mostly blues, R&B, pop, rock, top 40 and soul. Recently published "Where You Want Me," and "Straight and Narrow Line," (by B. Lusk and T. Fosko), recorded by B. Lusk.

*****ROCKER MUSIC/HAPPY MAN MUSIC**, #806, 50 Music Sq. W, Nashville TN 37203. (615)320-1177. Executive Producer: Dick O'Bitts. BMI, ASCAP. Music publisher and record producer (Rainbow Collections Ltd.). Publishes 50 songs/year; publishes 10 new songwriters/year. Pays standard royalty. Affiliate: Happy Man Music.

How to Contact: Call first to arrange personal interview. Prefers cassette with 4 songs and lyric sheet or lead sheet. SASE.
Music: "All types."

ROCKFORD MUSIC CO., Suite 6-D, 150 West End Ave., New York NY 10023. (212)873-5968. Affiliates: Corporate Music Publishing Company (ASCAP) and Stateside Music Company (BMI). Manager: L.A. Chielli. Music publisher, record company, record and video tape producer. BMI, ASCAP. Publishes 12 songs/year; publishes 4 new songwriters/year. Pays standard royalty.
How to Contact: Prefers cassette with any number songs and lyric sheet. SASE. Reports in 1-2 weeks.
Music: Blues, country, dance-oriented, easy listening, folk, jazz, MOR and top 40/pop. Recently published "I Sing You," and "Corporate Lady," (by Michael Greer), recorded by Danny Darrow (ballads); and "For My Tomorrow," (by Michael Green/Steven Schoenberg).

ROCKMORE MUSIC, 1733 Carmona Ave., Los Angeles CA 90019. (213)933-6521. Music publisher and record company. Contact: Willie H. Rocquemore. BMI. Publishes 4 songs/year; publishes 2 new songwriters/year. Pays 10% royalties USA; 50% foreign countries.
How to Contact: Prefers cassette with maximim 4 songs and lyric sheet. SASE. Reports in 1 month.
Music: Blues, dance-oriented, R&B, soul and top 40/pop. Recently published "I Can't Complain," (ballad), "Let's Just Fake It for Tonight," (rock), and "Summer Lovers," (MOR), recorded by Jennifer Jayson/Rockin! Records.

*ROCKSONG, 152 Goldham Hill, Penn., Wolverhampton WV2 3JA England. (902)345345. A&R Manager: David Roberts. PRS, MCPS, MRS, MPA. Music publisher, record company (Heavy Metal Records and labels in United Kingdom, Japan, Canada and Europe) and record producer. Publishes 2-300 songs/year; publishes 70-100 new songwriters/year. Pays negotiable royalty. Affiliates: Heavy Metal Music, Andersong Music.
How to Contact: Prefers cassette or VHS/Beta PAL System videocassette with 3 songs. "Send photos and bios if also an artist." Does not return unsolicited material. Reports in 3-4 weeks.
Music: Hard rock, AOR, country rock, melodic rock and heavy metal. Recently published "Stakk Attakk," recorded by W. Ratchild on Heavy Metal Records (rock); "East-West," recorded by Multi-Story on F.M. Records (AOR); and "Heart of Steel," recorded by Reckless on Heavy Metal America Records (metal).

ROCKY BELL MUSIC, Box 3247, Shawnee KS 66203. (913)631-6060. Affiliates: White Cat Music. Professional Manager: Frank Fara. Producer/Arranger: Patty Parker. Music publisher, record company (Comstock Records) and record producer. Member CMA, GMA, ACME, MACE, BCCMA, BBB. Publishes 60 songs/year; "50% of our published songs are from non-charted and developing writers." Pays standard royalties.
How to Contact: Arrange personal interview. Prefers cassette or VHS videocassette with 1-4 songs. SASE. Reports in 2 weeks.
Music: Adult contemporary and modern country. Recently released "Forever In Love," (by Dave Kalman), recorded by Carolyn Justice (country); "You're Spreadin' My Hurt Around," (by Inez Polizzi and George Allen), recorded by Billie J. Helmkay, (country); and "I Started Missing You Too Late," (by Mark Rone & Writer Blue), recorded by Don TeBeaux (pop/country).
Tips: "Immediate need for top 40 and adult contemporary tunes for our new US and Canadian pop division."

ROCKY'S RAGDOLL PUBLISHING, 210 Wildwood Dr., Trussville AL 35173. (205)655-4981. Contact: Rocky Evans. Music publisher. BMI. Member CMA. Publishes 8-12 songs/year; publishes 2-3 new songwriters/year. Works with lyricists and composers and teams collaborators. Pays standard royalty.
How to Contact: Prefers cassette with 1-5 songs and lyric sheet. SASE. Reports in 3 weeks.
Music: Mostly country and pop; also rock (country) and top 40/pop. Recently published "Ain't She Grand," (by H. Burke), recorded by Justin Dickens/Audiograph Records (country/pop); "Those Green Eyes," (by D. Phillips), recorded by Phillips/Showboat Records (pop); and "Looking for a Brand New Way," (by Chandler, Fleetwood and Dickens), recorded by Dickens/Audiograph Records (country).
Tips: "Songs should have simple lyrics, good hooks, and a sing along melody."

ROHLFING PUBLISHING COMPANY, 8404 W. McNab Rd., Tamarac FL 33321. (305)722-6010. Contact: Ray C. Rohlfing. Music publisher. BMI. Member NSAI, SFMA. Publishes 25-50 songs/year; publishes 10-20 new songwriters/year. Works with and develops songwriters and teams collaborators. Pays standard royalty.
How to Contact: Prefers cassette with 1-3 songs and lyric sheet. SASE. Reports in 1 month.

Music: Mostly country; also folk, R&B, MOR and gospel.
Tips: "Send songs that tell a complete story, have a dynamite hook, and a jump out chorus."

ROHM MUSIC, 10 George St., Box 57, Wallingford CT 06492. (203)265-0010. Affiliate: Trod Nossel Artists Records and Management (BMI). A&R Director: Rudy Szlavi. President: Thomas Doc Cavalier. Music publisher. BMI. Publishes 25-35 songs/year; publishes 2-4 new songwriters/year. Pays standard royalty.
How to Contact: Prefers cassette with 1-4 songs. SASE. Reports in 1 month."
Music: Rock, soul, R&B and top 40/pop. Recently published "I Fall in Love Too Much," and "Lover That Got Away," (by Christine Ohlman), recorded by Rebel Montey/TNA (rock); and "I'm On a Roll," written and recorded by Bob Mel/TNA (pop).
Tips: "Be a performing artist in our area. We generally only publish writers under contract to TNA Records."

RONDOR MUSIC (AUSTRALIA) PTY., LTD., 570 Military Rd., Mosman, Sydney, NSW 2088, Australia. 61-9696366. Managing Director: Bob Aird. Music publisher. APRA, Australasian Mechanical Copyright Owners Society. Member AMPAL, Country Music (Australia), Songwriters Association. Publishes 50-60 songs/year; publishes 8-10 new songwriters/year. Works with lyricists and composers and teams collaborators. Pays standard royalty; royalties paid to US songwriters through US publishing affiliate.
How to Contact: Prefers 15 ips reel-to-reel with 4-10 songs and lyric sheet. "Good quality demos are obviously more effective." Does not return unsolicited material. Reports in 3 weeks.
Music: Mostly ballads, top 40 and rock; also country, dance-oriented and MOR. Recently published "Our Love Is on the Faultline," (by Reece Kirk), recorded by Crystal Gale (country); "Crazy Dreams," (by John Swan), recorded by Lionheart (rock); and "Work Till You Drop," (by Chilton/Sutherland), by Kamsha (rock).
Tips: "Be able to write for specific projects. We need songs adaptable to several types of arrangements and treatments."

ROOTS MUSIC, Box 111, Sea Bright NJ 07760. President: Robert Bowden. Music publisher. BMI. Publishes 2 songs/year; publishes 1 new songwriters/year. Works with lyricists and composers and teams collaborators. Pays standard royalty.
How to Contact: Prefers cassette or videocassette with any number songs and lyric sheet. "I only want inspired songs written by talented writers." SASE. Reports in 1 month.
Music: Mostly country and pop; also church/religious, classical, folk, MOR, progressive, rock (soft, mellow) and top 40. Recently published "Always," and "Make Believe," (by Toy), recorded by Marco/Sision (pop); and "Henry C," written and recorded by Robert Bowden (pop).

ROPERRY MUSIC, 645 Madison Ave., New York NY 10022. (212)308-2636. General Manager: Jane Lowy. Music publisher, record company, record producer and personal management firm. BMI. Publishes varying number of songs/year; publishes 2 new songwriters/year. Pays standard royalty and uses standard publishing contract.
How to Contact: Call first about your interest. Prefers cassette with 1-3 songs. "Tell a little about yourself and include lyric sheets." SASE. Reports in 3 weeks.
Music: Mostly top 40/pop, MOR and easy listening; also children's and dance-oriented. Recently published "Just A Little Imagination," (by Patsy Maharam), recorded by Patsy (pop and adult contemporary); "Single Again," (by P. Maharam), recorded by Joey Latini (pop); and "You Are the Sun (Keep On Shining)," by Joey Latini.
Tips: "Song should be a complete tune—not just a beat or rhythm. It's not necessary to have a full-blown production; a simple piano/vocal, guitar/vocal is fine."

ROSE HILL GROUP, 1326 Midland Ave., Syracuse NY 13205. (315)475-2936. Affiliates: Katch Nazar Music (ASCAP) and Bleecker Street Music (BMI). A&R Director: Vincent Taft. Music publisher and record producer. BMI and ASCAP. Publishes 10-20 songs/year; publishes 2 new songwriters/year. Pays standard royalty.
How to Contact: Prefers cassette with 1-5 songs and lyric sheet. SASE. Reports in 2 weeks.
Music: Mostly top 40/pop, rock, dance; also MOR and jazz. Recently published "Jammed Tight," (by S. Baronian), recorded by Taksim/Star City Records (jazz); "Win Some, Lose Some," (by Zarm), recorded by Zarm/Hill Records (MOR); and "Lifeline," (by Taft), recorded by Manly Band/2 Sided Records (top 40/pop).

ROSEBUD PUBLISHING CO. INC., Rt. 20, Box 472, Tyler TX 76656. (214)593-0546. Vice President: Barbara St. Clair. Music publisher, record company, record producer, and recording consultants.

BMI. Publishes 55 songs/year. Pays standard royalty.
How to Contact: Prefers cassette or videocassette and lyric sheet. "Please be explicit about any legal contracts, etc., concerning submitted material." SASE. Reports in 3 weeks.
Music: Mostly country; also bluegrass, blues, children's, church/religious, folk, gospel and top 40/pop. Recently published "Good Times Are Fleeting Things," "If I Was Your Conscience," and "Go Powder Your Face," by Frank St. Clair.

BRIAN ROSS MUSIC, Box 2950, Hollywood CA 90078. Affiliates: Thrush (BMI), New High (AS-CAP) and IMC (ASCAP). President/Professional Manager: Brian Ross. Music publisher, record company (Starborn Records), record producer and worldwide music representatives and administrators. BMI; also member of all foreign performance societies. Member CCC, AIMP, NARAS. Publishes 200 songs/year; publishes 15-20 new songwriters/year. Sometimes hires staff writers. Works with lyricists and composers and teams collaborators. Pays about $1,000-1,500/month as an advance against future royalties from songs. Pays standard royalty.
How to Contact: Prefers cassette or videocassette with 1-6 songs and lyric sheet. Print your name on both cassette and cassette box. SASE. Does not assume responsibility for materials lost or damaged in the mail. Reports in 1 week.
Music: Mostly dance music, contemporary and MOR; also disco, new wave and techno-pop. Recently published "I'm on Fire" (by Robert Jason), recorded by Barry White (ballad); "Broken Dream" (by Joshua Perohia), recorded by Joshua (rock); and "Scream" (by Wayne Wright), recorded by The Younger Half (dance).
Tips: "Have a good hook and send up-temp dance music only! No ballads!"

ROUND SOUND MUSIC, 1918 Wise Dr., Dothan AL 36303. (205)794-9067. President: Jerry Wise. Music publisher. BMI. Member CMA, GMA. Publishes 10-20 songs/year, publishes 5-10 new song-writers/year. Pays standard royalty.
How to Contact: Write first about your interest. Prefers 7½ ips reel-to-reel or cassette with 1-6 songs and lyric sheet. SASE. Reports in 1 month.
Music: Country, easy listening, MOR, rock, soul and top 40/pop.
Tips: "Songs must be commercial."

ROWILCO, Box 8135, Chicago IL 60680. (312)224-5612. Professional Manager: R.C. Hillsman. Music publisher. BMI. Publishes 8-20 songs/year.
How to Contact: Arrange personal interview. Prefers 7½ or 15 ips ¼" reel-to-reel with 4-6 songs and lyric sheet. Submissions should be sent via registered mail. SASE. Reports in 3 weeks.
Music: Blues, church/religious, country, disco, easy listening, gospel, jazz, MOR, rock and top 40/pop.

ROYAL FLAIR PUBLISHING, 106 Navajo, Council Bluffs IA 51501. (712)366-1136. Music publisher and record producer. BMI. Publishes 25-30 songs/year; publishes 3-4 new songwriters/year. Pays standard royalties.
How to Contact: Query. Prefers cassette with 2-6 songs. SASE. Reports in 1 month.
Music: "Traditional country, bluegrass and folk. Recently published "Time After Time," and "None Come Near," written and recorded by R. Everhart/Folkways; and "Smoky Mountain Heartbreak," written and recorded by Bonnie Sanford/Folkways (all country).
Tips: "Song definitely has to have old-time country flavor with all the traditional values of country music. No sex, outlandish swearing, or drugs-booze type songs accepted. We have an annual Hank Williams Songwriting Contest and winners are granted publishing."

ROYAL K MUSIC, 6 Melrose Dr., Livingston NJ 07039. (201)533-0448. President Marc Katz. Music publisher, record company, record producer and personal manager. ASCAP. Publishes 5 songs/year; publishes 3 new songwriters/year. Pays standard royalty.
How to Contact: Prefers cassette with 1-3 songs and lyric sheet. SASE. Reports in 3 weeks.
Music: Mostly dance-oriented and rock; also top 40/pop.

*RUSHWIN PUBLISHING, Box K-1150, Buna TX 77612. (409)423-2521. General Manager: James Gibson. Professional Manager: Aline Gibson. Music publisher. BMI. Publishes 15-20 songs/year; publishes 2-3 new songwriters/year. Pays standard royalty.
How to Contact: Prefers cassette with 1-4 songs with lyric and/or lead sheet. SASE. Reports ASAP.
Music: Christian/gospel, all styles. Recently published "When Nobody Waves Good-bye," (by Wyndi Harp Moore), recorded by The Harbingers; and "Prayer Closet," (by Debbie Scruggs Murrell), recorded by The Third Day.

S.M.C.L. PRODUCTIONS, INC., Box 83, St. Bruno, Quebec J3V 4P8 Canada. (514)653-7838. Affiliates: A.Q.E.M. Ltee (CAPAC), Bag Enrg. (CAPAC), C.F. Music (CAPAC), Big Bazaar Music (CAPAC), Sunrise Music (CAPAC), Stage One Music (CAPAC), L.M.S. Ltee (CAPAC), ITT Music (CAPAC), Machine Music (CAPAC) and Dynamite Music (CAPAC). President: Christian Lefort. Music publisher and record company. CAPAC. Publishes 100 songs/year.
How to Contact: Prefers 7½ ips reel-to-reel with 4-12 songs and lead sheet. SAE and IRC. Reports in 1 month.
Music: Dance, easy listening, MOR and top 40/pop. Recently published "Where Is My Man," recorded by the Eartha Kitt/Able Records (dance); and "Sex Over the Phone," recorded by Village People/Celsius Records (dance).

S & R MUSIC PUBLISHING CO., 39 Belmont, Rancho Mirage CA 92270. (619)346-0075. Contact: Dolores Gulden. Affiliates: Meteor Music (BMI) and Boomerang Music (BMI). Music publisher. ASCAP. Member AIMP and NMPA. Publishes 100 songs/year; publishes 50 new songwriters/year. Pays standard royalty.
How to Contact: Prefers cassette with 1-4 songs and lyric sheet. SASE.
Music: "We are mostly interested in lyrics or melodies for instrumentals." Recently published "You're My Love Story," and "I Can Taste It," (by Jeffer), and "The Christmas Jamboree," (by Jeri Sullivan).

THE S.R.O. PUBLISHING GROUP, 189 Carlton St., Toronto, Ontario M5A 2K7 Ontario. (416)923-5855. Vice President: Pegi Cecconi. A&R Director: Val Azzoli. Music publisher, record company, record producer and management firm. CAPAC, PROCAN. Member CMPA. Publishes 30 + songs/year; publishes 1-2 new songwriters/year. Works with lyricists and composers. Pays standard royalty. Affiliates: Core Music Publishing, Mark-Cain Music and Brandy Music.
How to Contact: Prefers cassette only with maximum 2 songs and bio material and lyric sheet. Prefers studio produced demos. SAE and IRC. Reports in 12-16 weeks.
Music: Mostly rock; also progressive and top 40/pop. Recently published "Distant Early Warning," (by Lee/Lifeson/Peart), recorded by Rush/PolyGram (rock); "Criminal Mind," (by Gowan), recorded by Gowan/CBS (rock); and "Go For Soda," (by Mitchell/Dubois), recorded by Kim Mitchell/Bronze/Alert (rock).

*LARRY SABISTON MUSIC, Box 96, Route 2 West, Worthington IN 47471. (812)875-3722. President: Larry Sabiston. BMI. Music publisher and record producer. Publishes 8-15 songs/year; publishes 5-7 new songwriter/year. Pays standard royalty.
How to Contact: Prefers cassette or VHS videocassette (if a performer) with 1-6 songs and lyric sheet or lead sheet. "Prefer lead sheets. All material must be copyrighted by the person submitting it. Also enclose a letter telling us about your writing achievements to date." SASE. Reports in 2-8 weeks.
Music: Mostly humorous country, humorous gospel and humorous novelty; also humorous Christmas, humorous Easter and humorous political. Recently published: "L & M Braves," (by Robert McDonald), recorded by Phil Coley on Mudsock Records (country novelty); "Mudsock Rock," (by R. McDonald), recorded by P. Coley on Mudsock Records (rockabilly novelty); and "Someone There Beside You," (by Larry Sabiston), (gospel novelty).
Tips: "We have record labels wanting cute humorous country and MOR novelty songs—anything that'll make 'em laugh!' We're looking for 'silly' songs, also. We like songs with good hooks, catchy melodies and polished lyrics. Don't write poems. Write lyrics that unfold and say something."

SABRE MUSIC, Box 702, Snowdon Station, Montreal, Quebec, Canada H3X 3X8. Affiliate: Montina Music (CAPAC). Professional General Manager: D. Leonard. Music publisher. CAPAC. Member MIEA. Pays standard royalty.
How to Contact: Prefers 7½ or 15 ips reel-to-reel, cassette or record and lyric sheet. Does not return unsolicited material.
Music: Mostly top 40; also blues, country, dance-oriented, easy listening, folk, gospel, jazz, MOR, progressive, R&B, rock, soul and pop.

*SADHANA MUSIC PUBLISHING, Box 551, Graham NC 27253. (919)229-0358 or (419)474-4516. Art Director: Wesley Bulla. ASCAP. Music publisher and record company (Daymien Records & Tapes). Estab. 1984. Publishes 8-20 songs/year; publishes 3-5 new songwriters/year. Pays standard royalty.
How to Contact: Prefers cassette. SASE. Reports in 4-8 weeks.
Music: Mostly rock-dance. Recently published "None Like You," (by M. Dawson) and "End of the Rainbow," (by D. Gary/W. Bulla), recorded by Nikki Foxe on Daymien Records (rock singles); and *Sneak Preview*, (D. Gary/W. Bulla/M. Dawson/J. Pendleton), recorded by Pyramid on Daymien Records (rock LP).
Tips: "We are currently looking for 'pop-rock' for female vocalists."

*SALMO MUSIC, 331 E. 9th St., New York NY 10003. (212)473-7833. President: S.L. Mollica. AS-CAP. Music publisher. Estab. 1984. Publishes 10 songs/year; publishes 1-2 new songwriters/year. Pays standard royalty.
How to Contact: Write first and obtain permission to submit.

SASHA SONGS, UNLTD. & THE GRAND PASHA PUBLISHER, Division of The Pasha Music Org., Inc., 5615 Melrose, Hollywood CA 90038. (213)466-3507. President: Spencer D. Proffer. General Manager: Carol Peters. Send material to A&R Director. Music publisher, record production company and independent label distributed by CBS. BMI. Publishes 100 songs/year; publishes 3-4 new songwriters/year. Pays standard royalty.
How to Contact: Write first. Prefers cassette with 2-3 songs. SASE. Reports in 3 weeks.
Music: Mostly rock; also progressive. Recently published "Hot Cherie" (by Randy Bishop et al), recorded by Danny Spanos (rock); "Up the Creek" (by R. Nielsen and R. Bishop), recorded by Cheap Trick (rock); and "The Heat" (by R. Bishop), recorded by Heart (rock).
Tips: "Song needs strong conceptual lyrics; get a great industry attorney."

*SATRIL MUSIC, 444 Finchley Rd., London, NW2 2HY, England. (01)435-8063. Professional Manager: Chris Baker. PRS, MCPS. Music publisher, record company (Crash Records), and record producer (Henry Hadaway Organiation). Publishes 3-4 new songwriters/year. Pays standard royalty. Affiliated publishing firms: Totrill Music, Casino Music, Sava Music.
How to Contact: Prefers cassette. SASE.
Music: Mostly country and "chart material of all kinds."

SAUL AVENUE MUSIC PUBLISHING, Box 37156, Cincinnati OH 45222. (513)563-1919. President: Steve Halper. Music publisher. BMI. Member NMPA. Publishes 4 songs/year; publishes 1 new songwriter/year. Pays standard royalty.
How to Contact: Prefers cassette with 4 songs and lyric sheet. SASE. Reports in 3 weeks.
Music: Bluegrass, blues, gospel and R&B.

*SCHWARTZ MUSIC CO., INC., 20 F. Robert Pitt Dr., Monsey NY 10952. (914)425-7000. Vice President: Gene Schwartz. ASCAP, BMI. Music publisher. Publishes 7 songs/year. Pays standard royalty. Affiliated publishing firms: Laurie House Publishing, Rugelle Music, 3 Seas Music.
How to Contact: Prefers cassette and lyric sheet or lead sheet. SASE.
Music: Pop.

*SCORE PRODUCTIONS, INC., Box 95566, Atlanta GA 30347. (404)636-1211. Executive Vice President: Bob May. Music publisher and record company (Perfect Pitch). Publishes 50 songs/year; publishes 5 new songwriters/year. Pays standard royalty. Affiliated publishing firms: Deaf Monkey, Ape's Hit.
How to Contact: Prefers cassette with 3 songs and lyric sheet.
Music: "All styles except gospel."

SCOTTI BROTHERS MUSIC PUBLISHING, 2114 Pico Blvd., Santa Monica CA 90405. (213)450-4143. Affiliate: Flowering Stone and Holy Moley. Professional Manager: Richie Wise. Music publisher and record company. BMI, ASCAP. Member NMPA, AIMP, RIAA and CMA. Publishes 40 songs/year; publishes 2 new songwriters/year. Pays standard royalty.
How to Contact: Prefers cassette with 1-2 songs and lyric sheet. Does not return unsolicited material; "we report only if we're interested."
Music: Mostly top 40/pop and country; also easy listening, MOR and rock. Recently published "Eye of the Tiger" (by J. Peterick and F. Sullivan), recorded by Survivor/Scotti Bros.-CBS Records (rock); "How Do You Fall Out of Love," recorded by Janie Fricke/CBS Records (country-pop); and "Them Good Ol' Boys Are Bad" (J. Harrington and J. Pennig), recorded by John Schneider/Scotti Bros.-CBS Records (country).

SCULLY MUSIC CO., 800 South 4th St., Philadelphia PA 19147. (215)755-7000. Affiliate: Orange Bear Music (BMI). President: Walter Kahn. Music publisher and record production company. Member AGAC. Publishes 50 songs/year; publishes 25 new songwriters/year. ASCAP, BMI. Works with lyricists and composers and teams collaborators. Pays standard royalties.
How to Contact: Prefers 7½ ips reel-to-reel, cassette or VHS videocassette with 1-4 songs and lyric sheet or lead sheet. Prefers studio produced demos. SASE. Reports in 1 month.
Music: Mostly dance, pop, R&B; also MOR, top 40 and rock. Recently published "Love Stimulation," (by Monahan/Stokes/George), recorded by David St. George/Malaco (R&B); "Do You Have a Car," (by L. Williams), recorded by Kid Seville/Salsoul (R&B); and "Deetour," (by A. Cohen), recorded by Karen Young/Atlantic (pop).
Tips: Need songs that "suit the styles of the artists on the roster of affiliated Sunshine Records."

*SEA DREAM MUSIC, 236 Sebert Rd., Forest Gate, London E7 0NP England. (01)534-8500. Senior Partner: Simon Law. PRS. Music publisher and record company (Plankton Records). Publishes 50 songs/year; publishes 2 new songwriters/year. Pays 66⅔% royalty. Affiliated publishing firms: Scarf Music Publishing, Really Free Music, Ernvik Musik (Sweden).
How to Contact: Prefers cassette with 3 songs and lyric sheet. "Technical information about the recording is useful, as are the songwriter's expectations of the company—i.e., what they want us to do for them." SAE and IRC. Reports in 6 weeks.
Music: Mostly funk/rock, rock and blues; also gospel. Recently published "Micro On the Move," (by McCarthy Wenham), recorded by Intransit on Embryo Arts (funk); "Unusual Shade," written and recorded by Pete Ward on Plankton (pop/rock); and "The Divided," (by Steve Hunt), recorded by Intransit on Plankton (funk/rock).
Tips: "We are specifically interested in material with a Christian bias to the lyrics."

*AUGUST SEITH MUSIKVERLAGE, Haydnstrasse 2, D-8000 Munich Germany. (089)53 09 331. Music publisher. Publishes 150 songs/year. Affiliated publishing firms: Edition Riva, Palma Musikverlag, Florida Muskverlag.
How to Contact: Prefers cassette. Does not return unsolicited material.
Music: Recently published "Du Schönes Europa," (by Rudi Redl), recorded by Andreas Hauff on Koch (pop).

SEIXAS MUSIC, 913 Carmans Rd., Massapequa NY 11758. (516)798-8236. Contact: Ron Seixas. Music publisher. BMI. Publishes variable number of songs/year; publishes 2 new songwriters/year. Pays standard royalty.
How to Contact: Prefers cassette with 2 songs and lyric sheet. SASE. Reports in 3 week.
Music: Mostly "rock music with top 40 appeal and new music." Recently published "Tough Boy" and "Theory" (by R. Seixas), recorded by Seixas/Cargo records.

SESCO MUSIC/NICK & DAVE MUSIC, 1572 Park Crest Court, San Jose CA 95118. (408)265-2008. Professional Manager: Nick Sesnak. Music publisher, record company and record producer. BMI, ASCAP. Member AGAC. Publishes 8 songs/year. Pays standard royalty.
How to Contact: Prefers 7½ reel-to-reel, cassette or videocassette with 3-6 songs and lyric sheet. SASE. Reports in 3 weeks.
Music: Mostly children's, church/religious, country and MOR; also bluegrass and easy listening. Recently published "Seen the Wind" (by Sesnak), recorded by Half A Keg/Wine Country Records (country); and "Yesterday Morning" (by Sesnak), recorded by Half A Keg/Wine Country Records (top 40).

SEVENTH RAY PUBLISHING, T.B.M. Productions, Inc., Box 3771, Hollywood CA 90020. (213)467-0611. Affiliate: Hermosa Publishing (BMI). Producer: Alan Ames. Music publisher, record company and record producer. ASCAP. Member AMPAS, ATVAS, ITVA. Publishes 10-20 songs/year; publishes 3 new songwriters/year. Pays standard royalty.
How to Contact: Prefers cassette with 3-8 songs and lyric sheet. Prefers studio produced demos. SASE. Reports in 1 month.
Music: Mostly AOR, pop/rock and R&B/jazz; also blues, reggae, easy listening, MOR, progressive, soul and top 40/pop. Recently published "Nobody But You" (by Gay Martin), recorded by Gay Martin/Seventh Ray Records (reggae); "Love Who Are You" (by Teddy Christopher) (rock/ballad); and "Abundance" (by Fantuzzi) (R&B/fusion).
Tips: "Songs must have a competitive edge, good taste and quality. I want only the best!"

SEYAH MUSIC, Master Audio, Inc., 1227 Spring St. NW, Atlanta GA 30309. (404)873-6425. Affiliates: Paydirt Music and Lyresong Music. President: Babs Richardson. Music publisher and recording studio. BMI, ASCAP. Publishes 20 songs/year; publishes 1-2 new songwriters/year. Pays standard royalty.
How to Contact: Prefers cassette with 2-3 songs. SASE. Reports in 1 month.
Music: Country, disco, gospel, R&B, soul and top 40/pop. Recently published *Great News*, (by Troy Ramey), recorded by T. Ramey and the Soul Searchers/Nashboro Records (black gospel); "Try Jesus, " recorded by T. Ramey (gospel); "Tea Cups and Doilies," (by Mac Frampton), recorded by M. Frampton/Triumvirate Records (Broadway show type); and "Double Shot (of My Baby's Love)," recorded by Joe Stampley (country).

*SHAOLIN MUSIC, Box 387, Hollywood CA 90078. (213)372-9126. President: Richard O'Connor. ASCAP. Music publisher, record company, record producer and film and video director/producer. Estab. 1984. Publishes 30 songs/year; publishes 4 new songwriters/year. Pays standard royalty.

How to Contact: Prefers cassette or Beta videocassette with 2-4 songs and lyric sheet. Include bio, photos and reviews. SASE. Reports in 4 weeks.
Music: Mostly rock, pop, and blues. Recently published "Temptation," "We're Not Working Out," and "Carol," written and recorded by Richard O'Connor/Shaolin (rock).

SHAWNEE PRESS, INC., Delaware Water Gap PA 18327. (717)476-0550. Affiliates: Harold Flammer, Inc. (ASCAP), GlorySound, Templeton Music (ASCAP), Malcolm Music (BMI) and Choral Press (SESAC). Director of Publications: Lewis M. Kirby Jr. Music publisher and record company. ASCAP. Member NMPA, MPA, CMPA. Publishes 150-200 songs/year; publishes 25 new songwriters/year. Pays royalty negotiated at the time of purchase.
How to Contact: Prefers cassette and lead sheet. SASE. Reports in 2 months.
Music: Children's, choral, church/religious, classical, easy listening, folk, gospel, MOR and top 40/pop. "Shawnee Press is primarily a publisher of choral and instrumental music for educational or religious use." Recently published "Sing to the Lord," (by Robert Sterling), recorded by Sandi Patti/Impact Records (MOR gospel); "There's a Turning," written and recorded by Ken Medema; and "Black & White," (by Robinson and Arkin), recorded by Three Dog Night/ABC-Dunkill (top 40).
Tips: "Send material for review suitable for use in schools or churches or for publication/recording for gospel market. Primarily interested in choral music."

LARRY SHAYNE ENTERPRISES, Suite 120, 1334 Lincoln Blvd., Santa Monica CA 90401. (213)395-6680. Affiliate: Workers Union Music (BMI). Music publisher. ASCAP. Member SGA. Publishes 50 songs/year. Works with lyricists and composers and teams collaborators. Pays standard royalty.
How to Contact: Call first. Prefers cassette and lyric sheet. "I will not return cassettes unless SASE is enclosed." Reports in 2 weeks.
Music: Easy listening, R&B, top 40/pop, MOR and country. Recently published "Who Said Men Don't Cry," (by Kirg and Burkholder), recorded by Steve Higgs/Barber Records; "A House Is Not a Home" (by Bacharach and David), recorded by Luther Vandross/Epic Records; and "A Shot in the Dark" (by DeVorton), recorded by Patty Weaver/Warner Bros. Records.

SHELTON ASSOCIATES, 2250 Bryn Mawr Ave., Philadelphia PA 19131. (215)477-7122. A&R Director: Leo Gayton. Adminstrator: Richard Jackson. Music publisher. BMI. Publishes 12 songs/year; publishes 8 new songwriters/year. Pays standard royalty.
How to Contact: Prefers 7½ ips reel-to-reel or cassette with 3-5 songs. SASE. Reports in 6 weeks.
Music: Mostly R&B, top 40; also dance, easy listening, MOR, progressive, rock, soul and top 40/pop. Recently published "Turn'in Me Out" (by Eugene Curry and Ron Parnell) and "Why You Treat Me So Cold" (by E. Curry and Ken Murphy), both recorded by Lambchops/Pearl Harbor Records (R&B); "Where's the Beef," (by Victor Drayton and Exavier Wardlaw), recorded by the Uptown Band/Pearl Harbor Records (R&B); and "Love Tonight," (by Eugene Curry and George Guess), recorded by David Simmons/Atlantic Records (urban).

*SIDEWALK SAILOR MUSIC, Box 423, Station F, Toronto, Ontario M4Y 2L8 Canada. Affiliates: Etheric Polyphony (CAPAC), Scales of My Head Music (PROCAN), Cumulonimbus Music (PROCAN). Professional Manager: Allen Shechtman. Music publisher and record producer. Member CAPAC, CARAS, CIRPA, PROCAN. Publishes 2-3 songs/year; publishes 1 new songwriter/year. "We recoup any costs from publisher's income, then split publisher's side of income on a 25-75% basis with songwriter (25 percent)."
How to Contact: Prefers 7½-15 ips reel-to-reel or cassette with 3 songs and lyric sheet. "Check your songs before you send them to anyone. Make sure they are your best efforts and have been reworked to make them as accessible as possible." SAE and IRC. Reports in 3 months.
Music: Progressive, AOR, electronic, pop and country. Recently published "I'm Dancing Alone," (by Lloyd Landa), recorded by M. Evans (pop/country); "Open Up Our Hearts," (by L. Landa), recorded by Irene Atmay and Jesse Collins (R&B ballad); and "The River Song," (by L. Landa), recorded by I. Atmay (pop ballad).

*SIEBENPUNKT VERLAGS GMBH, Habsburger Platz 1, 8000 München 40 West Germany. (83)33 1808. General Manager: Mr. Schmidt. GEMA. Music publisher. Publishes 250 songs/year; publishes 7 new songwriters/year. Pays standard royalty or by contract.
How to Contact: Prefers cassette or VHS videocassette with 1-2 songs. SAE and IRC. Reports in 3 weeks.
Music: Rock, dance and pop; also fusion-jazz. Recently published "On the Air Tonight," and "After the Fall," (by Peter Bardens), recorded by Willy Finlayson.
Tips: "Get in contact with us as quickly as possible."

SILICON MUSIC PUBLISHING CO., Ridgewood Park Estates, 222 Tulane St., Garland TX 75043. President: Gene Summers. Vice President: Deanna L. Summers. Public Relations: Steve Summers. Music publisher. BMI. Publishes 10-20 songs/year; publishes 2-3 new songwriters/year. Pays standard royalty.
How to Contact: Prefers cassette with 1-2 songs. Does not return unsolicited material. "We are usually slow in answering due to overseas tours."
Music: Mostly rockabilly and 50's material; also country and MOR. Recently published "Loco Cat," (by Eddie Hill/Tom Toms), recorded by Gene Summers/White Label; "Baby Please Tell Me Why," (by John Rathburn), recorded by Pat Minter; and "Baby Are You Kidding," (by James McClung); recorded by Gene Summers on Jan Records.
Tips: "We are very interested in 50s rock and rockabilly *original masters* for release through overseas affiliates. If you are the owner of any 50s masters, contact us first! We have releases in Holland, Switzerland, England, Belgium, France, Sweden, Norway and Australia. We have the market if you have the tapes. In conjunction with Domino Records and overseas affiliates, we have established the International Rockabilly Music Hall of Fame. All candidates for induction consideration should be directed to: Awards and Induction Committee; c/o Silicon Music, BMI."

SILKWOOD MUSIC, #307, 1300 Division St., Nashville TN 37203. (615)242-4314. Manager: Kenny Earl. ASCAP, BMI, PRO. Music publisher, record company (Eagle Records), record producer (Eagle Association) and management firm. Publishes 20 songs/year; publishes 8 new songwriters/year. Pays standard royalty. Affiliated publishing firm: Creekwood Music.
How to Contact: Write or call first and obtain permission to submit. Prefers cassette or ¾" videocassette with 3 songs and lyric sheet or lead sheet. Does not return unsolicited material. Reports in 4 weeks.
Music: Mostly rock, pop and jazz; also 50s rock, big band and country. Recently published "Big Big," (by Joe Turley), recorded by Eagle on Eagle (jazz); "Harlem Nocturne," (by Bud Billings), recorded by Bob Davis & Prime Time on Eagle (swing); and "Maidens Prayer," (by B. Billings), recorded by Bob Davis & Prime Ties on Eagle (country).

SILVER BLUE PRODUCTIONS, LTD., Penthouse, 220 Central Park S., New York NY 10019. Affiliate: Silver Blue Music and Oceans Blue Music. President: Joel Diamond. Music publisher and record producer.
How to Contact: Prefers cassette with 3 songs and lead sheet. SASE. Reports in 3 weeks "only if we are interested in the material."
Music: Pop/rock crossover, dance, AC and country. Recently published "After the Lovin' " and "This Moment in Time" (by Richie Adams and Alan Bernstein), recorded by Englebert Humperdink (AC and top 40/pop); and "Let's Just Stay Home Tonight" (by Lottie Golden and Richard Scher), recorded by Helen Reddy.

SILVERFOOT PUBLISHING, 4225 Palm St., Baton Rouge LA 70808. (504)383-7885. President: Barrie Edgar. BMI. Music publisher, record company (Gulfstream Records) and record producer (Hogar Musical Productions). Publishes 20-50 songs/year; publishes 1-5 new songwriters/year. Pays standard royalty.
How to Contact: Prefers cassette with maximum 4 songs and lyric sheet.
Music: Mostly rock, blues ("not soul") and country. Recently published "You," (by Liscomb/Ratzlaff); "Leave You Girl," (by R. Liscomb); and "Picture on Page Ten," (by G. Ratzlaff); all recorded by B. Edgar on Cicadelic (rock).

SLATER PICHINSON MUSIC, INC., 11335 Ventura Blvd., Studio City CA 91604. (818)980-6800. President: Martin Pichinson. BMI, ASCAP and all foreign societies. Music publisher. Publishes varying number of songs/year; publishes varying number of songwriters/year. Employs songwriters on a salary basis. Pays standard royalty. Affiliated publishing firms: Songs of Cash, SlaPich Music, Black Cabinet Music, Lifeboat Music and Veridian Music.
How to Contact: Prefers cassette with 2-5 songs and lyric and lead sheets. Does not return unsolicited material.
Music: Mostly country, pop and rock; also gospel, children's and hard rock. Recently published "Be Bop on the Beach," (by Mike Love), recorded by The Flirts on Polydor (pop); "Goin' Down Hill," (by Y. Lincoln), recorded by John Anderson (country); "Heaven Sounding Sweeter," (by The Deweys), recorded by Jimmy Swaggert on Jim Records (gospel).
Tips: "We also purchase music catalogs with some track record."

SNUGGLEBUSH MUSIC COMPANY, 236½ Lasky Dr., Beverly Hills CA 90212. Affiliates: Snugglebug (ASCAP) and Iren Koster Music (BMI). Assistant to President: Karen Koster. Music publisher and record producer. BMI, ASCAP. Publishes 50 songs/year; publishes 2 new songwriters/year. Pays standard royalty or negotiates payment.

How to Contact: Prefers cassette or videocassette with 2 songs and lyric sheet. "SASE if it's to be returned." Reports in 2 weeks.

Music: Dance, easy listening, MOR, R&B, rock, soul and top 40/pop. Recently published "Rainbows," (by I. Koster), recorded by Jack Jones (pop); "I Won't Forget . . .," (by I. Koster), recorded by Stylistics (R&B); and "Superwoman," (by I. Koster), recorded by Dells (R&B).

*SO FAR SO GOOD MUSIC, 227 Brocket Place, Stafford TX 77477. (713)774-0433. President: Randy Soffar. ASCAP. Music publisher, record company (Z-Records) and record producer. Publishes 5-10 songs/year; publishes 0-3 new songwriters/year. Negotiates royalty. Affiliated publishing firms: Zong Publishing, Schwartz Songs.

How to Contact: Write or call first and obtain permission to submit. Prefers cassette, 15 ips reel-to-reel or VHS videocassette with 3-5 songs and lyric sheet. "Send promotional material, pictures, etc." SASE. Reports in 4-6 weeks.

Music: Mostly pop, rock and new wave; also techno pop and R&B. Recently published "The Teacher's A Punk," "The Way She Looks At Me," and "Real World," (by Randy Soffar), recorded by Z-Rocks on Z-Records (pop rock).

SONE SONGS, 10101 Woodlake Dr., Cockeysville MD 21030. General Manager: George Brigman. Music publisher, record company and record producer. BMI. Publishes 10-20 songs/year; publishes 1-2 new songwriters/year. Pays standard royalty.

How to Contact: Write first about your interest. Prefers 7½ ips reel-to-reel with 1-6 songs. No cassettes. Does not return unsolicited material. Reports in 1 month.

Music: Mostly hard rock, metal rock and progressive rock; also blues. Recently published "Mistress of Desire," "Iran in Japan," and "Cambodian Bossa Nova," (by G.F. Brigman), recorded by George Brigman/Split/Bonafide (rock).

Tips: "Know what a specific publisher needs."

SONG FARM MUSIC, Box 24561, Nashville TN 37202. (615)242-1037. President: Tom Pallardy. Music publisher and record producer. BMI. Member NSAI. Publishes 2-3 songs/year; publishes 1-2 new songwriters/year. Pays standard royalty.

How to Contact: Prefers cassette with maximum 2 songs and lyric or lead sheet. SASE. Reports in 1 month.

Music: Country, crossover, top 40/pop and R&B. Recently published "After Every Goodbye" (by Tom and Jo Pallardy), recorded by Lisa Ward/Whitehorse Records (positive/uptempo); "Only You Can Stop the Rain" (by T. Pallardy), recorded by Jerry Hopper (country); and "Another Heartache" (by Annette Lumsden), recorded by Carl Finney (country).

Tips: "Material should be submitted neatly and professionally with as good quality demo as possible. Songs need not be elaborately produced (voice and guitar/piano are fine) but they should be clear. Songs must be well constructed, lyrically tight, good strong hook, interesting melody, easily remembered; i.e., commercial!"

SONG OF SONGS MUSIC, Box 219, Langhorne PA 19047. (215)757-4144. Director: Barbara Riffe. Music publisher. ASCAP. Publishes 5 songs/year; publishes 1-5 new songwriters/year. Teams collaborators. Pays standard royalty.

How to Contact: Prefers cassette or videocassette with 2-4 songs and lyric sheet. SASE. Reports in 3 weeks.

Music: Top 40/pop, country, easy listening, folk, jazz, MOR and Spanish. Recently published "Candle Light," and "Livin' My Life with You," by Chuck Mitchell, on Song of Songs Records; and *A Collection of Love Songs*, by Sparky.

SONG TAILORS MUSIC CO., Box 2631, Muscle Shoals AL 35662-2631. (205)381-1455. Affiliate: I've Got the Music (ASCAP). Professional Manager: Richard Butler. Music publisher. BMI. Publishes 100 songs/year; publishes 1-2 new songwriters/year. Pays standard royalty.

How to Contact: Prefers cassette with 2 songs and lyric sheet. SASE. Reports "as soon as possible."

Music: Blues, country, dance, easy listening, folk, jazz, MOR, progressive, rock, soul and top 40/pop. Recently published "Let Your Heart Do the Talking," (by Robert Byrne/Alan Schulman), and "Love You Out of Your Mind," (by Robert Byrne/Brandon Banes), both recorded by Anne Murray/Capital (top 40/pop); and "One More Try for Love," (by R. Bryne/B. Barnes), recorded by Ronnie Milsap/RCA (country pop).

SONGS FOR TODAY, INC., 8 Mark Lane, New City NY 10956. (914)634-8282. Affiliates: Kenwood Music, Inc., Hillbrow Music Inc., Ember Music, Nathanial Music Group. Vice President: J.S.

Kruger. Music publisher. BMI, ASCAP, PRS. Publishes 50 songs/year; publishes 20 new songwriters/year. Pays standard royalty.
How to Contact: Prefers cassette with 1-4 songs and lyric sheet. Does not return unsolicited material. Reports in 4 weeks.
Music: Mostly country and soft rock; also easy listening, MOR, R&B, soul and top 40/pop. Recently published "Wish You Were Here Tonight," (by J. Sullins), recorded by Sheena Easton/EMI (pop); and "Letter to Home," (by C. Jackson), recorded by Glen Campbell/Atlantic (country).

SONGS FROM THE BOX, 5180-B Park Ave., Memphis TN 38119. (901)761-5074. Affiliate: Voice of Paradise (ASCAP). President: Mark Blackwood. Director of Publishing: B. Wood. Music publisher, record company and record producer. BMI. Publishes 30-40 songs/year; publishes 7 new songwriters/year. Works with lyricists and composers and teams collaborators. Pays standard royalty.
How to Contact: Prefers cassette or videocassette and lyric sheet. "Be sure that *both* demo tape and lyric sheet are provided." Does not return unsolicited material without SASE. Reports in 2 months.
Music: Mostly contemporary Christian; also gospel and Christian pop. "We are primarily interested in contemporary and MOR Christian style songs." Recently published "That Brighter Day," (by Tracy Zinn), recorded by the Blackwood Brothers/Voice Box (contemporary); "Lift Me Again," (by Calvan Gann), recorded by the Blackwood Brothers/Voice Box (MOR); and "No Matter What You're Goin' Through," (by Tony Pilcher), recorded by Robert Winston/Voice Box (contemporary).
Tips: "We like a well-structured song with a good hook, strong lead line and fundamental Christian lyric."

SON-TON MUSIC, 110 N. Main St., Fostoria OH 44830. (419)435-6525. Affiliate: Fresh Air Music. Contact: Ronald Hanson. Music publisher, record company and record producer. ASCAP. Publishes 12 songs/year; publishes 4 new songwriters/year. Pays standard royalty.
How to Contact: Prefers cassette with 2-8 songs and lyric sheet. SASE. Reports in 1 month.
Music: Mostly rock; also bluegrass, church/religious, country, dance-oriented, MOR, soul and top 40/pop. Recently published "Bottom of the Bottle" (by Fred Blackstone), recorded by Buzz Coady (country); "Sweet Night" (by K. Maiberger), recorded by The Rize Band (rock); and "Boffo" (by G. McGladdfry), recorded by Other Half (rock).
Tips: "Try to contact me personally. Find a group to record your song."

SOUND COLUMN COMPANIES, 46 E. Herbert Ave., Salt Lake City UT 84111. (801)355-5327. Affiliates: Ronarte Publications (ASCAP), Mountain Green Music (BMI) and Macanudo Music (SESAC). Professional Manager: Kelley Pollard. Music publisher. BMI, ASCAP. Member CMA. Publishes 15 songs/year; publishes 1 new songwriter/year. Hires staff writers. Pays standard royalty.
How to Contact: Query first. Prefers cassette with 1-3 songs and lyric sheet. SASE. Reports as time permits.
Music: Top 40/pop. Recently published "Cheyenne/Boston," (by Simpson/Romney), recorded by Dave Lemmon/SCP Records (country crossover); "Who Do You Know," (by Simpson/Romney), recorded by New Sound Column/SCP Records (pop-new music); and "Maggie," (by D. Lemmon), recorded by D. Lemmon/SCP Records (country).
Tips: "We very rarely accept outside submissions so be careful about song form and quality of demo."

*SOUND DIAGRAMS LTD., 21 Atholl Crescent, Edinburgh EH3 8HQ Scotland. (031)229-8946. PRS, ASCAP. Music publisher. Publishes 45 songs/year; publishes 2 new songwriters/year.
How to Contact: Write first and obtain permission to submit. Prefers cassette with 3 songs and lyric sheet. Does not return unsolicited material.
Music: Mostly rock/pop. Recently published "Louise," (by Callis), recorded by Homa League on A&M (pop); and "On American Broadway," (by Henderson), recorded by Win on London (pop).

SOUND IMAGE PUBLISHING, 6556 Wilkinson, North Hollywood CA 91606. (213)762-8881. President: Martin John Eberhardt. Vice President: David Chatfield. Music publisher, record company, record producer and video company. ASCAP. Member NARAS. Publishes 60 songs/year; publishes 10 new songwriters/year. Pays standard royalty.
How to Contact: Prefers cassette or VHS or Beta videocassette with 2-6 songs and lyric sheet. Does not return unsolicited material. Reports in 1 month.
Music: Mostly rock; also dance-oriented, R&B and top 40/pop. Recently published "Desperate Times," (by Saint), recorded by Million Miles; "We Get Along Just Fine," written and recorded by Mark Fosson; and "Your Loss My Gain," written and recorded by George Faber.

SOUNDS AMBIENT MUSIC, Box 499, Queens NY 11365. (212)969-2418. Affiliate: Human Sound Music (BMI). President: Marty Pekar. Music publisher. ASCAP. Publishes 10-30 songs/year. Pays standard royalty.

How to Contact: Prefers cassette and lyric sheet. SASE. Reports in 1 month.
Music: "We only publish authentic 50s style rock & roll/doo wop." Recently published "Baby Come Back to Me," by Manhattan Transfer.
Tips: "We publish songs that sound like they could have been hits for 50s artists (such as Randy & the Rainbows, the Mystics, the Jive Five). We record about 50% of the songs we decide to publish, but they must be pure, authentic 50s rock or don't even bother."

SOUTHERN CRESCENT PUBLISHING, Suite 5-J, 320 W. 30th St., New York NY 10001. (212)971-9151; and Suite 1003, 4545 Connecticut Ave. NW, Washington DC 20008. (202)362-2286. Affiliates; Sugar Mama Music (BMI) and Neck Bone Music (BMI). Vice President: Jonathan Strong. Music publisher, record company and record producer. BMI. Publishes 5 songs/year; publishes 1 new songwriter/year. Pays standard royalty.
How to Contact: Prefers cassette and lyric sheet. SASE. Reporting time "depends on free time; we try to be considerate and return material promptly."
Music: Rockabilly and traditional rock. Recently published (by Sugar Mama Music) "The Trouble with Girls," ("popabilly"); "Alley Cat," ("punkabilly"); and "Oh, Caroline," ("rockabilly"), all recorded by Billy Hancock/Ripsaw Records.

SPARROW/BIRDWING MUSIC, 9255 Deering, Chatsworth CA 91311. (818)709-6900. Affiliates: Birdwing Music (ASCAP), Sparrow Song (BMI), and His Eye Music (SESAC). Music publisher. Publishes 75-100 songs/year; publishes 2-4 new songwriters/year. Pays standard royalty.
How to Contact: Write or call first about your interest. Prefers cassette with 1-3 songs and lyric sheet. "A lead sheet is helpful, and a typewritten lyric sheet is essential. Also include a list of qualifications and credentials." SASE. Reports in 3-4 months.
Music: Mostly contemporary Christian styles (rock, light rock, MOR, new music).

BEN SPEER MUSIC, 54 Music Square W., Box 40201, Nashville TN 37204. (615)329-9999. Affiliates: Emmanuel Music, My Father's Music, Ben Speer Music. Promotion: Robin Mew. Music publisher. ASCAP, BMI, SESAC. Member GMA. Publishes 50 songs/year; publishes 11 new songwriters/year. Pays standard royalty.
How to Contact: Prefers cassette with 1-3 songs and lyric sheet. SASE. Reports in 4-6 weeks.
Music: Church/religious and gospel. Recently published "I'm Standing on the Solid Rock" (by Harold Lane), recorded by The Speer Family; "One More Hallelujah" (by Dave Clark), recorded by The Speer Family and The Florida Boys; and "In Gloryland" (by Harold Lane), recorded by The Singing Americans & The Florida Boys.
Tips: "Lyrics should be *unique* and have deep spiritual meaning."

*SPINNING GOLD INC., 221 W. 6th, Austin TX 78710. (512)331-7007. Administrator: Bob Rhino. Music publisher, record company and record producer. Employs songwriters on a salary basis.
How to Contact: Prefers cassette. Reports in 15 weeks.
Music: Mostly MOR, country and rock.

SPIRIT HORSE PRODUCTIONS & SONGS, 805 18th Ave. S., Nashville TN 37203. (615)327-3900. Affiliate: Shadowfax Music. Director: Steve Singleton. Music publisher. BMI. Member NMPA. Works with lyricists and composers and teams collaborators. Pays standard royalty.
How to Contact: Arrange personal interview for any Monday, or submit demo tape. Prefers cassette with maximum 3 songs and lyric sheet. SASE. Reports in 3 months.
Music: Bluegrass, blues, country, disco, easy listening, MOR, progressive, rock, soul and top 40/pop. Recently published "With You" recorded by Charly McClain; "The Faithful Kind" (by Singleton and Shell), recorded by Percy Sledge/Monument Records (R&B); "You're Work in Me" (by David Lindsey), recorded by Willie Jackson/Spring Records (contemporary R&B).

STANG MUSIC PUBLISHING, 168 Buckingham St., Hartford CT 06106. (203)524-5656. Producer: Jack Stang. Music publisher, record company and record producer. BMI. Publishes 20 songs/year; publishes 3 new songwriters/year. Pays standard royalty.
How to Contact: Prefers cassette with 1-3 songs and lyric sheet. SASE. Reports in 3 weeks.
Music: Dance-oriented, easy listening, MOR, R&B, rock and top 40/pop.

When contacting one of the markets listed in this book, please be sure you follow ALL submission instructions.

STARFOX PUBLISHING, Box 13584, Atlanta GA 30324. (404)872-4000. President: Alexander Janoulis. Vice President, Creative: Marie Sutton. General Manager: Hamilton Underwood. Music publisher. BMI. Publishes 30 songs/year; publishes 10-25 new songwriters/year. Works with composers. Pays 25-50% royalty.
How to Contact: Prefers reel-to-reel or cassette with 2-3 songs and lyric sheet. Does not return unsolicited material. Reports "as soon as possible, on material of interest and potential."
Music: Mostly country and top 40/pop; also blues, disco, MOR, progressive and rock. Recently published "Big Lollipop," (by Diamond Lil), recorded on Glamour & Grease Records (comedy); "Perils of Pauline," (by Phil Rosenberg and A. Janoulis), recorded on Hottrax Records (rock); and "Easier Said Than Done," (by Frank Amato and Nick Perugini), recorded on Hottrax Records (pop).
Tips: "Make subject relate to broad audience, have a good melody with repetitive hook and a good rhyme scheme."

STAR SONG PUBLISHING GROUP, 2000 21st Ave. S, Nashville TN 37212. (615)292-5222. Affiliates: Shepherd's Fold Music, Straight Way Music and Dawn Treader Music. President: Darrell A. Harris. General Manager: Dennis Worley. Music publisher. ASCAP, BMI, SESAC. Publishes 100 songs/year. Pays standard royalty.
How to Contact: Prefers cassette with 3 songs maximum and lyric sheet. "We would like as much background information as possible on the writer and his or her musical activities." SASE. Reports in 1 month.
Music: Contemporary gospel; and top 40/pop. "We are looking for well-constructed songs with a solid Christian lyrical content." Recently published "More Power to Ya," by Petra/Star Song Records; "The Sacrifice," by Wayne Watson/Milk & Honey Records; "Only One Lord," by Dallas Holm and Praise/Green Tree Records; and "Every Single Step," by Michael James Murphy/Milk & Honey Records.

STARTIME MUSIC, Box 643, LaQuinta CA 92253. (619)564-4823. Affiliate: Yo Yo Music (BMI). President: Fred Rice. Record producer, record company and music publisher (Yo Yo Music/BMI). Releases 10 singles/year; publishes 6 new songwriters/year. Teams collaborators. Pays standard royalty.
How to Contact: Prefers cassette or VHS videocassette with 1-2 songs and lead sheet. SASE. Reports in 6 weeks.
Music: Mostly top 40/pop, country and novelties; also rock. Recently published "My Palm Springs," (by Mary Gramm Turner), recorded by Robin Miller/Yo-Yo; "Palm Springs Party," (by Gary Whittaker/Robin Miller), recorded by R. Miller/Yo-Yo; and "Mini-Van," recorded by Vantastics (all pop/top 40).
Tips: "Like songs that have 'short story' endings, novelty twists or provocative subjects. Please consider the visual potential of your song—it should lend itself to a storyboard for future video production."

STEADY ARM MUSIC, Box 2277, Gainesville FL 32602. (904)378-8156. General Manager: Charles V. Steadham Jr. Professional Manager: Allen R. McCollum. Music publisher. BMI. Pays standard royalty.
How to Contact: Write first. Prefers cassette with 2-5 songs. Does not return unsolicited material. Reports "as soon as possible.".
Music: Bluegrass, country, dance, folk, MOR, rock (country), soul, top 40/pop, R&B, and comedy. Recently released "Micah" and "Enoch Ludford" (by Don Dunaway), recorded by Don Dunaway/Milltop Records (folk); "Kennesaw Line" (by Dunaway) recorded by Gamble Rogers/Mountain Railroad Records (folk); and "The Honeydipper" and "The Skylake Campfire Girls" (by Gamble Rogers), recorded by Rogers/Mountain Railroad Records (folk).

*STORZ GROUP OF COMPANIES, Box 1670, Hauptstr. 114, 3360 Osterode West Germany. (05522)7041. Music publishers and record company (Catena Vision, Arminia). Affiliated publishing firms: Musikverlag Storz KG, Edition Catena, Edition Storz.
How to Contact: Prefers cassette, reel-to-reel or VHS videocassette.

STREET CITY MUSIC, 8625 Santa Monica Blvd., Los Angeles CA 90069. (213)550-1216. Artist Relations: Bambi Bryens. Music publisher and record producer. BMI. Publishes 35 songs/year; publishes 3 new songwriters/year. Pays standard royalty.
How to Contact: Prefers cassette with 1-4 songs and lyric sheet. SASE. Reports in 3 weeks.
Music: Commercial rock and pop.

*STREET SINGER MUSIC, 117 W. 8th, Hays KS 67601. (913)625-9634. President: Mark Meckel. BMI. Music publisher, record company (MDM Records) and record producer (MDM productions). Publishes 15 songs/year; publishes 5 new songwriters/year. Employs songwriters on a salary basis. Pays standard royalty.

How to Contact: Prefers cassette with 2-4 songs and lyric sheet or lead sheet. Reports in 2 weeks.
Music: Mostly R&B, country and gospel; also rock/Christian, country R&B, and 50s rock. Recently published "This One's For You," (by M. Ferguson), recorded by Kim Haiger on MDM (slow rock); "Promise Givin," written and recorded by Bill Sanchez on MDM (Christian); and "Cadillac," written and recorded by C. Conlee on MDM (rock).
Tips: "Be willing to make changes and work with a producer."

JEB STUART MUSIC CO., Box 6032, Station B, Miami FL 33123. (305)547-1424. President: Jeb Stuart. Music publisher, record producer and management firm. BMI.
How to Contact: Query. Prefers cassette or disc with 2-4 songs and lead sheet. SASE. Reports in 1 month.
Music: Blues, church/religious, country, disco, gospel, jazz, rock, soul and top 40/pop. Recently published "We've Got to Change the Plan," "Baby Let's Get Together Tonight," "You Better Believe It Baby," and "Saucy Music," by Jeboria Stuart (jazz/pop/R&B).

*SUGARPLUM MUSIC CO., 1022 16th Ave. S., Nashville TN 37212. (615)255-5711. Affiliates: Gingham Music Co. (ASCAP), Calico Music Co. (SESAC). Administrative Assistant: Joe Allen. Music publisher. BMI. Member NMPA, CMA, NARAS and NSAI. Pays standard royalty.
How to Contact: Prefers 7½ ips reel-to-reel or cassette with 1-3 songs and lyric sheet. SASE. Reports in 3 weeks.
Music: Country, easy listening, MOR and country/pop. Recently published "Girls, Women & Ladies," "When You Fall in Love, Everything's a Waltz," "Love's Found You and Me," (*Maverick* Theme) and "Last Cowboy Song," by Ed Bruce/MCA Records (country); "Hand of the Man," recorded by B.J. Thomas/Myrrh Records; and "The Last Thing She Said," recorded by Ray Price.

*SULTRY LADY MUSIC, Suite 205, 380 Lafayette Rd., St. Paul MN 55107. (612)228-0719. Professional Manager: Thomas A. Del Vecchio. Music publisher. Estab. 1984. Publishes 1-2 songs/year; publishes 1 new songwriter/year. Pays standard royalty.
How to Contact: Prefers cassette with 3-5 songs "and a lyric sheet for each song. No submissions will be returned without SASE." Reports in 6-8 weeks.
Music: Mostly rock, MOR and jazz; also pop, top 40 and blues.

SULZER MUSIC, Dave Wilson Productions, 3530 Kensington Ave., Philadelphia PA 19134. (215)743-8549. Affiliates: Arzee Music (ASCAP), Asterisk Music (BMI), Rollercoaster Records (ASCAP), Rex Zario Music (BMI), Seabreeze Music (BMI), Wilson/Zario Publishers (BMI), Jack Howard Publishers (BMI), Country Bear Music (BMI) and Arcade Music (ASCAP). President: Dave Wilson. Vice President: Claire Mac. Music publisher, record company, record producer and bookings and management. Publishes 100-150 songs/year; publishes 50 new songwriters/year. BMI, ASCAP. Pays standard royalty.
How to Contact: Prefers cassette with 3-10 songs and lead sheet. SASE. Reports in 1 month. "Indicate whether BMI or ASCAP writer."
Music: Mostly country, easy listening, folk, top 40/pop, MOR and pop country. Recently published "Dixie Girl," (by Ralph Jarrell), recorded by Tom Bornemann/In Action (country); "Wildwood Days," recorded by Nite Shift/In Action (top 40); and "The Lonely Road," written and recorded by Paul Christoper/In Action (easy listening).

SU-MA PUBLISHING CO., INC., Box 1125, Shreveport LA 71163. (318)459-3751. Publishing Manager: Ms. Donnis Lewis. Music publisher. BMI. Publishes 75 songs/year. Pays standard royalty.
How to Contact: Prefers 7½ ips reel-to-reel, cassette or 8-track cartridge and lead sheet. SASE. Reports in 1 month.
Music: Country, gospel and soul.
Tips: "All songs must contain both lyrics and melody."

SUNBURY/DUNBAR MUSIC CANADA, LTD., 2245 Markham Rd., Scarborough, Ontario M1B 2W3 Canada. (416)299-9200. Affiliate: Dunbar Music Canada, Ltd. Administrator: Norma Barnett. Music publisher. CAPAC, PROCAN. Member CMPA and CARAS. Publishes 150-200 songs/year; publishes 5 new songwriters/year. Pays standard royalty.
How to Contact: Prefers cassette with 1-5 songs on demo. SAE and IRC. Reports in 1 month.
Music: Country, pop, jazz, hard rock, top 40 and MOR. Recently published "Here Comes the Rain Again," (by A. Lennoy and D. Stewart) recorded by Eurythmics/RCA (pop); "Standing Alone," written and recorded by White Wolf/RCA (rock); and "Crazy for Your Love," (by Pemington and Lemaire), recorded by Exile/Epic (country).

*SUNSET MUSIC, Box 500, The Production House, London E4 6AA England. (01)524 4245. Contact: Kevin Wyatt-Lown. PRS. Music publisher and record company (Coast Records). Publishes 100 songs/year; publishes 5 new songwritrers/year. Pays negotiable royalty. Affiliated publishing firms: Notable Music, Mummer Music.
How to Contact: Prefers cassette or VHS (PAL) videocassette with 4 songs and lyric sheet. "Every submission must include return package and postage to ensure reply." SAE and IRC. Reports in 4 weeks.
Music: Mostly comedy and novelty.
Tips: "All material must be highest quality commercial comedy with strong 'novelty' record single potential."

SWEET JUNE MUSIC PUBLISHING, 10125-227th Ave. Ct. E., Buckley WA 98321. (206)862-1877. Contact; Tom Thrasher. Music publisher. BMI. Publishes 12 songs/year; publishes 5 new songwriters/year. Pays standard royalty.
How to Contact: Prefers cassette with 2-5 songs and lyric sheet. SASE. Reports in 1 month.
Music: Mostly gospel and country; also bluegrass, church/religious, easy listening, folk, MOR and R&B. Recently published "For You—For Me," written and recorded by Tom Thrasher/C-M-I (gospel); "Someday the World," written and recorded by Todd Smith/C-M-I (gospel); and "Living Stream," written and recorded by Melissa Mason/C-M-I (gospel).

SWEET POLLY MUSIC, Box 521, Newberry SC 29108. (803)276-0639. Studio Manager: Polly Davis. Producer: Hayne Davis. Music publisher and record producer. BMI. Publishes 20-30 songs/year.
How to Contact: Prefers 7½ ips reel-to-reel or cassette with 4-8 songs and lyric sheet. "Include brief bio, list experience, credits etc. Express a desire to actively work on helping to produce/promote material. We are looking for professional writer/co-producer especially." SASE. Reports in 2 weeks.
Music: Country (contemporary), easy listening, MOR, rock and top 40/pop. Recently published "Rainy Days" (by Hayne Davis), recorded by Raw Material (country rock); "Down To The Lovin'," and "Back in 1956," (by H. Davis), recorded by Sugar & Spice (bubblegum/disco); and "If You Want My Love," by Hayne Davis.

SWEET SINGER MUSIC, The Mathes Company, Box 22653, Nashville TN 37202. Affiliate: Star of David (SESAC) and Sing Sweeter Music (ASCAP). President: Dave Mathes. BMI. Member CMA, GMA, NMPA, NARAS and AFM. Publishes 30-100 songs/year; publishes 6-20 new songwriters/year. Pays standard royalty.
How to Contact: Prefers 7½ ips reel-to-reel with 3-5 songs and lyric sheet.
Music: Mostly country and gospel; also bluegrass, blues, disco, easy listening, gospel, MOR, progressive rock (country), soul, top 40/pop and instrumental. Recently published "Simple Love Song," (by Pelleteri, Mathes, Bass), recorded by DeAnna/Rising Star Records (MOR); "If the Man on the Street Were You," (by Verlin Chalmers), recorded by Roy Drusky (gospel/country); and "Moonlight Honky Tonkin" (by Warner Mack/David McCaskell), recorded by W. Mack (country).
Tips: Needs "well-thought out lyrics, resulting from rewriting until satisfied that the song is as good as the top ten songs on the chart."

SWEET TOOTH MUSIC PUBLISHING, 2716 Springlake Ct., Irving TX 75060. (214)790-5172. General Manager: Kenny Wayne Hagler. Music publisher, record company, record producer, recording artist and traveling musician. BMI. Publishes 10-20 songs/year; publishes 5 new songwriters/year. Works with lyricists and composers and teams collaborators. Pays standard royalty.
How to Contact: Prefers cassette with 1-4 songs and lyric sheet. SASE, "be sure to include sufficient postage." Reports in 1 month.
Music: Mostly rock, country and R&B; also new rock, blues, MOR, soul and top 40/pop. Recently published "I Hope You Don't Lose," (by Michael Jeffrey), recorded by Kenny Wayne/Ace Records; "You've Got Those Eyes," (by William Blacker); and "8 Days Inn," (by Mark Roman), both recorded by Billy Blast Band/Candy (new rock).
Tips: "Compare all songs with the hits of today. Make sure the song has a good hook and is commercially appealing. I don't need B sides or LP filler."

SWING & TEMPO MUSIC PUBLISHING INC., 1995 Broadway, New York NY 10023 (212)787-1222. Vice President: Bill Titone. Music publisher and record producer. BMI. Publishes 50 songs/year. Pays standard royalty.
How to Contact: Prefers 7½ ips reel-to-reel with 2-4 songs and lyric sheet. SASE. Reports in 1 month.
Music: Jazz and R&B.

TABITHA MUSIC, LTD., 39 Cordery Rd., St. Thomas, Exeter, Devon EX2 9DJ, England 44-0392-79914. Affiliate: Dice Music. Managing Director: Graham Sclater. Music publisher and record produc-

er. MCPS, PRS. Member MPA. Publishes 25 songs/year; publishes 4 new songwriters/year. Pays negotiable royalty; royalties paid directly to US songwriters.
How to Contact: Prefers cassette or videocassette with 1-4 songs and lyric sheet. SAE and IRC. Reports in 2 weeks.
Music: Mostly MOR and pop; also country, dance-oriented, Spanish, rock, soul and top 40. Recently published "Dance Your Body," (by John Artes/Alan Bradbury), recorded by Flic/Towerbell; "No Love," written and recorded by Andy Ford/Tabitha (rock); and "Counterfeit Love," (by J. Artes/A. Bradbury), recorded by Beat the Heat/Domino (dance).

TAL MUSIC, INC., 16147 Littlefield, Detroit MI 48238. (313)345-1995. President: Edith Talley. Vice President A&R: Harold McKinney. Music publisher and record company. BMI. Publishes 2 songs/year. Pays standard royalty.
How to Contact: Call or write first to arrange personal interview. Prefers 7½ ips reel-to-reel or cassette and lead sheet. SASE. Reports as soon as possible.
Music: Choral, church/religious, country, dance, easy listening, gospel, jazz, rock, soul and top 40/pop. Recently published "In and Out of Love" (by Dennis Talley), recorded by the B.T. Band/D.T. Records (top 40); and "Party" (by D. Talley), recorded by the B.T. Band/D.T. Records (soul).
Tips: "Make sure the songs are on a quality demo and that lyrics are properly structured to flow with one idea."

*TANNEN MUSIC COMPANIES, 1650 Broadway, New York NY 10019. (212)582-1667. Contact: Paul Tannen. BMI, ASCAP. Music publisher and manager.
How to Contact: Prefers cassette. SASE.
Music: Mostly rock, country and dance.

TATA GRANDE PUBLISHING CO., 2107 Ansbury Dr., Houston TX 77018. (713)686-5108. Contact: Gabe Tucker. Music publisher. BMI. Publishes varying number of songs/year. Pays "per our songwriters contract."
How to Contact: Prefers 7½ ips reel-to-reel or cassette with 2-4 songs and lyric sheet. SASE. Reports in 1 week.
Music: Country and dance-oriented. Recently published "Hold Me" (by Bill Nash), recorded by Eddy Arnold/RCA Records (MOR); "Sorry" (by Bill Bramlett), recorded by River Road Boys/Longhorn Records (MOR/dance); and "Low Down Laid Off Blues" (by Tommy Howser), recorded by River Road Boys/Longhorn Records (country).

DALE TEDESCO MUSIC CO., 17043 Romar St., Northridge CA 91325. (818)885-0775. Affiliates: Dale Tedesco Music (BMI) and Tedesco Tunes (ASCAP). President: Dale T. Tedesco. General Manager: Betty Lou Tedesco. Music publisher. BMI, ASCAP. Publishes 20-50 songs/year; publishes 20-35 new songwriters/year. Works with composers and teams collaborators. Pays standard royalty.
How to Contact: Prefers cassette with 1-3 songs and lyric sheet. SASE. Reports in 2 weeks.
Music: Mostly dance-oriented, R&B instrumentals and pop; also country, jazz, MOR, rock, adult contemporary and soul.
Tips: "Want a very commerical vehicle with excellent lyrics and melodies."

*TELSTAR MUSIC VERLAGS GMBH, Beethovenstr. 3, 8000 Munchen 2, West Germany. (089)530 91 35/6. Music publisher. Publishes 40 songs/year; publishes 20 new songwriters/year. Pays standard royalty.
How to Contact: Prefers cassette with 3 songs and lyric sheet. SAE and IRC.
Music: Mostly dance and pop.

GUTHRIE THOMAS PUBLISHING COMPANY, Box 1027, Hermosa Beach CA 90254. (213)375-8385. President: Guthrie Thomas. Music publisher, record company, record producer and record broker. BMI. Publishes "hundreds" of songs/year; publishes 9 new songwriters/year. Pays standard royalty.
How to Contact: Prefers cassette with 5 songs and lyric sheet. Does not return unsolicited material. Reports in 1 month.
Music: Bluegrass, blues, classical, country, easy listening, folk, jazz, progressive, R&B and rock.

*THREE HEARTS MUSIC, 11260 Goodnight Lane, Dallas TX 75229. (214)241-5182. President: Gordon Perry. ASCAP. Music publisher and record producer. Publishes 30 songs/year; publishes 4 new songwriters/year. Pays standard royalty.
How to Contact: Prefers cassette or 15 ips reel-to-reel with 4 songs. Reports in 4 weeks.
Music: Mostly pop/rock and R&B. Recently published "Rock & Roll Me Again," (by Marc Benno),

recorded by The System on MCA (R&B); "Saddest Victory," written and recorded by Sandy Stewart on Modern (pop/rock); "If Anyone Falls," (by S. Stewart & S. Nicks), recorded by Stevie Nicks on Modern (pop/rock).

TIMBERTREE PUBLISHING, Rt. 8, 425 Orebank Rd., Kingsport TN 37664. (615)323-3152. Manager: J.W. Hutchins. Music publisher. BMI. Member AFTRA. Publishes 6-12 songs/year; publishes 1 new songwriter/year. Pays standard royalty.
How to Contact: Write or call first about your interest. Prefers cassette with 1-2 songs and lyric sheet. Does not return unsolicited material . Reports "if it's found favorable."
Music: Country, country rock and country gospel. Recently published "Don't Promise Forever," recorded by Mel Russell/Mountain Empire; "Someone Has Took Her," and "Maybe I'll Do Better," recorded by J.W. Hutchins/Tandem (country).

*TIME MINSTREL MUSIC, Box 241, Cameron MO 64429. (816)632-6039. Director: E.K. Bruhn. BMI. Music publisher, record company (Crusader), record producer (Crusader Records & Tapes) and video firm (Masterpeace Productions). Publishes 50 songs/year; publishes 10 new songwriters/year. Pays standard royalty.
How to Contact: Prefers cassette, 7½ ips reel-to-reel or ½ or ¾" videocassette with 1-3 songs and "optional" lyric sheet or lead sheet. "Include short write-up about your interests." SASE. Reports in 6 weeks.
Music: Mostly gospel, MOR and pop/country; also "clean" comedy show material. Recently published "Dedicated," (by Betty Jackson), recorded by Hope Jackson on Crusader (gospel); "Lie to Me Honestly," (by Ben Van Den Hoogenband and Kopperfield), recorded by Elaine Sanders on Crusader (country); and "Not the Same Anymore," (by Betty Jackson and Kopperfield), recorded by Kopperfield on Crusader (country).
Tips: "Complete your song idea—finish the story."

*TOGER MUSIK GMBH, Pferggasse 8, 8000 Munich 45, West Germany. (089)311 30 63. Contact: Jerry Toger. GEMA. Music publisher and management/PR firm. Publishes 50 songs/year; publishes 2 new songwriters/year. Pays standard royalty. Affiliated publishing firm: Toso Music Verlag.
How to Contact: Prefers cassette and lyric sheet and lead sheet. SAE and IRC. Reports in 1-2 weeks.
Music: Mostly pop; also rock.

TOMPAUL MUSIC CO., 628 South St., Mount Airy NC 27030. (919)786-2865. Owner: Paul E. Johnson. Music publisher, record company, record producer and record and tape distributor. BMI. Publishes 150 songs/year; publishes 65 new songwriters/year. Works with composers and teams collaborators. Pays standard royalties.
How to Contact: Prefers 7½ ips reel-to-reel with 3-5 songs and lead sheet. SASE. Reports in 1 month.
Music: Mostly country, bluegrass and gospel; also church/religious, easy listening, folk, MOR, rock, soul and top 40. Recently published "Liquor by the Drink," and "Changing of the Time," written and recorded by Carl Tolbert/Stark (country gospel); and "Paul's Ministry," written and recorded by Earl Upchurch/Stark (country gospel).

TOP DOG MUSIC, 71 Boylston St., Brookline MA 02147. (617)739-2010. President: Fred Berk. Music publisher, recording company and production company. BMI. Publishes 20 songs/year; publishes 1 new songwriter/year. Pays standard royalties.
How to Contact: Prefers cassette or videocassette with 1-6 songs. Reports in 3 weeks "if interested."
Music: Mostly rock; also country, rockabilly, progressive, soul and top 40/pop. Recently published "Driven to Drinkin'," recorded by Kenny Girard; "Devil Whiskey," recorded by Cabin Fever; "Fashion Girls," recorded by Points North; and "Firebreather," recorded by Northern Tier.

TOSHIBA-EMI MUSIC PUBLISHING CO., LTD., 5-21 Toranomon 2-Chome, Minato-ku, Tokyo 105 Japan. (03) (593) 1731. International Repertoire Division: Shig Yutani. JASRAC. Music publisher and record producer. Publishes 150 domestic songs/year; publishes 10-20 new songwriters/year. Pays standard royalty or "60% in case there are 2 songwriters."
How to Contact: Prefers cassette or Beta/VHS videocassette and lyric sheet.
Music: Mostly pop, rock and jazz; also easy listening music. Recently published "Nagare No Mama Ni," written and recorded by Maki Asakawa on Toshiba-EMI (blues); "Guts Da Aka Hel," written and recorded by Tamegoro Azuma on Tokuma-Japan (pop); and "You're Gonna Need Me," (by Kazuo Takeda), recorded by Creation on Kind (rock).

TOULOUSE MUSIC PUBLISHING CO., INC., Box 96, El Cerrito CA 94530. Executive Vice President: James Bronson, Jr. Music publisher, record company and record producer. BMI. Member AIMP.

Publishes 1 new songwriter/year. Hires staff writers. Pays standard royalty.
How to Contact: Prefers cassette with 2-4 songs and lyric sheet. SASE. Reports in 1 month.
Music: Bluegrass, gospel, jazz, R&B and soul.

*TRAFIC ENRG., #111, 180 Dorchester E., Montreal, Quebec, H2X 1N6, Canada. Marketing Director: Hamel Robert. CAPAC, SDE. Record company. Publishes 50 songs/year; publishes 3 new songwriters/year. Pays standard royalty.
How to Contact: Prefers cassette. Does not return unsolicited material.
Music: Mostly rock and French music; also jazz and blues.

TRAGREY MUSIC PUBLISHING, 17 Ponca Trail, St. Louis MO 63122. (314)821-2741. Producer: Greg Trampe. Music publisher, record producer and recording studio. BMI. Member NARAS. Publishes 50 songs/year. Pays standard royalty.
How to Contact: Write about your interest or arrange personal interview. Prefers 7½ ips reel-to-reel, cassette or videocassette with 1-4 songs and lyric sheet. Does not return unsolicited material. Reports in 1 month.
Music: Mostly top 40/pop, progressive and rock; also blues, church/religious, country, dance-oriented, easy listening, gospel, jazz, MOR, R&B and background library.

*TRAIL GOSPEL MUSIC, Box 3860, Kingsport TN 37664. (615)246-3845. Contact: Tilford A. Salyer. BMI. Music publisher. Estab. 1984. Publishes 20 songs/year. Pays standard royalty. Affiliated publishing firm: Nightwatch Music Co.
How to Contact: Prefers cassette. "Do not send anything that must be returned." Does not return unsolicited material. Reports in 6 weeks.
Music: Mostly gospel. Recently published "In Heaven Mammas Won't Cry," (by Dennis Bradley), recorded by Inspirations and the Brotherhood Quartet on Canaan Trail (gospel); "Enjoying the Trip," written and recorded by Lewis Harrah on Hearthside (gospel); and "O What A Sermon He Preached," written and recorded by Lewis Harrah on Trail (gospel).

TREE PUBLISHING CO., INC., 8 Music Square W., Nashville TN 37203. (615)327-3162. Affiliates: Cross Keys Publishing, Twittybird Music Publishing, Uncanny Music, Warhawk Music, Tree/ Harlan Howard Songs, Kentree Music, Stairway Music and Meadowgreen Music. President: Buddy Killen. Vice Presidents: Donna Hilley and Roger Sovine. Professional Managers/Song Pluggers: Dan Wilson, Judy Williams, Walter Campbell, Chuck Howard and Jeff Sillbar. Music publisher. BMI, ASCAP. Member NMPA.
How to Contact: Call first "to see if we're currently accepting material," then submit demo tape. Prefers cassette with 1-3 songs. "Voice and guitar or piano accompaniment is sufficient. There is no need to have full orchestra or band on track. We just need to hear the words and melody clearly." SASE. Reports in 10-12 weeks. "We will not return material unless proper postage is on SASE."
Music: Country, MOR, rock (hard or country), soul, top 40/pop and contemporary Christian.

TROUBLE BOY MUSIC, Box 256277, Chicago IL 60625. (312)399-5535. President: Tom Petreli. Music publisher. BMI. Publishes 5-15 songs/year; publishes 4 new songwriters/year. Pays standard royalty.
How to Contact: Prefers cassette or videocassette with 2-4 songs and lyric sheet. SASE. Reports in 1 month.
Music: Mostly new wave; also all types. Recently published "Oh That Man," and "Woman," (by Nadine Herman), recorded by N. Herman; and "Death," (by Jamie Christian), recorded by Torn Orphan (rock).

TRUSTY PUBLICATIONS, Rt. 1, Box 100, Nebo KY 42441. (502)249-3194. President: Elsie Childers. Music publisher and record company. BMI. Member CMA and NSAI. Publishes 3-5 songs/ year; publishes 3-5 new songwriters/year. Pays standard royalty.
How to Contact: Prefers 7½ ips reel-to-reel or cassette with 2-4 songs and lead sheet. SASE. Reports in 1 month.
Music: Mostly country and country/pop; also blues, church/religious, disco, easy listening, folk, gospel, MOR, soul and top 40. Recently published "Goodbye," and "This World's Too Big," written and recorded by Randy Hudson.
Tips: "Performing artists get the best shot with us."

TUMAC MUSIC PUBLISHING, Box 384, Senola GA 30276. (404)599-6935. Affiliate: Shandy Guff (BMI). Professional Manager: Phil McDaniel. General Manager: Joe McTamney. Music publisher, record producer and record company. ASCAP. Publishes 6 songs/year; publishes 1-2 new songwriters/year. Works with composers and teams collaborators. Pays standard royalty.

How to Contact: Prefers cassette with 1-3 songs and lyric sheet. SASE. Reports in 3 weeks.

Music: Mostly pop, ballads and R&B; also dance, easy listening, jazz (country), MOR, rock (adult/country), top 40/pop and country. Recently published "Why Couldn't I Just Love You," (by Beneteau), recorded by Ron Pereault/Lauri Records; "I'm a Spinner of Rainbows," (by Sheehy), recorded by Don Buckley/Tumac Records; and "I Am a Fallen Angel," (by McDaniel), recorded by Peggy Stuart/Tumac Records.

Tips: "Listen to what is being recorded. Learn to rewrite songs that are incomplete and continuously rejected. Songs should be simple and memorable with conversational *lyrics*."

TUTCH MUSIC PUBLISHING, 25 Bob Hill Rd, Ridgefield CT 06877. (203)438-5366. Professional Manager: Richie Kidd. Music publisher, record company and record producer. BMI. Member CMA, CSA. Publishes 20-25 songs/year; publishes 5-10 new songwriters/year. Works with lyricists and teams collaborators.

How to Contact: Write first. Prefers cassette with 2 songs. SASE. Reports in 2 weeks.

Music: Mostly country and pop; also dance-oriented, MOR/AOR and R&B. Recently published "Heaven Tonight," (by Paul Hoichkiss/M. Terry), recorded by Stonewall Jackson/Universal Records; and "Texas Heartache #1," (by P. Hotchkiss), recorded by Mickey Gilley/Columbia/Epic Records and Steve Michaels/Gilley Records.

Tips: "Songs should have good solid lyrics with a message; good vocal on the demo."

*THE TWL PUBLISHING GROUP, Box 372, Flint MI 48501-0372. (313)695-3790. Attention: A&R Department. ASCAP, BMI, SESAC. Music publisher. Publishes 10-20 songs/year; publishes 2-3 new songwriters/year. Pays standard royalty. Affiliated publishing firms: Lady Marion, Isle Cay Music, Sunscape.

How to Contact: "Solicited submissions only!" Write and obtain permission to submit. Prefers cassette with 2-3 songs and typed lyric sheet. SASE. Reports in 16 weeks.

Music: Mostly "highly commercial" pop, country and easy listening. Recently published "Don't Stop," (by M. Grabowski), recorded by Cerberus on Starstream (rock); *Champion*, and "What a Friend," written and recorded by Ron Moore on Morada (pop).

Tips: "The writer must be flexible and have the (obvious) potential to write not just one commercial success but many. The writer must also have a great amount of patience."

TWO FIFTY NINE MUSIC, Box 157, Richmond VA 23201. (804)359-0001. Affiliates: Liberator Music (BMI), Brat Music (BMI). President: Barry Gottlieb. Music publisher, record company and record producer. BMI. Publishes 20 songs/year; publishes 3 new songwriters/year. Pays standard royalty.

How to Contact: Write first about your interest. Prefers cassette with 1-3 songs and lyric sheet. SASE. "VHS videocassettes accepted." Reports in 2 weeks.

Music: Mostly "mainstream" rock, also top 40/pop. Recently published "Keep It Tight," (by Garrett/Holmes), recorded by Single Bullet Theory/Nemperor Records (rock); "Boys in Dresses," (by Peeples/Null/Hawkins), and "Rebecca," (by Bonham), recorded by Suzy Saxon & The Anglos/Brat Records (rock).

*ULTRAZEN RECORD COMPANY, Box 50634, Dallas TX 75250. (214)747-5370. Producer: James Stearns. BMI. Music publisher, record company, record producer and promotion and distribution firm. Publishes 6-18 songs/year; publishes 3-6 new songwriters/year. Pays standard royalty.

How to Contact: Prefers cassette or VHS videocassette with 5 or more songs and lyric sheet. "Include a list of recording equipment used to make demo." SASE. Reports in 12 weeks.

Music: Mostly "new music," rock and alternative music; also urban contemporary, modern country and international. Recently published *Secret Nights* and "Some Brazil," recorded by John Q. Public (new music); "Cut Off Jeans," (by Jimmy Mack), recorded by Rudy Wilson on JAH (R&B soul novelty); and "Spiral Shadows," by Will Wesch , recorded by Ultrazen on Ultrazen (rock).

Tips: "Know thy market. Develop your style, be patient and persistent."

UNIVERSAL STARS MUSIC, HC-80, Box 5B, Leerville LA 71446. Affiliate: Headliner Music. National Representative: Sherree Stephens. Music publisher. BMI. Publishes 12-24 songs/year; publishes 1 new songwriter/year. Pays standard royalty.

How to Contact: Prefers cassette with 1-6 songs and lyric sheet. Does not return unsolicited material. Reports in 1 month, if interested.

Music: Bluegrass, church/religious, country, folk, gospel and top 40/pop. Recently published "Jesus Amazes Me" (by Sherree Stephens), recorded by J.J. & S. Stephens; and "Wait Till You See My Miracle Home," recorded by J.J. & S. Stephens (religious).

VAAM MUSIC, Suite C-114, 3740 Evans St., Los Angeles CA 90027. (213)664-7765. Affiliate: Pete Martin Music. President: Pete Martin. Music publisher and record producer. ASCAP, BMI. Publishes 8 new songwriters/year. Pays standard royalty.
How to Contact: Prefers 7½ ips reel-to-reel or cassette with 1-4 songs and lyric sheet. SASE. Reports in 1 month.
Music: Country, easy listening, MOR, rock (general), soul and top 40/pop.

TOMMY VALANDO PUBLISHING GROUP, Suite 2110, 1270 Avenue of the Americas, New York NY 10020. (212)489-9696. Affiliates: Revelation Music Publishing Corp. and Fiddleback Music Publishing Co., Inc. President: Tommy Valando. General Manager: Arthur Valando. Professional Manager: Paul McKibbins. Music publisher. BMI, ASCAP. Member NMPA. Publishes varying number of songs/year. Pays standard royalty. Printed material percentage—rate varies.
How to Contact: Call first. Prefers cassette with 1-3 "clear" songs. SASE. Reports "as quickly as possible."
Music: Mostly MOR; also children's, country, easy listening and gospel. Recently published "She's Out of My Life" (by Tom Bahler), recorded by Michael Jackson/Epic Records (MOR); "Send in the Clowns" (by Stephen Sondheim) (MOR); and "Not A Day Goes By" (by S. Sondheim), recorded by Carly Simon/Warner Bros. Records (MOR).
Tips: "We prefer writer to perform own song to give a true idea of what he or she is trying to convey. Demo does not have to be elaborate."

VALCO MUSIC CO., 1327 Cobb St., Kalamazoo MI 49007. (616)342-5328. Contact: Victor Taylor. Music publisher, record company and record producer. BMI. Pays standard royalty.
How to Contact: Prefers reel-to-reel or cassette with 2-10 songs and lyric sheet. SASE. Reports in 3 weeks.
Music: Mostly country; "some" R&B.

*****VALENTINE MUSIKVERLAG**, Box 7718, D-2000 Hamburg 20 West Germany. (040) 43.00.339. General Manager: Arno H.V. Vught Jr. GEMA. Music publisher, record company (Bandleader Records, Range Records) and record producer. Publishes 350 songs/year; publishes 12 new songwriters/year. Pays standard royalty.
How to Contact: Write or call first to arrange personal interview. Prefers cassette or VHS videocassette and lyric sheet or lead sheet. SAE and IRC. Reports in 2 weeks.
Music: Mostly MOR, rock and country; also folk, background music and film music. Recently published "Never Saw the Roses," (by Post/Hurley), recorded by Mary O'Hara on Valentine (folk); and "I Love," (written and recorded by T.T. Hall on Range (country).
Tips: "Send full lead sheet and information about the writer(s)."

JERRY VAMPLE PUBLISHING CO., Box 23152, Kansas City MO 64141. President: Jerry Vample. Music publisher, record company and record producer. BMI. Publishes 15 songs/year; publishes 15 new songwriters/year. Pays standard royalty.
How to Contact: Write first. Prefers 7½ ips reel-to-reel or cassette with 2-4 songs and lyric sheet. SASE. Reports in 1 month.
Music: Church/religious, easy listening and gospel.

VERDE VISTA MUSIC, Suite 4, 2383 Union St., San Francisco CA 94123. (415)567-6935. President: S. White. Music publisher. ASCAP. Pays standard royalty.
How to Contact: Prefers cassette with maximum 3 songs and lyric sheet. SASE. Reports in 2 months.
Music: Inspirational/religious, country, easy listening, folk, gospel and MOR.

VIC-RAY PUBLISHING, Box 2277, Gainesville FL 32602. (904)378-8156. General Manager: Charles V. Steadham, Jr. Professional Manager: Allen R. McCollum. Music Publisher. ASCAP.
How to Contact: Write first. Prefers cassette with 2-5 songs and lyric sheet. Does not return unsolicited material. Reports "as soon as possible."
Music: Bluegrass, country, dance, folk, MOR, rock (country), soul, top 40/pop, R&B and comedy. Recently released *Live and Kickin'* featuring "Whiskey 'fore Breakfast," " The Scotsman," "Bounty Hunter," " Elma Turl" and "Kentucky Song" (by Mike Cross), recorded live by Mike Cross/Sugar Hill Records (country/rock).
Tips: "Submit 1-3 commercially viable songs on cassette accompanied by typed lyric sheets."

VIN-JOY MUSIC, 872 Morris Park Ave., Bronx NY 10462. (212)792-2198. Contact: Vice President. Music publisher, record company and record producer. BMI, ASCAP. Pays standard royalty.
How to Contact: Write first. Prefers cassette with 2-4 songs. SASE. Reports in 3 weeks.
Music: Easy listening, MOR and top 40/pop.

THE VIRGINIA ARTS PUBLISHING COMPANIES, Box 800, Louisa VA 23093. (703)967-2245. Affiliate: Notegun Music (BMI). Creative Director: Paul Brier. Music publisher, record company, record producer, recording studio and jingle producer. BMI. Publishes 20-30 songs plus background scores of TV shows/year; publishes 3 new songwriters/year. Works with lyricists and composers and teams collaborators. Pays standard royalty.
How to Contact: Prefers 7½ or 15 ips reel-to-reel, cassette or videocassette with 2-4 songs and lyric sheet. SASE. Reports in 2 weeks.
Music: Mostly children's; also top 40, bluegrass, country, dance-oriented, jazz, rock, TV and film scoring. Recently published "Where Would You Like to Go," written and recorded by Adele Abrahamse/ Virginia Arts (children's); "Economics USA," (by Paul Brier) (theme song for PBS TV series); and "Forever," (by Wayne Gentry), recorded by Goldstar/Virginia Arts (pop/country).
Tips: "Because so much of our material goes into TV for children, we look for natural, flowing, conversational lyrics with universal appeal."

VOKES MUSIC PUBLISHING, Box 12, New Kensington PA 15068-0012. (412)335-2775. President: Howard Vokes. Music publisher, record company, booking agency and promotion company. BMI.
How to Contact: Submit cassette and lead sheet. SASE. Reports "a few days after receiving."
Music: Bluegrass, country and gospel. Recently published "Blue, Blue, Blue," "My Heart Needs an Overhaul Job," "If All the Other Girls Were Like You," "I'm Going Out of Your Arms," "Honky Tonk Row," "The Sycamore Tree," "It Takes Six Men to Carry a Man to His Grave (But Only One Woman to Put Him There)," "Break the News, But Break It Gently," "Empty Victory," "West of the Yukon," "I'm Falling in Love Again," "City of Strangers," "Back When You Loved Me," and "Saddest Man That Walks Upon Two Feet."

*WALK ON WATER MUSIC, Rt. 2, Box 566-H, New Braunfels TX 78130. (512)629-4396. Producer/Manager: Brian C. Carr. ASCAP, BMI. Music publisher, record company, record producer and recording studios. Publishes 12 songs/year; publishes 2 new songwriters/year. Pays standard royalty.
How to Contact: Write first and obtain permission to submit. Prefers cassette, 7½ ips reel-to-reel or VHS videocassette with 2-3 songs and lyric sheet. Does not return unsolicited material. Reports in 4-6 weeks.
Music: Mostly AOR-pop/rock, new music and country. Recently published "Every One's a Spy," (by Morgan/Stirm), recorded by Secrets on Walk on Water (rock); "No Daddy Lads," written and recorded by Rusty Lawrence on Walk on Water (country); and "Jamaican Beaches," written and recorded by Norm Allen on Walk On Water (rock).

WALKWOOD PUBLISHING CO., Box 24454, Nashville TN 37202. (615)320-5492. General Manager: Dave Woodward. Administrative Assistant: Terry Walker. Music publisher. Estab. 1984. Pays standard royalty.
How to Contact: Prefers cassette or videocassette with 1-4 songs and lyric sheet. SASE.
Music: Country.

*WARNER BROTHERS JAPAN, Akasaka Makabe Bldg. 4-3, Akasaka 3-chome Minato-ku, Tokyo 107 Japan. A&R: Mark Suzuki. Music publisher. Publishes 500 songs/year; publishes 20 new songwriters/year. Pays 60% royalty. Affiliated publishing firms: Mind Music Publisher, Kitty Music, Uni Japan Music, and Standard Music.
How to Contact: Prefers cassette and lyric sheet and lead sheet. Send writer's bio with submission. Does not return unsolicited material. Reports in 2-3 weeks.
Music: Mostly pop and rock. Recently published "Romantic Ga Tomaranai," (by Kyohei Tsutsumi and Takashi Matsumoto), recorded by CCB on Polydor (pop); "Mienai Tsubasa," (by Masao Urino and Kisaburo Suzuki), recorded by Maiko Itoh on CBS Sony (pop); and "Koishite Carribean," (by K. Tsutsumi and T. Matsumoto), recorded by Yoko Oginome on Victor (pop).
Tips: "Light pop suitable for the Japanese would be most appreciated."

*KENT WASHBURN PRODUCTIONS, 10622 Commerce Ave., Tujunga CA 91042. (818)382-7155. Affiliates: Monard Music (ASCAP) and Pencott Publishing (BMI). Contact: Kent Washburn. Music publisher and record producer. Publishes 20 songs/year; publishes 3 new songwriters/year. Pays standard royalty.
How to Contact: Prefers cassette with 1-5 songs and lyric sheet. SASE. Reports in 1 month.
Music: Church/religious, contemporary gospel, R&B, soul and top 40/pop. Recently published "Don't Burn No Bridges," (by Romain Anderson), recorded by Jackie Wilson/Brunswick Records (R&B); "Resurrection," (by Washburn and Lupton), recorded by Paul Davis/Spirit Records (gospel); and "You Don't Even Know My Name," (by Kelly), recorded by Free Love/EMKAY Records (R&B).

WATONGA PUBLISHING CO., 2609 NW. 36th St., Oklahoma City OK 73112. (405)942-0462. Music publisher. ASCAP. Pays standard royalty.
How to Contact: Prefers 7½ ips reel-to-reel and lyric sheet.
Music: Country, R&B, rock, soul and top 40/pop.

WATTS CITY PRODUCTIONS, 11211 Wilmington Ave., Los Angeles CA 90059. (213)566-9982. President/Producer: Joe Fornis. Music publisher, record company and record producer. ASCAP. Publishes 10 songs/year; publishes 2 new songwriters/year. Pays standard royalty.
How to Contact: Prefers cassette with 4-12 songs. SASE. Reports in 3 weeks.
Music: R&B, soul and top 40/pop.

WEB IV MUSIC PUBLISHING, 2107 Faulkner Rd. NE, Atlanta GA 30324. Contact: Lynn Carroll. Music publisher. Pays standard royalty.
How to Contact: Submit demo tape and lyric sheet. "Please don't call." Prefers cassette with 3-4 songs and lyric sheet. SASE. Reports in 1 month.
Music: R&B, rock and top 40/pop.

*WEEDHOPPER MUSIC, #811, 225 Oxmoor Circle, Birmingham AL 35209. (205)942-3222. President: Michael Panepento. BMI. Music publisher. Publishes 5-10 songs/year; publishes 3 new songwriters/year. Pays standard royalty.
How to Contact: Write or call first and obtain permission to submit. Prefers cassette or 15 ips reel-to-reel with 3 songs. SASE. Reports in 3 weeks.
Music: Mostly AOR, R&B/jazz and rock; also all others. Recently published "Kings of Steel," (by J. Batton/D. White), recorded by Assault on Polymusic (heavy metal); "Dancin in the Wrong Shoes," (by S. McDavid), recorded Ian Hunter on Polymusic Records (AOR); and "Who's Been Sleeping in My Bed," (by S. McDavid), recorded by Scotti on Polymusic Records (AOR).

WEEZE MUSIC CO., Steven Scharf Productions, Suite 4N, 61 Jane St., New York NY 10014. (212)929-2068. Contact: Steve Scharf. Music publisher and record producer. BMI. Publishes 0-1 song/year; publishes 0-1 new songwriter/year. "No advance—if song is recorded by me, the publishing is either 100% or split 50%-50%." Pays standard royalty.
How to Contact: Call first. Prefers 7½ ips reel-to-reel or cassette with maximum 4 songs and lyric sheet. SASE.
Music: Mostly rock and R&B; also top 40/pop and adult contemporary.
Tips: "Unless I'm going to produce the song on a record, I would have no use to publish it. I don't run covers to other artists, because I'm primarily a producer."

RON WEISER PUBLISHING, 6918 Peach Ave., Van Nuys CA 91406. (213)781-4805. Contact: Ron Weiser. Music publisher, record company and record producer. BMI. Publishes 30-50 songs/year; publishes 6 new songwriters/year. Pays standard royalty.
How to Contact: Prefers cassette and lyric sheet. Does not return unsolicited material.
Music: Mostly rockabilly; also country and R&B. Recently published "Marie Marie," (by D. Alvin), recorded by Blasters (rockabilly); "The Newest Wave," (by R. Campi), recorded by Ray Campi (rockabilly); and "Tennessee & Texas," recorded by The Magnetics (rockabilly).

*BERTHOLD WENGERT (MUSIKVERLAG), Hauptstrasse 100, 7507 Pfinztal-Soellingen, West Germany. Contact: Berthold Wengert. Music publisher. Pays standard GEMA royalty.
How to Contact: Prefers cassette and lyric sheet or lead sheet. SAE and IRC. Reports in 4 weeks.
Music: Mostly light music and pop.

BOBE WES MUSIC, Box 28609, Dallas TX 75228. (214)681-0345. Affiliate: Wes Music (ASCAP). Publishes 20 songs/year. President: Bobe Wes. Music publisher. BMI. Pays standard royalty.
How to Contact: Prefers 7½ ips reel-to-reel or cassette. "State if songs have been copyrighted and if you have previously assigned songs to someone else. Include titles, readable lyrics and your full name and address. Give the same information for your co-writer(s) if you have one. State if you are a member of BMI, ASCAP or SESAC. Lead sheets are not required. Comments will follow only if interested." SASE.
Music: Blues, country, disco, gospel, MOR, progressive, rock (hard or soft), soul, top 40/pop, polka, and Latin dance. Published "It Won't Seem like Christmas (without You)," recorded by Elvis Presley (pop/country); "Blue Memories," and "I Don't Know What I'm Doing," recorded by Dean Martin; "Our Last Rendezvous," recorded by Stu Phillips; "A Railroad Bum," and "You're Slipping Away from Me," recorded by Jim Reeves.

WEYAND MUSIC PUBLISHING, 297 Rehm Rd., Depew NY 14043. (716)684-5323. Proprietor: C.D. Weyand. Music publisher. ASCAP. Member NMPA and AGAC. Works with composers. Pays negotiable royalty.
How to Contact: "Only fully written piano and orchestral arrangements will be considered. Please—no *lead* sheets. SASE a must. All material submitted must be complete and copyrighted by the person(s) making submission. Write first—important!"
Tips: "Instrumental and orchestral works must be of a professional nature when recorded on tape or on cassette and must include a full 'conductor' score for proper review."

WHITE CAT MUSIC Box 3247, Shawnee KS 66203. (913)631-6060. Affiliate: Rocky Bell Music (BMI). Music publisher. Professional Manager: Frank Fara. Producer: Patty Parker. Publishes 60 songs/year; "50% of our published songs are from non-charted and developing writers." Pays standard royalty.
How to Contact: Arrange personal interview or submit cassette or VHS videocassette with 1-4 songs. SASE. Reports in 2 weeks.
Music: Mostly pop and country; also country and contemporary gospel. Recently published "Sweet Love Affair," (by Dan Bagan), recorded by Dave Atwood (country); "Two of Me," (by Marcia Singer and Brian Connie), recorded by Carolyn Justice (country); and "For All Those Years," (by Ron Jolemore), recorded by Peter Chipman (adult contemporary).
Tips: "Urgently need adult contemporary-pop songs for new Top 40 division servicing US and Canada. Save your ballads for top stars when you're established."

DON WHITE PUBLISHING/DEW MUSIC, 2020 Ridge Ave., Philadelphia PA 19121. (215)765-4889. Contact: P. Donald White. Music publisher, record company and record producer. ASCAP, BMI. Pays standard royalty.
How to Contact: Prefers 7½ ips reel-to-reel and lyric sheet. SASE. Reports in 3 weeks.
Music: Country.

WHITE WAY MUSIC CO., 65 W. 55th St., New York NY 10019. Affiliates: Sally Music (BMI) and Langley Music (BMI). President: Eddie White. Vice President: Peter White. Music publisher and record producer. ASCAP. Publishes 65 songs/year. Pays standard royalty.
How to Contact: Prefers cassette with 1-5 songs and lead sheet. SASE. Reports in 2 weeks.
Music: Bluegrass, blues, church/religious, country, easy listening, folk, gospel, MOR, rock, soul and top 40/pop.

*****WILCOX MUSIC ORGANIZATION**, 1099A Finchley Rd., London NW11, England. (01)455-6620. Managing Director: Herb W. Wilcox. PRS, MCPS, SGGB. Music publisher, record company (Zodiac Records) and record producer (Zodiac-Wilcox). Publishes 10 songs/year; publishes 6 new songwriters/year. Pays negotiable royalty.
How to Contact: Prefers cassette and lyric sheet. Reports in 4 weeks.
Music: Mostly jazz, rock and blues; also ballads, instrumentals and gospel.

SHANE WILDER MUSIC, Box 3503, Hollywood CA 90078. (818)891-1185. President: Shane Wilder. Music publisher and record producer. BMI. Publishes 30 songs/year; publishes 18 new songwriters/year. Pays standard royalty.
How to Contact: Prefers cassette or videocassette with 3-10 songs and lyric sheet. "Include SASE if you wish tape returned." Reports in 1 month.
Music: Mostly soft and country rock; also country, easy listening and MOR.

DON WILLIAMS MUSIC GROUP, Suite 809, 1888 Century Park. E., Los Angeles CA 90067. (213)556-2458. Affiliates: Redstripe Music (BMI), Pacific View Music (ASCAP), Wishbone Music (ASCAP) Aphrodite Music, Archimedes Music, Antoninus Music, Athena Music, Diogenes Music, Espeseth Music, Bag of Tunes, Inc., Big Elk Music, Aurelia Music, Aurelius Music, Happy Hooker Music, Hitman Music, Horseshoe Canyon Music, Jock Bartley Music, La De Ole Music, Poppa Willie Music, Roger Linn Music, Slap Shot Music, Thorkus Publishing Co., and Yano Music. Contact: Randall Rumage. Music publishing/administration and record production. BMI and ASCAP. Publishes 40 songs/year; publishes 10-20 new songwriters/year. Works with lyricists and composers and teams collaborators. Pays standard royalty.
How to Contact: Prefers "cued" cassette or videocassette with 2-3 songs and lyric sheet. Prefers studio produced demos. "Prefer VHS format if sending videocassette. List name, address and telephone number on package." SASE. Reports in 2-3 weeks.
Music: Mostly R&B, pop/rock and country; also easy listening, jazz, MOR. Recent publishing and administrative credits: "Water From the Moon," recorded by Melissa Manchester; "When The Boys Meet the Girls," recorded by Sister Sledge; and "Heart to Heart," recorded by Kenny Rogers.

THE WILLIS MUSIC COMPANY, 7380 Industrial Rd., Florence KY 41042. (606)283-2050. Affiliates: Huntzinger, Delhi Publications Inc., and Ralph Jusko Publications Inc. Editor: David B. Engle. Music publisher. Member SESAC. Publishes 10-12 new songwriters/year. Pays 10% of retail price or outright purchase.
How to Contact: Prefers cassette with 1-3 songs and lyric sheet. SASE. Reports in 12 weeks.
Music: Children's, choral, church/religious, classical, folk, gospel, jazz and pop. Recently published "Spending Christmas with You," (by Offutt) (pop); "Jesus, I Love You So," (by Galyean) (religious); and "Psalm 67," (by Edwards) (sacred solo).

WILSING MUSIC PUBLISHERS, Rt. 3, Box 100-N, Stuart VA 24171. (703)694-6128. Contact: Frank W. Singleton. Music publisher and record company (Spinn Records). BMI. Works with lyricists and composers and teams collaborators. Publishes 2 songs/year; publishes 2 new songwriters/year. Pays standard royalty.
How to Contact: Prefers 7½ or 15 ips reel-to-reel or cassette and lyric sheet. SASE. Reports in 1 month.
Music: Mostly country; also bluegrass, church/religious, folk and gospel. Recently published "Unclaimed Soldier," and "Live Here with the Blues," (by Tommy Riddle), recorded by T. Riddle/Spinn Records (country).
Tips: "Don't give up."

LUTHER WILSON MUSIC CO., 312 S. Mill St., Kansas City KS 66101. (913)621-1676. Contact: Luther Wilson Jr. Music publisher, record producer, music copying and record company (LWJ Records). ASCAP. Publishes 40-60 songs/year; publishes 6 new songwriters/year. Works with lyricists and composers and teams collaborators. Pays standard royalty.
How to Contact: Prefers cassette with minimum 4 songs and lyric sheet. SASE. Reports in 3 weeks.
Music: Mostly top 40 and R&B; also bluegrass, blues, country, dance-oriented, easy listening, folk, gospel, jazz, MOR, rock and soul. Recently published "Destination Motherland," "Mo Nise Si E (I Love You)," and "Lots of Love" (by Tanya Wood and Luther Wilson Jr.), recorded by Roy Ayers/Polydor Records (jazz/easy listening); and "I Am Here for You," (by Vickie D. Chiney/Luther Wilson, Jr.), recorded by E.L. Overton/Neco (R&B).
Tips: "Use good quality tapes and get voice out front. We openly encourage songwriters to send us material. Send only the songs with strong catchy hooks and lyrics. Listen to the radio for ideas."

WINDHAM HILL MUSIC, Box 9388, Stanford CA 94305. Music publisher, record company and record producer. BMI. Member NARAS, RIAA. Publishes 100 songs/year; publishes 12 new songwriters/year. Pays standard royalty.
How to Contact: Prefers cassette with 1-3 songs and lyric sheet. SASE. Reports in 1 month; "have been enormously backlogged."
Music: Mostly jazz; also classical. Recently published "Thanksgiving" (by George Winston); recorded by G. Winston/Windham Hill Records (jazz/AC); "On the Threshold of Liberty" (by Mark Isham), recorded by M. Isham/Windham Hill Records(jazz); and "New Electric India" (by Shadowfax), recorded by Shadowfax/Windham Hill Records (jazz).
Tips: "We are not looking for material by others for specific artists to perform. Our recordings are made by the songwriters themselves. We want composers/musicians."

WISHBONE, INC., Box 2631, Muscle Shoals AL 35662-2631. (205)381-1455. Affiliates: Song Tailors Music Co. (BMI), Terry Woodford Music (ASCAP), I've Got the Music Co. (ASCAP) and Creative Source Music (BMI). Professional Manager: Richard Butler. General Manager: Kevin Lamb. Music publisher, record producer, studio and video production company (Flying Colors Video). BMI, ASCAP. Publishes 100 songs/year; publishes 1-2 new songwriters/year. Hires staff writers. Pays standard royalty.
How to Contact: Prefers cassette with 2 songs and lyric sheet. SASE. Reports as soon as possible. Submit to the attention of Richard Butler.
Music: Mostly top 40/pop, country, dance-oriented, easy listening, MOR, progressive, R&B, rock and soul. Recently published "Let Your Heart Do the Talking," (by Robert Byrne/Alan Schulman), recorded by Anne Murray/Capitol (country/pop); "One More Try for Love," (by R. Bryne/Brandon Banes), recorded by Ronnie Milsap/RCA (MOR); and "She's Going Out of My Mind," (by Mac McAnally), recorded by Jimmy Buffett/MCA (country).
Tips: "Be up-to-date with various artists' styles."

WOODRICH PUBLISHING CO., Box 38, Lexington AL 35648. (205)247-3983. Affiliate: Mernee Music (ASCAP). President: Woody Richardson. Music publisher and record company. BMI. Publishes 25 songs/year; publishes 5 new songwriters/year. Pays 50% royalty less expenses.

How to Contact: Prefers 7½ ips reel-to-reel or cassette with 2-4 songs. Prefers studio produced demos. SASE. Reports in 1 month.

Music: Mostly bluegrass, black gospel and country; also blues, choral, church/religious, easy listening, folk, gospel, jazz, MOR, progressive, rock, soul and top 40/pop. Recently published "I'm Calling You," (by Rex Elliott), recorded by Bitter Creek (country); and "Jesus Is the Only Way," written and recorded by Wayne Yocum (bluegrass).

Tips: "Send a good demo and include a lyric sheet, but written music is not necessary."

WOOMERA MUSIC PTY., LTD., 17 Radford Rd., Reservoir, Victoria 3073 Australia. Affiliate/US: Jaspar Music. Affiliate/Canada: Banff & Melbourne Music. Director: Ron Gillespie. Music publisher and record company. APRA, AMCOS. Member AMPA. Will listen to songs submitted by US songwriters, but only when submitted through US publishing affiliates. Pays standard royalty; royalties paid to US songwriters through US publishing affiliate.

How to Contact: Prefers cassette with 2-5 songs and lyric sheet. Does not return unsolicited material. Reports if interested.

Music: Mostly country; also folk and top 40/pop.

WORD MUSIC, Division of Word, Inc., Box 1790, Waco TX 76796. (817)772-7650. Affiliates: Rodeheaver (ASCAP), Myrrh (ASCAP), Dayspring (BMI) and The Norman Clayton Publishing Co. (SESAC). A&R Dept.: Bubba Smith, Word Records, Suite 302, 2300 Hillsboro Rd., Nashville TN 37212. Music publisher and record company. ASCAP. Member GMA. Publishes 25 songs/year; publishes 1-3 new songwriters/year.

How to Contact: Prefers cassette with 1-3 songs and lead sheet. SASE. Reports in 10 weeks.

Music: Choral anthems and octavos; also children's, choral, church/religious. "Songs of a commercial, solo nature should not be submitted. Please send a demonstration tape of a choir singing your anthem to choral music editor."

Tips: "Lead sheets, or final form—anything submitted—should be legible and understandable. The care that a writer extends in the works he submits reflects the work he'll submit if a working relationship is started. First impressions are important."

*WORKSHOP RECORDS, Box 49507, Austin TX 78765. (512)452-8348. Contact: Dan Huckabee. Music publisher, record company and record producer. Publishes 10 songs/year; publishes 2 new songwriters. Pays standard royalty.

How to Contact: Write or call first and obtain permission to submit or to arrange personal interview. Prefers cassette or videocassette with lyric sheet. Reports in 1 week.

Music: Interested in all types of music. Recently published "Anawac," (by Conrad Diesler), "Cook Whip," (by Mike Light), and "Saguaro," (by Mike Stevens), all recorded by Austin Lounge Lizzards (humorous).

REX ZARIO MUSIC, 3010 N. Front St., Philadelphia PA 19133. (215)426-5682. Affiliates: Jack Howard Publishing (BMI), Seabreeze Music (BMI), Valley Brook Publishing (ASCAP), Arcade Music Co. (ASCAP). Production Manager: Lucky Taylor. Music publisher, record company and record producer. BMI. Publishes 15-25 songs/year. Pays standard royalty.

How to Contact: Prefers 7½ ips reel-to-reel or cassette with 4-6 songs and lyric sheet. SASE. Reports in 1 month.

Music: Country, MOR, rock and bluegrass. Recently published "Night Wine," (by Lucky Taylor, Doris Frye, Rex Zario and Jesse Rogers), recorded by J.Rogers/Arcade Records (MOR); "Go Man Go, Get Gone," (by L. Taylor, D. Frye & R. Zario), recorded by R. Zario/Rollercoaster Records in England (country); and "Worlds Apart," (by Ray Whitley & R. Zario), recorded by R. Whitley/Arzee (country).

Geographic Index_____

The US section of this handy geographic index will quickly give you the names of publishers located in the music centers of Los Angeles, Nashville and New York. The International section lists, geographically, markets for your songs in Australia, Canada, Germany, Japan, The United Kingdom and New Zealand.

Find the names of companies in this index, and then check listings within the Music Publishers section for addresses, phone numbers and submission details.

UNITED STATES

LOS ANGELES

Alexis
Arista Music Publishing Group
Arpell/Pinellas Music Publishing
Audio Music Publishers
Bal & Bal Music Publishing
Bee Ray Music
Beechwood
Black Stallion Contry Publishing
Boggy Depot Music
Tommy Boyce & Melvin Powers Music Enterprises
Bug Music
Creative Entertainment Corporation
De Walden Music International, Inc.
Dupuy Records/Productions/Publishing, Inc.
Eagle Rock Music Co.
Emandell Tunes
Equinox Music
Free & Show Music
The Fricon Entertainment Co., Inc.
Al Gallico Music Corp.
Gold Hill Music, Inc.
The Grand Pasha Publisher
Heaven Songs
Highest Praise Publishing
Kellijai Music Limited/ Ja'Nikki Songs
Kenwon Music
Keristene Music, Ltd.
Kingsport Creek Music Publishing
Stuart Lanis Music, Inc.
Loring Music Co.
Doug Moody Music
Michael O'Connor Music
O'Lyric Music
Peer-Southern Organization
Philippopolis Music
Players Press Inc.
Gary Revel Music

Rhythms Productions
Rockmore Music
Brian Ross Music
Sasha Songs, Unlimited
Scotti Brothers Music Publishing
Seventh Ray Publishing
Shaolin Music
Larry Shayne Enterprises
Slater Pichinson Music, Inc.
Snugglebush Music Co.
Sound Image Publishing
Sparrow/Birdwing Music
Street City Music
Dale Tedesco Music Co.
Guthrie Thomas Publishing
VAAM Music
Kent Washburn Productions
Watts City Productions
Ron Weiser Publishing
Shane Wilder Music
Don Williams Music Group

NASHVILLE

Acoustic Music, Inc.
Americus Music
Angelsong Publishing Co.
Another Ear Music
ATV Music Corp.
Beau-Jim Music Inc.
Believe'n Productions
Bil-Kar Music
Brandwood Music Inc.
Brentwood Publishing
Broadman Press
Calvary Music Group Inc.
Glen Campbell Music
Chip 'N' Dale Music Publishers
Covered Bridge Music
Denny Music Group
Door Knob Music Publishing, Inc.
The Drake Music Group
Dream City Music
Bobby Fischer Music
Al Gallico Music Corp.
Heavy Jamin' Music
James Hendrix, Composer and Publisher

Humanform Publishing Co.
Iffin Publishing Co.
Jackpot Music
Jaclyn Music
Dick James Organization
Gene Kennedy Enterprises, Inc.
Kimtra Music/Hatband Music
Jimmy Kish Music Publishing Co.
Lantern Music Publishing
Lodestar Music
Mr. Mort Music
Multimedia Music Group
My Dee Dee Music
Nashcal Music
Nautical Music Co.
Newcreature Music
Newwriters Music
Old Guide Publishing Inc.
Peer-Talbot Music Group
Power Play Publishing
Pyramid Records
Ric Rac Music
Rocker Music/Happy Man Music
Silkwood Music
Song Farm Music
Ben Speer Music
Spirit Horse Productions & Songs
Star Song Publishing Group
Sugarplum Music Co.
Sweet Singer Music
Tree Publishing Co., Inc.
Walkwood Publishing Co.

NEW YORK

Ace Adams Music/Adam Puertas Music
April Fool Music Publishing Company, Inc.
Bag Lady Music
Beautiful Day Music
Big Mike Music
Blue Umbrella Music Publishing Co.
Bush/Lehrman Productions
Camerica Music

Chargo Music
The Chu Yeko Musical Foundation
Copyright Service Bureau Ltd.
David Music
Earl Music Co.
Human Sound Music
Iguana Music, Inc.
Jeneane & Jude Music
Johnny Angel Music
Jondi Music
Largo Music, Inc.
Little Wizard Music Publisher
Mark of Aries Music
Mind to Sound Music Publishing
Ivan Mogull Music Corp.

Mustevic Sound Publishing
My! My! Music Publishing Inc.
Nonpareil Music
Notable Music Co. Inc.
NRP Music Group
Number 9 Musical Enterprises, Inc.
Pavillion Productions/Promotion, Inc.
Peer-Southern Organization
Personal Music Publishing Inc.
Prescription Company
Publishing Ventures
Gerald W. Purcell Associates
Raybird Music
Red Cow Music

Ren Maur Music Corp.
Ridge Music Corp.
Rockford Music Co.
Roperry Music
Salmo Music
Seixas Music
Silver Blue Productions, Ltd.
Sounds Ambient Music
Southern Crescent Publishing
Swing & Tempo Music Publishing Inc.
Tannen Music Companies
Tommy Valando Publishing Group
Vin-Joy Music
Weeze Music Co.
White Way Music Co.

INTERNATIONAL

AUSTRALIA

Chappell & Co. (Aust.) Pty.
Image Music Pty., Ltd.
Leosong Copyright Service Pty. Ltd.
Opal Records/Matrix Music
Rondor Music (Australia) Pty., Ltd.
Woomera Music Pty, Ltd.

CANADA

Alternative Direction Music Publishers
Attic Publishing Group
Berandol Music Ltd.
David Case Artist Productions, Inc.
Do Sol Publishing
Editions Nahej
Halben Music Publishing
Lapelle Music Publishing
Master's Collection Publishing & T.M.C. Publishing
Montina Music
Musicworks Publishing Company
Musinfo Publishing Group,
Northern Comfort Music
Noteworthy Publishing Co.
On Record Music
On the Wing Music Publishing Co.
People City Music Publishing Inc.
Praise Industries Corp.
S.M.C.L. Productions, Inc.
The S.R.O. Publishing Group
Sabre Music
Sidewalk Sailor Music
Sunbury/Dunbar Music

Canada, Ltd.
Trafic Enrg.

ENGLAND

Asterisk Music
Automatic Music Co. Ltd.
Bearsongs
Black Gold Record Productions, Ltd.
Button Music
Frank Chacksfield Music/ Eros Music
Complete Music Limited
Creole Music Ltd.
Cyhoeddiadau Sain
Express Music (London) Ltd.
Folktracks
Garron Music
Golden Arrow Records
Gwynn Publishing Co.
Hedley Music Group
Hollywood Music
Horizon Recording Studios, Ltd.
Jammy Music Publishers Ltd.
Jason Music/Mooreside Music
Keep Calm Music Limited
L E Music
Le Matt Music, Ltd.
Alfred Lengnick & Co. Ltd.
Marylebone Music
Mawson and Wareham (Music), Ltd.
Phab Music
R.J. Music
Rocksong
Satril Music
Sea Dream Music

Sound Diagrams Ltd.
Sunset Music
Tabitha Music Ltd.
Wilcox Music Organization

WEST GERMANY

Boogietunes Musikproduktion GmbH
R.D. Clevere Musikverlag
Cool Cat Music
CSB Kaminsky GmbH
Funkturm-Verlage Musikproduktion/Funky Records Produktion
Gorilla Musik-Verlag GmbH
Hammer Musik GmbH
Idee Musik Verlag
Juicy Peeple
Kroepcke Musikverlage
Mento Music Group KG
Roba Music
August Seith Musikverlage
Siebenpunkt Verlags GmbH
Storz Group of Companies
Telstar Music Verlags GmbH
Toger Music GmbH
Valentine Musikverlag
Berthold Wengert (Musikverlag)

ITALY

Conypol Music, Inc.

JAPAN

MCA Music Japan
Nichion, Inc.
Toshiba-EMI Music Publishing Co., Ltd.
Warner Brothers Japan

NEW ZEALAND

Pegasus Music

Record Companies

Record companies provide or arrange for the production, manufacture, distribution and marketing of recorded music. Even if many of these costs are eventually passed on to the consumer, record companies must initially risk thousands of dollars on a song or artist in hopes of seeing a profit. For this reason most record companies are extremely selective regarding the songs and artists they record.

To discover and develop new songs and artists a record company relies on its Artist & Repertoire, or A&R department. These people provide the record company's link with the creative side of the music business. Often they can be seen in a city's better known live music venues looking for new songs for artists already on their rosters, or new talent to sign. Obviously artists who are also songwriters are most in demand.

In addition to visiting clubs, record company A&R people often audition material and artists via the mail. If you are both a songwriter and an artist be sure to include a professional 8x10 glossy photo, a short biography and any clippings of reviews you might have, along with your demo submission.

The A&R Departments of foreign record companies as well as foreign branches of US record companies are also looking for new talent for their rosters. The steadily growing worldwide demand for American and English music represents ample justification for their efforts to sign foreign songwriters or license foreign product for release in their own country. To help songwriters and artists take advantage of this growing new market we have greatly increased the number of foreign record companies listed in this edition. Each has expressed a willingness to work with songwriters from other countries; some already have. Others indicate that they have not yet, but would be willing to listen to material from foreign songwriters. (See "Exploring the International Music Marketplace," by Brian Ross in the front of this edition.)

The geographic index at the end of this section will quickly refer you to record companies from such important music markets as Canada, England, Germany, Australia, and Japan; as well as the major music centers in the United States.

Use the two major music trade magazines, *Billboard* and *Cash Box*, to keep in touch with the activities of record companies both here and overseas.

A&M RECORDS, INC., 1416 N. La Brea, Hollywood CA 90028. (213)469-2411. Record company and music publisher (Almo Irving Music). Releases 100 singles and 50-60 albums/year. Works with artists and songwriters on contract.
How to Contact: "Direct all material through a publisher." Prefers studio produced demos. SASE.
Music: Pop, R&B and top 40. Recently released "Somebody," by Bryan Adams (pop/rock single); "Be Your Man," by Jesse Johnson (R&B/dance single); and "Oh Girl," by Boy Meets Girl (pop/rock single).
Tips: Looking for "female pop vocalists and male and female R&B artists. The more commercial and 'coverable,' the better."

A&M RECORDS INC., 595 Madison Ave., New York NY 10022. (212)826-0477. A&R Director: Nancy Jeffries. Record company.
How to Contact: Prefers cassette with 1-5 songs. SASE. Reports in 6-8 weeks.
Music: Dance-oriented, progressive, R&B, rock and top 40/pop.

A&M RECORDS OF CANADA, LTD., 939 Warden Ave., Scarborough Ontario M1L 4C5 Canada. (416)752-7191. Vice-President, A&R: Michael Godin. Record company and music publisher (Almo; Irving) Member CRIA. Works with artists on contract. Pays statutory rate to publishers for each record sold.
How to Contact: Prefers cassette or videocassette with 3-5 songs and lyric sheet. "Be aware of the time it takes to listen and respond. Be patient." SAE and IRC. Reports in 1 month.
Music: Progressive, rock and top 40/pop. Recently released *Synchronicity*, by the Police; *Body and Soul*, by Joe Jackson; and *Cuts Like a Knife*, by Bryan Adams (all rock LPs). Other artists include Payola$, Peter Pringle, The Arrows.

Tips: "Listen to the new records being released regularly and be aware of what you are competing with for radio airplay, sales, concerts, video, etc.

ABACUS, Box 186, Cedarburg WI 53012 (414)284-7058. Labels include Abacus and New Dawn Records. Producer: Bob Wiegert. Record company, record producer and music publisher (RobJen Music). Works with musicians on salary for in-house studio work; songwriters on contract. Pays negotiable royalty to artists on contract; statutory rate to publishers for each record sold.
How to Contact: Write first about your interest. Submit cassette only with 1-3 songs and lyric sheet. Does not return unsolicited material. Reports in 1 month.
Music: "If the song is commercial we will use it. Interested in top 40." Recently released "Hollywood" and "So Alone," both recorded by Leslie Ashford; and "Alabama," and "I Think It's Gonna Rain," by Stills & Scott (country rock singles). Other artists include Katie Mcgivin.

ALEAR RECORDS, Box 574, Sounds of Winchester, Winchester VA 22601. (703)667-9379. Labels include Master Records, Winchester Records and Real McCoy Records. Record company, music publisher (Jim McCoy Music, Clear Music, New Edition Music/BMI), record producer and recording studio. Releases 20 singles and 10 albums/year. Works with artists and songwriters on contract; musicians on salary. Pays 2% minimum royalty to artists; statutory rate to publishers for each record sold.
How to Contact: Prefers 7½ ips reel-to-reel or cassette with 5-10 songs and lead sheet. SASE. Reports in 1 month.
Music: Bluegrass, church/religious, country, folk, gospel, progressive and rock. Recently released "Like Always," by Al Hogan (country single); and *Mr. Bluegrass Here's to You*, by Carroll County Ramblers (bluegrass LP).Other artists include Alvin Kesner, Jubilee Travelers, Jim McCoy, and Middleburg Harmonizers.

ALFIE RECORDS, A division of Sound Syndicate, 1041 N. Orange Dr., Hollywood CA 90038. President: Al Durand. Labels include Sound Syndicate. Owner: Al Durand. Record company, record producer and music publisher. ASCAP. Works with artists and songwriters on record contract. Pays 8-10% royalty to artists on contract; statutory rate to publisher for each record sold.
How to Contact: Call first to obtain permission to submit, then submit cassette with 2-6 songs and lyric sheet. SASE. Reports in 3 weeks.
Music: Mostly MOR, R&B and country. Recently released "Plain Jane," by D. Johnson (MOR single).

*ALVERA RECORD AND MUSIC PUBLISHING, Box 9404, Tulsa OK 74157. (918)396-1333. President: Al Clauser. Labels include: AV C-International, Churchbell, Osage, Target, and Arrow. Record company, music publisher and record producer. Works with musicians/artists and songwriters on contract; musicians on salary for in-house studio work. Pays variable royalty to artists on contract.
How to Contact: Call first and obtain permission to submit or to arrange personal interview. Cassette only. SASE. "Submissions will not be returned if not covered by proper postage and stamped envelope. Reports in 4 weeks.
Music: Mostly country, gospel and rock; also pop and jazz. Recently released "I'd Rather Be An Old Time Christian," recorded by Al Clauser on Goodtimes (gospel LP); "Don't Monkey with Me," (by Goodman), recorded by Alvera on Osage (country single); and "Think About Love," (by Frisco), recorded by Alvera on Alvera Records (pop single). Other artists include Jeannie Reykert; June Harmer; Bob Cline; Rocky Caple; Umy Youngblood; Shirley Connett; Billy Dozier; Kate Smith; and Joe Schat.

AMALGAMATED TULIP CORP., 117 W. Rockland Rd., Libertyville IL 60048. (312)362-4060. Labels include Dharma Records. Director of Publishing and Administration: P. Johnson. Record company and music publisher. Works with musicians on salary; artists and songwriters on contract. Pays royalty to artists and songwriters on contract.
How to Contact: Prefers cassette with 2-5 songs. SASE. Reports in 1-3 months.
Music: Rock (progressive and easy listening) and top 40/pop. Recently released *Songs by the Group Milwaukee*, by Milwaukee; "Sunday Meetin' In the Morning," by Ken Little and the Band; and "This Feels Like Love to Me," by Animation.

*AMBIENT SOUND RECORDS, Box 499, Queens NY 11365. (718)969-2418. President: Marty Pekar. Labels include Human America Records. Record company and music publisher (Sounds Ambient/Human Sound). Releases 2 singles/year and 2 LP's/year.
How to Contact: "We look for songs, not artists. We have a full roster of artists who were popular in the '50s and early '60s. We are absolutely not interested in contemporary songs or artists."
Music: Other artists include The Jive Five, The Blue Emotions, Randy & The Rainbows, Baby Washington, The Mystics, and Johnnie & Joe.

*AMERICAN COMMUNICATIONS ENTERPRISES (A.C.E.), Box 444, Taylor MI 48180. (313)782-4973. President: John D. Lollio. Labels include A.C.E. Records, Mystery Train. Record company and record producer. Releases 5 singles/year and 2 LP's/year. Works with musicians/artists and songwriters on contract. Pays 6% royalty to artists on contract.
How to Contact: Prefers cassette and lyric sheet or lead sheet. SASE. Reports in 2 weeks.
Music: Mostly country and gospel. Recently released "Falling Water," recorded by Johni Dee on ACE (country single); "I'm Still Around," (by Carnes/Parson), recorded by W.P. Carnes on ACE (contemporary single); and *It Keeps Right on a Hurtin*, (by Tillotson), recorded by Johni Dee on ACE (country single and LP). Other artists include Marty Parker, David Atkins and Le Moine.

*AMERICAN COWBOY SONGS, INC., Rt. 7, Box 251, Mt. Juliet TN 37122. Chief Executive Officer: Alfred H. Le Doux. Record company, music publisher (Wyoming Brand Music/ASCAP, Prune Danish Music/BMI) and record producer. Releases 5 singles/year and 3 LP's/year. Pays statutory rate to publishers for each record sold.
How to Contact: Prefers cassette with maximum 3 songs and lyric sheet. SASE. Reports in 2 weeks.
Music: Mostly western theme ballads. "We specialize in songs with western themes." Recently released *Even Cowboys Like a Little Rock & Roll*, recorded by Chris LeDoux on American Cowboy (country LP); and *Summer Thunder*, and recorded by Tony Glenn on American Cowboy (western country LPs); and *You Make Me Feel Like a Winner*, by Kyle Evans (country).

AMERICAN MUSIC COMPANY/CUCA RECORD AND CASSETTE MANUFACTURING COMPANY, Box 8604, Madison WI 53708. Labels include American, Cuca, Jolly Dutchman, Age of Aquarius, Top Gun, Sound Power and Night Owl Records. Vice-President: Daniel W. Miller. Record company and music publisher (American Legend Music/ASCAP and Apple-Glass Music/BMI). Works with artists and songwriters on contract. Pays 10% royalty to artists on contract; 50% royalty to songwriters on contract.
How to Contact: Prefers reel-to-reel tape (but will accept cassettes) with 2-20 songs; include photo and complete information. SASE. "No calls, please." Reports within 6 months.
Music: "Old time" (polkas, waltzes), bluegrass, folk and ethnic. Recently released "Hupsadyna," by Styczynski (ethnic single); *Polka 76*, by Meisner (ethnic LP); and "Muleskinner Blues," by the Fendermen.
Tips: "Cuca has an extensive catalog and is known as "America's leading line of ethnic and old-time music." Artists may have a superior chance of having their material released on Cuca, American or affiliated labels, if they present *studio-quality* tapes of *all original* material."

AMHERST RECORDS, 1800 Main St., Buffalo NY 14208. (716)883-9520. General Manager: David E. Parker. Record company. Works with artists on contract.
How to Contact: Prefers cassette with 3 songs and lyric sheet. Does not return unsolicited material.
Music: Mostly R&B and pop; also all other styles.

*ANGELSONG RECORDS/MASTERSTOUCH RECORD PRODUCTION, 2714 Westwood Dr., Nashville TN 37204. (615)297-2246. President: Mabel Birdsong. Producer: Joe L. Wilson. Labels include Birdsong Records. Record company and record producer. Works with musicians/artists and songwriters on contract; musicians on salary for in-house studio work.
How to Contact: Write or call first and obtain permission to submit. Prefers cassette with maximum 4 songs and lyric sheet. Does not return unsolicited material. Reports in 2 weeks.
Music: Mostly gospel, country and MOR; also pop. Recently released *Easier*, (by Pam Tillis and Jan Buck), recorded by Sandy Craft on Angelsong (country LP and single). Other artists include Byron Walls; and Mike Jarmallo.

ANTHEM RECORDS OF CANADA, 189 Carlton St., Toronto, Ontario M5A 2K7 Canada. (416)923-5855. Managing Director: Val Azzoli. Press & Publicity: Lesley Clark. Record company. Releases 5-10 singles and 4-8 albums/year. Works with artists on contract.
How to Contact: Submit demo tape.
Music: Top 40 and AOR. Recently released *Grace Under Pressure*, by Rush/AOR Records (top 40/LP); and "New World Man," by Rush/AOR Records (top 40 single). Other artists include Coney Hatch, Ian Thomas, Moe Koffman and the Boys Brigade.

APEXTON RECORDS MFG. CORP., 44-27 Purves St., Long Island City NY 11101. (212)937-4038. Manager: Derek Ropiak. Record company, record producer, music publisher and pressing plant. Releases 5 singles and 2 albums/year. Works with artists on contract.
How to Contact: Call or write first to arrange personal interview. Prefers cassette with 1-3 songs and lyric sheet. Does not return unsolicited material. Reports in 2 weeks.

Music: Mostly R&B; also children's, dance-oriented and top 40/pop. Recently released "Can't Wait to Get to You," "Unity Rap," and "Education" (R&B singles).

APON RECORD COMPANY, INC., 44-16 Broadway, Box 3082, Long Island City, NY 11103. (212)721-5599. Contact: Don Zemann. Record company, record producer and music publisher (Apon Publishing Company). Releases 15 albums/year. Works with artists and songwriters on contract. Pays according to special agreements made with individual songwriters; statutory rate to publishers for each record sold.
How to Contact: Call first. Prefers 15 ips reel-to-reel or cassette with 1-12 songs and lyric sheet. SASE. Reports in 1 month.
Music: Church/religious, classical, dance-oriented, easy listening, folk and international. Recently released *Polka Fever*, by Slawko Kunst (polka LP); *Russian Gypsy Melodies*, by Sandor Lakatos (gypsy music LP); and *Budvarka*, by Alojz Skolka Ensemble (folk/pop LP).

*APPLE PYE RECORDS, INC., 128 Colonial Pkwy., Yonkers NY 10710. (914)337-4462. President: Charles Manna. Record company, music publisher (Charles Mann Publishing) and record producer (Manna Productions). Releases 5-10 singles/year and 2 LP's/year. Works with musicians/artists and songwriters on contract; musicians on salary for in-house studio work.
How to Contact: Prefers cassette with 3-5 songs and lyric sheet or lead sheet. Does not return unsolicited material. Reports in 5 weeks.
Music: Mostly rock, dance and jazz. Recently released "Today Frye," written and recorded by Tony Frye on Apple (rock EP). Other artists include Roxy Perry, Jo Ellen Arena, Nick Moroch, Anthony Frisaura, and Lori Allison.

APRIL RECORDS, Box 8263., Haledon NJ 07508. (201)942-6810. Labels include Alsaman, Arch, Kela, Afro and Cummings Records. Vice President: Gauntiett Cummings. Record company, music publisher (Dragon International Music) and record producer. Releases 3 singles and 1 album/year. Works with artists and songwriters on contract. Pays standard royalty to artists and to songwriters on contract; statutory rate to publishers for each record sold.
How to Contact: Prefers 7½ ips reel-to-reel, cassette or record with 3-5 songs and lyric sheet. SASE. Reports in 1 month.
Music: Mostly gospel. Recently released *Africa Stands Alone*, by Culture (reggae LP); *Africa Shall Stretch Forth Her Hands* and *Small Street at Her Hands*, by the Mighty Threes (reggae LPs); and "Being A Woman", by Yolanda Brown and Rhonda Durand (disco single).

AQUARIUS RECORDS, #200, 6265 Cote de Liesse Rd., St. Laurent, Quebec, Canada H4T 1C3. (514)735-5303. A&R/Promotion Director: Keith Brown. Record company and music publisher (Slalom/PRO, Crescent/CAPAC). Member CRIA and CIRPA. Releases 9 singles and 3 albums/year. Works with musicians/artists on contract.
How to Contact: Prefers cassette. "We pay postage on international submissions as non-Canadian postage is useless to us. No videocassettes or master tapes, please, due to customs." Reports in 2 months.
Music: Mostly rock/CHR, rock/AOR and metal rock; also comedy. Recently released "Lamp at Midnight,' (rock single) and *Boy in the Box*, (rock LP), written and recorded by Corey Hart on Aquarius; and *One for the Road*, (by C. Hart), recorded by April Wine (rock LP).

ARIANA RECORDS, 808 S. Pantano Rd., Tucson AZ 85710. (602)885-5931. President: James M. Gasper. Vice President: Thomas M. Dukes. Record company, record producer and music publisher (Myko Music). Releases 2 singles and 1 album/year. Works with artists and songwriters on contract; musicians on salary.
How to Contact: Prefers videocassette with 3-5 songs and lyric sheet. Does not return unsolicited material. Reports in 1 month.
Music: Mostly R&B, rock, dance rock, top 40/pop and AOR. Recently released *Extreme Closeup* by Gasper (pop rock LP and single); *Talk About Your Feelings*, by Mobile Cubes (new wave cassette); and *Stranger's Eyes*, by No Refunds (R&B cassette).
Tips: "Be professional, first impressions are very important."

*ARIOLA-EURODISC GMBH, Steinhauser Strasse 3, 8000 Munich 80, West Germany. (089)4136-442. A&R Managers: Holger J. Magnussen and Hans Scherer. Labels include Ariola, Arista, Hansa. Distributes Chrysalis Island, Bronze, Towerbell, Red Bus, CGD, Record Shack. Record company. Releases 270 singles/year and 250 LPs/year. Works with musicians/artists on contract; musicians on salary for in-house studio work.
How to Contact: Prefers cassette. SAE and IRC. Reports in 2 weeks.
Music: Mostly pop, MOR and rock.

*ARMINIA MUSIKPRODUKTION-ERICH STORZ, Box 1670, Hauptstr. 114, 3360 Osterode, West Germany. (05522) 7 30 41. Contact: Juditha Storz. Record company, music publisher and record producer. Works with musicians/artists and songwriters on contract.
How to Contact: Prefers cassette and lyric and lead sheets. SAE and IRC. Reports in 2 weeks.
Music: Mostly folk music; also pop.

ART ATTACK RECORDS, INC./CARTE BLANCHE RECORDS, Box 31475, Ft. Lowell Station, Tucson AZ 85751. (602)881-1212. Contact: William Cashman. Record company, music publisher (Cardio Music) and record producer. Member RIAA. Releases 2 singles and 2 albums/year. Works with artists on contract; mechanical rate negotiable.
How to Contact: Prefers cassette or videocassette with 3-10 songs and lyric sheet. "We are interested in the artist's performance abilities and would need to see photos and biographical materials as well as to hear the music." Does not return unsolicited material. Reports in 1 month.
Music: Rock, jazz and progressive.

*ASA RECORDS, 31 Music Sq. W., Nashville TN 37203. (615)242-1580. President: Albert Jolson. Labels include Masterlink Studios and Swanee Records. Record company and music publisher (Al Jolson's Black & White Music, Jolie House Music). Works with songwriters on contract; musicians on salary for in-house studio work.
How to Contact: Prefers cassette with any number of songs and lyric sheet. SASE. Reports in 4-6 weeks.
Music: Mostly country and rock.

*ASSOCIATED RECORDING COMPANIES, 2250 Bryn Mawr Ave., Philadelphia PA 19131. (215)477-7122. Labels include Pearl Harbor, Jaguar and Jenges Records (Shelton Associates). A&R Directors: Ted Brown, Leo Gaton. Administrator: Richard Jackson. Record company and music publisher. Releases 12 albums and 7 singles/year. Works with artists and songwriters on contract. Pays 6-9% royalty to artists on contract; standard royalty to songwriters on contract; statutory rate to publishers for each record sold.
How to Contact: Prefers 7½ ips reel-to-reel or cassette with 3-5 songs. SASE. Reports in 2 weeks.
Music: Mostly R&B and top 40; also easy listening, MOR, soul and pop. Recently released "Turnin Me Out," recorded by Lambchops/Pearl Harbor (R&B); "Wheres The Beef," recorded by Uptown Band/Pearl Harbor (R&B); and "Love Tonight," by David Simmons/Pearl Harbor (R&B).
Tips: "Looking for artists with a finished product. Very high royalty rate."

ATLANTIC RECORDING CORP., 9229 Sunset Blvd., Los Angeles CA 90069. (213)205-7460. Labels include Atco and Custom Records. Contact: Paul Cooper. Record company. Works with artists on contract.
How to Contact: Prefers cassette with 3-5 songs. SASE. Reports in 2 weeks.
Music: Blues, disco, easy listening, folk, jazz, MOR, progressive, R&B, rock, soul and top 40/pop.

ATTIC RECORDS LTD., 624 King St. W., Toronto, Ontario M5V 1M7 Canada. (416)862-0352. Labels include Attic and Viper. President: Al Mair. Record company and music publisher (Attic Publishing Group). Member CARAS, CRIA. Releases 25 singles and 30 albums/year. Works with artists and songwriters on contract. Pays statutory rate to publishers for each record sold.
How to Contact: Call first. Prefers cassette with 3-5 songs and lyric sheet. SAE and IRC. Reports in 3 weeks.
Music: Blues, MOR, rock and top 40/pop. Artists include Anvil, Bobcats, Nylons, Downchild, The Lincolns, Steppenwolf and Kamahl.

*AUTOGRAM & FOLK RECORDS, Burgstr.9, 4405 Nottuln 1, West Germany. (02502) 6151. A&R: Willy Schwenken. Labels include Autonom, Folk-Record, Autophon and Doctor. Record company. Releases 5 singles/year and 25 LP's/year. Works with musicians/artists and songwriters on contract. Pays "above average" royalty to artists on contract.
How to Contact: Prefers cassette with minimum 8 songs and lyric sheet. Returns unsolicited material. Reports in 1-10 weeks. "No stylistic imitations, no cover versions and no 'overproduced' music. Make it simple and impressive/expressive."
Music: Mostly ethnic folk music, blues and contemporary guitar music; also classical, contemporary, bluegrass and historical (reissues). Recently released *2nd Album for Sale*, written and recorded by Rod MacDonald on Autogram (LP); *Almost True*, (by Tony Maude), recorded by Tony Maude and Paul Millns on Autogram (LP); and *Wilder Falke*, (by Norbert Hanewinkel), recorded by Wanderfalk on Autogram (song/folk-rock LP). Other artists include Guthrie Thomas, Eric Bogle, Gerry Lockran, Harry Welling, Colum Sands and Toatendierk.

AXBAR RECORDS, Box 12353, San Antonio TX 78212. (512)735-3322. Labels include Axbar, JA-TO, Prince, and Charro. Producer: Joe Scates. Record company, record producer, music publisher (Axbar Productions/BMI and Axe Handle Music/ASCAP) and distributors of country music products. Member CMA. Releases 12-15 singles and 3-5 albums/year. Works with artists and songwriters on contract; musicians on salary. Works with composers. Pays 8% maximum royalty to artists on contract; statutory rate to publishers for each record sold.
How to Contact: Prefers 7½ ips reel-to-reel or cassette with 1-5 songs and lyric sheet. "Send us only your best shots." SASE. Reports ASAP. "but don't rush us."
Music: Mostly country, MOR crossover and comedy; also blues, western, and soft rock. "No hard rock or reggae." Recently released "Welcome Fool," by Mark Chesnutt (country single); "Heartache County," by Ray Sanders (country single); and "Once More With Feeling," by Carla Neet and Jerry Blanton (country pop single).
Tips: "We like interesting titles with good hook lines."

AZRA RECORDS, Box 411, Maywood CA 90270. (213)560-4223. Labels include Azra, Metal Storm, Iron Works, Soif, Not So Famous David's Records and Condor Classics. Artist Development: David T. Richards. Record company. Releases 5 singles and 10-20 albums/year. Works with artists on contract. "Artists usually carry their own publishing." Pays statutory rate to publishers for each record sold.
How to Contact: Prefers cassette or VHS videocassette with 3-5 songs and lyric sheet. Include bio and photo. SASE. Reports in 2 weeks.
Music: Mostly heavy metal, hard rock and novelty tunes. Recently released "Ground Zero," by Zak Daniels (rock single); and *Ample Destruction*, by Jag Panzer (heavy metal LP). Other artists include Centaurus, Evasions, Theodore Thrasher, Dark Angel, and Leige Lord.
Tips: "We prefer groups that have been together a minimum of 6 months and solo artists who can write for specific projects."

BAGATELLE RECORD COMPANY, 400 San Jacinto St., Houston TX 77002. (713)225-6654. President: Byron Benton. Record company, record producer and music publisher (Floyd Tillman Music Co.). Releases 20 singles and 10 albums/year. Works with songwriters on contract; musicians on salary for in-house studio work. Pays negotiable royalty to artists on contract.
How to Contact: Prefers cassette and lyric sheet. SASE. Reports in 2 weeks.
Music: Mostly country; also gospel. Recently released "This is Real," by Floyd Tillman (country single); "Lucille," by Sherri Jerrico (country single); and "Everything You Touch," by Johnny Nelms (country single). Other artists include Jerry Irby, Bobby Beason, Bobby Burton, Donna Hazard, Danny Brown and Sonny Hall.

BAL RECORDS, Box 369, La Canada CA 91011. (818)952-1242. President: Adrian Bal. Record company, record producer and music publisher (Bal & Bal Music). Releases 4 singles/year. Works with artists and songwriters on contract. Works with lyricists and composers and teams collaborators. Pays 10% minimum royalty to artists on contract; statutory rate to publishers for each record sold.
How to Contact: Prefers cassette or videocassette with 3 songs and lyric sheet. SASE. Reports in 1 month.
Music: Blues, church/religious, country, easy listening, jazz, MOR, R&B, rock, soul and top 40/pop. Recently released "Los Angeles," by Rich Martin (ballad single); and "Song of the Pasadena Rose Parade," by Jack Heinderich (swing single).

BAM-CARUSO RECORDS, 9 Ridgmont Rd., St. Albans, Herts., England. 44-0727-32109. Labels include Waldo's Records. General Manager: Phil Smee. Record company and music publisher (Waldo's Music). Releases 5 singles and 5 albums/year. Works with artists on contract; musicians on salary for in-house studio work. Pays 2-12% royalty to artists on contract; pays 6¼% to publishers for each record sold. Royalties paid directly to US songwriters and artists.
How to Contact: Prefers cassette with minimum 2 songs and lyric sheet plus photos if possible. Does not return unsolicited material. Reports in 1 month.
Music: Mostly 60s music—new psychedelic bands, beat groups, R&B, etc.; also folk. Recently released "The Whale Zoo," by Clive Pig & The Hopeful Chinamen (rock single); "Competition," by Rabbi Joseph Gordan (psychedelic single); and "London Swings at Happening 44," by various artists (60s psychedelic).
Tips: "We specialize in compilations of small bands. We will consider any good song or band that shows promise."

*BAYWEST RECORDS, Suite 398, 2554 Lincoln Blvd., Marina del Rey CA 90292. (213)822-7629. President: Ron Patton. Labels include Marina Sound Records. Record company, music publisher (Free

& Show Music/ASCAP, Honeymaker Music/BMI) and record producer. Releases 3 singles/year and 1 LP/year. Works with musicians/artists and songwriters on contract. Pays 6-8% royalty to artists on contract.
How to Contact: Write or call first and obtain permission to submit. Prefers cassette or videocassette with 3-5 songs and lyric sheet or lead sheet. Prefers studio produced demos. SASE. Reports in 4 weeks. "Have a finished product."
Music: Mostly R&B dance, pop/rock and contemporary Christian; also country/pop, gospel and jazz. Recently released "Hook Me," (by Laurie Roberts & Ron Patton), recorded by LeRoy "Ace" Miller on Baywest (R&B dance single); "Don't Blame Me," (by L. Roberts and R. Patton), recorded by Michael Peyser on Baywest (top 40 pop/rock single); and "Your Key Fits," (by L. Roberts, R. Patton, T. Elliot, and M. Peyser), recorded by Laurie Roberts on Baywest (R&B/pop dance LP).

BEAU-JIM RECORDS INC., Box 84, Hermitage TN 37076. President: Buddy Hooper. Record company, music publisher (Beau-Di Music Inc.), record producer and management firm. Member CMA, NSAI, NMA, AGAC. Releases 4 singles and 1 album/year. Works with artists and songwriters on contract.
How to Contact: Prefers cassette or videocassette with 3-5 songs on demo. SASE. Reports in 3 weeks.
Music: Country. Artists include Debbie Kay and Joe Neddo.

BEE HIVE JAZZ RECORDS, 1130 Colfax, Evanston IL 60201. (312)328-5593. Producer: Susan L. Neumann. Record company, music publisher and record producer. Works with musicians on salary; artists and songwriters on contract. Pays 50% royalty to artists on contract; standard royalty to songwriters on contract.
How to Contact: Write or call first. SASE. Reports in 1 month.
Music: Jazz only. Recently released *Baritone Madness*, by Nick Brignola (jazz LP); *Fire & Filibree*, by Curtis Fuller (jazz LP); and *Neo/Nistico*, by Sal Nistico (jazz LP).

*BELLA MUSICA TONTRAEGER GMBH, Albert-Schneble-Str. 2, 7582 Buehlertal, West Germany. (07223) 7014. Contact: Juergen Rinschler. Labels include Emston. Record company, music publisher and record producer. Releases 10 singles/year and 10 LPs/year. Works with musicians/artists and songwriters on contract.
How to Contact: Prefers cassette. SAE and IRC. Reports in 2 weeks.
Music: Mostly pop/rock and country (German); also jazz. Recently released "Ich Habe Keinen Job," written and recorded by Bernd Schoene on Bella Musica (rock single); *Concierto de Riga*, written and recorded by Andres El Leton (LP); and "Ich Danke," (by Reinhard Heck/Baldur Seifert), recorded by Juergen Thomas on Bella Musica (single). Other artists include Franco Cordi, Martina, Big Ben, Peter Patrick, Miki Reo, Andreas and Bernd, Theo Ansy, Andreas Fon and Manni Daum.

BELMONT RECORDS, 259A Beech St., Belmont MA 02178. (617)489-4510. Labels include Waverley Records. President: John Penny. Record company, record producer and music publisher (Penny Thoughts Music/BMI). Releases 8 singles and 2 LPs/year. Pays statutory rate to publishers for each record sold.
How to Contact: Write first. Prefers cassette. SASE. Reports in 2 weeks.
Music: Mostly country and contemporary; also country rock. Recently released "You're Making It Easy," and "Help Yourself To My Heart," by Liz Boardo (country singles); and *I Spent Last Year In A Barroom*, by Bayou Boys (country LP).

*BERANDOL RECORDS, 11 St. Joseph St., Toronto, Ontario M4Y 1J8 Canada. (416)924-8121. A/R Director: Tony Procewiat. Labels include Plumtree. Record company. Releases 5 singles/year and 5 LP's/year. Works with musicians/artists on contract. Pays variable royalty to artists on contract.
How to Contact: Prefers cassette with 2-5 songs. SAE and IRC.
Music: Mostly hip-hop, R&B and funk; also children's, classical and heavy metal. Recently released *Party Album* recorded by Beastles on Berandol (dance LP); *Magic Singing Animal Farm*, recorded by David Walden on Beandol (children's album); and "Scene Stealer," recorded by Jennifer Jones on Berandol (pop single). Other artists include Sandy Offenheim, Toronto Pops Orchestra, Rob Liddell, and Music Builders.

*BGM RECORDS, 10452 Sentinel, San Antonio TX 78217-3824. (512)654-8773. Contact: Bill Green. Labels include Zone 7. Record company, music publisher (Bill Green Music) and record producer. Releases 10 singles/year and 1-2 LP's/year. Works with songwriters on contract.
How to Contact: Prefers cassette. SASE. Reports in 4-8 weeks.
Music: Mostly contemporary country and traditional country. Recently released *Texas Songwriter*,

written and recorded by David Price on BGM (country LP); "Louisiana Heatwave," and "Me & Margarita," written and recorded by Bobby Jenkins on Zone 7 (country single). Other artists include Diana Hart, Jack Young, and Bo Garza.

BGS PRODUCTIONS LTD., Newtown St., Kilsyth, Glasgow G65 0JX, Scotland. 44-0236-821-81. Labels include Country House Records and BGS Chord. Directors: Dougie Stevenson and Bill Garden. Record company, record producer and music publisher (Garron Music). Member ARRS, PPL, MCPS. Releases 10 singles and 20 albums/year. Works with artists and songwriters on contract. Statutory rate paid to publishers for each record sold. Royalties paid to US songwriters and artists through US publishing or recording affiliate.
How to Contact: Prefers cassette or videocassette with 3-6 songs and lyric sheet. SAE and IRC. Reports in 1 month.
Music: Mostly country, MOR and folk; also dance-oriented, easy listening, gospel, jazz, R&B and top 40/pop. Recently released *You're My Hero*, by Lena Martell (country ballad LP); *From Scotland With Love*, by Sydney Devine (Scottish ballad LP); and "Going Home," by The Pipes & Strings of Scotland (instrumental single).
Tips: "We are more interested in artists who make live appearances."

BIG BEAR RECORDS, 190 Monument Rd., Birmingham, B16 8UU, England. 44-021-454-7020. Labels include Big Bear, Truckers Delight and Grandstand Records. A&R Director: Jim Simpson. Record company, record producer and music publisher (Bearsongs). Releases 12 singles and 6 albums/year. Works with artists and songwriters on contract. Teams collaborators. Pays 8-10% royalty to artists on contract; 6¼% to publishers for each record sold. Royalties paid directly to the songwriters and artists or through US publishing or recording affiliate.
How to Contact: Prefers 7½ or 15 ips reel-to-reel, cassette or videocassette and lyric sheet. SAE and IRC. Reports in 2 weeks.
Music: Blues, jazz, R&B and soul. Artists include Roy Ree & Energee, The Gangsters, Muscles and many jazz and bluesmen.

*****BIG L PRODUCTIONS LTD., INC.**, Box 2015, Garland TX 75041. President: Mr. Lonnie Salazar. Labels include I.C.A. Records, Hungry Bear Publishing, Happy Bear Publishing, Scuffy Bear Publishing. Record company, music publisher and record producer. Releases 15 singles/year and 6 LP's/year. Works with musicians/artists and songwriters on contract; musicians on salary for in-house studio work. Pays 6% royalty to artists on contract.
How to Contact: Call first and obtain permission to submit or arrange personal interview.

BIG MIKE MUSIC/BILDO MUSIC, 408 W. 115th St., New York NY 10025. (212)222-8715. Labels include Right On! and Big Mike Records. Manager: Bill Downs. Record company and music publisher. Releases 10 singles and 3 albums/year. Works with artists and songwriters on contract. Pays 4-6% royalty.
How to Contact: Prefers cassette or videocassette with 1-2 songs and lead sheet. Prefers studio produced demos. Does not return unsolicited material. Reports in 1 month.
Music: Mostly dance and rock "with big band backing." Recently released "Check It Out," by Tim Serrcy (soul/dance single); "Rocket Cruiser," (rock-soul single Europe); and "Loneliness is Driving Me Crazy," (gospel-soul single).
Tips: "Looking for high tech sound with drum breaks and passages for dancing between vocals."

BLACK ROSE RECORDS, 827 Meridian, Nashville TN 37207. (615)227-0920. A&R Director: David L. Bean. Labels include Roxy Records, Ritz Records, Limelight Records, and Gospeltone Records. Record company. Releases 10+ singles/year and 6+ LP's/year. Works with musicians/artists and songwriters on contract; musicians on salary for in-house studio work. Pays 5-12% royalty to artists on contract.
How to Contact: Prefers cassette or ¾" U-matic videocassette and lyric sheet. SASE. Reports in 1-6 weeks. Send "quality material with unique artists on a good demo."
Music: Mostly country and contemporary.

BLIND PIG RECORDS, Box 2344, San Francisco CA 94126. (415)526-0373. Contact: Edward Chmelewski. Record company, record producer and music publisher (Viper Music/BMI). Member NAIRD. Releases 3-6 albums/year. Works with artists on contract. Pays negotiable royalty to artists on contract; negotiable rate to publishers for each record sold.
How to Contact: Prefers cassette "unless artist has finished master tape (LPs only); then send copy of complete tape. Include lyric sheet and any promo/press material, including recent itineraries." SASE. Reports in 2-3 months.

Music: Blues, R&B (40s, 50s) and rock (rockabillly). Recently released *Everybody Needs It*, by Ellen McIlwaine and Jack Bruce (rock/rhythm LP); *It's All Rock & Roll*, by Steve Nardella (rock/rockabilly LP); and "Drinking TNT and Smoking Dynamite," by Buddy Guy and Jr. Wells.

*BLUE GEM RECORDS, C-114, 3740 Evans St., Los Angeles CA 90027. (213)664-7765. President: Pete Martin. Record company, music publisher (Vaam Music/BMI, Pete Martin/ASCAP) and record producer (Pete Martin Productions). Releases 12 singles/year and 5 LP's/year. Works with musicians/artists and songwriters on contract. Pays varying royalty to artists on contract.
How to Contact: Prefers cassette with 3 songs and lyric sheet. SASE. Reports in 3-4 weeks.
Music: Mostly pop/top 40, rock and country; also R&B. Recently released "Feeling Love," (by Ray Hepinstal), recorded by Ray & Annie on Blue Gem (top 40 single); "Do It," (by Reynolds Ohai), recorded by Reynolds Inc. on Hi-Lite (country single); and *Stoned Cold Heart*, (by Sherry Campbell and Robbie Campbell), recorded by Night Vision on Blue Gem (rock LP). Other artists include Kamie Redell, P.S. Lambert, Hot Flash, Cosme, Meza and Victoria Limon.

BLUE ISLAND RECORDS, Box 171265, San Diego CA 92117-0975. (619)477-4442. Contact: Donna Parker. Labels include BOB. Contact: Bob Gilbert. Record company, record producer and music publisher (Blue Island Publishing and Bob Gilbert Music). Releases 5 singles/year. Works with artists and songwriters on contract. Pays 12% royalty to artists on contract; statutory rate to publishers for each record sold.
How to Contact: Prefers cassette with 3 songs and lyric sheet. SASE. Reports in 3 weeks.
Music: Country, MOR, rock, top 40/pop and disco/dance.
Tips: "I review *every* song presented. So many in this industry only listen to selected songs per tape. I listen to all songs because you never can tell who will present the next hit song."

BLUE-TOWN, Suite 206, 1508 Harlem, Memphis TN 38174. (901)274-2726. A&R: Joe Kish, Reginald Eskridge. Record company, record producer and music publisher (GCS, Beth Ridge and Chartbound Publications). Releases 10 singles and 3 albums/year. Works with artists and songwriters on contract; musicians on salary for in-house studio work. Pays minimum 4% royalty to artists on contract; statutory rate to publishers for each record sold.
How to Contact: Prefers 7½ or 15 ips reel-to-reel with 3-7 songs and lyric sheet. Reports in 1 month.
Music: R&B, blues and soul. Recently released "Rainbow Love," by Howard Everett (soul single); and "Please Dad," by Miles Broom (R&B-soul single); "Strings of My Heart," (R&B/blues single), and *Stepping Out*, (R&B/blues album), by Eddie Mayberry.

BOLIVIA RECORDS, 1219 Kerlin Ave., Brewton AL 36426. (205)867-2228. Labels include Known Artist. President: Roy Edwards. Record company, record producer and music publisher (Cheavoria Music Co.). Releases 8 singles and 4 albums/year. Works with artists and songwriters on contract; musicians on salary for in-house studio work. Pays royalty to artists on contract; statutory rate to publishers for each record sold.
How to Contact: Write first. Prefers cassette with 3-5 songs and lyric sheet. SASE. Reports in 1 month.
Music: Country, easy listening, MOR, R&B and soul. Recently released "Make Me Forget," by Bobbie Roberson (country/MOR single); "Always and Forever," by Jim Portwood (country single); and "Music Inside," by Ray Edwards (MOR single).

BOOT RECORDS, LTD., 1343 Matheson Blvd. E., Mississauga, Ontario L4W 1R1 Canada. (416)625-2676. Labels include Boot, Cynda, Generation, Boot Master Concert Series and Boot International Records. General Manager: Peter Krytiuk. President: Jury Krytiuk. Record company and music publisher (Morning Music Ltd./CAPAC). Releases 40 singles and 20 albums/year. Works with musicians on contract. Pays 9-12% royalty to artists on contract; pays statutory rate to publishers for each record sold. "We operate on a lease basis with the artist paying the cost of the session."
How to Contact: Prefers 7½ or 15 ips reel-to-reel or cassette with 3-6 songs. "Prefers some originals and some standards." Does not return unsolicited material. Reports in 1 week.
Music: Mostly easy listening, folk and reggae/top 40; also classical, polka, bluegrass, country, dance, MOR and rock. Recently released "Draggin' This Ball & Chain," by Joe Firth/Paul Weber (country single; *Dobro Theatre*, by Mickey Andrews (MOR LP); and *Man From Snowy River*, by Bruce Rowlands (soundtrack LP).
Tips: "Enough material should be recorded so that we would be considering an LP, not just a 45."

The asterisk before a listing indicates that the listing is new in this edition. New markets are often the most receptive to freelance contributions.

BOUQUET RECORDS, Bouquet-Orchid Enterprises, Box 18284, Shreveport LA 71138. (318)686-7362. President: Bill Bohannon. Record company and music publisher (Orchid Publishing/BMI). Releases 3-4 singles and 2 albums/year. Works with artists and songwriters on contract. Pays 5% maximum royalty to artists on contract; pays statutory rate to publishers for each record sold.
How to Contact: Prefers cassette with 3-5 songs and lead sheet. SASE. Reports in 1 month.
Music: Religious (contemporary or country-gospel), country ("the type suitable for Barbara Mandrell, Ricky Skaggs, Lee Greenwood, etc.") and top 40/pop ("the type suitable for Kenny Rogers, Oak Ridge Boys, etc."). Recently released "Freeborn Man," by Bill Bohannon (country single); *Broken Pieces*, by Linda Hair Grissam (country gospel LP); and "A Little More Like You," by Adam Day (top 40/pop).
Tips: "Submit material that relates to what is currently being charted. A strong story line will help."

BOYCE & POWERS MUSIC, 12015 Sherman Rd., North Hollywood CA 91605. (213)875-1711. President: Melvin Powers. Record company and music publisher. Releases 12 singles/year. Works with songwriters on contract.
How to Contact: Prefers cassette or disc with minimum 3 songs and lyric sheet. SASE. Reports in 1 month.
Music: Country and MOR. Recently released "Who Wants a Slightly Used Woman?," by Connie Cato (country single); "Mr. Songwriter," by Sunday Sharpe (country single); and "Willie Burgundy," by Teresa Brewer (MOR single).

BOYD RECORDS, 2609 NW 36th St., Oklahoma City OK 73112. (405)942-0462. President: Bobby Boyd. Record company and music publisher. Releases 12 singles and 4 albums/year. Works with artists and songwriters on contract. Pays negotiable royalty to artists on contract; statutory rate to publishers for each record sold.
How to Contact: Prefers 7½ ips reel-to-reel with 3-12 songs and lyric sheet. "Do not send anything that has to be returned." Reports in 2 weeks "if we like it."
Music: Country, R&B, soul and top 40/pop. Recently released "Say You Love Me (One More Time)," by Dale Ward (country single); "There's No Way to Measure Love," by Dale Greear (country single); "Snap Your Fingers," by Debbie Smith (top 40 single); "One Teardrop at a Time," by Tina Camarillo (pop/country single); "Flip the Switch," by Cherie Greear; "Legends Never Die," by Jim Whitaker (pop single); and "We Miss You Red Sovine," by Marvin Ray (country LP and single). Other artists include Faye Haley and Bobby Barnett.

BRANCH INTERNATIONAL RECORDS, Box 31819, Dallas TX 75231. (214)750-0720. A&R: Mike Anthony. Record company. Works with artists and songwriters on contract. Pays 6-8% royalty to artists on contract; standard royalty to songwriters on contract.
How to Contact: Prefers cassette with 3-5 songs and lyric sheet. SASE. Reports in approximately 1 month.
Music: Country and gospel. Recently released "No Satin Sheets to Cry On," by Janet Cave; and "Old Man on the Square," by Charlie Seybert. Other artists include George Brazzel, Digger Wyatt and Jack Wyatt.

BRAT RECORDS, Box 157, Richmond VA 23201. (804)359-0001. President: Barry Gottlieb. Record company, record producer and music publisher. Releases 2 singles and 1 album/year. Works with musicians and artists on contract. Negotiates royalty paid to artists on contract. Pays statutory rate to publishers for each record sold; may pay lower rate for writer/performer.
How to Contact: Write first. Prefers cassette with 1-3 songs and lyric sheet. SASE. "VHS videocassettes accepted." Reports in 2 weeks.
Music: Mostly rock; also top 40/pop. Recently released "Boys in Dresses," (rock single), and *Suzy Saxon & The Anglos*, by Suzy Saxon & The Anglos (rock LP).

BREAD 'N HONEY RECORDS, Box 3391, Ventura CA 93006. (805)644-1821. Contact: Mark Craig. Record company, record producer and music publisher (Bread 'N Honey/ASCAP, and Honeybread/BMI). Releases 5-6 albums/year. Member GMA. Pays statutory rate to publishers for each record sold.
How to Contact: Prefers cassette and lyric sheet. SASE. Reports in 3 weeks.
Music: Gospel. Recently released "Silver And Gold," by Johnny Hall; "Walk On The Clouds," by Karen Kelley; and "The Very Best In Me," by Kathie Sullivan.

BRENTWOOD RECORDS, INC., Box 1028, Brentwood TN 37027. (615)373-3950. Contact: Music Editor. Record company and music publisher. Member GMA, CBA. Releases 5 albums/year. Works with musicians/artists and songwriters on contract.
How to Contact: Prefers cassette with 2-4 songs and lyric sheet. SASE.

Music: Mostly gospel. Recently released *Beside Still Waters*, recorded by Don March Orchestra on Brentwood (traditional gospel LP); *Good News Car Tunes*, (by Steve Elkins), recorded by Good News Travelers on Brentwood (children's gospel LP); and *A Fresh New Touch*, recorded by Bridge on Brentwood (adult contemporary gospel LP).

BRIDGES RECORDS, 9701 Taylorsville Rd., Louisville KY 40299. (502)267-9658. Labels include Rondo. Administrator: J.D. Miller. Record company, record producer and music publisher (Falls City Music Co.). Releases 10 singles and 5 albums/year. Works with artists and songwriters on contract; musicians on salary for in-house studio work. Pays statutory rate to publishers for each record sold.
How to Contact: Prefers cassette or videocassette with 1-4 songs and lyric sheet. SASE. Reports in 2 weeks.
Music: Mostly gospel and country; also church/religious and top 40/pop. Recently released "Hands Off the Merchandise," by Gaither Vocal Band/Benson Records (gospel); and "Little Gold Circles," by Mark Grey/Warner Bros. Records (country/pop).

*BRING OUT YOUR DEAD RECORDS, Box 160951, Sacramento CA 95816. (916)756-4941. Contact: Connie O'Donnell. Record company and music publisher (Dex Deadbolt Music). Releases 2 LP's/year. Works with musicians/artists on contract. Pays 10-15% royalty to artists on contract.
How to Contact: Prefers cassette with 3-4 songs. Does not return unsolicited material. Reports in 6 weeks.
Music: Mostly innovative rock. Other artists include True West, and 28th Day.

*BROADWAY/HOLLYWOOD PRODUCTIONS, Box 10051, Beverly Hills CA 90213-3051. (818)761-2646; (213)596-7666. Producer: Doris Chu. Labels include Take Home Tunes!, Original Cast, Broadway Baby, Disco and The C.Y. Musical Foundation. Record company, music publisher and record producer. Releases 2 LP's/year.
How to Contact: Prefers cassette or VHS videocassette with any number of songs. SASE. Reports in 20 weeks. "Film score writers needed. Send samples."
Music: Mostly rock/pop, music videos and films. Recently released "Dracula Goes to London," and "Mean City," (by Fred Grat), recorded by Sweet Chariot (music videos).

BUDDAH RECORDS, INC., 18th Floor, 1790 Broadway, New York NY 10019. Labels include Sutra and Beckett Records. Director: Phil Kahl.
How to Contact: Prefers 7½ ips reel-to-reel or cassette with 1-3 songs and lyric sheet. SASE. Reports in 1 month.
Music: Blues, choral, country, dance, easy listening, folk, jazz, MOR, progressive, R&B, rock, soul and top 40/pop.

BULL CITY RECORDS, Box 99, Rougemont NC 27572. (919)477-4077. Manager: Freddie Roberts. Record company, record producer and music publisher (Freddie Roberts Music). Releases 5 singles and 1 album/year. Works with artists and songwriters on contract; musicians on salary for in-house studio work. Pays 5-12% royalty to artists on contract; statutory rate to publishers for each record sold.
How to Contact: Write or call first about your interest or to arrange personal interview. Prefers 7½ ips reel-to-reel, cassette or videocassette with 1-5 songs and lyric sheet. "Submit a clear, up-to-date, demo." SASE. Reports in 3 weeks.
Music: Mostly country, MOR, top 40/pop; also bluegrass, church/religious, gospel and rock country. Recently released "I Can't Help It," by Rodney Hutchins (southern/rock single); *Forever Yours*, by Freddie Roberts (country LP); and "Shackled," by Doug McElroy (country/rock single). Other artists include Sleepy Creek, Eldorado, Billy McKellar, Les Howard Lacey, and Brenda Owens.

CALIFORNIA INTERNATIONAL RECORDS & VIDEO, Box 2818, Newport Beach CA 92663. President: Joseph Nicoletti. Creative Director: Cheryl Nicoletti. Record company, record producer and music publisher (ASCAP). Member NARAS, AFTRA and SAG. Releases 2-3 singles/year. Works with musicians on salary; artists and songwriters on contract. Pays 3-5% royalty to artists on contract; statutory rate to publishers for each record sold.
How to Contact: Write first. Prefers cassette or VHS videocassette with 1-3 songs and lead sheet. SASE. Reports in 1 month.
Music: Mostly gospel rock and R&B; also rock-oriented (new wave, pop, classical), great ballads, MOR and top 40/pop. Recently released "Let's Put the Fun Back in Rock 'n Roll," by Freddie Cannon and the Belmonts (pop/rock single) and "Child of Technology" and "Streetwise," by Joseph Nicoletti (pop rock/rock ballad singles).

THE CALVARY MUSIC GROUP, 142 8th Ave. N., Nashville TN 37203. (615)244-8800. Labels include Calvary, Lifestream, Frontline and Heart Song. Artist Development: Nelson S. Parkerson, Jr. Re-

cord company, record producer, music publisher and distribution company. Member GMA. Releases 10 singles and 12 albums/year. Works with artists and songwriters on contract. Pays statutory rate or negotiates rate to publishers for each record sold.
How to Contact: Prefers cassette or videocassette with 1-3 songs and lyric sheet. SASE. Reports in 1 month.
Music: Mostly gospel; also choral and church/religious.

CAMBRIA RECORDS & PUBLISHING, Box 374, Lomita CA 90717. (213)541-1114. Labels include Charade. Director of Recording Operations: Lance Bowling. Record company and music publisher. Releases 3 albums/year. Works with musicians on salary for in-house studio work. Pays negotiable royalty to artists on contract; statutory rate to publisher for each record sold.
How to Contact: Write first. Prefers cassette. SASE. Reports in 1 month.
Music: Mostly classical; also jazz, nostalgia and crossover. Recently published *Dizzy Fingers*, by Leigh Kaplan and Lincoln Mayorga (nostalgia duo-piano LP); *Piano Music of Madeleine Drung*, by L. Kaplan (classical LP); and *Shades of Drung*, by Kaplan, Shelly Manne, Bill Perkins, Ray Brown, Rod Shank (crossover LP).

CANDY RECORDS, 2716 Springlake Ct., Irving TX 75060. (214)790-5172. Labels include Sweet Tooth, Lil' Possum and Holli Records. General Manager: Kenny Wayne Hagler. Record company, record producer and music publisher (Sweet Tooth Music/BMI). Releases approximately 4 singles and 5 albums/year. Works with artists on contract. Pays 5% royalty to artists on contract; statutory rate to publishers for each record sold.
How to Contact: Prefers cassette with 3-4 songs and lyric sheet. "Send only quality material." SASE. Reports in 1 month.
Music: Mostly country and rock; also soul, blues and top 40/pop. Recently released "Green Eyes", by Reign (country rock single); *In Motion*, by Kenny Wayne & The Komotions (top 40 LP); *Born with the Blues and Raised on Rock and Roll*, by the Billy Blast Band (rock/blues LP); and " 'Bout a Broken Heart," by Michael Jeffrey (country single). Others artists include Carter Holcomb.

*****CANYON CREEK RECORDS**, Box 31351, Dallas TX 75231. (214)750-0720. A&R: Mike Anthony. Record company, music publisher (Eagle Nest) and record producer (Lemon Square). Estab. 1984. Works with musicians/artists and songwriters on contract. Pays 50% royalty to writers on contract.
How to Contact: Write first and obtain permission to submit.

CANYON CREST RECORDS, 6316 Garnet, Alta Loma CA 91701. (714)980-1716. A&R: Mark Larson. Record company and record producer. Estab. 1983. Releases 5 singles and 2 albums/year. Works with artists on contract.
How to Contact: Call first. Prefers 15 ips reel-to-reel, cassette or videocassette with 3-5 songs and lyric sheet. Does not return unsolicited material; "we will contact if interested. Reports in 2 weeks.
Music: Mostly progressive, jazz and international; also children's, church/religious, dance-oriented, easy listening, MOR, Spanish and top 40/pop.

CAPITOL RECORDS, INC., 1750 N. Vine St., Hollywood CA 90028. (213)462-6252. Record company. Releases 170 singles/year. Works with artists.
How to Contact: "Have an agent, manager or publisher submit material for you and submit the best-quality demo you can afford." SASE. Reports in 4-6 weeks.
Music: All styles. Recently released *Rhyme and Reason*, by Missing Persons (rock LP). Other artists include The Tubes, Billy Squier, Duran Duran and Queen.

CAPSTAN RECORD PRODUCTION, Box 211, East Prairie MO 63845. (314)649-2211. Contact: Joe Silver. Record company, music publisher and record producer. Works with artists on contract. Pays 3-5% royalty to artists on contract.
How to Contact: Write first about your interest. Prefers cassette with 2-4 songs and lyric sheet. SASE. Reports in 1 month.
Music: Country, easy listening, MOR, country rock and top 40/pop. Recently released "Dry Away the Pain," by Julia Brown (easy listening single); "Country Boy," by Alden Lambert (country single); "Yesterdays Teardrops," by The Burchetts (country single); and "Round & Round," by The Burchetts. Other artists include Shuri Castle, Skidrow Joe and Fleming.

CARGO RECORDS, Box 111, Massapequa NY 11758. (516)798-8236. Contact: Ron Seixas. Record company and record producer. Member AFMSC. Works with artists on contract. Pays variable royalty to artists on contract; statutory rate to publishers for each record sold.

How to Contact: Prefers cassette with minimum 2 songs and lyric sheet. SASE. Include photograph. Reports in 3 weeks.
Music: Rock music with top 40 appeal and new wave. Recently released "Tough Boy," (dance-rock single) and "Theory," (new wave single) by Seixas.

CAROUSEL RECORDS, INC., 1273½ N. Crescent Hts. Blvd., Los Angeles CA 90046. (213)650-6500. A&R: Stuart Lanis. Record company, music publisher and record producer. Works with musicians on contract.
How to Contact: Prefers cassette with 3-6 songs and lyric sheet. SASE. Reports in 3 weeks.
Music: Children's, country, church/religious, classical, easy listening, gospel, MOR, and top 40/pop.

CARRIE RECORDS CO., Box 90639, 902-42nd Ave. N., Nashville TN 37209. (615)321-3319. President: James Hendrix. Record company and music publisher (Mester Music/BMI). Releases 8 singles and 4 albums/year. Works with songwriters on contract. Pays 2-4% royalty to artists on contract; statutory rate to publishers for each record sold.
How to Contact: Prefers cassette with 3-4 songs and lyric sheet. SASE. Reports in 1 month.
Music: Church/religious, gospel, R&B, and top 40/pop. Recently released "An Everlasting Love," by Keith Chism; "Song of the Oppressed Christian," by Daniel Zimmerman; and "Thank You Jesus for Dying for Me" (by James Hendrix), recorded by Michael Hunter. Other artists include Cornelius Grant, Ellison Family, Michael Hunter and P-Wee & The Psalmsters.

CASA GRANDE RECORDS, Box 113, Woburn MA 01801. (617)933-1474. Labels include Don-Mar Records and Strawhut Records. Manager: Frank Paul. Record company, record producer and music publisher (Donna Music Publishing Company and Antone Music Publishers). Number of releases/year varies. Works with artists and songwriters on contract. Pays 3% minimum royalty to artists on contract.
How to Contact: Prefers cassette with 3-6 songs and lyric sheet. SASE. Reports as soon as possible.
Music: Children's, country, easy listening, folk, gospel, MOR, Spanish, R&B, rock, soul and top 40/pop. Recently released *Happy Birthday Baby*, by TuneWeavers (R&B LP and single).

CASTELAR RECORDS, 2322 S. 64th Ave., Omaha NE 68106. (402)554-0123. President: Nils Anders Erickson. Record company, record producer, music publisher and sound and light company. BMI. Releases 12 singles and 6 albums/year. Works with artists and songwriters on contract; musicians on salary for in-house studio work. Pays 20-80% royalty to artists on contract; statutory rate to publishers for each record sold.
How to Contact: Write first. Prefers cassette with 1-3 songs. SASE. Reports in 1 month.
Music: Mostly rock; also all other types. Recently released *Hit & Run* and *Tom Ware* (rock LPS); and *Dark Nights* (rock LP-EP).

*CENTURY RECORDS, INC., 1429 Hawthorne St., Pittsburgh PA 15201. (412)781-4557. President: Edward J. Moschetti. Labels include Star Records. Record company. Works with songwriters on contract.
How to Contact: Prefers cassette. SASE.
Music: Country.

CHA-CHA RECORDS, 15041 Wabash Ave., South Holland IL 60473. (312)339-0307. Labels include Cha-Cha (rock) and Cap (country). President: Donald L. De Lucia. Record company, record producer, and music publisher (Don-Del Music/BMI and Don-De/ASCAP). Releases 2 singles and 2 albums/year. Works with artists on contract. Pays 3%/record to artists on contract; statutory rate to publishers for each record sold.
How to Contact: Prefers 7½ ips reel-to-reel with 4-6 songs and lyric sheet. SASE. Reports in 1 week.
Music: Country, rock, and top 40/pop. Recently released *99 Chicks*, by Ron Haydock and the Boppers (rock LP). Other artists include Don Glasser and Lois Castello.

CHAPMAN RECORDS, 228 W. 5th St., Kansas City MO 64105. (816)842-6854. Contact: Chuck Chapman. Record company and music publisher. Releases 15 singles and 12 albums/year. Works with artists on contract. Pays 5-50% royalty to artists on contract, pays statutory rate to publishers for each record sold. Charges for some services: "We charge for recording services for music that we don't publish."
How to Contact: Prefers cassette or videocassette with minimum 3 songs. Prefers studio produced demos. SASE. Reports in 1 month.
Music: Mostly country; also bluegrass, choral, church/religious, classical, dance, easy listening, folk, gospel, jazz, MOR, progressive, rock, soul and top 40/pop. Recently released "Nothing Between," by S. Frank Frazier (black gospel single); "I'm So Glad," by Ira Wilkes (R&B single); and "Love Affair," by Bruce Ghale (country single).

*CHARTA RECORDS, 44 Music Sq. E., Nashville TN 37203. (615)255-2175. President: Charlie Fields. Labels include Delux and Sun-Rize. Record company, music publisher and record producer. Releases 10 singles/year and 6-8 LPs/year. Works with musicians/artists on contract; musicians on salary for in-house studio work. Pays standard royalty to artists on contract.
How to Contact: Call first to arrange personal interview. Prefers cassette or reel-to-reel with 2-3 songs and lyric sheet and lead sheet. Does not return unsolicited material. Reports in 2-3 weeks.
Music: Mostly MOR, blues and country. Recently released "Don't Talk to Me," (by Micky Jupp), recorded by Wendel Adkins on DeLux (MOR single); "Memory of You," (by Paul Hotchkiss and M.E. Terry), recorded by Ken Scott on Charta (MOR single); and "Manatte," written and recorded by David Walsh on Charta (single). Other artists include The Marshall & The Lady, Donna Darlene, Jack Elliott, Steven & Debby Brown, and The Rhoads.

CHATTAHOOCHEE RECORDS, 5300 Sepulveda Blvd., Van Nuys CA 91411. (213)788-6865. Contact: Chris Yardum. Record company and music publisher (Etnoc/Conte). Member NARAS. Releases 4 singles/year. Works with artists and songwriters on contract.
How to Contact: Prefers cassette with 2-6 songs and lyric sheet. SASE. Reports in 2-3 weeks.
Music: Top 40/pop.

CHERRY RECORDS, 9717 Jensen Dr., Houston TX 77093. (713)695-3648. Manager: A.V. Mittelstadt. Record company, record producer and music publisher (Publicare). Releases 5 singles and 2 albums/year. Works with artists and songwriters on contract. Pays 5% minimum royalty for artists on contract; statutory rate to publishers for each record sold.
How to Contact: Prefers cassette with 1-5 songs and lyric sheet. SASE. Reports in 3 weeks.
Music: Mostly country; also R&B, rock, soul and top 40/pop. Artists include Randy Cornor.

THE CHU YEKO MUSICAL FOUNDATION, Box 10051, Beverly Hills CA 90213. (818)761-2646. Branch: Box 1314, Englewood Cliffs NJ 07632. (201)224-5811. Messages: (201)567-5524. Labels include The Chu Yeko Musical Foundation, Take Home Tunes! Record Co., Original Cast Records and Broadway Baby Records. Producer: Doris Chu. Record company and music publisher (Broadway/Hollywood International Music Publishers/ASCAP). Releases 5-10 albums/year. Works with songwriters on contract. Teams collaborators. Pays 1-10% royalty to artists on contract; statutory rate to publishers for each record sold.
How to Contact: Prefers cassette or VHS videocassette with any number of songs and lyric sheet. SASE. Reports in 1 month.
Music: Pop, rock, R&B and musicals in entirety.
Tips: "Need female singer or rock/pop/group touring L.A./CA area."

*CIMIRRON/RAINBIRD RECORDS, 607 Piney Point Rd., Yorktown VA 23692. (804)898-8155/595-4191. Professional Managers: Lana Puckett and Kim Person. Record company, music publisher (Hot Knobs Music), record producer (Humdinger Productions) and Wistaria Recording Studio. Releases 5 singles/year and 2 albums/year. Works with musicians/artists and songwriters on contract.
How to Contact: Write or call first and obtain permission to submit. Prefers cassette or Beta videocassette with 1-5 songs and lyric sheet. SASE. Reports in 3-4 weeks. Also submit bio, credits and glossy photograph.
Music: Mostly country, easy listening and pop; also gospel, bluegrass and children's music. Recently released "Love Ain't What It Seems," (by L. Puckett & K. Person), recorded by Lana Puckett on Cimirron (pop single); and "Hard Habit to Break," written and recorded by Lana Puckett on Cimirron (country single). Other artists include Kim Person and Bill Gurley.

CINNAMON RECORDS, Box 4029, Winston-Salem NC 27105. (919)723-1822. President: Joseph Daniels. Record company, record producer and music publisher (Jo-Wee Publishing House). Releases 2 singles/year. Works with artists on contract; musicians on salary for in-house studio work.
How to Contact: Prefers cassette or ¾" U-matic videocassette with 3-8 songs and lyric sheet. Reports in 1 month.
Music: Mostly reggae; also R&B and soul. Recently released "I Like Reggae," by Cinnamon Reggae (reggae single). Other artists include Jo Dread, Truth & Rights, Connie Florance, Janice Miller, and The Dread Orchestra.

CLARUS MUSIC, LTD., 340 Bellevue Ave., Yonkers NY 10703. (914)591-7715. President: S. Fass. Record company, record producer and music publisher. Member MENC, NYSSMA, RIAA. Releases 1-2 albums/year. Works with artists and songwriters on contract. Pays current royalty rate to artists on contract; statutory rate to publishers for each record sold.
How to Contact: Prefers cassette with 4-10 songs and typed lyric sheet. SASE. Reports in 1-3 months.
Music: Children's.

CLAY PIGEON RECORDS, Box 20346, Chicago IL 60620. Labels include Clay Pigeon International and Patefonas Records. President: V. Beleska. A&R Director: Rudy Markus. Record company. Releases 3-5 singles and 2-5 albums/year. Works with musicians on salary; artists and songwriters on contract. "Royalties on records start at 2% of retail. All acts negotiate with us individually. Four percent is common. Royalties paid to publishers are often at 2¢ per selection, per record sold."
How to Contact: "Inquire by mail first (do not phone), describing yourself and your material in some depth. We cannot consider any material without a written query." Prefers 7½ ips reel-to-reel, cassette or disc with 1-5 songs. SASE. Reports in 2-8 weeks.
Music: Avant-garde, new wave, MOR, progressive, rock and top 40/pop. Recently released "Tribe of Dolls," by Vyto B (modern rock single); "Band That Never Made It," by Bena Neva Mada (modern rock single); and "I'm Sure Now," by Seetz Executive (MOR ballad).
Tips: "Cover letter should explain songwriter's background, type of songs written and why songs are unique enough to be listened to.

CLOUDBURST RECORDS, Box 31, Edmonton KY 42129. (502)432-3183. President: Rev. Junior Lawson. Record company and music publisher (Holy Spirit Music). Releases 3 singles and 4 albums/year. Works with songwriters on contract. Pays 4¢ royalty to artists on contract.
How to Contact: Call first. Prefers 7½ ips reel-to-reel or cassette and lyric sheet. SASE. Reports in 3 weeks.
Music: Mostly southern gospel; also country, gospel, MOR and progressive. Recently released *Introducing the Cornerstones* and *Extra! Extra!*, by The Cornerstones (southern gospel LPs); and *Old-Fashioned Ways*, by the Sounds of Joy (southern gospel LP). Other artists include The New Apostles and The Helmsmen.

COAST TO COAST RECORDS, Box 8958, Arlington Station, Jacksonville FL 32239. Record company and music publisher (Frankly Music/BMI, J.D. Music/ASCAP). Releases 2 albums/year. Works with musicians on contract and songwriters on salary.
How to Contact: Prefers cassette with 2-3 songs and lyric sheet. Does not return unsolicited material. Reports in 2 weeks.
Music: Disco, MOR and R&B.

*****COMMA RECORDS & TAPES**, Postbox 2145, 6078 Neu-Isenburg, West Germany (6102)5640. General Manager: Roland Bauer. Labels include: Big Sound, Comma Int'l, Max-Banana-Tunes. Record company. Releases 25 singles/year and 20 LP's/year. Works with musicians/artists and songwriters on contract. Pays 7-10% royalty to artists on contract.
How to Contact: Prefers cassette, reel-to-reel or U-matic or VHS (PAL) videocassette and lyric sheet. Reports in 2-3 weeks.
Music: Mostly pop, disco, rock, R&B and country; also musicals.

*****COMMAND RECORDS**, Box 1869, Hollywood CA 90078. (213)564-1008. Vice President/CEO: Kent Washburn. Record company, music publisher (Highest Praise Publishing) and record producer (Mighty "T" Productions). Releases 4 LP's/year. Works with musicians/artists and songwriters on contract. Pays 5-10% royalty to artists on contract.
How to Contact: Prefers cassette with 4 songs and lyric sheet. SASE. Reports in 8 weeks.
Music: Mostly gospel, R&B and pop. Recently released *Words Can't Express*, written and recorded by P. Nicholas on Command Records (gospel LP); *Dedicated*, recorded by P. Nicholas on Command Records (gospel LP); and *This Is My Story*, recorded by Vernessa Mitchell on Command Records (gospel LP). Other artists include Rodney Friend.

COMMON CAUSE RECORDS, 880 NE. 71st, Miami FL 33138. (305)759-1405. Labels include Common Cause Records. President: Carlos Oliva. Record company, record producer and music publisher (Avilo Music/BMI, Oliva Music/SESAC, Santa Clara Music/ASCAP). Member NARM. Releases 10 singles and 10 albums/year. Works with artists on contract. Pays 10-15% royalty to artists on contract; statutory rate to publishers for each record sold.
How to Contact: Prefers cassette and lyric sheet. Include bio and/or resume. SASE. Reports in 6 weeks.
Music: Dance-oriented, MOR, Spanish and rock. Recently released *Friends*, by Friends, *Paco-Paco*, by Paco-Paco; and *Hay Carino*, by Clouds (all Latin contemporary LPs). Other artists include Mary Pacheco, Marco Rizo, Nelson Galanos, and Orquesta La Tremenda.

COMPO RECORD AND PUBLISHING CO., Box 15222, Oklahoma City OK 73115. (405)677-6448. President: Yvonne De Vaney. General Manager: Sonny Lane. Record company and music publisher (Country Classics Music/BMI). Releases 4-6 singles and 1-2 albums/year. Works with artists and songwriters on contract. Pays 5% minimum royalty to artists and songwriters on contract; statutory rate to publishers for each record sold.

How to Contact: Prefers cassette with 4-8 songs and lead sheet. SASE. Reports in 3 weeks.

Music: Country, gospel and MOR. Recently released "Teach Me To Live Without You" and "I'm Just Fool Enough," by Yvonne DeVaney (country singles); and "Take Me Back Into Your World," by Gary McCray (country single).

Tips: "We like simple melodies with strong lyrics."

COMSTOCK RECORDS LTD., Box 3247, Shawnee KS 66203. (913)631-6060. Canadian, United States and European distribution on Paylode & Comstock Records. Production Manager/Producer: Patty Parker. President: Frank Fara. Record company, music publisher (White Cat Music/ASCAP, Rocky Bell Music/BMI), record producer, and management and promotions firm. Releases 24-30 singles and 2-4 albums/year. Works with artists and songwriters on contract; musicians on salary. Pays royalty to artists on contract; standard royalty to songwriters on contract; pays statutory rate to publishers for each record sold. Member CMA, GMA, ACME, MACE, BCCMA, BBB, and British & French C&W Associations.

How to Contact: Arrange personal interview. Prefers cassette with 1-4 songs. "Enclose stamped return envelope if cassette is to be returned." Reports in 2 weeks.

Music: Adult contemporary and pop country; also country and contemporary gospel. Recently released "Heartbeat," by Priscilla Wright (AC single); *This Song's For You*, by Beth Owen (contemporary gospel lP and single); and *Endlessly*, by Anne Lord (country LP and single). Other artists include Peter Chapman, Pegasus, R.J. McClintock, Doug Peters, Don Malena, Bobby Gibson and the O'Roark Brothers.

Tips: "We have an immediate need for top 40/pop and adult contemporary material for our new USA/Canada division, Paylode Records."

COUNTERPART CREATIVE STUDIOS, 3744 Applegate Ave., Cincinnati OH 45211. (513)661-8810. President: Shad O'Shea. Record company, music publisher (Hurdy Gurdy Music Co., Counterpart Music/BMI) and jingle company. Member RIAA. Releases 24 singles and 6 albums/year. Works with musicians on salary; artists and songwriters on contract. Pays 5% royalty to artists on contract; statutory rate to publishers for each record sold.

How to Contact: Write first. Prefers 7½ ips reel-to-reel with 1-2 songs. Does not return unsolicited material. Reports in 1 week.

Music: Bluegrass, blues, children's, choral, church/religious, classical, country, dance, easy listening, folk, gospel, jazz, MOR, progressive, rock, funk, soul and top 40/pop. Recently released "McLove Story," by Shad O'Shea/Plantation Records; "Hot Fun in the Summertime," by Dayton/Capitol Records; "Freakazoid" and "Wet My Whistle," by Midnight Star/Warner Bros. Records; and "Ready for the Saddle," by David Anderson/Fraternity Records.

COUNTRY INTERNATIONAL, 23 Music Circle E., Nashville TN 37203. (615)327-4656. President: Sherman Ford. Vice President, Promotion: Tom Dean. Record company. Works with artists and songwriters on contract; musicians on salary for in-house studio work. Pays statutory rate to publishers for each record sold.

How to Contact: Prefers 7½ ips reel-to-reel or cassette with 1-4 songs and lyric sheet. SASE. Reports in 2 weeks.

Music: Country.

*COUNTRY SHOWCASE AMERICA, 11350 Baltimore Ave., Beltsville MD 20705. (301)937-7201. President: Francis Gosman. Record company. Releases 2 singles/year. Works with musicians/artists on contract. Pays negotiable royalty to artists on contract.

How to Contact: Prefers cassette and lyric sheet. SASE.

Music: Mostly country. Recently released "Sweet Yesterdays," (by Marrino & Gellspie), recorded by Country Cavalier on CSA (country single). Other artists include Johnny Anthony.

COUNTRY STAR PRODUCTIONS, 439 Wiley Ave., Franklin PA 16323. (814)432-4633. Labels include Country Star, Process and Mersey Records. Contact: Norman Kelly. Record company and music publisher (Country Star/ASCAP, Process and Kelly/BMI). Releases 10-15 singles and 3-5 albums/year. Member AFM and AFTRA. Works with artists and songwriters on contract; musicians on salary for in-house studio work. Works with lyricists and composers. Pays 6% royalty to artists on contract; statutory rate to publishers for each record sold.

How to Contact: Write first. Prefers 7½ ips reel-to-reel or cassette with 1-4 songs. SASE. Reports in 2 weeks.

Music: Mostly country; also bluegrass, easy listening, folk, MOR, rock and top 40/pop. Recently re-

leased "Porch Light," by J.C. Young (country single); "It's Pickle Time Again," by Bonnie Baldwin (country single); and "A Step from Your Heart," by Denver Bill (country single).
Tips: "Send only your best efforts."

COURRIER RECORDS, 1650 Broadway, New York NY 11021. (212)247-2159. Labels include Overseas Wax. President: Morton Wax. Record company, record producer and music publisher (David Music, Inc./BMI). Works with artists and songwriters on contract. Pays standard royalty to artists on contract; statutory rate to publishers for each record sold.
How to Contact: Prefers cassette and lyric sheet. Does not return unsolicited material. Reports ASAP.
Music: All kinds.

COWBOY JUNCTION PUBLISHING CO., Highway 44 W., Lecanto FL 32661. (904)746-4754. Contact: Elizabeth Thompson. Record company, record producer and music publisher. Releases 3 singles and 2 albums/year. Pays 50% royalty to artists on contract.
How to Contact: Prefers cassette with 1-4 songs and lyric sheet. SASE. Reports in 1 month.
Music: Country, gospel and bluegrass. Recently released *The Story of Freda and Bud*, by Buddy Max (country LP); *Carrots and Taters*, by Leo Vargason (bluegrass LP); and "Sweet Little Butterfly," by B. Max.

*COWGIRL RECORDS, Box 6085, Burbank CA 91510. Contact: Vice President. Record company and music publisher (Kingsport Creek). Works with musicians/artists and songwriters on contract; musicians on salary for in-house studio work.
How to Contact: Prefers cassette or videocassette with any number of songs and lyric sheet or lead sheet. Does not return unsolicited material.
Music: Mostly country and gospel. Recently released *Tennessee Cowgirl*, "Wash Your Hands," and "Only Life I Know," written and recorded by Melvena Kaye.

THE CREATION CO., 939 Felix Ave. lwr, Windsor, Ontario N9C 3L2, Canada. (519)256-6604. Labels include JLT Records, Sky Light Records and Alternative Records. President: Jim Thomson II. Record company, record producer and music publisher (On the Wing Music). Releases 3 singles and 2 albums/year. Works with artists and songwriters on contract. Pays statutory rate or negotiates rate for first use.
How to Contact: Prefers cassette or videocassette with 4-6 songs and lyric sheet. "Send bio." Does not return unsolicited material. Reports in 3 weeks "if interested."
Music: Mostly gospel, MOR and rock; also bluegrass, blues, children's, church/religious, easy listening, folk, jazz, progressive, country, soul and top 40/pop. Recently released "Old Gypsy Moon," by Jim Thomson II (swing/MOR single); *Raw*, by Preflyte (heavy metal LP); and *War & Peace*, by Jim Thomson II (folk-rock LP).

CREOLE RECORDS LTD., 91/93 High St., Harlesdew, London NW10, England. 44-01-965-9223. Labels (England): Creole, Ecstacy, Dynamic, Polo, Cactus, Replay, Blast from the Past. Labels (US): Creole Music, Inc. Managing Director (record demos): Bruce White. Publishing Manager (publishing demos): Steve Tantum. Record company, record producer and music publisher. Member BPI, PP and IRPI. Releases 18 singles and 10 albums/year. Also works with artists and songwriters on contract. Works with lyricists and composers and teams collaborators. Pays 10-16% royalty to artists on contract; 6¼% to publishers for each record sold.
How to Contact: Prefers cassette or videocassette with 2-4 songs and lyric sheet. SAE and IRC. Reports in 2 weeks.
Music: Pop, rock, dance, ballads, R&B and reggae. Recently released *Call Me*, by Sylvester (pop/dance LP); "White Horse," by Laid Back (pop/dance single); and "That Feeling," by Zoot Alors (pop/dance single). Other artists include The Pinkees, Pete McDonald, City IQ, Liquid Gold, Ellie Hope, Adrian Baker, Bob Puzey (writer), Terry Hanton, Enigma, Ricky Anderson, Peter Green, and The Pioneers.

CRITIQUE RECORDS INC., 400 Main St., Reading MA 01867. (617)944-0423. Professional Manager: Harry King. Record company, record producer and music publisher (Solid Smash). Releases 10 singles and 2 albums/year. Works with artists on contract.
How to Contact: Prefers cassette or videocassette with 1-3 songs and lyric sheet. SASE. Reports in 1 month.
Music: Mostly R&B and dance; also country, rock, soul and top 40/pop. Recently released "Dear Michael," by Kim Fields (pop/R&B single); and "Breaking Up Is Hard on You," by American Comedy Network (pop single).

CURTISS RECORDS, Box 4740, Nashville TN 37216. (615)865-4740. President: Wade Curtiss. Record company and producer. Works with artists and songwriters on contract. Pays 8¢/record royalty to artists on contract; 2½¢/record royalty to songwriters on contract.
How to Contact: Prefers 7½ ips reel-to-reel with 2-8 songs and lead sheet. SASE. Reports in 3 weeks.
Music: Bluegrass, blues, country, disco, folk, gospel, jazz, rock, soul and top 40/pop. Recently released "Book of Matches," by Gary White; and "Rompin' " and "Punsky," by the Rhythm Rockers.

DA CAR RECORDING, 297 Rehm Rd., Depew NY 14043. (716)684-5323. Proprietor and Producer: C.D. Weyand. Record company and music publisher (Weyand Music Publishing/ASCAP). Member NMPA, Songwriter's Guild and Harry Fox Agency. Works with composers. Works with artists and songwriters on contract as negotiated; pays negotiated rate. Releases 2 singles/year.
How to Contact: Write first, then submit professional, studio produced demo tape. Prefers cassette or 7½ ips reel-to-reel on 5-inch reel with 1-5 songs and leader tape between songs. "Full piano arrangement *must* be included with tape or cassette. With orchestral or instrumental works—full score is a *must* for proper review of material. Only copyrighted material will be listened to; all other will be returned." SASE.
Music: Mostly classical; also dance, easy-listening and jazz. "No rock music—please." Recently released "A Father for Christmas," by Gertrude and Carlton Weyland (Christmas) and "To Seal Our Love," (wedding song).
Tips: "Keep vocal distinct and out front. Full band required. We favor arrangements featuring strings. No electronic sounds. SASE a must! Write first. Material submitted must be of 'master tape' quality. We will not listen to homemade tapes."

DAN THE MAN PRODUCTION/WESTBURY RECORDS, Box 702, Cleveland OH 44107. (216)251-1618. President: Daniel L. Bischoff. Record company, record producer and music publisher (Dan The Man Music Publishing Co./ASCAP). Estab. 1982. Releases 6-10 singles and 1-3 albums/year. Works with artists and songwriters on contract. Pays statutory rate to publishers for each record sold.
How to Contact: Prefers cassette or videocassette with 2-4 songs and lyric sheet. SASE. Reports in 6-8 weeks.
Music: Mostly country and novelty; also country, easy listening, folk, R&B, top 40 and rock. Recently released "The King Went on a Journey" and "Telephone Gossip," by Johnny Wright (country singles).
Tips: Looking for "novelty records, catchy tunes."

DANSAN RECORDS, 14 Soho St., London W1V 6HB, England. 44-01-437-2245. Labels include Dansan, Leisure, 'O'Liver "D" and Blank Records. Managing Director: David Marcus. Record company, record producer and music publisher (Jason Music, Mooreside Music). Releases 4 singles and 8-10 albums/year. Works with artists and songwriters on contract. Pays 2-15% royalty to artists on contract; pays royalty for each record sold "as laid down by MCPS." Royalties paid to US songwriters and artists through US publishing or recording affiliate. Has not yet, but would listen to material from US songwriters and artists.
How to Contact: Write first and obtain permission to submit. Prefers cassette. Does not return unsolicited material. Reports in 1 month.
Music: Mostly dance-oriented and MOR; also country, easy listening and R&B. Recently released *Play It Again Bryan*, by Bryan Smith (MOR LP); *Andy's Dance Party*, by Andy Ross (MOR LP); and *Dancing Guitars*, by Bert Weedon (MOR LP).

DAYMIEN RECORDS, Box 551, Graham NC 27253. (919)229-0358. A&R Director: Wesley Bulla. Record company and music publisher (Sadhana Music Publishing). Estab. 1984. Releases 4 singles and 2 albums/year. Works with musicians and songwriters on contract; musicians on salary for in-house studio work. Pays 5-25% royalty to artists on contract.
How to Contact: Prefers cassette with 4-5 songs and lyric sheet. Reports in 4-8 weeks.
Music: Rock-dance. Recently released *Sneak Preview*, (by D. Gray/W. Bulla/M. Dawson/J. Pendleton), recorded by Pyramid (rock LP); and "Hold On," (by D. Gray/W. Bulla), recorded by Nikki Fox (rock single).

DESTINY RECORDS, 31 Nassau Ave., Wilmington MA 01887. (617)658-8391. Owner: Larry Feeney. Record company, record producer and music publisher (Seismic Music). Releases 4 singles and 1 album/year. Works with artists and songwriters on contract; musicians on salary for in-house studio work. Pays 50% rate to artists on contract; statutory rate to publishers for each record sold.
How to Contact: Write first. Prefers cassette with maximum 2 songs on demo. Does not return unsolicited material. Reports in 6 months.
Music: Mostly rock; also bluegrass, blues, church/religious, country, dance-oriented, easy listening,

folk, jazz, MOR, progressive, R&B, soul and top 40/pop. Recently released "Decisions," by Rude Awakening (rock single); "Prisoners," by Tinted Glass (rock single); and "When You Thought I Had It," by True Desire (R&B single).

DEUCE RECORDS, (formerly Rock Candy Records), 104 Reade St., New York NY 10003. President: Robert Warren. Record company and music publisher. "Currently not seeking new artists to record." Pays standard royalty to artists; statutory rate to publishers for each record sold.
How to Contact: Prefers cassette and lyric sheet. SASE. Reports in 1 month.
Music: Contemporary top 20 and danceable pop/new wave. Artists include Diva.

DHARMA RECORDS, 117 W. Rockland Rd., Box 615, Libertyville IL 60048. (312)362-4060. Labels include Future and Homexercise. Vice President: Rick Johnson. Record company, record producer and music publisher (Amalgamated Tulip Corp.). Releases 3 singles and 2 albums/year. Works with artists and songwriters on contract. Pays negotiable royalty to artists on contract; negotiable rate to publishers for each record sold.
How to Contact: Write first about your interest. Prefers cassette with 3-5 songs and lyric sheet. Prefers studio produced demos. SASE. Reports in 1 month.
Music: Mostly rock, top 40/pop and country; also easy listening, MOR and progressive rock. Recently released *Active Music for Children*, by Bill Hooper (education LP); "Oh Boy," by Oh Boy (pop rock single); and *Not Marmosets Yet*, by Conrad Black (rock LP).

DOMINO RECORDS, LTD., Ridgewood Park Estates, 222 Tulane St., Garland TX 75043. Labels include Front Row Records. Contact: Gene or Dea Summers. Public Relations/Artist and Fan Club Coordinator: Steve Summers. Record company and music publisher (Silicon Music/BMI). Releases 5-6 singles and 2-3 albums/year. Works with artists and songwriters on contract. Pays negotiable royalties to artists on contract; standard royalty to songwriters on contract.
How to Contact: Prefers cassette or VHS videocassette with 1-3 songs. Does not return unsolicited material. SASE. Reports ASAP.
Music: Mostly 50's rock/rockabilly; also country and R&B. Recently released "Ballad of Moon Dog Mayne," by Ricky Ringside (country/folk single); "Excuse Me For Living," by Joey Johnson (country single); "When Love Calls," by Gene Summers (R&B single); and "A Beautiful Love Affair," by Joe Hardin Brown (50's rock single).
Tips: "If you own masters of 1950s rock and rock-a-billy, contact us first! We will work with you on a percentage basis for overseas release. We have active releases in Holland, Switzerland, Belgium, Australia, England, France, Sweden, Norway and the US at the present. We need original masters. You must be able to prove ownership of tapes before we can accept a deal. We're looking for little-known, obscure recordings. We have the market if you have the tapes!"

DRAGON RECORDS, INC., 872 Morris Park Ave., Bronx NY 10462. (212)792-2198. Labels include Agon Records. Contact: President. Record company and record producer. Works with artists and songwriters on contract. Pays statutory rate to publishers for each record sold.
How to Contact: Write first. Prefers cassette with 2-4 songs. SASE. Reports in 3 weeks.
Music: Easy listening, MOR and top 40/pop.

DTI RECORDS, Box 6143, San Rafael CA 94903. (415)883-8245. Contact: Derek Tracy. Record company and record producer. Member NAIRD. Releases 3-5 albums/year. Works with artists on contract. Pays standard royalty to artists on contract; statutory rate to publishers for each record sold.
How to Contact: Prefers cassette or videocassette with 3-5 songs and lyric sheet. SASE.
Music: Mostly contemporary rock. Recently released "Only Lovers Left Alive," and "Made in the States," by Yanks (rock EPs).

***D-TOWN RECORDS (OF CALIFORNIA), INC.**, #21, 1605 N. Martel, Hollywood CA 90046-3515. (213)851-9418. President: Kenneth H. Smith. Labels include Platinum Sound, KHS/Futura and DROC. Record company, music publisher (Keristene Music, Ltd.) and record producer (Platinum Sound Productions). Releases 6 singles/year and 8 LP's/year. Works with musicians and songwriters on contract; musicians on salary for in-house studio work. Pays 7½ to 33⅓% royalty to artists on contract.
How to Contact: Write or call first and obtain permission to submit. Prefers cassette or VHS videocassette with maximum 3 songs. Does not return unsolicited material. Reports in 6-8 weeks. "Our current policy is to review only finished product. The exception is outstanding demos."
Music: Mostly heavy metal, rock and "dance floor"; urban rock, country and R&B. Recently released *A Day In Paradise*, written and recorded by Merrell Fankhauser/D-Town (rock LP); *Scratch Break*, recorded by Broken Toys/Platinum Sound (urban LP); and *D-Town '83-'84*, recorded by various artists/DROC. Other artists include Cindy Bandes, Rich Landar, Debby Clinton, William Dean, and Diane Anderson.

DUPUY RECORDS/PRODUCTIONS/PUBLISHING, INC., Suite 200, 10960 Ventura Blvd., Studio City CA 91604. (818)980-6412. President: Pedro Dupuy. Record company, record producer and music publisher (Dupuy Publishing, Inc./ASCAP). Releases 5 singles and 5 albums/year. Works with artists and songwriters on contract; musicians on salary for in-house studio work. Pays negotiable rate to publishers for each record sold.
How to Contact: Write or call first or arrange personal interview. Prefers cassette with 2-4 songs and lyric sheet. SASE. Reports in 1 month.
Music: Easy listening, jazz, MOR, R&B, soul and top 40/pop. Artists include Gordon Gilman, David Loeb, Michael Gruwell and Robert Buttera.
Tips: Needs "very definite lyrics with hook."

DYNAMIC ARTISTS RECORDS, Box 25654, Richmond VA 23260. (804)225-7810. President: Joseph J. Carter Jr. Record company, music publisher, booking agency, management firm and production firm (Hot Gold Music Publishing Co./BMI). Releases 6 singles and 2 albums/year. Works with musicians on salary; artists and songwriters on contract; statutory rate to publishers for each record sold. Pays 9-12% royalty to artists on contract.
How to Contact: Prefers cassette or VHS videocassette with 1-3 songs. SASE. Reports in 60 days.
Music: Mostly R&B and pop; also dance and rock. Recently released "Without You Tonight," by Waller Family (ballad single); *Love Moods*, by Waller Family (soul and pop LP); and "I Want to Sing This Song for You," by Starfire (pop/R&B single). Other artists include the Dynamic Soul Orchestra and Legacy.

DYNAMITE, 5 Aldom Circle, West Caldwell NJ 07006. (201)226-0035. Branch: Box 386, Tutwiler MS 38963. Labels include Dynamite, Deadwood, Tar Heel, True Love, Cactus, Peek Records and Deadwood-Dynamite cassette tapes. Contact: Gidget Starr (gospel music) or Jim Hall (other music). Record company, record producer and music publisher. Works with artists and songwriters on contract. Pays 5% royalty to artists on contract; statutory rate to publishers for each record sold.
How to Contact: Write first about your interest. Prefers 7½ ips reel-to-reel or cassette with 5 songs and lyric sheet. Does not return unsolicited material. Reports in 2 weeks.
Music: Bluegrass, blues, country, gospel and rock. Artists include Doc Hopkins and Tune Twisters, Sal Franco and Charlie Bailey.

E.L.J. RECORD CO., 1344 Waldron, St. Louis MO 63130. President: Eddie Johnson. Record company, record producer and music publisher (Quinones/BMI). Works with musicians on salary; artists and songwriters on contract. Releases 6 singles and 3 albums/year. Pays 3% minimum royalty to artists on contract; statutory rate to publishers for each record sold.
How to Contact: Prefers 7½ ips reel-to-reel or cassette with 4 songs and lead sheet. SASE. Reports in 2 weeks.
Music: Mostly top 40; also easy listening, blues, church/religious, R&B, soul and pop. Recently released "Strange Feeling," by Eddie Johnson (top 40 single); "Tables are Turned," by Bobby Scott (top 40 single); and "Hold Me," by Ann Richardson (soul single). Other artists include Joe Buckner, LeRoy Harris, Vivian Harper and Bill Shank.

EAGLE RECORDS, Box 1027, Hermosa Beach CA 90254. (213)375-8385. Labels include Pastels, Sailor and Carmen Records. President: Guthrie Thomas. Record company, record producer and music publisher (Guthrie Thomas Publishing Company/BMI). Releases 40 singles and 60 albums/year. Works with artists and songwriters on contract; musicians on salary for in-house studio work. Pays varying royalty to artists on contract; statutory rate to publishers for each record sold.
How to Contact: Prefers cassette with 5-10 songs and lyric sheet. SASE. Reports in 1 month.
Music: Mostly jazz, country, folk, classical and rock; also country, easy listening, progressive and top 40/pop. Recently released *John Nilsen* (instrumental LP); *Guthrie Thomas* (country folk LP); and *Josh White* (blues LP).

EARTH RECORDS CO., Rte. 3, Box 57, Troy AL 36081. (205)566-7932. Record company, record producer and music publisher. Releases 2-3 singles/year. Works with artists and songwriters on contract. Pays statutory rate to publishers for each record sold.
How to Contact: Write or call first to arrange personal interview to play demo tape. Prefers cassette with 2-9 songs. SASE. Reports in 2 weeks.
Music: Children's, country, easy listening, gospel and top 40/pop. Recently released "Ship Away," by C. Carter (soul single).

EAST COAST RECORDS INC., 604 Glover Dr., Runnemede NJ 08078. (609)931-8389. President: Anthony J. Messina. Record company and music publisher. Releases 10 singles and 3 albums/year.

Works with artists and songwriters on contract. Pays 4-7% royalty to artists on contract; standard royalty to songwriters on contract.
How to Contact: Prefers 7½ ips reel-to-reel or cassette with 3-12 songs and lyric sheet. SASE. Reports in 3 weeks.
Music: Classical, MOR, rock, and top 40/pop. Recently released "Remembering," by Lana Cantrell (MOR single from LP); "Drifting Away," by Uproar (rock single); and *England Made Me* (soundtrack from the motion picture), by London Philharmonic (classical LP). Other artists include Duke Williams & the Extreams, Lynn Redgrave, Byron Blues & The Gangsters, Lotus, and David Christopher.

ECHO RECORDS, 824 83rd St., Miami Beach FL 33141. (305)865-8960. Record company, record producer and music publisher (Dana). Releases 2 singles and 1 album/year. Pays statutory rate to publishers for each record sold.
How to Contact: Write first. Prefers 7½ or 15 ips reel-to-reel or cassette as demo. SASE. Reports in 1 week.
Music: Classical and ethnic (Polish).

ECLIPSE RECORDS, 118 5th St., Box 176, Taylorsville NC 28681. (704)632-4735. Contact: Harry Deal. Record company, music publisher and record producer. Works with artists and songwriters on contract.
How to Contact: Prefers cassette with 2-3 songs and lyric sheet. SASE. Reports in 2-3 weeks.
Music: Country, dance, folk, MOR, R&B, rock, soul and top 40/pop.

EMI AMERICA/LIBERTY RECORDS, 1370 Avenue of the Americas, New York NY 10019. (212)757-7470. A&R Director (EMI-America): Caroline Prutzman. Record company and music publisher (Screen Gems). Releases several singles and albums/month.
How to Contact: Prefers reel-to-reel or cassette and lyric sheet. SASE. Reports in 3 weeks.
Music: All types of music except R&B. Recently released "You Could Have Been With Me," by Sheena Easton; "Freeze Frame," by J. Geils Band; and "Bette Davis Eyes," by Kim Carnes. Other artists include, Marty Balin, Gary U.S. Bonds, John Hall, Earl Klugh, Melba Moore, Michael Murphy, Cliff Richard, Peter Tosh, Kasim Sulton, Powder Blues Band, Kenny Rogers, Dottie West and many others.
Tips: "Mail in no more than 3 songs on a cassette at a time. Include a SASE that will support all the materials sent as we keep nothing on file."

*EMKAY RECORDS, 10622 Commerce Ave., Tujunga CA 91042. (818)352-7155. Contact: Kent Washburn. Record company, record producer and music publisher (Monard Music/ASCAP, Pencott Publishing/BMI). Releases 2-3 singles and 1-2 albums/year. Works with artists and songwriters on contract. Pays 5-12½% royalty to artists on contract; statutory rate to publishers for each record sold.
How to Contact: Prefers cassette with 2-4 songs and lyric sheet. SASE. Reports in 1 month.
Music: Mostly R&B and soul; also gospel, jazz, soul and top 40/pop. Recently released *A Life In a Day*, by Justin Thyme (jazz LP); *Free Love*, by Free Love (R&B LP); and "Don't Burn No Bridges," by Hypnotics (R&B single).

EQUA RECORDS, 1800 Mowry Ave., Fremont CA 94538. (415)794-6637. President: Warren M. Johnson. Record company and music publisher (Equa Music/ASCAP, Mepro Music/BMI). Member CMA. Releases 4-5 singles/year. Works with artists and songwriters on contract. Pays statutory rate to publishers for each record sold.
How to Contact: Prefers cassette with 3-6 songs and lyric sheet. SASE. Reports in 3 weeks.
Music: Country. Recently released "No Place to Hide," "It Ain't My Concern" and "Goin' Home Alone," by Gail Zeiler (country singles).

EURO TEC RECORDS AND TAPES, Box 3077, Ventura CA 93006. (805)642-8269. Labels include ETR. Vice President: Bruce Caplin. Record company, record producer, music publisher and management consultants. Estab. 1982. Releases 3-5 singles and 1-3 albums/year. Works with artists and songwriters on contract. Pays 12-15% royalty to artists on contract; statutory or variable rate to publishers for each record sold.
How to Contact: Write or call first. Prefers 15 ips reel-to-reel, cassette or videocassette with 1-12 songs. SASE. Reports in 60 days.
Music: Dance, rock, top 40, pop, Latin rock, AOR, MOR and CHR (Contemporary Hit Radio). Recently released *Rock Rolls On*, by Michael Bruce (AOR/CHR LP); "Too Young," by M. Bruce (rock-AOR single); and "Dance Tonight," by Carol Stewart (dance single).

EXECUTIVE RECORDS, 11 Shady Oak Trail, Charlotte NC 28210-7409. (704)554-1162. Executive Producer: Butch Kelly Montgomery. Record company, record producer, music publisher (Butch Kelly

Production) and songwriter. Member AGAC. Releases 2 singles/year and 1 album/year. Works with artists on contract; musicians on salary for in-house studio work. Pays 50% to artists on contract; statutory rate to publishers for each record sold.
How to Contact: Prefers cassette or videocassette with 3 songs and lyric sheet and pictures. SASE. Submit pictures with demo. Reports in 1 month.
Music: Mostly R&B and pop; also dance-oriented, soul and top 40. Recently released "Fantasy II," by Melisa Kelly (pop single); "13 Years," by L.A. Stars (R&B single); and "Super Star," by L.A. Stars (rap single).

F&L RECORDS, Suite #902, 50 Music Square W., Nashville TN 37203. (615)329-2228. Labels include Progress Records. General Manager: Bobby Fischer. Record company, record producer, music publisher (Bobby Fischer Music Group), national record promoter and distributor. Member NSAI, CMA, CPA, FICAP. Releases 10 singles/year. Works with artists and songwriters on contract. Pays maximum royalty to artists on contract; statutory rate to publishers for each record sold.
How to Contact: Prefers cassette with 2-3 songs and lyric sheet. SASE. Reports "when time permits."
Music: Country and progressive. Recently released "Chances Are," by Melissa; "Til Dawn Do Us Part," by Boyd Chisum; and "He's Steppin' Out," by Bucky Allred. Other artists include Danny White, Linda Nail and Wyvon Alexander.

FACTORY BEAT RECORDS, INC., 521 5th Ave., New York NY 10175. (212)757-3638. Labels include RER, Ren Rome and Can Scor Productions, Inc. President: Rena L. Feeney. Record company, record producer and music publisher (Ren-Maur Music Corp.), Member NARAS, BMI and Songwriters Guild. Releases 4 singles and 2 albums/year. Works with musicians on salary for in-house studio work. Pays 4-12% royalty to artists on contract; statutory rate to publishers for each record sold.
How to Contact: Submit cassette and lyric sheet only. SASE. Reports in 3 weeks.
Music: R&B, rock, soul and top 40/pop.

FAMOUS DOOR RECORDS, Box 92, Station A, Flushing NY 11358. (718)463-6281. Contact: Harry Lim. Record company. Member NARAS. Releases 6 albums/year. Works with artists on contract. Pays 5% in royalty to artists on contract; statutory rate to publishers for each record sold.
How to Contact: Write first. Prefers cassette with minimum 3 songs. Prefers studio produced demos. SASE. Reports in 1 month.
Music: Jazz. Recently released *Miles & Miles of Swing*, by The Butch Miles Sextet; *Holllywood Swing*, by The Jack Lesberg Sextet; and *Slick Funk*, by The John Bunch Quartet.
Tips: Looking for "good instrumentals."

FARR RECORDS, Box 1098, Somerville NJ 08876. (201)725-3850. Contact: Candace Campbell. Record company and record producer. Member RIAA. Releases 30 singles and 30 albums/year. Works with artists and songwriters on contract. Pays negotiable royalty to artists on contract; statutory rate to publishers for each record sold.
How to Contact: Prefers cassette with 4 songs and lyric sheet. SASE. Reports in 2 weeks.
Music: Mostly pop and folk; also country, dance-oriented, easy listening, MOR, rock, soul and top 40.

*FIFTH STREET RECORDS, 228 W. 5th St., Kansas City MO 64105. (816)842-6854. Contact: Chuck Chapman. Record company and promotional service. Releases 15 singles and 12 albums/year. Works with artists as service and contract. Pays negotiable royalty, statutory rate to publishers for M.L.
How to Contact: Prefers cassette or videocassette with maximum 3 songs. SASE. Reports in 3 months.
Music: Mostly country and black gospel; also jazz, MOR and southern gospel. Recently released "I'm So Glad," by Ira Wilkes; "Love Affair," by Bruce Ghale; and "Nothing Between," by S. Frank Frazier.

50 STATES RECORDS & TAPES, Box 314, Hendersonville TN 37075. (615)824-8308. A&R Director: Johnny Howard. Record company, record producer and music publisher (Chap's Music). Releases 12 singles and 6 albums/year. Works with artists and songwriters on contract. Pays negotiable royalty to artists on contract; statutory rate to publishers for each record sold.
How to Contact: Prefers cassette with 1-5 songs and lyric sheet. SASE. Reports in 3 weeks.
Music: Mostly country and top 40; also bluegrass and gospel. Recently released "England, America Loves You," by Fabulous Fryers (country/pop single); *You Lay So Easy On My Mind*, by Jack Paris (country/pop LP); and "Keep Your Hands Off My Baby," by Sharry Hanna (country/pop single).

*FIRST DYNASTY RECORDS, 4747 Central Ave., St. Petersburg FL 33713. (813)321-8649. A&R: Lee C. Bevilacqua. Record company, music publisher (Lisa's Theme Music, Inc.), record producer (Mike Douglas & Assoc. Inc.) and music research and marketing corporation. Releases 12 singles/year and 12 LP's/year. Works with musicians/artists and songwriters on contract. Pays negotiable royalty to artists on contract.

How to Contact: Prefers cassette or 7½ ips reel-to-reel and lyric sheet. SASE.

Music: Mostly Christian contemporary, gospel and country gospel. Recently released "Neath the Shadow of His Wings," and "Life Without You," written and recorded by Mike Rudasill on First Dynasty (country/gospel single); and "Fig Tree," (by Marilyn Rice), recorded by The Joint Heirs on First Dynasty (country gospel single).

415 RECORDS, Box 14563, San Francisco CA 94114. (415)621-3415; 522-9828. President: Howie Klein. Record company and music publisher (Very Safe Music/BMI and Even Safer Music/ASCAP). Releases 4 singles and 4 albums/year. Works with artists on contract. Pays statutory rate to publishers for each record sold.

How to Contact: Prefers cassette or Beta/VHS videocassette with 1-5 songs. SASE.

Music: Rock and new wave. Recently released *I'll Do You*, by Wire Train (rock single and album); *Un-Alone*, by Translator (rock single and album); *China*, by Red Rockers (rock single and album).

FOUR WINDS RECORD PRODUCTIONS INC., Box 11547, East Station, Memphis TN 38111. (901)525-5414. Contact: A&R Department. Record company. Works with artists on contract; musicians on salary for in-house studio work. Pays 4-10% royalty to artists on contract; statutory rate to publishers for each record sold.

How to Contact: Write or call first. Prefers cassette or 7½ ips reel-to-reel with 2-4 songs. Reports in 1 month.

Music: Mostly country; also R&B and bluegrass.

FRANNE RECORDS, Box 8135, Chicago IL 60680. (312)224-5612. Labels include Superbe Records. A&R Director/Executive Producer: R.C. Hillsman. Record company, music publisher and producer. Works with artists and songwriters on contract. Pays 3½% royalty to artists and songwriters on contract.

How to Contact: Write or call to arrange personal interview or submit demo tape. Prefers 7½ or 15 ips ¼" reel-to-reel or cassette with 4-6 songs and lyric sheet. Send material "by registered mail only." SASE. Reports in 3 weeks.

Music: Church/religious, country, disco, gospel, jazz, MOR, rock and top 40/pop. Recently released "He's Love" and "You Better Get Right," by Allen Duo (gospel singles).

FUN CITY RECORDS CO., 281 W. 6th St., Mansfield OH 44902. Executive Producer: Larry Rawls. Record company and record producer. Releases 4 singles/year. Works with songwriters on contract. Pays 10¢-30¢/record sold to artists on contract; statutory rate to publishers for each record sold.

How to Contact: Prefers cassette with 3-5 songs and lyric sheet. Does not return unsolicited material. Reports in 3 weeks.

Music: Mostly R&B and top 40/pop; also contemporary gospel. Recently released "Love So Divine" and "Let's Stay Together," by Rawls Brothers (R&B/ballad singles); "Ready for De Funk," by Larry Rawls (R&B/top 40 single); and "Sunshine," by Shellis Payne (pop single).

FUTURE STEP SIRKLE, Box 2095, Philadelphia PA 19103. (215)844-8736. Labels include Molecules of Force Records. A&R Director: S. Deane Henderson. Record company, record producer, music publisher (Communciation Concept) and management firm. Releases 6-10 singles and 3-6 albums/year. Works with artists and songwriters on contract. Pays 4-10% royalty to artists on contract; statutory rate to publishers for each record sold.

How to Contact: Prefers cassette or VHS videocassette with 4-8 songs and lyric sheet. "Lyrics only are returned." Reports in 2 weeks.

Music: Mostly R&B, funk, rock and heavy metal; also dance-oriented, easy listening, gospel, MOR, soul and top 40/pop. Recently published *Hot Number*, by Racers (rock LP); *Save Me Jesus*, by Offspring Gospel (gospel LP); and "Exercise," by M.D.F. (dance single). Other artists include Dean Morrow, Shonee, 4 Way Ping and Nasty Rumors.

*MICHAEL GALE ENTERTAINMENT, 29 S. Erie, Toledo OH 43602. (419)244-8599. Manager, A&R: Reen Shaw. Labels include Toledo Records, My Reen Records, Park J. Tunes, and Jamestune Records. Record company, music publisher (Keeny/York Publishing) and record producer (MDS Productions). Releases 10 singles/year and 3 LP's/year. Works with musicians/artists and songwriters on contract. Pays standard royalty to artists on contract.

How to Contact: Prefers cassette with 3 songs and lyric sheet. Does not return unsolicited material. Reports in 6 weeks.

Music: Mostly country, jazz and rock; also MOR. Recently released "Rich Man," "Jesse," and "Oh

Them Hens," (by Michael Drew Shaw) all recorded by Hotlix on Reen (rock singles). Other artists include Suzy Rice, Mark Kieswetter, Lori Lefevre and Dan Faehnle.

GCS RECORDS, Suite 206, 1508 Harlem, Memphis TN 38114. (901)274-2726. Labels include Del-A-Ron Records, Great-Day Records and Blue-Town Records. A&R Directors: Daniel Boga and Willie Blair. Record company and music publisher. Releases 40 singles and 7 albums/year. Works with artists on record contract and musicians on salary for in-house studio work. Also works with composers and teams collaborators. Pays 3-7% royalty to artists on contract; statutory rate to publishers for each record sold.
How to Contact: Write or call about your interest or arrange personal interview. Prefers 7½ or 15 ips reel-to-reel, or VHS videocassette or cassette with 3-5 songs and lyric sheet. SASE. Reports in 1 month.
Music: Mostly R&B; also top 40/pop, gospel, blues and dance. Recently released "Never Say What You Want to Do," by Amnisty; "Spending My Time," by Cheryl Fox; and "Across the Miles," by Lee Moss (all R&B singles).

*GEMINI RECORDS, INC., 8 Canberra Dr., Knoxville TN 37923. (615)690-8521. President: Rick Bowen. Labels include Chantilly Records. Record company. Releases 7 singles/year and 4 LP s/year. Works with musicians/artists and songwriters on contract; musicians on salary for in-house studio work. Pays 7% royalty to artists on contract.
How to Contact: Prefers cassette with 4 songs and lyric sheet. SASE. Reports in 2 weeks.
Music: Mostly rock/pop, jazz and soft rock; also blues, gospel and country. Recently released *Want My Love*, written and recorded by R. Bowen on Gemini (pop LP); *Guilty*, written and recorded by Sue Robinson on Gemini (rock LP); and *Letmotif*, written and recorded by Marcus Shirley on Chantilly (jazz LP). Other artists include: Carl Marshall, Deny Joe Landry, Sunshine People, TC & Company, and Mavis Thall.

GERVASI RECORDS, Box 4547, Redding CA 96099. (916)222-1401. Marketing: Dienna Gervasi. Record company, music publisher and management firm. Member CMA and AMC. Releases 4 singles and 1 album/year. Works with songwriters on contract. Pays statutory rate to publishers for each record sold.
How to Contact: Prefers cassette with 3-5 songs and lyric sheet. SASE. Reports in 2 weeks.
Music: Mostly country and country rock. Recently released "I Still Love Your Body," by Tommy Overstreet (country single); "Wishful Drinkin" and "Look of a Lovin Lady," by Wyvon Alexander (country singles).

GHOST RECORDS, 1905 Pesos Place, Kalamazoo MI 49008. (616)375-2641. Labels include Ghost and Jobie Records. President: Don Jobe. Record company. Releases 5-8 singles and 2 albums/year. Works with artists and songwriters on contract.
How to Contact: Prefers 7½ ips reel-to-reel and lead sheet. SASE. Reports in 1 month.
Music: Mostly country rock; also easy listening, rock, soul, top 40/pop and country/western. Recently released "Nadine" by the Ghosters (top 40 single); and "Bendin' Over Backwards," by Dan Stersic and The Country Squires (country single). Other artists include Jim Hallberg and the Tru-Tones.

GMT RECORDS, Box 25141, Honolulu HI 96825. (808)737-7059. President: Gil M. Tanaka. Record company, record producer and music publisher (Music Publishers of Hawaii). Works with artists and songwriters on contract. Pays 15-50% royalty to artists on contract; statutory rate to publishers for each record sold.
How to Contact: Prefers cassette with 1-6 songs and lyric sheet. SASE. Reports in 1 month.
Music: Mostly top 40/pop; also country, easy listening, jazz and rock. Recently released *Kevin I.*, by Kevin I. (top 40/pop LP); *Morning Light*, by Paul Flynn (top 40/pop LP); and *Music Man*, by Music Magic (jazz LP).

GOLD GUITAR RECORDS, 1450 Terrell, Beaumont TX 77701. (409)832-0748. President: Don Gilbert. Record company, record producer and music publisher (Don Gilbert Music/BMI). Releases 10 singles/year. Works with songwriters on contract; musicians on salary for in-house studio work. Pays 8-15% royalty to artists on contract; statutory rate to publishers for each record sold.
How to Contact: Prefers 7½ ips reel-to-reel or cassette with 2-10 songs and lyric sheet. SASE. Reports in 1 month.
Music: Religious music only. Recently released "Five Rooms of Memories" and "The Other One," by Don Gilbert (country singles). Other artists include Sherry Black, George Lee and Scottie.

GOLDEN RULE RECORD PRODUCTION CO., INC., Box 11547, East Station, Memphis TN 38111. (901)525-5414. Contact: A&R Department. Record company. Releases 4 singles and 2 albums/

year. Works with artists on contract; musicians on salary for in-house studio work. Pays 4-10% royalty to artists on contract; statutory rate to publishers for each record sold.
How to Contact: Write first. Prefers cassette or 7½ ips reel-to-reel with 2-4 songs. Reports in 1 month.
Music: Church/religious and gospel.

GOLDUST RECORD CO., 115 E. Idaho Ave., Las Cruces NM 88005. (505)524-1889. Contact: Emmit H. Brooks. Record company, music publisher (Enchantment Music/BMI) and recording studio. Member CMA. Releases 8-12 singles and 8 albums/year. Works with artists and songwriters on contract; musicians on salary for in-house studio work. Pays 4-6% royalty to artists on contract; standard royalty to songwriters on contract; statutory rate to publishers for each record sold.
How to Contact: Prefers cassette with 1-5 songs. "We do not wish to review material which has been previously released." Send SASE if return of material is requested. Reports in 1 month.
Music: Country, easy listening, MOR, rock (soft or country), top 40/pop and fiddle instrumentals. Recently released "Crazy and Lonely," by Jeff Moore (country single); *Twin Fiddles*, by Tammy and Junior Daugherty (country instrumental LP); *Shock Treatment*, by Voltz (rock LP); *The Clay Mac Band in Austin*, by Clay Mac Band (country LP); and "Mississippi" by Dana Bivens (country single). Other artists include Hyram Posey, Wes Nivens, David Ruthstrom, Dick Jonas, Jake Brooks, Raintree, Claudia Jones, Desperados, Breeze, Terry Lee, Bill Lendrom and Kim Litton.

GRANDVILLE RECORD CORP., Box 11960, Chicago IL 60611-0960. (312)561-0027. Executive Producer/President: Clifford Rubin. Record company, record producer and music publisher (Billetdoux Music/BMI). Releases 5 singles and2 albums/year. Works with artists and songwriters on contract; musicians on salary for in-house studio work. Pays 3-6% royalty to artists on contract; statutory rate to publishers for each record sold.
How to Contact: Prefers cassette with 3-6 songs and lyric sheet. SASE. Reports in 1 month.
Music: Mostly R&B; also blues, country, gospel, jazz, MOR, rock, soul and top 40/pop. Recently released "Tell Me Lies," by Randy Terry (rock/pop single); *Mama Was Right*, by Malcolm Simmons (blues/funk LP); and "Lie to Me," by M. Simmons (blues/funk single). Other artists include Larry Caballero, Burning Corvairs, and La John.
Tips: "We want commercial hooks with lyrics that are to the point as well as universal."

GRASS ROOTS RECORD & TAPE/LMI RECORDS, Box 532, Malibu CA 90265. (213)858-7282. Labels include LMI Records. President: Lee Magid. Record company, record producer and music publisher (Alexis/ASCAP, Marvelle/BMI). Member AIMP, NARAC. Releases 10 singles and 4 albums/year. Works with artists and songwriters on contract. Pays 2½-5% royalty to artists on contract; pays negotiable royalty to publishers for each record sold.
How to Contact: Prefers cassette with 3 songs and lyric sheet. "Please, no 45s." SASE. Reports in 1 month minimum.
Music: Mostly pop/rock, R&B, country, jazz/rock and blues; also bluegrass, children's and Spanish. Recently released "How Do You Keep Music Playing," by Nan Brennan (pop/jazz vocal single); "Pagliacci Swings," by Russ Gary Big Band Express (jazz single); and *Have Horns, Will Travel*, by Russ Gary Big Band Express (jazz LP). Other artists include Gloria Lynne, Arthur Prysock, Carl Bean and the L.A. Jazz Choir.

***GULE RECORDS INC.**, #410, 7046 Hollywood Blvd., Hollywood CA 90028. (213)462-0502. A&R: Harry Gordon. Record company, music publisher (Bee Ray Music) and record producer (Harry Edward Co.). Works with songwriters on contract.
How to Contact: Prefers cassette. SASE. Reports in 2 weeks.
Music: Mostly country and gospel.

***GULFSTREAM RECORDS**, 4225 Palm St., Baton Rouge LA 70808. (504)383-7885. President: Barrie Edgar. Record company, music publisher (Silverfoot) and record producer (Hogar). Works with musicians/artists and songwriters on contract; or pays musicians per session. Pays 3-10% royalty to artists on contract.
How to Contact: Prefers cassette with 4 songs and lyric sheet. SASE.
Music: Mostly rock, blues (not soul) and country. Recently released "Louisiana's Basin Child," by Top Secret on Hogar (rock single).

***HACIENDA RECORDS**, 1236 S. Staples, Corpus Christi TX 78404. (512)882-7066. Producers: Arnold Garcia and Rick Garcia. Labels include: Las Brisas. Record company, music publisher (Dark Heart Music, El Palacio Music, Roland Garcia Music) and record producer. Releases 20-100 singles/year and 5-20 LP's/year. Works with artists and songwriters on contract; musicians on salary for in-house studio work. Pays royalties or per LP to artists on contract.

How to Contact: Prefers cassette. Does not return unsolicited material. Reporting time varies.
Music: Mostly rock, Spanish and country; also gospel. Recently released "Ready as Hell," (by Jim D. Ricky R. Johnny C.), recorded by Jim Dandy's Black Oak Arkansas on Hacienda (rock single & LP), "It's Majic," (by Pio Trevino), recorded by Majic on Hacienda (English single from Spanish LP); and "Ran Kan Kan," (by Tito Puente, recorded by Steve Jordan on Hacienda (Spanish single). Other artists include Romance, Gary Hobbs, Fuego, Janie C., Steve Borth, Rowdy Friends, and Vida Alegre.

HAPPY BEAT RECORDS, Suite 303, 14045 S. Main, Houston TX 77035. (713)641-0793 or 645-5391. Labels include MSB Records. President: Roger L. Cummings. Record company, music publisher (Sirloin Music Publishing/BMI), promotion and distribution firm. Releases 5 singles and 3 albums/year. Works with artists and songwriters on contract; musicians on salary for in-house studio work. Works with lyricists and composers and teams collaborators. Pays negotiable royalty to artists on contract; negotiable rate to publishers for each record sold.
How to Contact: Prefers cassette with 3-6 songs and lyric sheet. "Don't send your master and state speed on videocassette box. Artists should include photo." SASE. Reports in 1 month.
Music: Mostly rock, soul and dance; also blues, jazz, R&B and top 40/pop. Recently released "Let the Music in Your Mind," by Chance (dance single); and *Drum Licks*, by Friction (drum songs EP). Other artists include Carl Adams, Steve Cummings, Carl Stewart and Invasion.

HARD HAT RECORDS AND CASSETTES, 519 N. Halifax Ave., Daytona Beach FL 32018. (904)252-0381. Labels include Hard Hat, Maricao, Blue Bandana and Indian Head. President: Bobby Lee Cude. Record company, record producer and music publisher (Cude & Pickens Publishing/BMI). Releases 6 singles and 12 albums/year. Works with artists and songwriters on contract; musicians on salary for in-house studio work. Works with lyricists and composers and teams collaborators. Pays 3-5% royalty to artists on contract; statutory rate to publishers for each record sold.
How to Contact: Write first. Prefers cassette with 1-6 songs and lyric sheet. Prefers studio produced demos. SASE.
Music: Mostly country; also easy listening, gospel, MOR, top 40/pop and Broadway show. Recently released *Heard You Married Him Today*, *Inter-State Blues*, and *Country Blues*, recorded by Blue Bandana Country Band (cassettes).

HARD-BOILED RECORDS, 484 Lake Park Ave., Box 6, Oakland CA 94610. (415)482-4854. A&R Director: Dan Orth. Record company, record producer and music publisher (Dynamo Publishing Co./BMI). Releases 1 single/year. Works with artists and songwriters on contract; musicians on salary for in-house studio work. Pays 10-50% royalty to artists on contract; statutory rate to publishers for each record sold.
How to Contact: Write or call first. Prefers cassette with 1-3 songs and lyric sheet. SASE. Reports in 1 month.
Music: Mostly pop, rock and new wave; also country, easy listening, folk, MOR and R&B. Recently released "Cruisin' the Strip," by Phil Phillips (hard rock single); and "It Takes More," by P. Phillips (pop rock single).
Tips: "We are interested in anyone with extraordinary songwriting or musical talent."

HE ROSE RECORDS, 1098 Rose Ave., El Centro CA 92243. (619)352-5774. A&R Department: Danny Berg. Record company and music publisher. Member GMA. Releases 2 singles and 2 albums/year. Works with artists and songwriters on contract. Pays 7% of $8.98 list; statutory rate to publishers for each record sold.
How to Contact: Prefers cassette with 1-3 songs and lyric sheet. SASE. Reports in 6 months.
Music: Mostly contemporary/Christian; also choral, gospel and church/religious. Recently released *Jonah and the Whalers* and "I Need Him/Broken Together," by Don Charles (contemporary Christian LP and single).

*HEARTHSIDE RECORDS, Box 3860, Kingsport TN 37664. (615)246-3845. President: Tilford A. Salyer. Labels include Trail, Trinity, Olive and TSR records. Record company. Releases 20 singles/year and 16 LP's/year. Works with musicians/artists and songwriters on contract; musicians on salary for in-house studio work. Pays 10% royalty to artist on contract.
How to Contact: Prefers cassette. Does not return unsolicited material. Reports in 6 weeks.
Music: Mostly Southern gospel and contemporary Christian. Recently released *Enjoying The Trip*, written and recorded by Lewis Harrah on Hearth Side (country gospel LP); *Follow Me*, written and recorded by Ellason Castiglione on Trinity (contemporary gospel LP); *Premiere Issue*, recorded by Barry Gregory on Trinity (contemporary gospel LP). Other artists include Ray Branham Family, Royalmen Quartet, Dumplin' Valley Boy, Brotherhood, Singing Disciples, and the Holloways.

HEAVY METAL RECORDS, 152 Goldthorn Hill, Penn, Wolverhampton, WV2 3VA England. 44-(0902)-345345. Labels include Heavy Metal America, Heavy Metal Worldwide and FM. A&R Manager: David Roberts. Record company, record producer and music publisher. Releases 40 singles and 40 albums/year. Works with musicians/artists and songwriters on contract.
How to Contact: Prefers cassette with 2-4 songs. Does not return unsolicited material. Reports in 2-3 weeks.
Music: Mostly heavy metal/hard rock, AOR/FM rock and "alternative" guitar-based rock. Recently released *On a Storytellers Night*, written and recorded by Magnum on FM (commercial/hard rock LP); *East/West*, written and recorded by Multi-Story (progressive/AOR rock LP); and *Brightest Starz*, written and recorded by Starz on Heavy Metal America (hard rock LP). Other artists include Wrathchild, Restless, Runestaff, Eloy, Marionette, Pet Hate, Black Oak Arkansas, Briar, Diano and the Rejects.

HIGH POCKETS RECORDS, 527 Meadow Dr., West Seneca NY 14224. (716)675-3974. President: Nick Gugliuzza. Record company and music publisher. Releases 5 singles and 14 albums/year. Works with artists and songwriters on contract. Pays 4-7% royalty to artists on contract; statutory rate to publishers for each record sold.
How to Contact: Prefers cassette with 1-3 songs and lyric sheet. SASE. Reports in 1 month.
Music: Mostly rock; also bluegrass and blues. Recently released *Undeniable*, *Don't Shoot My Dog*, and *Down in the Valley*, by Paul Benhatzel (rock LPs). Other artists include Don Tomasullo, John Druzak and Mike Dunn.

*HME RECORDS, 250 W. 57th St., New York NY 10107. (212)664-8888. A&R: Bob Cutarella or Jack Littlejohn. Labels include Zoo York Records. Record company. Releases 25 singles/year and 12 LP's/year. Works with musicians/artists and songwriters on contract. Pays negotiable royalty to artists on contract.
How to Contact: Prefers cassette or ¾" VHS videocassette with 3 songs ("seven second space between songs") and lyric sheet. Does not return unsolicited material. 'Videos may be picked up." Reports in 2-6 weeks.
Music: Mostly pop-rock and R&B/dance; also country, blues and jazz. Recently released *Black Cars*, recorded by Gino Vannelli on HME (rock/dance LP); *No Muss . . . No Fuss*, recorded by Donnie Iris on HME (rock LP); and *Surrender*, recorded by Robin Clark on HME (R&B/dance LP). Other artists include John Palumbo, Younger Bros., Finn and the Sharks, Diane Richards, Michael Cody, and the Fabulous Thunderbirds.
Tips: "We have no 'ears.' Don't make us figure it out. Send well produced, well recorded, well arranged demos. Do it right."

HOLLYROCK RECORDS, Suite 170, 14116 E. Whittier Blvd., Whittier CA 90605. (213)945-5449. A&R Director: Dave Paton. Record company, record producer and music publisher (Heaven Songs/BMI). Releases 2 singles and 4 albums/year. Works with artists and songwriters on contract; musicians on salary for in-house studio work. Pays negotiable royalty to artists on contract; statutory rate to publishers for each record sold.
How to Contact: Prefers 7½ ips reel-to-reel or cassette with 3-6 songs and lyric sheet. SASE. Reports in 2 weeks.
Music: Country, easy listening, folk, jazz, MOR, progressive, rock and top 40/pop. Recently released "Everything" (movie soundtrack).

HOLY SPIRIT RECORDS, INC., 27335 Penn St., Inkster MI 48141. Labels include God's World and Aspro Records. Contact: Elder Otis G. Johnson. Record company, music publisher (Manfield Music/BMI, Stephen Enoch Johnson Music/ASCAP and God's World Music/SESAC) and record producer. Releases 4 singles and 2 albums/year. Works with artists and songwriters on contract. Works with lyricists and composers. Pays 4% minimum royalty to artists on contract; statutory rate to publishers for each record sold.
How to Contact: Write or call first. Prefers 7½ ips reel-to-reel or cassette with 3 songs and lyric sheet. SASE. Reports in 1 month.
Music: Church/religious, country, easy listening and gospel. Recently released "To Be With You," and "I Found You," by Valorie Jean Reha and Otis G. Johnson; and "Dream Girl," by Annexus.

HOMESTEAD RECORDS, Box 256577, Chicago IL 60625. (312)399-5535. President: Tom Petreli. Record company and record producer. Releases 8-15 singles and 2-5 albums/year. Works with artists on contract; musicians on salary for in-house studio work.
How to Contact: Prefers cassette or videocassette with 2-4 songs and lyric sheet. SASE. Reports in 1 month.
Music: Mostly country; also bluegrass, church/religious and Spanish. Recently released *Arizona*, by Arizona Country (country LP). Other artists include Tom Petreli, Tempe and Messa.

*HOTTRAX RECORDS, 26 17th St., Atlanta GA 30309. (404)872-4000. Vice President, A&R: Marie Sutton. Labels include: Dance-A-Thon, Hardkor. Record company and music publisher (Starfox Publishing). Releases 12 singles/year and 3-4 LPs/year. Works with musicians/artists and songwriters on contract. Pays 5-7% royalty to artists on contract.
How to Contact: Prefers cassette with 3 songs and lyric sheet. SASE. Reports in 8 weeks.
Music: Mostly top 40/pop, rock and country; also hard core punk and jazz-fusion. Recently released *P Is For Pig*, written and recorded by The Pigs on Hottrax (top 40/pop LP); "The World May Not Like Me," (by Mike Fitzgerald), recorded by Mike Angelo on Hottrax (rock single); and *Introducing The Feel*, written and recorded by The Feel on Hottrax (new rock LP). Other artists include Burl Compton (country), Michael Rozakis & Yorgos (pop), Starfoxx (rock), The Night Shadows (rock), and The Bop (new wave).

HULA RECORDS INC., Box 2135, Honolulu HI 96805. (808)847-4608. Labels include Hawaii Call's Music Group, Inc. and Surfside Records, Inc. President: Donald P. McDiarmid III. Record company, record producer and music publisher (Kona-Kai Distribution Co.). Releases 5 albums/year. Works with artists on contract. Pays statutory rate to publishers for each record sold.
How to Contact: Prefers cassette and lyric sheet. SASE. Reports in 3 weeks.
Music: Hawaiian.

HUNGARIA RECORDS, INC., Box 2073, Teaneck NJ 07666. (201)836-4869. General Manager: Stephen Kotansky. Record company and record producer. Releases 2-3 albums/year. Works with artists on contract. Payment negotiable.
How to Contact: Write first. Prefers cassette with 1 song. SASE. Reports in 1 month.
Music: Hungarian folk music only. Recently released *HRLP 001*, by Kallo's Zoltan (Hungarian folk LP); *HRLP 002*, and *HRLP 004*, by Teka Ensemble (Hungarian folk music/LP); and *HRLP 003*, by Kodaly Quartet.

HYBRID RECORDS, Box 333, Evanston IL 60204. (312)274-9126. President: Graham Carlton. Record company, record producer and music publisher (Graham Carlton Music Co.). Releases 130 singles and 40 albums/year. Works with artists and songwriters on contract; musicians on salary for in-house studio work. Pays maximum 14% royalty to artists on contract; statutory rate to publishers for each record sold.
How to Contact: Prefers cassette or videocassette with 1-5 songs and lyric sheet. SASE. Reports ASAP.
Music: Mostly country and soul; also bluegrass, blues, dance-oriented, easy listening, folk, jazz, MOR, progressive, R&B, rock, top 40/pop and humorous. Recently released "Al Capone Clone," by Hustlers, Inc. (dance single); and "More & More," by Annie Wynne (country single).

IGL AUDIO, Shore Acres, Box 100, Spirit Lake IA 51360. (712)336-2859. President: John Senn. Record company, record producer and music publisher (Okoboji Music). Releases 10 singles and 6 albums/year. Works with artists and songwriters on contract; musicians on salary for in-house studio work. Pays 8% maximum royalty to artists on contract; statutory rate to publishers for each record sold.
How to Contact: Prefers cassette with 1-5 songs and lyric sheet. SASE. Reports in 1 month.
Music: Mostly modern country (rock/pop) and church/religious; also gospel and top 40/pop. Recently released "Love Tender Love," by DJ & the Runaways (country single); and *American Heritage*, by American Heritage (religious LP). Other artists include Vegas and Becky Weber.
Tips: "We are looking for both up-tempo and slower-type country, pop and gospel songs with strong modern lyrics and melodies."

*IMAGINARY RECORDS, 239-A E. Thach Ave., Auburn AL 36830. (205)821-JASS. Proprietor: Lloyd Townsend, Jr. Record company, music publisher record producer (Almost Audible Audio) and distribution firm. Releases 1 single/year and 2 albums/year. Works with musicians/artists and songwriters on contract. Pays 10-15% royalty to artists on contract.
How to Contact: Prefers cassette or 7½ ips reel-to-reel with 4 songs and lyric or lead sheet. SASE. Reports in 4 weeks.
Music: Mostly jazz, blues and rock; also classical, folk and spoken word. Recently released "Fast Food Driver," (by Thom Freeman), recorded by Slow Natives on Imaginary (rock single); "Jagged Edges," (rock EP) and *Serve and Protect*, (rock LP) (by Paul Presley), recorded by The Moderns on Imaginary (rock); and *Star Maker*, by Somtow Sucharitkul (avant-garde LP). Other artists include Judy Roderick, Philip Walker, Bob Richardson and Rick Bell.

IN ACTION, 3530 Kensington Ave., Philadelphia PA 19134. (215)288-4750. Labels include Arcade, Lisa and Claire. Vice President: Claire Mac. Record company, record producer and music publisher (Sulzer Music/BMI and Arcade Music/ASCAP). Releases 10 singles and 10 albums/year. Works with

Close-Up

Bobby Bare
Songwriter/Performer/TV Show Host
Nashville, Tennessee

Photo by Beverly Parker

If you ask in Nashville who is one person in the music business who has done a great deal for the songwriter, you probably will hear the name Bobby Bare quite a few times. Bare, host of The Nashville Network's "Bobby Bare and Friends," is known around Nashville as "The Songwriter's Friend" for his never ending support of the songwriter.

In fact, Bare's popular cable show serves to further this support. "I think it's drawing attention to the people, who really control the direction our music goes, the songwriters. It's an area people really haven't had a chance to look at." Although his guests include many of the famous and not-so-famous writers in country and pop music today, Bare steers clear of the usual TV-interview personal questions. "I'm not going to put somebody on the spot," says Bare, "and besides the real stars of the show are the songs."

Bare's own music career started when he joined a band at age 16. At 19 he left his home outside the small southern Ohio town of Ironton in search of a record contract in California. After several years of odd jobs, parking cars and driving an ice cream wagon, Bare finally found success in "All-American Boy," a song he had quickly recorded just before his induction in the Army in 1959.

Later, in Nashville Bare met Shel Silverstein, a songwriter, playwright and *Playboy* cartoonist who was to become one of Bare's best friends and constant writer/collaborator. After being introduced to Silverstein by country great Chet Atkins, Bare recorded one of his tunes, "Sylvia's Mother." He was so impressed by the result he asked Silverstein to write enough material for an album and a long time working relationship was born. From the first project, *Lullabies, Legends and Lies* through at least a dozen other records to the latest

release, *Drinkin' From The Bottle, Singin' From The Heart*, Bare and Silverstein developed into one of Nashville's most successful and unusual teams.

Through the late 60's and early seventies Bare became known as somewhat of an innovator on the Nashville music scene, credited with producing and recording country music's first concept albums, and more importantly, with being the first Nashville artist to gain total artistic control over his work. Bare exercises this freedom when choosing material for his next record, waiting until he can assemble enough *good* songs for an album, rather than coming up with just a couple of good songs and filling out the rest of the record with less than adequate cuts so as to meet somebody's deadline.

Considered a maverick by some for his sometimes irreverent, tongue-in-cheek approach to the songs he records and writes like "Drop Kick Me Jesus (Through the Goalposts of Life)," and "Pour Me Another Tequila, Sheila," Bare realizes it's not the performance so much as the song that counts. "There's no way you can take a bad song, or even a mediocre one, and sweeten it up enough to where it will really be an unforgettable hit record, because it's really the song that makes it. If you don't have a good song, you're not really going to have a hit that people will remember."

artists and songwriters on contract. Pays 5¢/record for each record sold; statutory rate to publishers for each record sold.
How to Contact: Prefers cassette with 2-6 songs and lyric sheet. SASE. "Indicate whether BMI or ASCAP writer." Reports in 1 month.
Music: Country, easy listening and MOR. Recently released "Dixie Girl," by Tom Bornemann/In Action (country single); "The Lonely Road," by Paul Christopher/In Action (easy listening single); and "So Much In Love," by Frank Langley/Acapella (easy listening single).

JAMAKA RECORD CO., 3621 Heath Ln., Mesquite TX 75150. (214)279-5858. Labels include Felco, Candlelight, Plano and Texas Tea. Contact: Jimmy Fields. Record company, record producer and music publisher (Cherie Music/BMI). Releases 10 singles and 2 albums/year. Works with artists and songwriters on contract; musicians on salary for in-house studio work. Pays royalties to artists on contract; statutory rate to publishers for each record sold.
How to Contact: Prefers 7½ ips reel-to-reel or cassette with songs and lyric sheet. "A new singer should send a good tape with at least 4 strong songs, presumably recorded in a professional studio." SASE. Reports in 2 months.
Music: Bluegrass, church/religious, country, easy listening, progressive country, R&B, rock and top 40/pop. Recently released *Heart Achin' Blues*, by Suzan Stotts (progressive country LP); and "Your Convenience," by Bobby Crown (country single). Other artists include Boots and His Buddies, George McCoy, Joe Bill, Saucers, V-Notes, The Carmacks, Billy Taylor, Bobby Crown, The Twisters, Jimmy Fields and Straight Jackets.
Tips: "Songs should have strong lyrics, with a good story, whether country, rock or pop."

JAY JAY PUBLISHING, 35 NE 62nd St., Miami FL 33138. (305)758-0000. Contact: Walter Jagiello. Record company, record producer and music publisher (BMI). Releases 6 singles and 6 albums/year. Works with lyricists and composers and teams collaborators. Pays standard royalty.
How to Contact: Prefers cassette with 2-6 songs and lyric sheet. SASE. Reports in 1 month.
Music: Mostly polkas and waltzes; also country, novelty and easy listening. Recently released "God Bless Our Polish Pope," "Jelly Bean Polka" and "Polish Feelings," by Li'l Wally (polka singles); "I'd Rather Have a Hooker Than a Wife," by J. Rowland/Bonfire (country); and "There's A Full Moon Out Tonight," by D. Rowland.
Tips: "Send your demos by registered mail to ensure that they aren't lost."

*****JET RECORDS**, #200, 8730 Sunset Blvd., Los Angeles CA 90069. (213)652-0811. A&R Director: David A. Quint. Record company and management firm. Releases 8 singles/year and 4 LP's/year. Works with musicians/artists and songwriters on contract; musicians on salary for in-house studio work. Pays negotiable royalty to artists on contract.
How to Contact: Prefers cassette with 4 songs and lyric sheet. SASE. Reports in 3 weeks.
Music: Mostly hard rock, heavy metal and pop rock; also rock ballads. Artists include Air Supply, Lita Ford and Black Sabbath.

JRM RECORDS, Box 993, Salem VA 24153. (703)387-0208. Label includes Dominion. President: Jack Mullins. Record company and music publisher (Powhatan Music and Double Jack Publishing). Releases 6-8 singles and 6-8 albums/year. Works with artists and songwriters on contract. Teams collaborators. Pays 5-15% to artists on contract; statutory rate to publishers for each record sold.
How to Contact: Prefers cassette or videocassette with 1-3 songs on lyric sheet. SASE. Reports if interested.
Music: Crossover country, bluegrass, country and R&B. Recently released "Crazy in the Dark," by Donna Dean (crossover country single); "Til You Get it Right," by Roy James (country rock single); and "This Morning When You Said Goodbye," by Simpson Allen (pop country single).

KEYNOTE RECORDS, 4322 Mahoning Ave., Youngstown OH 44515. (216)793-7295. Executive Producer: Richard M. Hahn. Record company, record producer and music publisher (Al-Kris Music/BMI). Releases 5 singles and 2 albums/year. Works with artists and songwriters on contract. Pays 3-5% royalty to artists on contract; statutory rate to publishers for each record sold.
How to Contact: Query by letter first. Prefers cassette with 3-5 songs and lyric sheet. "Must have decent quality tape and clear lead or lyric sheet." SASE. Reports in 3 weeks.
Music: Children's, country, folk, gospel, MOR and top 40/pop. Recently released "Here Come the Browns", by Kardiak Kids (MOR single); "Jubilee" and "His Lovin", by Cycles (top 40 single); "Help Me I'm Falling," by Kirsti Manna (MOR ballad single). Other artists include Phil Hickman, Jim Stack, The B-Minors, Ken Crosslin, Leigh Fisher, and Gary Kekel.

KICKING MULE RECORDS, INC., Box 158, Alderpoint CA 95411. (707)926-5312. Head of A&R: Stefan Grossman. Record company and music publisher (Kicking Mule Publishing/BMI, Desk

Drawer Publishing/ASCAP). Member NAIRD. Releases 12 albums/year. Works with artists on contract. Pays 10-16% royalty to artists on contract; standard royalty to songwriters on contract.
How to Contact: Prefers reel-to-reel or cassette with 3-5 songs. SASE. Reports in 1 month.
Music: Bluegrass, blues and folk. Recently released *Mooncoin*, by Mickie Zekley (Irish traditional LP); *New York Banjo Ensemble Plays Gershwin* (pop music LP); *Blue Hula Stomp*, by Bob Brozman (pop music blues LP). Other artists include Michael Rugg, Neal Hellman, Bert Jansch, John Renbourn, Stefan Grossman, John James, Happy Traum, Fred Sokolow, Bob Stanton, Bob Hadley, Leo Wijnkamp, Jr., Mark Nelson, Lea Nicholson and Hank Sapoznik.
Tips: "We are a label mostly for instrumentalists. The songs are brought to us by the artists but we contact the artists because of their playing, not their songs. First, listen to what we have released and don't send material that is outside our interests. Secondly, learn to play your instrument well. We have little interest in songs or songwriters, but we are quite interested in people who play guitar, banjo, or dulcimer well."

KIDERIAN RECORD PRODUCTS, 4926 W. Gunnison, Chicago IL 60630. (312)399-5535. Labels include Homestead, Newbary, Sonic Wave, Virgin Vinal, Trinity, Far Star, Twin Lakes, Tempe and Stang Records. President: Ray Peck. Record company, record producer and music publisher (KRPCO). Releases 25-30 singles and 5-6 albums/year. Works with artists and songwriters on contract; musicians on salary for in-house studio work. Pays statutory rate to publishers for each record sold.
How to Contact: Prefers cassette with 4-6 songs and lyric sheet. Reports in 1 month.
Music: Bluegrass, blues, children's, choral, classical, country, dance-oriented, easy listening, folk, gospel, jazz, MOR, progressive, Spanish, R&B, rock, soul, top 40/pop and new wave. Recently released *Gary Cross Live*, by Gary Cross (country LP and single); *Rich Rags Syncopated Love*, by Rich Rags (new wave LP and single); and *Tricky Zingers*, by Creme Soda (power pop LP and single). Other artists include Boyz (Paul), Tom Petreli, The 80's, Ray Peck, The Trouble Boys, Wall Street, Pirate, Mammoth, Nadine Herman, Torn Orphan, Destiny, Puppetteer, Alicja, Ted Wika, Lucky Guess and Deceivor.

KILGORE RECORDS, INC., 706 W. Mechanic St., Leesville LA 71446-3446. (318)239-7121. Labels include Gotown Records. President: John E. Kilgore. Record company, record producer and music publisher (Gotown Publishing Company/BMI). Releases 3 singles/year. Works with artists and songwriters on contract. Pays minimum 3% royalty to artists on contract; statutory rate to publishers for each record sold.
How to Contact: Prefers cassette with 4-6 songs and lyric sheet. SASE. Reports in 6 months.
Music: Mostly gospel; also church/religious, R&B and soul. Recently released "Change in My Life," by Sensational (gospel single); and "Pass Me Not," by Golden Links (gospel single). Other artists include Echoes of Heaven, Sister Alfredia Allen Jones, Anita Anderson, Samuel Wallace, The Gospelerettes, The Gospel Harmonettes and Mildred Dorsey.

KIM RECORDS, 2305 Hungary Rd., Richmond VA 23228. (804)264-0539. Contact: W.H. Smith. Record company, record producer, music publisher (Festive Music/BMI) and agent. Works with songwriters on royalty contract. Pays 5% minimum royalty to artists on contract; statutory rate to publishers for each record sold.
How to Contact: Prefers reel-to-reel or cassette and lyric sheet. SASE. Reports in 1 month.
Music: Mostly country; also R&B, rock and top 40/pop.

KING OF KINGS RECORD CO., 38603 Sage Tree St., Palmdale CA 93550. Branch office: 171 Pine Haven, Daytona Beach FL 32014. (904)252-4849. President: Leroy Pritchett. A&R Director: Charles Vickers. Record company and music publisher. Releases 1 single and 1 album/year. Works with composers and teams collaborators. Pays statutory rate to publishers for each record sold.
How to Contact: Submit lead sheet only. SASE. Reports in 1 month.
Music: Country, church/religious and gospel. Recently released "Let Your Light Shine," "The Other Side of the Rainbow," and *The Magic of Gospel*, by Charles Vickers (gospel singles and LP).
Tips: "Send 2 or 3 songs, only your best."

KING-J RECORD CO., (subsidiary of Joe King Productions, Inc.), 80 Yesler, Seattle WA 98104. (206)622-5316. Labels include New Meadows and Cora and King J Records. Contact: Joe King. Record company and music publisher (Joe King Music/BMI). Releases 10 singles and 3 albums/year. Works with musicians on salary for in-house studio work and songwriters on contract.
How to Contact: Prefers cassette with 6-8 songs and lyric sheet. SASE. Reports in 2 weeks.
Music: Country. Recently released "Honky Tonk Woman," by Joe King; and "I Won't Cry No More," by Julie Ann Vath.

SID KLEINER MUSIC ENTERPRISES, 3701 25th Ave. SW, Naples FL 33999. (813)455-2696. Labels include Musi-Poe, Top-Star, This Is It, Token, and Country-King Records. Contact: Sid Kleiner. Record company and consulting firm to music industry. Releases 10 albums/year. Works with musicians and songwriters on contract. Charges for some services: "We may, at our option, charge *actual* production expense. We are not get-rich-quickers or rip-off artists. But we are too small to pay all of these bills!"

How to Contact: Prefers cassette and lead sheet. SASE, "otherwise materials aren't returned." Reports in 3 weeks.

Music: Bluegrass, country, easy listening, folk, jazz, and "banjo and guitar soloists and features." Recently released *Burd Boys on Stage* and *Chartbusters and Other Hits* (country LPs), by the Burd Boys; and *Find a Simple Life*, by Dave Kleiner (folk/rock LP). Other artists include Sid Kleiner.

L.M.I. (LEE MAGID, INC.), Box 532, Malibu CA 90265. (213)858-7282. President: Lee Magid. Record company, record producer and music publisher (Alexis Music/ASCAP, Marvelle Music/BMI, and Lou-Lee Music/BMI). Releases 8 singles/year and 4 albums/year. Works with artists, songwriters and self-contained groups on contract. Pays 2½-5% royalty to artists on contract; standard royalty to songwriters on contract. Pays negotiable rate to publishers for each record sold.

How to Contact: Prefers cassette or videocassette with 3-4 songs and lyric sheet. SASE. Reports in 3 weeks.

Music: Mostly country, rock, pop and jazz; also blues, gospel, R&B and soul. Recently released "Jelly Roll," by Carl Bean (rock single). Other artists include "Rags" Waldorf Band, Lyn Turner, Sandy Landers, Art Reynolds, Rene Heredia, the Jazz Choir, Papa John Creach, Nan Brennan, and Four Freshman.

Tips: "Send a good clear demo. Try to get some financial help to back up talent."

*LA LOUISIANNE RECORDS, 711 Stevenson St., Lafayette LA 70501. (318)234-5577. Labels include Tamm and Belle. President: (Mr.) Carol J. Rachou, Sr. Record company, record producer, recording studio and music publisher (La Lou Music/BMI). Releases 10-20 singles and 4-6 albums/year. Works with artists and songwriters on contract. "We also deal with promoters, managers, agents, etc." Pays statutory rate to publishers for each record sold.

How to Contact: Prefers 7½ ips reel-to-reel or cassette with 1-6 songs and lyric sheet. "If possible, submit different musical variations of songs (tempos, styles, keys, etc.)." SASE.

Music: Primarily produces Cajun/French but also produces some blues, church/religious, classical, country, folk, gospel, jazz, MOR, progressive, R&B, rock, top 40/pop, comedy, French comedy and instrumental. Recently released *Lache Pas La Patate* (Gold record in Canada), by Jimmy C. Newman (French Cajun LP); *A Cajun Tradition Vol. 2*, by Nathan Abshire (French Cajun LP); *Cajun Fiddle*, by Rufus Thibodeaux (Cajun/country LP); *That Cajun Country Sound*, by Eddy Raven (French and English Cajun/country LP); and *Authentic French Music*, by Ambrose Thibodeaux (traditional Cajun LP). Other artists include Vin Bruce, Aldus Roger, Merlin Fontenot, L.J. Foret, Blackie Forestier, The Dusenbery Family, Alex Broussard and Bud Fletcher.

LADD MUSIC CO., 401 Wintermantle Ave., Scranton PA 18505. (717)343-6718. Labels include White Rock Records. President: Phil Ladd. Record company, music publisher and producer. Releases 12-24 singles and 1-3 albums/year. Works with artists and songwriters on contract. Pays negotiable rate to artists on contract; 4% royalty to songwriters on contract.

How To Contact: Prefers cassette with 1-6 songs and lead sheet. SASE. Reports in 2 weeks.

Music: Blues, children's, choral, country, easy listening, MOR, rock, soul and top 40/pop. Recently released "Miss Lucy," by Big Al Downing (rock single); and "Once in Awhile," by Clyde Stacy (MOR single).

LAMON RECORDS, Box 25371, Charlotte NC 28212. (704)537-0133. Labels include Panhandel Records. Contact: Dwight or Carlton Moody. Record company, record producer and music publisher (Laymond Publicity Co./BMI and CDT Products/ASCAP). Releases 25 singles and 12 albums/year. Works with artists and songwriters on contract; musicians on salary for in-house studio work. Pays statutory rate to publishers for each record sold.

How to Contact: Write first and obtain permission to submit. Prefers cassette with minimum of 2 songs. Prefers studio produced demos. SASE. Reports in 1 month.

Music: Mostly beach, country and R&B. Recently produced "My Turn to Sing with Willie," (by Bob Bush), recorded by Cathy Moody (country); "Merry Christmas," (by C. Fulton/J. Dillard), recorded by Billy Scott; and "Play Me Tonight," written and recorded by A. Tucker (country).

LANDMARK (AUDIO OF NASHVILLE), Box 148296, Nashville TN 37214. (615)868-3407. Labels include Looking Glass, Smokehouse. Producers: Bill Anderson, Jr. or D.D. Morris. Record com-

pany, record producer and music publisher (Newcreature Music/BMI). Releases 4 singles and 4 albums/ year. Works with artists and songwriters on contract; musicians on salary for in-house studio work. Pays statutory rate to publishers for each record sold.
How to Contact: Prefers 7 1/2 ips reel-to-reel or cassette with 4-10 songs and lyric sheet. SASE. Reports in 1 month.
Music: Country, gospel, jazz, R&B, rock and top 40/pop. Artists include Joanne Cash, Rhonda Ingle, Dottie Lee Snow, and Vernon Oxford.

LANDSLIDE RECORDS, 450 14th St. NW, Atlanta GA 30318. (404)873-3918. President: Michael Rothschild. Record company and music publisher (Frozen Inca/BMI). Member NARAS. Releases 2 singles and 5 albums/year. Works with artists and songwriters on contract. Pays 5-15% royalty to artists on contract; statutory rate to publishers for each record sold.
How to Contact: Write or call first. Prefers cassette with 4-10 songs and lyric sheet. SASE. Reports in 1 month.
Music: Mostly progressive and dance-oriented; also blues, jazz, R&B, rock and soul. Recently released *Isles of Langerham*, by The Late Bronze Age (progressive LP); *Dancing Under the Streetlights*, by The Brains (progressive/new music LP); and *Middle of the Night*, by Bruce Baxter (pop/new music LP). Other artists include David Earle Johnson, Defuser, The Heartfixers, Curlew, Dan Wall, It and Marianna Pace.
Tips: "Don't be afraid to go to extremes in presenting your work."

LANOR RECORDS, 329 N. Main St., Box 233, Church Point LA 70525. (318)684-2176. Labels include Lanor and Joker Records. Contact: Lee Lavergne. Record company and music publisher. Releases 12-18 singles and 2-3 albums/year. Works with composers. Works with artists and songwriters on contract. Pays 3-5% royalty to artists on contract.
How to Contact: Prefers cassette or videocassette with 2-6 songs. SASE. Reports in 2 weeks.
Music: Mostly country; also rock, and soul. Recently released "Devil Went Down to New Iberia," by Johnny Smith (Cajun country single); "I Heard That Whistle," by B.D. Thomas (country single); and "The Pill," by Pat Smith (country single). Other artists include Doris Bijeaux, Glenn T. and Aldus Roger.

*LAURIE RECORDS/3C RECORDS, 20 F Robert Pitt Dr., Monsey NY 10952. (914)425-7000. Vice President: Gene Schwartz. Labels include Rust Records. Record company. Releases 10 singles/ year and 7 LP's/year. Works with musicians/artists and songwriters on contract; musicians on salary for in-house studio work. Pays varying royalty to artists on contract.
How to Contact: Prefers cassette and lyric sheet. SASE.
Music: Mostly rock and MOR.

LAVAL RECORDS, 1327 Cobb St., Kalamazoo MI 49007. (616)342-5328. Contact: Vic Laval. Record company, record producer and music publisher (Valco Music/BMI). Releases 15 albums/year. Works with artists and songwriters on contract. Pays 3-5¢/single sold and 60-80¢/album sold to artists on contract; statutory rate to publishers for each record sold.
How to Contact: Prefers 7 1/2 ips reel-to-reel or cassette with 4-8 songs and lyric sheet. SASE. Reports in 2 weeks.
Music: Blues, church/religious, country, gospel, R&B, rock and soul. Recently released *Don't Tax Me In*, by Joe Blue (blues LP); *Stoop Down Baby*, by Chick Willis (blues LP); and *The Best of Jimmy Lynch*, by Jimmy Lynch (soul LP). Other artists include Eddie Vespa, Frisco, Linc Terry, John Brown, Tommy Brown and The Terry's.

LAZER RECORDS, 7330 Sycamore Ave., Philadelphia PA 19126. (215)635-2878. President: A. Gravatt. Record company, record producer and music publisher. Works with artists and songwriters on contract. Pays negotiable royalty to artists on contract; negotiable rate to publishers for each record sold.
How to Contact: Write first about your interest. Prefers cassette and lyric sheet. SASE. Reporting time varies.
Music: Dance-oriented, easy listening, MOR, progressive, R&B, rock, soul and top 40/pop.

LE MATT MUSIC LTD., c/o Stewart House, Hill Bottom Rd., Highwycombe, Buckinghamshire, England. 44-0525-220400 or 0494-36301/36401. Labels include Swoop, Genouille, Pogo and Check Records. Contact: Ron or Cathrine Lee. Record company, record producer and music publisher (Le Matt Music, Ltd., Lee Music, Ltd., and Pogo Records, Ltd.) Member MPA, PPL, PRS, MCPS. Releases 25 singles and 20 albums/year. Pays negotiable royalty to artists on contract; MCPS rates to publishers for each record sold. Royalties paid to US songwriters and artists through US publishing or recording affiliate.

How to Contact: Include bio and photo. Prefers 7½ or 15 ips reel-to-reel, cassette or videocassette with 1-3 songs and lyric sheet. SAE and IRC. Reports in 3 weeks.
Music: Bluegrass, blues, country, dance-oriented, easy listening, MOR, progressive, R&B, disco, new wave, rock, soul and top 40/pop. Recently released "I Do Love You," by Penny Arcade (MOR single); "I'm Only Looking," by Daniel Boone (reggae single); and "I'm a Rep" and *The Chromatics*, by The Chromatics (rock single and LP). Other artists include Emmitt Till, Touche, Orphan, Nightmare, Jonny Moon, Ian "Sludge" Lees and Kyro Groucho.

LEGEND RECORDS AND PROMOTIONS, 1102 Virginia St. SW, Lenoir NC 28645. (704)758-4170. Labels include Legend Records. President: Mike McCoy. Record company, record producer and music publisher (Nancy Jane Publishing). Releases 2 singles/year. Works with songwriters on contract. Pays 10% maximum royalty to artists on contract; statutory rate to publishers for each record sold.
How to Contact: Prefers cassette with 1-4 songs and lyric sheet. SASE. Reports in 1 month.
Music: Mostly country rock, rock and rockabilly; also church/religious, gospel, R&B, "outlaw" country, and bluegrass. Recently released "My Baby Loves Old Rock and Roll," "From My Land to Graceland," and "Rock and Roll Outlaw," all by Mike McCoy (singles).
Tips: "Analyze your songs very carefully and write with the times; lyrics must be good; story should sound real."

*LIGHT RECORDS, #304, 4001 W. Alameda, Burbank CA 91505. (818)842-1010. Vice President, Director of A&R: Gary Whitlock. Record company and music publisher (Lexicon Music). Releases 25 singles/year and 25 LPs/year. Works with musicians/artists and songwriters on contract.
How to Contact: Call first and obtain permission to submit. Prefers cassette with 2-3 songs and lyric sheet. SASE. Reports in 3-4 weeks. "Check out who is recording prior to submitting 'blind' material."
Music: Gospel only. Artists include Allies, Bryan Duncan, Douglas Miller, Sandra Crouch, and Walter Hawkins.

LITTLE GIANT RECORDS, Box 205, White Lake NY 12786. (914)583-4471. Label includes Killer Records. A&R Director: Mike Pell. Record company, record producer and music publisher (Karjan Music Publishing Co./SESAC). Releases 6 singles and 6 albums/year. Works with artists and songwriters on contract. Pays standard royalty to artists on contract; statutory rate to publishers for each record sold.
How to Contact: Prefers cassette with 1-3 songs and lyric sheet. SASE. Reports in 3 weeks.
Music: Country, easy listening, MOR, R&B and top 40/pop. Recently released *Presenting T. Barry Kaminski* (MOR LP); *Country Songs and Dreams* by Chuck Wilson (country LP); and *You Requested This* by Mickey Barnett (MOR LP). Other artists incude Bobby Gold, The Third Edition, Jason Ross, Kenny Adams and Amanda.

LITTLE RICHIE RECORDS, 1700 Plunket, Box 3, Belen NM 87002. (505)864-7441. Labels include LRJ and Chuckie records. Manager: Curt Huckabone. Record company, record producer and music publisher (Little Richie Johnson Music/BMI). Releases 10 singles and 2-4 albums/year. Works with artists on contract.
How to Contact: Call first. Prefers cassette with 4-6 songs. SASE. Reports in 1 month.
Music: Country.

LONGHORN RECORDS, Box 1995, Studio City CA 91604. (213)656-0574. Contact: Lil Rodell and Harvey Appell. Record company and music publisher (Udder Publishing/BMI and Golden Gilt/ASCAP). Releases 6 singles and 6 albums/year. Works with artists and songwriters on contract and individual basis; musicians on salary for in-house studio work.
How to Contact: Arrange personal interview. Prefers 15 ips reel-to-reel or cassette and lead sheet. SASE.
Music: Mostly country and bluegrass; also western swing and folk. Recently released "I Do My Crying at Night," and "Houston Bounce," by the River Road Boys (country singles); and "The Other Man," by Billy Mize (country single). Other artists include Bob White and Clyde Brewer.

LUCIFER RECORDS, INC., Box 263, Hasbrouck Heights NJ 07604. (201)288-8935. Branch: Box 263, Brigantine NJ 08203. (609)266-2623. President: Ron Luciano. Record company, booking agency and music publisher. Works with artists and songwriters on salary and contract.
How to Contact: Arrange personal interview. Prefers cassette with 4-8 songs. SASE. Reports in 3 weeks.
Music: Dance, easy listening, MOR, rock, soul and top 40/pop. Recently released "I Who Have Nothing," by Spit-N-Image (rock single);"Lucky," and "Smoke Ya," by Legz (rock single); and "Loves a Crazy Game," by Voyage (disco/ballad single). Other artists include Diamond Jym, Charles Lamont and Lee Estrada (tribute to Elvis).

LUNA RECORDS CORP., 434 Center St., Healdsburg CA 95448. (707)433-4138. Labels include Luna, Lugar, Yuriko and Sony Records. President: Abel De Luna. Record company, booking agency and music publisher (Yema Publishing/ASCAP and De Luna Publishing/BMI). Releases 30 singles and 20 albums/year. Works with artists and songwriters on contract. Pays 8% royalty to artists on contract; statutory rate.
How to Contact: Prefers cassette with 5-10 songs and lead sheet. Does not return unsolicited material. Reports in 3 weeks.
Music: Children's and Latin. Recently released "El Solitario," by Los Pasteles Verdes (Spanish 45 and LP); "Que Me Entierren Cantando," by Los Huracanes Del Norte (Spanish 45 and LP); and "Te Vas O Quedar Liorando," by La Banda Int'de Ray Camacho (Spanish 45 and LP). Other artists include Los Luceritos de Michoacan, Los Astros, Los Buhos, Tany Ponce, Grupo Santa Maria, Los Flamantes Del Norte, and Los Errantes Del Norte.

LUV RECORDS, 3784 Realty, Dallas TX 75244. (214)241-7854. Label includes Kenco Records. President: K.J. Hughes. Record company, record producer, music publisher (Luvco Music/BMI and Kenco Publishing Co./ASCAP) and 24-track recording studio. Member CMA, TMA. Releases 12-15 singles and 8-12 albums/year. Works with artists and songwriters on contract; musicians on salary for in-house studio work. Pays 3¢/song to artists on contract; statutory rate to publishers for each record sold.
How to Contact: Prefers cassette with 1-3 songs and lyric sheet. SASE. Label tape with address and phone number. Reports in 1 month.
Music: Mostly country and novelty; also bluegrass, R&B and top 40/pop. Recently released *I Am a Promise*, by Joe Alan (Christian LP); "Dallas Does It," by Nancy Allyson Parrish (MOR single); and "Too Good to Be True," by Michael Wicks (novelty single). Other artists include Carlette, Roger Howell, Westridge, and The Gloryland Express.

M.E.C.A., 7764 NW. 71st St., Miami FL 33166. A&R: Mark Blanchard. Record company and music publisher. Releases 10 singles and 3 albums/year. Works with artists and songwriters on contract. Pays 10-18% royalty to artists on contract; statutory rate to publishers for each record sold.
How to Contact: Prefers cassette with 1-3 songs and lead sheet. SASE. Reports in 6-8 weeks. "No reports issued unless material is accepted or unless we wish additional material for review."
Music: Dance, progressive, rock, soul and top 40/pop. Recently released "Give It Up," and "Are You Ready," by KC (top 40/pop/dance).
Tips: "We need music for male pop singers and rock groups."

M.R.C. RECORDS, Box 2072, Waynesboro VA 22980. (703)949-0106. Labels include MRC, Lark and Echo Records. Contact: John Major. Record company, music publisher and recording studio. Releases 10 singles and 20 albums/year. Pays 5-7% royalty to artists on contract; statutory rate to publishers for each record sold.
How to Contact: Prefers cassette and lyric sheet. SASE. Reports in 2 weeks.
Music: Bluegrass, gospel, country, easy listening, dance, MOR, rock (country, hard), soul and top 40/pop. Recently released "Honky Tonk Angel," by Joey Davis (country single).
Tips: "Don't submit songs with tunes purchased from advertisements. Make sure your songs say what people want to hear."

*M.R.I. CASSETTES, #117, 4047 N. Beltline, Irving TX 75038. (214)258-7955. Producer: Mike Itashiki. Record producer. Releases 3-5 cassettes/year and 1-2 albums/year. Works with musicians/artists on contract.
How to Contact: Prefers cassette with 1-4 songs and lyric sheet. Does not return unsolicited material. Reports in 2 weeks.
Music: Mostly novelty, educational and ethnic; also classical, pop and religious. Recently released "Cassette Para Sobrevivir," (by Mike Itashiki), recorded by Jose Diaz on M.R.I. (novelty cassette); "Biblia Español," recorded by Martin Villa on M.R.I. (religious cassette); and "Wedding Music," recorded by Dial-A-Quartet on M.R.I. (novelty cassette).

*MAIN TRIPP RECORDS INC., 2804 Beechtree Dr., Sanford NC 27330. (919)774-8926. Vice President/General Manager: John W. Edwards. Record company and music publisher. Releases 20 singles/year and 4 albums/year. Works with musicians/artists and songwriters on contract; musicians on salary for in-house studio work. Pays 3-10% royalty to artists on contract; statutory rate to publishers for each record sold.
How to Contact: Prefers cassette or 7¹/₂ ips reel-to-reel with any number of songs and lyric sheet; "we also accept 8-track, record, or lead sheet." SASE. Reports in 2 weeks.
Music: Mostly country, country rock and gospel; also bluegrass. Recently released "Love Is," "Put Me Down Easy," and "Love Gone Right," all written and recorded by Bill Tripp on Atteram (country

singles). Other artists include Joe Stuart, Brock Brothers, and Tommy & Donny Green.
Tips: "Don't write to please the publisher, let creativity lead."

MAJEGA RECORDS, 240 E. Radcliffe Dr., Claremont CA 91711. (714)624-0677. President: Gary K. Buckley. Record company. Works with artists and songwriters on contract; musicians on salary for in-house studio work. Pays negotiable royalty to artists on contract; standard royalty to songwriters on contract; statutory rate to publishers for each record sold.
How to Contact: Prefers cassette with 1-4 songs and lead sheet. SASE. Reports in 3 weeks.
Music: Country, easy listening, gospel, MOR, rock (country or pop) and top 40/pop. Recently released *To God, with Love* and *Country Love*, recorded by Jerry Roark (gospel/country LPs); "Songwriter," (pop single) and *Buche*, (top 40 LP) by Rick Buche; *Steppin' Out*, by The Gospelmen (gospel LP); "Our America," by June Wade and the Country Congregation (country/gospel single); "Is It Right," "Touch Me Now," "It's Alright," and "What You Doin' to Me," by Borderline (top 40 singles); and *Sky's the Limit* by Michael Noll (top 40 LP).

MAJOR LABEL RECORD CO., Box 651, Worthington OH 43085. (614)846-2026. President: Richard H. Deitch. Record company and music publisher (XC Music Publishing/ASCAP). Releases 1 single/year. Works with artists and songwriters on contract. Works with lyricists and composers and teams collaborators. Pays negotiable royalty to artists on contract; statutory rate to publishers for each record sold.
How to Contact: Prefers cassette or videocassette with 1-6 songs and lyric sheet. SASE.
Music: Rock, top 40/pop, country, MOR and new wave. Recently released "War Museum", by XL (rock single).

MALACO RECORDS, Box 9287, Jackson MS 39206. (601)982-4522. Labels include Malaco and Chimneyville Records. Producers: Wolf Stephenson, Tommy Couch. Record company, music publisher and record producer. Works with artists and songwriters on contract and salary. Pays standard royalty.
How to Contact: Prefers cassette with 1-5 songs and lyric sheet. SASE. Reports in 1 month.
Music: R&B music only. Other artists include Z.Z. Hill, Denise Lasalle, Latimore and Little Milton.

MANHATTAN RECORDS, 1370 Avenue of the Americas, New York NY 10019. (212)547-6401. Vice President, A&R: Bruce Garfield. Record company and music publisher.
How to Contact: Prefers cassette with 4 songs and lyric sheet. SASE. Reports in 3 months.
Music: All styles.

MANQUIN, Box 2388, Toluca Lake CA 91602. (818)985-8284. Contact: Manny Rodriquez. Record company, music publisher, record producer, management firm and public relations firm. Works with artists and songwriters on spec only. Pays standard royalty to artists and songwriters on contract.
How to Contact: Prefers cassette with 2-3 songs and lead sheet. SASE. Reports in 8 weeks.
Music: Country and Latin only.

MARIA RECORDS, Box 295, Riverdale NY 10463. (212)549-0502. President: John Clark. Record company, record producer, music publisher (Johnny Angel Music) and artist booking agent. Releases 2 singles/year. Works with artists on contract. Pays minimum 5% royalty to artists on contract; statutory rate to publishers for each record sold.
How to Contact: Prefers cassette with 2-4 songs and lyric sheet. Prefers studio produced demos. SASE. Reports in 1 month.
Music: Mostly top 40 and rock; also dance and pop. Recently released "Be My Baby," by Mystique (top 40 single).

MARMIK, 135 E. Muller Rd., East Peoria IL 61611. (309)699-7204. President: Martin Mitchell. Record company and music publisher. Releases 12-15 singles and 6-10 albums/year. Works with musicians and songwriters. Pays negotiable royalty. Sometimes buys material from songwriters outright; payment negotiable.
How to Contact: Query first. Prefers reel-to-reel or cassette with 2-10 songs. "With first submission include an affidavit of ownership of material." SASE. Reports in 2 weeks.
Music: Mostly Christian, MOR and country; also blues, children's, choral, church/religious, easy listening, and gospel. Recently released "Be My Sunshine," and "The Good Ol Days," written and recorded by Danny Schaeffer (country); and "Why Did I Do That?," written and recorded by Mack Dunning (country).
Tips: "The country seems to be going into a happier time now. Keep songs up-tempo and positive."

MASTER TRAK SOUND RECORDERS, Miller Building, 413 N. Parkerson, Box 1345, Crowley LA 70526. (318)783-1601. Labels include Master-Trak, Showtime, Kajun, Blues Unlimited and Par T.

Contact: Jay Miller. General Manager and Chief Engineer: Mark Miller. Recording studio and record companies. Works with artists on royalty basis; musicians on salary for in-house studio work. Pays 4% and 5% artist royalty. (No studio charges to contract artists.) Studio available on an hourly basis to the public. Works with musicians on salary; artists and songwriters on contract. Pays 4-5% royalty to artists on contract. Charges for some services: "We charge for making audition tapes of any material that we do not publish."
How to Contact: Prefers cassette and lead sheet. SASE. Reports in 1 month.
Music: Mostly country; also blues, church/religious, dance, folk, gospel, MOR, progressive, rock and soul. Recently released *Lerory Broussard*, and *The Lagniapee Gang*; *Cajun Fiddling & Singing Now & Tommorrow*, by Hadley Castille; and "Buckwheat Zydeco," by Buckwheat Zydeco.

THE MASTER'S COLLECTION LIMITED, Box 362, Station A, Rexdale, Toronto, Ontario M9W 5L3, Canada. (416)746-1991. Labels include Sharon, T.M.C., The Master's Collection, Pilgrim and Little Pilgrim. President: Paul J. Young. Record company and music publisher (T.M.C. Publishing/ CAPAC and Master's Collection Publishing/PROCAN). Member CIRPA. Releases 3-6 singles and 10-12 albums/year. Works with artists and songwriters on contract. Pays 2%-10% royalty to artists on contract; statutory rate to publishers for each record sold.
How to Contact: Write first. Prefers cassette with 3-6 songs. Does not return unsolicited material. Reports in 1 month.
Music: Mostly Christian gospel ("any style"); also church/religious. Recently released "Trusting You, Jesus," by Frank and Debbie, "Mobile," by Andrew Donaldson; and "Crown of Glory, Crown of Thorns," by Ruth Fazel. Other artists include Rick Piche, Mark Moore, Wiz Bryant and Gene MacLellan.

*MAWSON AND WAREHAM (MUSIC) LTD., Midgy Ha, Sharperton, Morpeth, Northumberland NE65 7AS England. (0669)40252. Labels include Rubber Records, MWM Records, Black Crow Records, Vallium Records. Record company, music publisher and record producer. Releases 6 LPs/year. Works with musicians/artists and songwriters on contract. Pays 4-8% royalty to artists on contract.
How to Contact: Prefers cassette with 4 songs. SAE and IRC. Reports in 4 weeks.
Music: Mostly folk, blues and country. Recently released *Under the Rain*, (by Rab Noakes) and *On the Other Side*, (by Alan Hull) on Black Crow (LP); and *At Last It's*, (by Mike Elliott) on Rubber Records (LP). Other artists include Allan Taylor, Joe Hutton, Alex Glasgow, Maxie and Mitch, and Bobby Thompson.

*MAZINGO'S, INC., 4317 Rounding Run Road, Matthews NC 28105. (704)542-7000. President: Ben W. McCoy. Record company. Payment negotiable.
How to Contact: Prefers cassette or 8-track (cartridge) with 2-8 songs and lead sheet. SASE. Reports in 1 month.
Music: Bluegrass, blues, children's, choral, church/religious, classical, country, folk, gospel, jazz, polka, progressive, soul, and top 40/pop.

MCA RECORDS, Suite 400, 1701 West End Ave., Nashville TN 37203. (615)244-8944. Contact: A&R Department. Record company. Releases 60 singles and 30 albums/year. Works with artists on contract. Does not accept unsolicited or unpublished material.

MCP/DAVISOUND, Box 521, By-Pass 76, Newberry SC 29108. (803)276-0639. Labels include Mother Cleo, Cleo and Cub Records. Producer/Director: Hayne Davis. Studio Manager: Polly Davis. Record company, music publisher (Sweet Polly Music/BMI), recording studio, and production company producing music for films, features and commercials. "MCP is a unique, small (but multifaceted) company engaged in numerous activities for the communications/entertainment industry." Releases 6 singles and 2 albums/year. Works with artists and songwriters on contract; musicians on salary for in-house studio work. "We also work with co-producers, supplying our facility and talent for outside use for a front fee. We hire talent (vocalists, musicians and writers) of varying types, styles and capabilities at varying intervals, depending on the requirements and frequency of the work project and the individual's capabilities." Charges for some services: offers studio facilities for rental by "outside" songwriters, producers and publishers.
How to Contact: Prefers cassette with 2-8 songs and lead sheet. "We are not responsible for return of tapes, lead sheets, etc. on unsolicited material. If, however, appropriate packaging and return postage are included, we make every effort to return materials and notify the sender by personal letter." SASE. Reports in 2 weeks.
Music: Modern country, disco, easy listening, MOR, rock and top 40/pop. Recently released "Sheila," by James Meadows (modern country single); "Too Far Gone," by Curt Bradford (modern country single); and "If You Want My Love," by Hayne Davis.

MDS-NORTHCOAST, 29 S. Erie, Toledo OH 43602. (419)244-8599. Labels include MDS, Northcoast, Heritage, Jamestune, Purple Gwano and Toledo. Assistant to the President: Jennifer Lynne. Record company, record producer and music publisher (Keeny-York, Park J. Tunes). Releases 6 singles and 2 albums/year. Works with artists and songwriters on contract. Pays negotiable royalty to artists; statutory rate to publishers for each record sold.
How to Contact: Prefers cassette with 5-10 songs and lyric sheet. SASE. Reports in 1 month.
Music: Mostly pop; also country, easy listening and MOR.

MEDA RECORD CO., 8130 Northlawn, Detroit MI 48204. (313)934-0106. West Coast: 8569 Horner, Los Angeles CA 90035. (213)657-2649. A&R Director: Joe Hunter. Record company, record producer and music publisher (Mertis Music Company). Releases 4 singles and 4 albums/year. Works with artists and songwriters on contract. Pays 4-12% royalty to artists on contract; statutory rate to publishers for each record sold.
How to Contact: Prefers cassette with 4-8 songs and lyric sheet. SASE. Reports in 1 month.
Music: Mostly gospel, R&B and pop; also jazz and top 40. Recently released "You Don't Know," by Lorine Thompson (gospel single); "I'm Guilty," by Lorene Daniels (gospel single); and "God's Grace," by the Bethel Baptist Church East Mass Choir of Detroit.

*MEGATONE RECORDS, #206, 2269 Market, San Francisco CA 94114. (415)621-7475. A&R: Marty Blecman. Record company, music publisher (Masculine Music/BMI, Marsan/ASCAP) and record producer. Releases 20 singles/year and 5 LP's/year. Works with musicians/artists and songwriters on contract; musicians on salary for in-house studio work. Pays 20% (wholesale) royalty to artists on contract.
How to Contact: Prefers cassette with 2-4 songs. SASE. Reports in 4 weeks. "24-track masters are the best bet."
Music: Mostly disco, R&B dance and pop rock. Recently released "Rock the Box," (by Kessie), recorded by Sylvester on Megatone (R&B disco single); "And Dance," written and recorded by Billy Preston on Megatone (R&B dance single); and "Last Call," written and recorded by Jo-Lo on Megatone (disco single). Other artists include Jeanie Tracey, Sarah Dash, Modern Rocketry, Kenny James, The 49rs, and Sehennie Payne.

MELODEE RECORDS, Box 1010, Hendersonville TN 37077. (615)451-3920. General Manager: Dee Mullins. Record company, record producer, music publisher (My Dee Dee Music/ASCAP, Mel-Dee Music/BMI), and promotion and distribution firm. Member NARM, Music Expo, MIDEM. Releases 10-20 singles and 20-30 albums/year. Works with artists and songwriters on contract; musicians on salary for in-house studio work. Pays standard royalty to artists on contract; statutory rate to publishers for each record sold.
How to Contact: Write or call first about your interest, or arrange personal interview to play demo tape. Prefers cassette with 1-4 songs and lyric sheet. Prefers studio produced demos. SASE. Reports in 1 month.
Music: Mostly country, MOR and bluegrass; also folk, gospel, rock (country) and top 40/pop. Recently released "I Can't Keep My Hands Off You," by Dee Mullins (country crossover single); and "Holdin On, Hangin On," by Carlson Roberts and Kelly Harland (country crossover single). Other artists include Jo Countess, Polly Ford, Ronnie Osbahr, Hank Marshall and Joy Lewis.

MERCANTILE RECORDS, Box 2271, Palm Springs CA 92263. (619)320-4848. President: Kent Fox. Record company, record producer and music publisher. Works with artists on contract.
How to Contact: Prefers cassette with 3-12 songs and lyric sheet. SASE. Reports in 1 month.
Music: Country, easy listening, rock and top 40/pop.

MIRROR RECORDS, INC., 645 Titus Ave., Rochester NY 14617. (716)544-3500. Labels include Mirror and House of Guitars Records. Vice President: Armand Schaubroeck. Record company and music publisher. Works with artists and songwriters on contract; musicians on salary for in-house studio work. Pays 33% royalty to artists on contract; negotiable royalty to songwriters on contract.
How to Contact: Prefers 7½ ips reel-to-reel or cassette. Include photo with submission. SASE. Reports in 2 months.
Music: Folk, progressive, rock, punk and heavy metal. Recently released "I Shot My Guardian Angel," by Armand Schaubroeck Steals; and "She Told Me Lies," by the Chesterfield Kings.

MODERN RECORDS INC., 1438 N. Gower St., Box 3, Los Angeles CA 90028. (213)465-5144. A&R Director: Rick Roger. Record company, record producer and music publisher (Modern Music Publishing). Member RIAA, NARAS, NARM. Releases varying number of singles and albums/year. Works with artists and songwriters on contract; musicians on salary for in-house studio work. Pays statutory or varying rate to publishers for each record sold.

How to Contact: Prefers cassette with 2-4 songs and lyric sheet. SASE. Reports in 2 weeks.

Music: Mostly rock and AOR; also country, dance-oriented, folk, MOR, R&B and top 40/pop. Recently released "Stand Back," "If Anyone Falls," "Nite Bird" and "Wild Heart," by Stevie Nicks (rock singles). Other artists include Sandy Stewart.

MONOTONE RECORDS, 281 E. Kingsbridge Rd., Bronx NY 10458. (212)582-3240. President: Murray Fuller. Record company, record producer and music publisher (Sun Island Music Publishing Co.). Releases 1 single/year. Works with artists and songwriters on contract. Pays 3-5% royalty to artists on contract; statutory rate to publishers for each record sold.

How to Contact: Prefers cassette with 3-5 songs and lyric sheet. SASE. Reports in 6 weeks.

Music: Blues, dance-oriented, easy listening, jazz, R&B, soul and top 40/pop.

MONTICANA RECORDS, Box 702, Snowdon Station, Montreal, Quebec H3X 3X8 Canada. (514)345-4142. Labels include Dynacom and Monticana Records. General Manager: David P. Leonard. Record company, record producer, and music publisher (Montina Music/BMI). Member MIEA. Works with artists and songwriters on contract. Pays negotiable royalty to artists on contract; statutory rate to publishers for each record sold.

How to Contact: Prefers 7½ or 15 ips reel-to-reel, phonograph record or VHS videocassette and lyric sheet. Does not return unsolicited material.

Music: Mostly top 40, blues, country, dance-oriented, easy listening, folk, gospel, jazz, MOR, progressive, R&B, rock and soul.

MOPRO INC., 5950 Beech Dell Dr., Cincinnati OH 45238. (513)281-4954. President: Helen Y. Morr. Record company and record producer. Member IAJRC, NAIRD, NARAS. Releases 3 albums/year. Works with artists on contract. Pays statutory rate to publishers for each record sold.

How to Contact: Write first and obtain permission to submit. Prefers cassette with 2-3 songs. Does not return unsolicited material. Reports in 2 weeks.

Music: Jazz and big band. Recently released *Live at Carmelo's*, by Blue Wisp Big Band (jazz big band single); and *No Net*, by Marshall Vente/Project Nine (jazz LP). Other artists include Cal Collins and Ron Boustead.

*MOR RECORDS, 17596 Corbel Court, San Diego CA 92128. (619)485-1550. President: Stuart L. Glassman. Record company and record producer. Releases 6 singles/year. Works with musicians on salary for in-house studio work.

How to Contact: Prefers cassette. Does not return unsolicited material. Reports in 6-8 weeks.

Music: Mostly pop instrumental/vocal MOR; also novelty songs. Recently released "As Time Goes By," recorded by Al Rosa on MOR (pop single); "Shifting, Whispering Sands," recorded by Wally Flaherty on MOR (pop single); and "You'll Never Know/Colors of My Life," recorded by Frank Sinatra, Jr., on MOR (pop single).

*MOTORCOACH RECORDS, 630 W. Adler Rd., Marshfield WI 54449-2653. President: Daniel Korn. Record company, music publisher and record producer. Releases 1 single/year and 1 LP/year. Works with musicians/artists and songwriters on contract; musicians on salary for in-house studio work. Pays 100% royalty to artists on contract.

How to Contact: Write and obtain permission to submit. Prefers cassette, reel-to-reel or videocassette with 8-10 songs and lyric sheet or lead sheet. SASE. Reports in 2 weeks.

Music: Mostly rock, jazz and country; also blues, classical and soul. Recently released "Skin and Bones," "This Empty Space," and "The Mirage," written and recorded by Daniel Korn on Sojourn. Other artists include Robert Pue, Gary Nilsen, and Paula Van Holland.

*MUSHROOM RECORDS PTY, LTD., 9 Dundas Lane, Albert Park, Victoria 3206 Australia. (03)690-3399. Label Manager: Michelle Higgins. Labels include Liberation Records, White Label Records. Record company and music publisher. Releases 50 singles/year and 20 LP s/year. Works with musicians/artists and songwriters on contract.

How to Contact: Prefers cassette or videocassette. Does not return unsolicited material. Reports in 4 weeks.

Music: Mostly pop, rock and dance.

MUSICANZA CORPORATION, 2878 Bayview Ave., Wantagh NY 11793. Record company and music publisher (ASCAP). Works with artists and songwriters on contract.

How to Contact: Submit lead and lyric sheet.

Music: "We will only accept original children's songs." Recently released *Dolly Dimples*, by many artists (children's LP); and *Yeaster Bunny*, by many artists (children's LP).

MUSTEVIC SOUND, INC., 115-18 222nd Ave., New York NY 11411. (212)276-2078. Producer: Steve Reid. Record company, music publisher (Mustevic Sound Publishing/BMI) and record producer. Member BMA and SIRMA. Releases 3-4 singles and 1-7 albums/year. Works with artists and songwriters on contract. Pays 17-85% to artists on contract; standard royalty to songwriters on contract; statutory rate to publishers for each record sold.
How to Contact: Write first. Prefers cassette with 1-3 songs. SASE. Reports in 3 weeks.
Music: Mostly jazz, fusion and ethnic rock. Recently released *Space Place*, by Steve Reid (fusion LP); "One Hard Fall," by Mike Singer (rock single); and "I Know, You Know," by Beverly Reid (blues single).
Tips: "Please send only copyrighted material."

MYSTIC OAK RECORDS, 1727 Elm St., Bethlehem PA 18017. (215)865-1083. Talent Coordinator: Bill Byron. Record company and record producer. Releases 8 singles and 15 albums/year. Works with artists on contract. Pays 3-10% royalty to artists on contract; statutory rate to publishers for each record sold.
How to Contact: Write first and obtain permission to submit. Prefers 15 ips reel-to-reel or cassette or videocassette with 3-6 songs. Include bio and performance information. SASE. Reports in 1 month if interested.
Music: Mostly synth-pop and dance-oriented rock; also folk and top 40/pop. Recently released "In Your Dreams," by Office Toys (dance-oriented rock EP). Other artists include Trendsetters, Psychic Warriors, Steve Brosky and the BBC, and The Polygraphs.
Tips: "Be professional in all respects and work toward being able to formulate "hit" songs. Also, send videos with return postage (if you wish them returned). Videos allow us to evaluate an act's entire image and presentation."

MYSTIC RECORDS, INC., Doug Moody Productions Inc., 6277 Selma Ave., Hollywood CA 90028. (213)464-9667. Labels include Mystic, Solar, Clock, Ghett-O-Way, Atmosphear and Mystic Classique. President: Doug Moody. Coordinator: Nancy Faith. Record company, music publisher and production firm. Also originates film and TV music and syndicated radio show. Releases 20 singles and 30 albums/year. Works with artists and songwriters on contract; musicians on salary for in-house studio work. Pays standard rates; some advances.
How to Contact: Prefers cassette and lyric sheet. Reports in 1 month. SASE.
Music: Blues, country, easy listening, gospel (modern, rock or pop), MOR, punk, rockabilly, soul, top 40/pop and "spoken word plays (up to 1 hour)." Has own 16 track recording and video facilities.
Tips: "Mystic also releases collector item records, limited editions in picture disc or shaped records."

NASHBORO RECORDS, 128 Sixth Ave S., Nashville TN 37203. (615)227-5081. Labels include Creed, Ernie's, Kenwood, Excello, Abet, Mankind, Nasco Records and AVI. Vice President/A&R: John Jossey. Record company. Pays standard royalty to artists and songwriters.
How to Contact: Prefers cassettes and lyric sheet. "Please include address and phone number." SASE. Reports in 1-2 months.
Music: Gospel and jazz. Recently released "That's My Son," "Prayer," and "He Won't Let You Fall," by Excello (gospel LP).

*NEW COLONY, 455 Massieville Rd., Chillicothe OH 45601. (614)663-4030. Manager: (Ms.) Willi Pack. Record company. Works with musicians/artists on contract.
How to Contact: Prefers cassette with maximum 3 songs and lyric sheet. "Lyric sheets a must." Does not return unsolicited material. Reports in 4 weeks.
Music: Mostly country, gospel, R&B and MOR. Recently released *Southbound All The Way*, recorded by Southbound on New Colony (country LP); and *Harvest Moon*, by Joe Waters on New Colony (country LP). Other artists include Star Taylor and Richard Montgomery.

NEW DAWNING RECORDS, Dyer Rt., Cowen WV 26206. (304)226-3424. Secretary: Gladys Spearman. Record company and music publisher (Broad River Publishing Co./BMI). Releases 1 album/year. Works with artists and songwriters on contract. Teams collaborators.
How to Contact: Prefers cassette with 3-6 songs and lyric sheet. "Be sure cassette tape is clear. Songs should have meaning based on the word of God." SASE. Reports in 1-3 months.
Music: Country gospel. Recently released *I Feel the Winds of Heaven Blowing in My Face*, *In One Ear and Out the Other*, and *Come Lord Jesus*, by The Singing Spearman's (gospel LPs).

NEW WORLD RECORDS, Suite 11, 2309 N. 36th St., Milwaukee WI 53210. (414)445-4872. Labels include New World and More-Love Records. President: Marvell Love. Record company, music publisher (Jero Limited/BMI) and record producer. Releases 2-3 singles and 1 album/year. Works with

artists and songwriters on contract; musicians on salary for in-house studio work. Pays 3¹/₂-5% royalty to artists on contract; standard royalties to songwriters on contract; statutory rate to publishers for each record sold.
How to Contact: Prefers cassette with 3-5 songs and lyric sheet. SASE. Reports in 3 weeks.
Music: Mostly R&B, pop and gospel; also soul and top 40. Recently released "Miss You in the Morning," by Jim Spencer (love ballad single); "Been So Long," by Action (love ballad single); and "Sunset Lady," by Marvell Love (reggae single).

NICKEL RECORDS, 168 Buckingham St., Hartford CT 06106. (203)524-5656. Producer: Jack Stang. Record company, record producer and music publisher (Stang Music Publishing). Releases 4 singles and 2 albums/year. Works with artists and songwriters on contract; musicians on salary for in-house studio work. Pays 4-7% royalty to artists on contract; statutory rate to publishers for each record sold.
How to Contact: Prefers cassette with 1-3 songs and lyric sheet. SASE. Reports in 3 weeks.
Music: Mostly dance and top 40/pop; also easy listening, MOR, R&B and rock. Recently released "Do Your Best," "Into the Night," and *Portraits*, by Carol Hahn (dance singles and top 40 LP). Other artists include Kevin Dahill and Matt Towsend.

*NIGHTHAWK RECORDS, Box 15856, St. Louis MO 63114. (314)576-1569. Managing Director: Robert Schoenfield. Record company, music publisher (Blackheart Music/BMI) and record producer (NH Records). Releases 2-4 singles/year and 3-5 LP's/year. Works with musicians/artists and songwriters on contract. Pays negotiable royalty to artists on contract.
How to Contact: Prefers cassette with 4-6 songs and lyric sheet. SASE. Reports in 3 weeks.
Music: Mostly reggae, blues and R&B. Recently released *Serious Thing*, (by A. Griffiths), recorded by Gladiators on Nighthawk Records (reggae LP); *Give Me Power*, (by A. Porter), recorded by Itals on Nighthawk Records (reggae LP); and *Travel With Love*, (by Justin Hinds), recorded by J.H. Dominoes on Night Records (reggae LP).

NINE PINES CO., Old Antrim Rd., Hancock NH 03449. Creative Director: Dick Nevell. Record company.
How to Contact: Prefers cassette with minimum 6 songs and lyric sheet. SASE. Reports in 1 month.
Music: "Particularly interested in performance, art, and new music; jazz.". Recently released "*Surprise: A Ballet Suite*, (ballet cassette); *Snooze*, by D. Nevell (mixed LP); and *Live At The Marble Palace*, by Canterbury Folk (folk LP).

NORTH AMERICAN LITURGY RESOURCES, 10802 N. 23rd Ave., Phoenix AZ 85029. (602)864-1980. Labels include NALR and Livingsong. Music Editor: Henry Papale. Record company, record producer and music publisher (NALR/BMI). Releases 5-8 albums/year. Works with artists on contract; musicians on salary for in-house studio work. Pays statutory rate to publishers for each record sold.
How to Contact: Prefers cassette with 5-12 songs and lyric sheet. SASE. Reports in 1 month.
Music: Children's, choral, church/religious, liturgical and Christian rock and inspirational. Recently released *No Greater Love*, by Tom Kendzia (Christian rock LP); *Color the World*, by Rev. Carey Landry (Christian LP); and *Here In Our Midst*, by Michael Joncas (Catholic LP). Other artists include St. Louis Jesuits, The Dameans, Tutti Camarata, Ellis and Lynch, Abraham Kaplan and Tom Conry.
Tips: "Be familiar with our recordings. Free catalogs and brochures supplied on request."

NUCLEUS RECORDS, Box 111, Sea Bright NJ 07760. President: Robert Bowden. Record company and music publisher (Roots Music/BMI). Member AFM (US and Canada). Releases 1 single/year. Works with songwriters on contract. Pays up to 7-10% royalty for each record sold.
How to Contact: Prefers cassette or videocassette with any number songs and lyric sheet. Prefers studio produced demos. SASE. Reports in 1 month.
Music: Mostly country and pop; also church/religious, classical, folk, MOR, progressive, rock (soft, mellow) and top 40. Recently released "Always," and "Make Believe," by Marco Sison (pop singles).

*NUMBERS, 153 Telson Rd., Markham, Ontario L3R 1E7 Canada. (416)477-3524. Director A&R: Maggie Hues. Labels include Flip and Sommersault. Record company and national and promoter with distribution. Estab. 1984. Works with musicians/artists on contract.
How to Contact: Call first to arrange personal interview. Prefers cassette and lyric sheet. Does not return unsolicited material. Reports in 2-3 weeks. "Label interested in licensing all markets." Promotion company has national distribution.
Music: Mostly pop, rock and dance/crossover; also heavy metal (export). Artists include Sign System, Crypton, and Sam 7.

O.L. RECORDS, INC., 10051 Greenleaf, Santa Fe Springs CA 90670. (213)946-1524. President: Overton Lee. Record company, record producer, video production and music publisher (Boggy Depot, Overton Lee Music). Releases 6 singles and 2 albums/year. Works with artists and songwriters on contract. Pays statutory rate to publishers for each record sold.
How to Contact: Prefers cassette with 1-3 songs and lyric sheet. Reports in 3-4 months.
Music: Mostly country and bluegrass; also blues and gospel.

OHIO RECORDS, Box 655, Hudson OH 44236. (216)650-1330. Labels include Deco. A&R Director: Russ Delaney. Record company, record producer and personal manager. Member BMI, RIAA, CMA, FICAP. Releases 2 singles and 1 album/year. Pays standard royalty; pays statutory rate to publishers for each record sold.
How to Contact: Prefers cassette with 6 songs minimum and lyric sheet. Tapes returned only with SASE. Reports in one month. "Sometimes we hold material until we're ready for a recording session."
Music: Country. Recently released "Can You Go Back to That Ole Jukebox" (country single); "Taste of the Blues," (country single); and *He e e re's Ethel*, (country LP) by Ethel Delaney.
Tips: "I manage several artists who also write for the Ohio label and on occasion we do look for good commercial material from outside writers."

OLD HAT RECORDS, 3442 Nies, Fort Worth TX 76111. (817)834-3879. Labels include Old Hat Records. President: James Michael Taylor. Record company, booking agency, music publisher (Royal T Music/ASCAP) and production company. Member TMA. Releases 4 singles and 2 albums/year. Works with artists and songwriters on contract.
How to Contact: Arrange personal interview or submit demo tape. Prefers cassette with 6-12 songs and lyric sheet. SASE. Reports in 1 month.
Music: Children's, choral, country, folk, rock and top 40/pop. Recently released *Water Under the Bridge*, by Texas Water (country LP); *Texas Rain*, by Texas Water (country/progressive LP); *First Unk*, by Bob French (folk LP); and "What To Do with the Pictures," by James M. Taylor (country single).

***ON TIME RECORDS, INC.**, Box 314, New York NY 10037. Contact: Director of A&R. Record company. Releases 12 singles/year and 6 LPs/year. Works with musicians/artists and songwriters on contract; musicians on salary for in-house studio work.
How to Contact: Prefers cassette, reel-to-reel or videocassette with 3 songs and lyric or lead sheet. SASE. Reports in 6-8 weeks.
Music: Mostly urban dance, R&B dance and R&B/funk. Recently released "Spicey (You're So Spicy)," recorded by Cherokee on On Time (urban dance single); "You Do It," recorded by Shyvonne (R&B funk and dance single); and "Pushin' the Nation," recorded by The Majestic MO's on On Time (rap dance single). Other artists include Jumar Starr, First Rate, T.N.T. and Grand Whamo Mellow "T".

100 GRAND RECORDS, A Division of One Hundred Grand Music, 11 Norton St., Newburgh NY 12550. (914)561-4483. President: Gregg Bauer. Record company, record producer and music publisher. Releases 5 singles and 2 albums/year. Works with artists and songwriters on contract. Pays negotiable royalty to artists on contract; statutory rate to publishers for each record sold.
How to Contact: Prefers cassette or videocassette with 3-5 songs and lyric sheet. SASE. Reports in 1 month.
Music: Mostly rock, dance and MOR; also choral, easy listening, folk, jazz, progressive, soul and top 40/pop. Recently released "One of the Girls," "Another Stroke," and "My Fantasy Girl," by Art Nouveau (dance rock).

ORANGE RECORDS, c/o Jeffrey E. Jacobson, Esq., 150 Fifth Ave., New York NY 10011. (212)691-5630. Labels include Scattawane, Praise, Fraser, Ariga, and Auravox. President: Dave Peel. Record company.
How to Contact: Prefers cassette with 1-4 songs and lyric sheet. SASE. Reports in 1 week.
Music: Mostly progressive; also blues, classical, country, R&B, rock and soul.

ORIGINAL CAST RECORDS, Box 10051, Beverly Hills CA 90213. (818)761-2646. Labels include Take Home Tunes!, Disco Records, Broadway Baby Demos, The C.Y. Musical Foundation and The Chu Yeko Musical Foundation. Producer: Doris Chu. Record company, record producer, music publisher (Broadway/Hollywood International Music Publishers and The Chu Yeko Musical Foundation) and TV and film producer. Member NARAS. Releases 2-7 albums/year. Works with artists and songwriters on contract; musicians on salary for in-house studio work. Pays maximum 10% of profits to artists on contract; statutory rate or 50-75% of statutory rate to publishers for each record sold.
How to Contact: Prefers cassette or VHS videocassette and lyric sheet. SASE. "Send only top 40 pop/rock and R&B type songs." Reports in 1-3 months.

Music: Mostly musicals; also pop church religious, rock (any type) and top 40/pop. Recently released *Martin Charnin Mini-Album*, by Robert Guillame; *81 Proof*, by various artists (MOR LP); and *Of Love and Sex* (MOR LP).
Tips: "We are currently interested in a woman singer with a group and pop/rock groups with original top 40 songs."

*OUTLET RECORDING CO. LTD., Outlet House, H8 Smithfield Square W., Belfast BT1 1JE, Nothern Ireland. (0232)222826. Managing Director: William McBurney. Labels include: Top Spin, Homespun, Praise. Record company and music publisher (Outlet-Ulster Music). Releases 20 singles/year and 30 LPs/year. Works with musicians/artists and songwriters on contract. Pays 5% royalty to artists on contract.
How to Contact: Prefers cassette and lyric sheet ("required"). Does not return unsolicited material. Reports in 4 weeks.
Music: Mostly country and gospel. Recently released *Belfast*, (by Alex Quinn), recorded by Barn Brack on Homespun (single and LP); and *Rathlin Island*, (by B. Conner), recorded by Pat Woods on Homespun (single and LP). Other artists include Susan McCann, Ann Breen, and Gene Fitzpatrick.

LEE MACE'S OZARK OPRY RECORDS, INC., Box 242, Osage Beach MO 65065. (314)348-3383. Labels include Kajac, Ven Jence, Vision, KRC and Red Rock Records. General Manager: Lee Mace. Record company, music publisher and record producer. Works with artists and songwriters on contract; musicians on salary for in-house studio work. Pays 3-8% royalty to artists on contract; standard royalty to songwriters on contract.
How to Contact: Arrange personal interview. Prefers 7½ ips reel-to-reel or cassette with 2-4 songs and lead sheet. SASE. Reports in 2 weeks.
Music: Bluegrass, blues, church/religious, country, gospel and R&B. Recently released "Waylon Sing to Mama," by Darrell Thomas (country single); *Lee Mace 25 Years*, by the Ozark Opry (country LP); and *Songs Like We Sing*, by Lee Mace & the Ozark Opry (country LP).

P.M. RECORDS, INC., 20 Martha St., Woodcliff Lake NJ 07675. (201)391-2486. President: Gene A. Perla. Record company, music publisher (Perla Music/ASCAP) and record producer. Works with artists on contract.
How to Contact: Prefers cassette and lead sheet. SASE.
Music: All types. Recently released *Secret Places*, by Nina Sheldon (jazz vocal LP); *Pharoah's Gold*, by Bob Ackerman and Claude Johnson (jazz LP); *Con Brio*, by Con Brio (jazz LP); and *Day Dream*, by Pam Purvis (jazz vocal LP).

PACIFIC CHALLENGER RECORDS, 2940 E. Miraloma Ave., Anaheim CA 92806. (714)992-6820. Labels include Moonridge. Record company, record producer and music publisher (Pacific Challenger Music/Moonridge Music). Releases 8 singles and 4 albums/year. Works with artists and songwriters on contract. Pays statutory rate to publishers for each record sold.
How to Contact: Prefers cassette with 2-4 songs and lyric sheet. Does not return unsolicited material. Reports in 1 month.
Music: Mostly country; also gospel, country rock and top 40/pop. Recently released "Waltzes & Western Swing," by Donnie Rohrs (country single); *Social Errors*, by Don Hinson (comedy LP); and "Hurtin' Kind of Love," by Ron Shaw (country single).

*PALO ALTO RECORDS/TBA RECORDS, Suite A-280A, 755 Page Mill Rd., Palo Alto CA 94304. (415)856-4355. Contact: Al Evers or Jean Catino. Labels include Tall Tree Records. Record company and music publisher (Palo Publishing, Page Mill Publishing). Releases 4-5 singles/year and 15-20 LP's/year. Works with musicians/artists on contract.
How to Contact: Write or call first and obtain permission to submit. Prefers cassette with 3 songs and lyric sheet. "We do not guarantee return of unsolicited material." Reports in 2-3 weeks. "Be familiar with the artists requiring material, and submit accordingly."
Music: Mostly black/urban contemporary, pop and adult contemporary. Recently released *Live From San Francisco*, by Maynard Ferguson on Palo Alto (jazz LP); *American Eyes*, by Rare Silk on Palo Alto (jazz vocal LP); and "Live From New York," by Phil Woods on Palo Alto (jazz single). Other artists include George Howard, Dianne Reeves, Generation Band, Victor Feldman, McCoy Tyner, Richie Cole, and Free Flight.

PANDA RECORDS, 19146 Twig Ln., Cupertino CA 95014. (408)252-1580. Labels include Bumble-B, Vaudys, Kim and Apex Records. A&R Director: D. Richards. Record company and music publisher (Apex Music Publishing). Releases 6 singles/year. Works with artists and songwriters on contract. Pays royalty to artists for each record sold; statutory rate to publisher for each record sold.

How to Contact: Write first. Prefers cassette with maximum 2 songs on demo. Reports in 1 week.
Music: Religious, country and easy listening. Recently released *Too Many Tears*; *Hurry Back to Me*; and *Let's Pretend* (all LPs).

PARADE, 88 St. Francis St., Newark NJ 07105. (201)344-4214. Labels include Peter Pan, Power, Connection and Jammo. Vice President, Product Development/A&R Director: Joey Porello. Record company. Releases 10-20 singles and 5-10 albums/year. Works with artists and songwriters on record contract. Pays 4¢ royalty to artists on contract; statutory rate to publishers for each record sold.
How to Contact: Prefers cassette with 1-3 songs and lyric sheet. SASE. Reports in 1 month.
Music: Mostly dance, children's and MOR; also country, R&B and rock. Recently released *Aerobics*, by Joanie Greggains (exercise LP); and "Can't Judge a Book," by Cookie (dance single).

*PARAGOLD RECORDS & TAPES, 7020 Baldwin, Lawton OK 73505. (405)536-6463. Director: Teresa Bernard. Record company, music publisher (Rainbarrel Music Co.) and record producer. Releases 2 singles/year and 2 LPs/year. Works with musicians/artists and songwriters on contract.
How to Contact: Prefers cassette with 2 songs and lyric sheet or lead sheet. SASE. Reports in 6 weeks.
Music: Mostly country. Recently released "Ghost of Grand Ol Opry," written and recorded by Johnny Bernard on Paragold (country single); "Daddy's Last Letter," (by J. Bernard), recorded by JLyne on Paragold (country single); and "Don't Turn Me On Today," (by Ray Davis), recorded by J. Bernard on Paragold (country single). Other artists include Justin Christie, 7th Heaven Band, and Sunset Cowboys.

PARASOUND, INC., 2631 Clay, San Francisco CA 94115. (415)563-0202. President: Bernie Krause. Record company and music publisher. Releases 1-3 singles and 1-3 albums/year. Works with artists and songwriters on contract. Payment negotiable.
How to Contact: Prefers 7½ ips reel-to-reel or cassette or videocassette with 3-6 songs and lyric sheet. SASE. Reports in 3 months.
Music: New wave, jazz and electronic. Recently released *Citadels* by Bernie Krause (jazz-fusion LP).

*PARC RECORDS, Box 7877, College Park Station, Orlando FL 32854. (305)299-0077. A&R: Andy Deganahl. Record company and music publisher (Mister Sunshine Music, Inc.). Estab. 1985. Releases 8 singles/year and 4-5 LPs/year. Works with musicians/artists and songwriters on contract.
How to Contact: Prefers cassette or videocassette with 3-5 songs and lyric sheet. SASE. Reports in 4 weeks. "Picture and write ups are appreciated."
Music: Mostly contemporary hit music/top 40 and rock/pop. Recently released "The Deed is Done," recorded by Molly Hatchet on Epic; and *Four-In-Legion*, recorded by Four-In-Legion on CBS Associated. Other artists include Stranger, Secret Service, and John Kurzweg.

*PARHAM SOUND STUDIO, Rt. 3, Box 243-B, Stephenville TX 76401. (817)965-4132. Contact: Carroll Parham. Labels include Scotty Records of Texas, Cedar Valley Records. Record company, music publisher (Cedar Valley Publishing) and record producer. Releases 9 singles/year and 4 LPs/year. Works with musicians/artists and songwriters on contract; musicians on salary for in-house studio work. Pays standard royalty to artists on contract.
How to Contact: Prefers cassette. Does not return unsolicited material. Reports in 8 weeks. "Please make sure demo is clean and presentable."
Music: Mostly country and gospel. Recently released "Tuccumcari," (by Stan Knowles), recorded by Charlotte Brown on Scotty (country single); *Grown Older*, written and recorded by J.W. Seals on Scotty (gospel single and LP); and "Past is Past," (by Martin-Parham), recorded by C.C. Martin on Cedar Valley (country single). Other artists include Gene Williams, Tommy Kent, Delores Ayres, Joe Bass & Double Mountain Boys, and Lana Newman.

PARIS RECORDS, Suite 103, 12111 Strathern St., North Hollywood CA 91605. (818)768-7597. President: Jeff Gordon. Record company, music publisher (Gordon Music Co. Inc.) and management firm. Releases 2 albums/year. Works with artists and songwriters on contract. Pays statutory rate to publishers for each record sold.
How to Contact: Prefers cassette with 2-4 songs and lyric sheet. Does not return unsolicited material. Reports in 2 weeks.
Music: Mostly rock; also jazz, progressive and top 40/pop. Recently released *Bravados* and *Suicide Bridge*, by Failsafe (rock LPs); *Greg Chapman*, by G. Chapman (rock/top 40 EP); and "Hold Me Tight," by Robert White.

FRANK PAUL ENTERPRISES, Box 113, Woburn MA 01801. (617)933-1474. Labels include Casa Grande, Don-Mar and Strawnut Records. General Manager: Frank Paul. Record company, booking agency and music publisher. Works with artists and songwriters on contract. Pays 3% minimum royalty to artists and songwriters on contract.

How to Contact: Prefers cassette with 3-6 songs and lead sheet. SASE. Reports in 1 month.
Music: Blues, children's, choral, church/religious, classical, country, dance, easy listening, folk, gospel, MOR, rock, soul and top 40/pop. Recently released "Happy, Happy Birthday Baby," by the Timeweavers (R&B single); and "God Said He Would Fight My Battle," by the Fabulous Bullock Brothers (gospel single).

PAUSA RECORDS, Box 10069, Glendale CA 91209. (818)244-7276. Label includes Pausa Jazz Origin Records. Contact: Bill Stillfield. Record company and record producer. Releases 18 albums/year. Works with artists on contract. Pays statutory rate or "75% of statutory rate on mid-line albums" to publishers for each record sold.
How to Contact: Write first. Prefers cassette with 2-6 songs. SASE. "Do not send manuscript with lyrics." Reports in 1 week.
Music: Jazz. Recently released *Dan Siegel*, by D. Siegel; *Tom Grant*, by T. Grant; and *Again*, by Rob McConnell (all jazz LPs). Other artists include Judy Roberts, Pat Coil, Laurel Masse, Puttin On the Ritz, Billy Mitchell, Cal Collins, Willie Dixon, Art Van Damme, Mundell Lowe, Steve Narahara, Grant Geissman, Luis Arteaga, Made In Brasil and Don Latarski.

PCRL/DISQUES FLEUR, INC., 2364 Sherbrooke E., Montreal, Quebec H2K 1E6, Canada. (514)526-2831. Labels include Sterling, Quatre Saisons, Foreign Exchange, Boitadisc, Mayerling, Collection and Previll. Professional Manager: Carole Risch. Record company, record producer, and music publisher (Crisch Music/PROCAN and Notre Musique/CAPAC). Member ADISQ. Releases 25 singles and 10 albums/year. Works with artists and songwriters on contract. Pays 4%-16% royalty to artists on contract; statutory rate to publisher for each record sold.
How to Contact: Prefers 15½ ips reel-to-reel or cassette with 3-7 songs and lyric sheet. SAE and IRC. Reports in 3 weeks.
Music: Easy listening, MOR (ballads), rock and top 40/pop. Recently produced *C'est Magnifique*, by Santa Esmeralda (rock/latin American LP); *Un Coup d'Amour*, by Richard Cocciante (MOR LP); and "T'es Plus Une Star," by C. Michel (top 40/pop single). Other artists include Bernard Blane, Deveze, Diane Juster, Julie Arel, Alain Delorme, Michel Murty, Marie-France Paquin, Marie Myriam, Herbert Leonard and Mia Rochos.

PENTAGRAMM RECORDS, Box 384, 116 Wendy Dr., Holtsville NY 11742. (516)654-8459. President/A&R Director: Art Poppe. Record company, record producer and music publisher (Little Wizard Music). Releases 5 singles and 5 albums/year. Works with artists and songwriters on record contract. Pays statutory rate to publishers for each record sold.
How to Contact: Write first. Prefers cassette or videocassette with 3 songs. SASE. Reports in 3 weeks.
Music: Country, dance-oriented, easy-listening, MOR, R&B, rock, soul and top 40/pop.

PENTHOUSE RECORDS, Suite 1002, 924 Westwood Blvd., Los Angeles CA 90024. (213)824-9831. A&R/Director: Toni Biggs. Record company and music publisher (Tonina Music Publishing). Releases 5 singles and 5 albums/year. Works with artists and songwriters on contract. Pays 5-8% royalty to artists on contract; statutory rate to publishers for each record sold.
How to Contact: Prefers cassette or videocassette with lyric sheet and photographs of artist. SASE. Reports in 2 weeks.
Music: Mostly rock, R&B and dance-oriented; also country, easy listening, jazz, progressive, soul, top 40/pop and space wave/mod hot. Recently released *Caligula*, by various artists (soundtrack LP); *Threshold*, by Threshold (disco LP and single); and *Carlin on Campus*, by George Carlin (comedy LP).

PERMIAN RECORDS, 3122 Sale St., Dallas TX 75219. (214)522-8900. Vice President, Promotion: Ralph Witsell. Record company and music publisher (Banjo Man Music, Inc./BMI, Saratoga Trunk Music, Inc./ASCAP). Member CMA, TMA. Releases 6 singles and 2 albums/year. Works with artists and songwriters on contract. Pays royalty to artists on contract; statutory rate to publishers for each record sold.
How to Contact: Prefers cassette with maximum 2 songs and lyric sheet. SASE. Reports in 3 weeks.
Music: Mostly country. Recently released *Just Dottie*, by Dottie West (country LP); "Green Eyes," and "That's What Your Lovin' Does to Me," by Kathy Twitty (country singles). Other artists include Katy Moffatt.

PERSONAL RECORDS, INC., Suite 12A, 211 West 56th St., New York NY 10019. (212)246-5520. Labels include Oh My! Records Inc. A&R Director: Terry Lind. Record company and music publisher (Personal Music Publishing and My! My! Music Publishing). Member RIAA, NARM. Releases 20-30 singles and 5-10 albums/year. Works with artists and songwriters on contract; musicians on salary for in-house studio work. Pays according to individual contracts.

How to Contact: Prefers 15 or 30 ips reel-to-reel, cassette or videocassette with 3-5 songs and lyric sheet. Prefers studio produced demos. SASE. Reports in 2 weeks.
Music: Mostly dance, R&B and top 40; also MOR, rock and soul. Recently released "Come Inside," by Fancy (R&B/dance single); *Made In America*, by The Flirts (pop/dance LP); and "Born to Love," by Claudja Barry (pop/dance single). Other artists include Executive, Die Zwei, Stephen Eicher, Kiz, Kenny Beck, Klinte Jones and Cerrone.

*PLAYBONES RECORDS, Box 7718, 2000 Hamburg 20, West Germany. (040) 4300339. Producer: Arno v. Vught. Labels include Rondo Records. Record company, music publisher (Mento Music Group KG.) and record producer (Arteg Productions). Releases 10 singles/year and 8 LPs/year. Works with musicians/artists and songwriters on contract. Pays 12% on 90% royalty to artists on contract.
How to Contact: Write or call first to arrange personal interview. Prefers cassette or VHS videocassette and lyric or lead sheet. SASE. Reports in 2 weeks.
Music: Mostly instrumentals, country and jazz; also background music, rock and gospel. Recently released "On a Rainy Day," written and recorded by R. Bankel on Playbones (single); "Lonely Boy," written and recorded by C. Sargent on Playbones (single); and "Kirlian Effect," written and recorded by A. Bellaiche on Playbones (single). Other artists include H.J. Knipphals, Gaby Knies, Jack Hals, H. Hausmann, Crabmeat and M. Frommhold.

POLKA TOWNE RECORDS, 211 Post Ave., Westbury NY 11590. President: Teresa Zapolska. Record company, music publisher, record producer and booking agency. Works with artists and songwriters on contract.
How to Contact: Prefers cassette with 1-3 songs. SASE for report and SASE for return of cassette. "We review music once a month."
Music: Mostly polkas; also waltzes.

POLYGRAM RECORDS, 810 7th Ave., New York NY 10019. (212)399-7051. Contact: A&R Director. Record company. Works with artists on contract.
How to Contact: Call first for submission policy. Prefers cassette. SASE.
Music: Rock, R&B and top 40/pop. Recently released *Flashdance* soundtrack; *Grace Under Pressure*, by Rush; and *Pyromania*, by Def Leppard. Other artists include John Cougar Mellencamp, Bar Kays, Cameo, Scorpions, Big Country, ABC, Bon Jovi and Kiss.

POWER UP, (formerly Logo III), Suite 101, 413 Cooper St., Camden NJ 08102. (609)963-3190. President: Michael Nise. Labels include Power House Recording. Record company, music publisher and record producer. Releases 6 singles and 4 albums/year. Works with artists and songwriters on contract, musicians on salary for in-house studio work. Pays standard royalty to artists on contract; statutory rate to publishers for each record sold. Payment negotiable.
How to Contact: Prefers cassette or VHS videocassette with 1-3 songs. SASE. Reports in 1 month.
Music: Mostly R&B and pop/crossover; also children's, church/religious, country, dance, easy listening, folk, gospel, jazz, rock, soul and top 40/pop.

THE PRESCRIPTION CO., 70 Murray Ave., Port Washington NY 11050. (516)767-1929. President: David F. Gasman. Record company, record producer and music publisher (Prescription Co./BMI). Releases a varying number of singles and albums/year. Works with artists and songwriters on contract. Pays statutory rate to publishers for each record sold.
How to Contact: Call or write first. Prefers cassette with any number of songs and lyric sheet. Does not return unsolicited material. Reports in 1 month. "Send all submissions % Mitch Vidur (General Manager) with SASE or no returns."
Music: Bluegrass, blues, children's, country, dance-oriented, easy listening, folk, jazz, MOR, progressive, R&B, rock, soul and top 40/pop. Recently released "You Came In," "Seasons" (pop/country singles) and "Rock 'n Roll Blues," (rock single) by Medicine Mike.

*PRIME CUT RECORDS, 439 Tute Hill, Lyndonville VT 05851. (802)626-3317. President A&R: Bruce James. Record company and record producer. Releases 3-10 singles and 2 albums/year. Pays statutory rate to publishers for each record sold. Works with artists on contract.
How to Contact: Prefers cassette with 1-5 songs and lyric sheet. "Songs should be hit material no longer than 3½ minutes each." SASE. Reports in 8 weeks.
Music: Country and top 40/pop. Recently released "It's Over," by Fox (top 40 single); "Frightning," by Phase 3 (pop single); and "Coming Around," by Jackie O (country single). Other artists include Rockestra, Littlewing and Champlain.
Tips: "Artist should have strong desire to *make it*. Think and write hit records; songs should have two hooks in each tune, lyrics should be personal and intimate."

PRINCESS PRODUCTIONS LIMITED, Suite 202, 217 W. Alameda, Burbank CA 91502. (818)842-8900. Labels include Bouvier and Credence. A&R Director: Steve Dancz. Record company, record producer and music publisher (Kellijai Music Limited and Ja'Nikki Songs). Releases 6 singles and 3 albums/year. Works with artists and songwriters on contract. Pays 6-10% royalty to artists on contract; statutory rate to publishers for each record sold.
How to Contact: Prefers cassette with 1-5 songs and lyric sheet. SASE. Reports in 3 weeks.
Music: Mostly R&B, blues and pop; also dance-oriented, rock and soul. Recently released "Joy" and *Men of the Music*, by The Band A.K.A. (R&B/pop single and LP); "Precious & Special" and *Flash*, by Stacye Branche (R&B/pop single and LP). Other artists include Clement Forrest, Condottiere and Suzanne Wallach.

PRODUCTION CONNECTION, INC., 1422 McGill College, Montreal, Quebec H2Y 2Z9, Canada. (514)287-9574. Labels include Focus, Bobinason, Vierge and Horizon. President: Yves Godin. Vice President: Alaen Deland. Record company, record producer and music publisher (Les Editions LaBobine). Releases 15 singles/year. Works with artists on contract. Pays 4-8% royalty to artists on contract; statutory rate to publishers for each record sold.
How to Contact: Prefers cassette with minimum 5 songs and lyric sheet. SAE and IRC. Reports in 2 weeks.
Music: Dance-oriented, easy listening, rock and top 40/pop. Recently released "If You Can Count," by Cesarez (electro pop single); "Snap," by Beauflash (electro rock single); and "SOS Anonyme," by Dwight Druick (pop rock single).

QUINTO PRODUCTIONS/RECORDS, Box 2388, Toluca Lake CA 91602. (818)985-8284. Labels include Quinto, Suzi, Fun, Top 'n' Bottom and Clovermint Records. Contact: Quint Benedetti. Record company, music publisher and demo producer. Works with songwriters on contract. Pays standard royalty.
How to Contact: Prefers cassette with 2-4 songs and lyric sheet. SASE. Reports in 2 months.
Music: Musical comedy and Christmas songs only. "We are presently scouting for new musical comedy material for possible recording and stage production locally." Recently released *Chocalonia*, by original cast (rock musical LP); *The Lavender Lady*, by Agnes Moorehead (one-woman show LP); and *Topsy or Sorry about That Harriett*, by the original cast (LP).

R.E.F. RECORDS, 404 Bluegrass Ave., Madison TN 37115. (615)865-6380. Contact: Bob Frick. Record company, record producer and music publisher (Frick Music Publishing Co./BMI). Releases 10 albums/year. Works with artists and songwriters on contract. Pays 3-5¢ royalty to artists on contract; statutory rate to publishers for each record sold.
How to Contact: Call first. Prefers 7¹/₂ ips reel-to-reel or cassette with 2-10 songs and lyric sheet. SASE. Reports in 1 month.
Music: Country, gospel, rock and top 40/pop. Recently released *Release Me*, by Bob Scott; *Bob Scott Picks on Henry Slaughter*, by B. Scott and H. Slaughter; and *I Can't Help Myself*, by B. Scott and family (all gospel LPs). Other artists include Scott Frick, Larry Ahlborn, Francisco Morales, Candy Coleman, and Peggy Beard.

RA-JO INTERNATIONAL, Suite 192, 100-19 Alcott Pl., Bronx, NY 10475. (212)379-2593. Labels include Abbco. A&R Producer: Joe Adams. Record company. Releases 10 singles and 3 albums/year. Works with musicians/artists and songwriters on contract. Pays 10% royalty to artists on contract.
How to Contact: Call first and obtain permission to submit. Prefers cassette and lyric sheet. SASE. Reports in 2 weeks.
Music: Mostly rock, blues and pop. Recently released "Honk Tonk," (by Doggett), recorded by Beach Boys on Capitol (pop); "Somebody's Fool," (by A. Adams), recorded by Michael Jackson on Motown (pop); and "No More In Life," (by A. Adams), recorded by Arthur Prysock on Bloor (pop). Other artists include Tiny Tim, DeDe Sharp, Larry Johnson, Joe Tex, Johny Calvin and P.J. Jones.

RAINA RECORDING CO., 1818 E. Ardmore Dr., Phoenix AZ 85040. (602)276-2039. Vice President: Odessa Payton. Record company, record producer and music publisher (LA-NAI). Releases 6 singles/year. Works with artists and songwriters on contract. Pays standard royalty to artists on contract; statutory rate to publishers for each record sold.
How to Contact: Prefers cassette with 4 or more songs and lyric sheet. SASE. Reports in 3 weeks.
Music: Country, jazz and R&B. Recently released "Love Knows," by Lawrence Carroll (jazz single); "I Am at the Crossroads," by Bobby Barnes (R&B single); and "Imitations," by The Johnson Family (gospel single).

RAINBOW RECORDS/ARROW MINISTRIES, 506 Cottonwood St., Woodland CA 95695. (916)655-3328. President: Dennis Litchfield. Record company, record producer and music publisher

(Poiema Music Publishing/BMI). Works with artists and songwriters on contract. Pays $.015/record minimum to artists on contract; statutory rate to publishers for each record sold.
How to Contact: Prefers cassette or videocassette with 4-10 songs and lyric sheet. Reports in 1 month.
Music: Mostly contemporary Christian rock; also gospel, gospel rock and MOR. Recently released *Face to the Son*, by Dennis Litchfield (contemporary Christian rock LP); and *Through Every Storm*, by Emaous Road (contemporary Christian MOR LP).

RAVEN RECORDS, 1918 Wise Dr., Dothan AL 36303. (205)793-1329. Labels include Studio Four Records. President: Jerry Wise. Record company and music publisher (Round Sound Music/BMI). Member CMA and GMA. Releases 3-6 singles and 5-10 albums/year. Works with artists and songwriters on contract. Pays 2-20% royalty to artists on contract; standard royalty to songwriters on contract; pays statutory rate to publishers for each record sold.
How to Contact: Write first. Prefers 7½ ips reel-to-reel or cassette with 1-6 songs and lyric sheet. SASE. Reports in 1 month.
Music: Country, easy listening, MOR, rock, soul and top 40/pop.

RCA RECORDS, 6363 Sunset Blvd., Los Angeles CA 90028. (213)468-4039. A&R/West Coast: Paul Atkinson. Record company. Works with artists and songwriters on contract. Not currently accepting unsolicited material.
Music: Top 40/pop only.
Tips: "We're interested in a simple demo with piano and voice for songs. The same applies for artists, but get vocals out front."

RECORD COMPANY OF THE SOUTH (RCS), 5220 Essen Lane, Baton Rouge LA 70809. (504)766-3233. President: Cyril E. Vetter. Record company, music publisher and record producer. Works with musicians on salary; artists and songwriters on contract. Pays 3-7% royalty to artists on contract; standard royalty to songwriters on contract.
How to Contact: Write first. Prefers cassette (7½ ips reel-to-reel OK) with 1-10 songs and lyric sheet. SASE. Reports in 1 month.
Music: Country, MOR, R&B, rock (hard and country), soul, top 40/pop and new music. Recently released "Suddenly Single," by Butch Hornsby (country single); *Don't Take It Out on the Dog*, by Butch Hornsby (country LP); and *Safe with Me*, by Irma Thomas (pop single and LP). Other artists include Luther Kent, Gregg Wright and Floyd Brown.

RED BUD RECORDS, A Division of CAE, Inc., 611 Empire Mill Rd., Bloomington IN 47401. (812)824-2400. Labels include Sirius Music. General Manager: Rick Heinsohn. Record company and record producer. Member NARAS. Releases 1 single and 4 albums/year. Works with musicians and artists on contract. Pays statutory rate to publishers for each record sold.
How to Contact: Call first and obtain permission to submit. Prefers cassette with 2-10 songs. SASE. "Include bio and gig list." Reports in 1 month.
Music: Mostly jazz and folk; also bluegrass and rock. "We'll listen to anything." Recently released *Chicago Style*, by Friedlander & Hall (swing LP); *Solo Guitar*, by Royce Campbell (jazz LP); and *Buffalo Gal*, by Leftwich and Higginbotham (folk LP). Other artists include Bill Wilson, Eric Rosser, Jan Henshaw, High Ground, Electricity and Kiethe-Lowrie Duet.

RED DOT RECORDS-MARULLO PRODUCTIONS, 1121 Market, Galveston TX 77550. (409)762-4590. Labels include Red Dot, Rotab, Graffiti. President: A.W. Marullo Sr. Record company, record producer and music publisher (A.W. Marullo Music/BMI). "We also lease masters from artists." Releases 7 singles and 1 album/year. Works with artists and songwriters on contract; musicians on salary for in-house studio work. Pays 10-12% royalty to artists on contract; statutory rate to publishers for each record sold.
How to Contact: Prefers cassette with 4-7 songs and lyric sheet. SASE. Reports in 6 weeks.
Music: Mostly country; also hard rock and country rock. Recently released "Long Tall Texan," by Brown Brothers (country/pop single); "Elayne," by George G. Lee (rock single); and *Made to be Played*, by Geo (rock LP).

RED HORSE RECORDS, Box 163, West Redding CT 06896. (203)438-5366. Labels include Bluebird Country Records, Tutch and Red Kastle. Professional Manager: R. Kidd. Record company, record producer and music publisher (Tutch Music Publishing/BMI). Member CMA and CSA. Releases 4-5 singles and 1 album/year. Works with songwriters on contract; musicians on salary for in-house studio work. Pays 4-10% royalty to artists on contract; statutory rate to publishers for each record sold.
How to Contact: Write first. Prefers cassette with minimum 2 songs. SASE. Reports in 2 weeks.
Music: Mostly country and top 40/pop; also dance-oriented, easy listening, R&B and rock. Recently

released "Nashville Plastic," by Paul Hotchkiss; "Ease the Pain," by Fran Taylor; and "Love Was Meant to Be," by Patty Terry. Other artists include Gerry Malone, Malone and Hutcher, Gerri Roth, Country Touch, Hutcher Brothers and Kristian Bivona.

REVONAH RECORDS, Box 217, Ferndale NY 12734. (914)292-5965. Contact: Paul Gerry. Record company and booking agency. Releases 2-4 albums/year. Works with artists and songwriters on contract. Teams collaborators; pays negotiable royalty to artists on contract. Pays statutory rate to publishers for each record sold.
How to Contact: Arrange personal interview. Prefers reel-to-reel, cassette, videocassette or 8-track cartridge and lead sheet. SASE. Reports in 1 month.
Music: Bluegrass, country, folk and gospel. Recently released *The Fiddler & His Lady*, by Tater Tate (bluegrass LP); *Back Home in Madison County*, by Red Rector (bluegrass LP); *Saturday Night*, by Bristol Mountain Bluegrass (bluegrass LP); and *Before the Fire Comes Down*, by Northern Lights (bluegrass LP). Other artists include Mac Martin, the Shenandoah Cutups, Stacy Phillips, Simon St. Pierre, Gene Elders, Fred Pike, Roger Bellow, Del McCoury, The Stuart Family, Mountain Grass, Walter Hensley, Clinton King, Jerry Oland and The Gospelites.

*RIC RAC RECORDS, % Ric Rac, Inc., Box 712, Nashville IN 47448. (812)837-9569. President: R.L. Hanson. Labels include Country Bump. Record company, music publisher, record production and promotion firm. Releases 2-3 singles/year and 2 LP's/year. Works with musicians/artists and songwriters on contract. Pays 3-6% royalty to artists on contract.
How to Contact: Write first and obtain permission to submit. Prefers cassette with 1-4 songs and lyric or lead sheet. SASE. Reports in 6-8 weeks. "Do not make phone inquiries as to status of material submitted. Material submitted to A&R must be represented by publisher."
Music: Mostly country, rock and gospel; also folk and easy listening (MOR). Recently released "Before I'm Fool Enough," (by Allen Reynolds), recorded by Rick Hanson on Ric Rac (country single), "Momma Sing Us a Song," written and recorded by Kathy Shepard on Ric Rac (country single); and "Laced with Love," written and recorded by Rick Hanson on Ric Rac (country single). Other artists include Jack Lawles.

RIPSAW RECORD CO., Suite 5-J, 320 W. 30th St., New York NY 10001. (212)971-9151. President: Jonathan Strong. Record company (Southern Crescent Publishing/BMI), record producer, and music publisher. Releases 1-5 singles and 1-2 albums/year. Works with artists and songwriters on contract. Payment negotiable with artists on contract; standard royalty to songwriters on contract; statutory rate to publishers for each record sold.
How to Contact: Prefers cassette and lyric sheet. SASE. "Invite us to a club date to listen." Reports as soon as possible.
Music: Rockabilly and "traditional" rock. Recently released *Wanted: True Rock 'N' Roll*, by Billy Hancock (traditional rock EP); "Hot Rod Man," by Tex Rubinowitz (rockabilly single); and "Wheels on Fire," by Kid Tater & the Cheaters (rockabilly single).
Tips: "Keep it rockabilly."

RITE RECORD PRODUCTIONS, INC., 9745 Mangham Dr., Cincinnati OH 45215. (513)733-5533. Labels include Gateway and Arc Records. Studio Manager: Phil Burkhardt. Record company, record producer and music publisher. Member RIAA. Releases 25 singles and 25 albums/year. Works with musicians and artists on record contract.
How to Contact: Call first. Prefers 7¹/₂ or 15 ips reel-to-reel or cassette with 1-3 songs. SASE. Reports in 1 month.
Music: Country, rock and top 40/pop.

RMS TRIAD RECORDS, 6267 Potomac Circle, West Bloomfield MI 48033. (313)661-5167. Contact: Bob Szajner. Record company, record producer and music publisher. Releases 3 albums/year. Works with artists on contract. Pays negotiable royalty to artist on contract; statutory rate to publishers for each record sold.
How to Contact: Write first about your interest. Prefers cassette with 2-4 songs. SASE. Reports in 3 weeks.
Music: Jazz. Recently released "Since I've Had a Change of Heart," and "I Just Came to Thank You Lord," by J.J. and Sherrie Stephens (religious singles); and "Jesus Amazes Me," by S. Stephens (religious single). Other artists include Frank Isola, Roy Brooks, Ray McKinney and Ed Pickens.

ROBBINS RECORDS, HC80, Box 5B, Leesville LA 71446. Labels include Headliner Stars Records. National Representative: Sherree Scott. Record company and music publisher (Headliner Stars Music and Universal Stars Music/BMI). Releases 12 singles and 3 albums/year. Works with artists and songwriters on contract. Pays standard royalty to artists on contract; statutory rate to publishers for each record sold.

How to Contact: Prefers cassette with 1-6 songs and lyric sheet. Does not return unsolicited material. Reports only if interested.

Music: Mostly church/religious; also bluegrass, country, folk, gospel, and top 40/pop. Recently released *Jesus Amazes Me* and *Wait Till You See My Miracle Home*, by J.J. and Sherree Stephens (religious LPs); and *I Just Came to Thank You Lord*, by Sherree Stephens (religious LP). Other artists include Renee Wills.

ROCKEN MUSIC CORP., Box 12752, Memphis TN 38182-0752. (901)725-5387. Labels include Rocken Rhythm Records. President: Bill Lusk. A&R Director: Mike Noland and Don Von Maurer. Record company, record producer, music publisher (Rocken Rhythm/BMI) and management, promotion and booking agency. Member Memphis Music Association and The Blues Foundation. Releases varying number of singles and albums/year. Works with artists and songwriters on contract; musicians on salary for in-house studio work. Pays negotiable rate to artists on contract; statutory rate to publishers for each record sold.

How to Contact: Prefers cassette with 1-4 songs and lyric sheet. "Specify the number of songs on the tape." SASE, "but we keep tape on file." Reports if interested.

Music: Mostly blues, pop/R&B, soul and top 40. Other artists include Clarence "Gatemouth" Brown, The Field Stones, Wampus Cats, GTO and Kenneth Jackson.

ROCKIN! RECORDS, 1733 Carmona Ave., Los Angeles CA 90019. (213)933-6521. Labels include Rockmore Records. Manager: Perry Rocquemore. A&R Director: Willie H. Rocquemore. Record company, music publisher (Broadcast Music/BMI) and record producer. Member RIAA. Releases 1 album/year. Works with artists and songwriters on contract. Teams collaborators. Pays 10-15% royalty to artists on contract, pays statutory rate to publishers for each record sold.

How to Contact: Prefers cassette with 4 songs maximum and lyric sheet. SASE. Reports in 1 month.

Music: Pop rock, ballad and soul. Recently released "I Can't Complain," "Let's Just Fake It for Tonight," "Hello Good Times," and "Summer Lovers," all by Jennifer Jayson. Other artists include Jennifer Well.

Tips: "Listen to top 40 hits on radio."

*ROGUE RECORDS, Box 568, Woodland Hills CA 91365. (818)992-4922. Contact: A&R Department. Record company and music publisher (Arpell/Pinellas Music Publishing). Releases 3 singles and 1 LP/year. Works with musicians/artists on contract.

How to Contact: Prefers cassette with 3-4 songs and lyric sheet. SASE. Reports in 2 weeks.

Music: Mostly pop, rock and R&B. Recently released "Still Thinking of You," recorded by Bob Gulley on Rogue (A/C single).

ROLLIN' ROCK RECORDS, 6918 Peach Ave., Van Nuys CA 91406. (213)781-4805. Labels include Rockabilly Rebel, Rockabilly Uprising. Contact: Ron Weiser. Record company, record producer and music publisher (Ron Weiser Publishing, Rockin' Ronny Music). Releases varied number of singles and 4-5 albums/year. Works with artists and songwriters on contract; musicians on salary for in-house studio work. Pays 4-7% royalty to artists on contract; statutory rate to publishers for each record sold.

How to Contact: Prefers cassette and lyric sheet. Does not return unsolicited material.

Music: Mostly rockabilly and 50s R&B and rock; also country and R&B. Artists include Ray Campi & His Rockabilly Rebels, The Blasters and American Music.

ROPERRY RECORDS, 645 Madison Ave., New York NY 10022. (212)308-2636. General Manager: Jane Lowy. Record company, record producer, music publisher and personal management firm. Releases approximately 3 singles and 1-2 albums/year. Works with artists and songwriters on contract. Rates paid to artists and publishers "dependent on contract."

How to Contact: Call first about your interest. Prefers cassette with 1-3 songs and lyric sheet. SASE. "Include picture and biography." Reports in 3 weeks.

Music: Mostly top 40/pop, MOR and easy listening; also children's. Recently released "Joggin'," by Patsy (pop/dance/MOR single); "Just a Little Imagination," by Patsy (adult/contemporary single); and "Kid Santa Claus," by Patsy (pop LP). Other artists include Joey Latini, and Joey Morgano.

*ROUNDTREE RECORDS, 2700 Champa, Denver CO 80220. Creative Director: Jon Chandler. Record company, music publisher, and record producer (JMC Music Group). Releases 2 singles/year and 1 LP/year. Works with musicians/artists and songwriters on contract; musicians on salary for in-house studio work. Pays 7-15% royalty to artists on contract.

How to Contact: Call first and obtain permission to submit. Prefers cassette with 3-4 songs and lyric

sheet. Does not return unsolicited material. Reports in 3-5 weeks.
Music: Mostly country, pop and dance. Recently released "Sidekicks," and "151," written and recorded by Jon Chandler on Roundtree (country singles). Other artists include Ken Perkins and Kenny Waughan.

ROYAL T MUSIC, 3442 Nies, Fort Worth TX 76111. (817)834-3879. Labels include Old Hat. President: James Michael Taylor. Record company, music publisher (Royal T Music/ASCAP) and booking agency. Member TMA. Releases 4 singles and 2 albums/year. Works with artists and songwriters on contract.
How to Contact: Prefers 7^1/$_2$ ips reel-to-reel or cassette with 6-12 songs and lead sheet. SASE. Reports in 1 month.
Music: Children's, choral, country, folk, MOR, rock and top 40/pop. Recently released *Water Under the Bridge*, by Texas Water (country/pop LP); and *The Mansfield Tapes*, by James Michael Taylor (folk, country LP).

RSO RECORDS, 1775 Broadway, New York NY 10019. (212)975-0700. Director of A&R: James Dayley. Record company, music publisher and record producer. Releases 5 singles/year and 10 LP's/year. Works with musicians/artists and songwriters on contract.
How to Contact: Prefers cassette or VHS videocassette with 4 songs. SASE. Reports in 4 weeks. Include photo, bio, press clippings, etc. with submission.
Music: Mostly rock and pop; also video music.

RTP INTERNATIONAL, 180 Pond St., Cohasset MA 02025. (617)383-9494. Label includes Sequel. Artist Relations: Richard F. Tinory Jr. Record company, record producer and music publisher (Old Boston Publishing).
How to Contact: Call first. Prefers cassette with 1-3 songs. Does not return unsolicited material.

*RUTLAND RECORDS, 71 Rutland Rd., Chesterfield, Derbyshire S40 1ND, England. 44-0246-79976. Labels include Rutland Records. Director: Tony Hedley. Record company, record producer, music publisher (Hedley Music Group/MCPS) and promotions company. Releases 4 singles and 2 albums/year. Works with artists and songwriters on contract. Pays negotiable royalty to artists on contract; 6^1/$_2$% to publishers for each record sold. Royalties paid directly to US songwriters and artists or through US publishing or recording affiliate. Has not yet but would listen to material from US songwriters and artists.
How to Contact: Write first. Prefers cassette with 1-4 songs and lyric sheet. SAE and IRC. Reports in 2 weeks.
Music: Mostly pop and rock (hard and country); also folk, progressive, soul and top 40/pop; "we also want to expand into country music." Artists include Dagaband, J.J. Jones Elastic Band and Bitch.
Tips: "We are looking for good country material suitable for UK artists as well as chart potential pop and rock."

SAIN (RECORDIAU) CYF., Llandwrog, Caernarfon, Gwynedd, LL54 5TG, Wales. 44-0286-831-111. Labels include Sain, Cambrian, Tryfan, Welsh Teldisc, Ty Ar Y Graig. Directors: O.P. Huws and Dafydd Iwan. Record company, record producer, music publisher (Cyhoeddiadau Sain) and record distributor. Member APRS. Releases 10 singles and 40 albums/year. Works with 10 new songwriters/year. Works with artists and songwriters on contract. Pays 4-10% royalty to artists on contract; 6^1/$_4$% to publishers for each record sold, pro rated per song. Has not yet, but would listen to material from US songwriters and artists.
How to Contact: Prefers cassette with 1-5 songs and lyric sheet. SAE and IRC. Reports in 1 month.
Music: Mostly choral (Welsh language), folk, folk/rock and classical; also children's, church/religious, classical, country, MOR and rock. Recently released *Ave Maria*, (by Bach/Gounod), recorded by Aled Jones (classical LP); "Uncle Sam Meets the Welch Dragon," (by Copland/Randall), recorded by Pendyrus Male Choir (classical/MOR); and *Welsh Songs for Peace*, by various artists (folk/MOR). Other artists include Omega, Ar Log, Dafydd Iwan, Tecwyn Ifan, Ficar, Derec Brown, Margaret Williams, Cilmeri, Pendyrus Choir, Brythoniaid Choir, Rhos Choir, Leah Owen, Eirlys Parri, Hogia'r Wyddfa, Meic Stevens and Caryl Parry Jones.
Tips: "Music should be relevant to the 'scene' in Wales."

SAVOY RECORDS, 342 Westminister Ave., Box 279, Elizabeth NJ 07208. Contact: Milton Biggham. Record company and music publisher (Savgos Music, Inc./BMI, Jonan Music, Inc./ASCAP and Arisav Music, Inc./SESAC). Member RIAA. Releases 50 albums/year. Pays statutory rate to publishers for each record sold.
How to Contact: Query with SASE. Reports in 2 weeks.

Music: Contemporary and traditional gospel. Recently released *I Want to Know What Love Is*, by New Jersey Mass Choir (contemporary gospel LP); *Love Lifted Me*, by Revival Temple (traditional gospel LP); and *I'm Going to Hold Out*, by Georgia Mass Choir (traditional gospel LP).

SCARAMOUCHE RECORDS, Drawer 1967, Warner Robins GA 31099. (912)953-2800. Director: Robert R. Kovach. Record company and record producer. Releases 4 singles and 1 album/year. Works with artists and songwriters on contract. Works with lyricists and composers and teams collaborators. Pays 3-5% royalty to artists on contract; pays statutory rate to publishers for each record sold.
How to Contact: Prefers cassette or videocassette with 3-5 songs and lyric sheet. SASE. Reports in 2 months.
Music: Blues, country, easy listening, R&B, rock, soul and pop. Recently released "Real Country Livin'," by Little Budy (country single); and "When Your Light Comes On," by Theresa Justus (pop single). Other artists include Napoleon Starke.
Tips: "Submit it! We listen to each and every tape we receive."

SCENE PRODUCTIONS, Box 1243, Beckley WV 25801. (304)252-4836. Labels include Rising Sun and Country Road Records. Executive Professional Manager/Producer: Richard L. Petry. Record company, record producer and music publisher (Purple Haze Music/BMI). Member of AFM. Releases 1-2 singles and 1-2 albums/year. Works with artists and songwriters on contract. Pays 4-5% minimum royalty to artists on contract; standard royalty to songwriters on contract; statutory rate to publishers for each record sold. Charges "initial costs, which are conditionally paid back to artist."
How to Contact: Write first about your interest (recording only). Prefers cassette with 2-5 songs and lyric sheet. Prefers studio produced demos. SASE. Reports in 1 month.
Music: Mostly pop, top 40, R&B crossover and country crossover; also MOR, light and commercial rock. Recently released *Premier*, by Tim Brophy (pop LP); "Can't Get Over Losing You," by Dave Runion (country single); and "High Cost of Loving," by Pam Daniel (country single).
Tips: "Songs should be well-thought-out and well-constructed—songwriting is a craft."

SCP RECORDS, Division of the Sound Column Companies, 46 E. Herbert Ave., Salt Lake City UT 84111. (801)355-5327. Labels include Big Sky Records. A&R Professional Manager: Clive Romney. Record company, record producer and music publisher (Ronarte Publications/ASCAP, Mountain Green Music/BMI and Macanudo Music/SESAC). Member CMA. Releases 3 singles and 4 albums/year. Works with artists and songwriters on contract; musicians on salary for in-house studio work. Pays negotiable royalty to artists on contract; statutory rate to publishers for each record sold.
How to Contact: Write first. Prefers cassette with 1-3 songs. SASE. "Demand varies—some artists have their own material. Query first as to demand." Reports as soon as possible. "Once in awhile we get seriously behind—but you'll eventually be heard."
Music: Mostly top 40/pop and crossover country; also easy listening and MOR. Recently released "I'll Build You a Rainbow," by Sun Shade 'N Rain (contemporary gospel single); *Too Good to be Through*, by Dave Lemmon (country single and LP); *I Promise You*, by Heidi Magleby (contemporary gospel cassette); and *Wanna Sing for You*, by Dave Compton (jazz/pop LP/cassette). Other artists include Brett Raymond and Power & Light.

SHADOW RECORDS, 1517 W. Lake, Minneapolis MN 55408. (612)825-0766. President: Charlie Campbell. Record company and music publisher (Boss Apple Tunes). Releases 1 album/year. Works with musicians and artists on record contract. Pays 2¼¢ royalty to artists on contract; statutory rate to publishers for each record sold.
How to Contact: Call first. Prefers cassette.
Music: Blues, jazz, R&B, reggae and calypso.

*SHAOLIN RECORDS, Box 387, Hollywood CA 90078. (213)372-9126. A&R: Jennifer Olds. Record company, music publisher, record producer and film and video firm. Estab. 1984. Releases 4 singles and 3 LP's/year. Works with musicians/artists and songwriters on contract.
How to Contact: Prefers cassette or Beta videocassette with 2-4 songs and lyric sheet. SASE. Reports in 8 weeks. "Include bios, photos and reviews."
Music: Mostly rock, pop and blues. Recently released *Temptation*; *Coyote in a Graveyard*, and "Out of My Mind," all written and recorded by Rirchard O'Connor on Shaolin (rock LPs and single). Other artists include JJ & The Streethearts, Second Chance and The Rich.

*SHEPERD RECORDS, 2307 N. Washington Ave., Scranton PA 18509. (717)347-7395. A&R: Fran Grogan. Record company. Releases 1-3 singles/year and 1-3 LPs/year. works with musicians/artists and songwriters on contract; musicians on salary for in-house studio work.
How to Contact: Prefers cassette with 1-2 songs. Does not return unsolicited material. Reports in 6 weeks.

Close-up

Byron Hill
Songwriter
Nashville, Tennessee

Photo by Don Putnam

"There's a lot of business that has to be done in songwriting," says Nashville's Byron Hill, a 31-year-old native of Winston-Salem, North Carolina. "It's not just the creative end of it. You've got to go out and show your songs, find out which artists are recording when and what kind of songs they need. Nowadays, the songwriter who's not able to write and keep up with the business end too, is gonna have a tough time."

In 1978, Hill left his hometown to join what he calls that "big sea of writers in Nashville." He signed as a staff songwriter for ATV (Associated Television) Music, a British company which published some of The Beatles' material. In their Nashville offices he started doing odd jobs, such as emptying ash trays and copying demo tapes. The first songs he wrote at ATV, he recalls, were pretty bad.

Hill says the feedback and critique he received from Roger Bowling ("Lucille," "Coward of the County") and other successful songwriters on Nashville's Music Row helped him break into the songwriting business and establish himself. He doesn't believe he would have developed as a songwriter if he had moved to New York City or Los Angeles instead.

While at ATV, Hill co-wrote "Fool Hearted Memory," which became the first number-one record on the *Billboard* magazine charts for country star George Strait. Among Hill's other best known songs are "Pickin' Up Strangers," released on Johnny Lee's *Lookin' for Love* album, and "Two Hearts One Love," a pop song on Kenny Rogers' latest album, *What About Me?* Hill left ATV in 1984 to form his own publishing company.

A lot of ideas for song titles come to Hill when he's driving, so he keeps a small tape recorder in his car. He later makes a list of those titles, which he uses in songwriting sessions.

"I must have thousands of titles," he said. "Whenever I do sit down and write, I take out those lists and look and see which ideas hit me good that particular day. I'm always listening to what people say. I get a lot of ideas out of things people say in conversations."

Hill says it always feels good to write a hit song and hear it played on the radio. But not every song can be a hit, and when a record company rejects his work, he says it's hard sometimes to get over the disappointment.

"The disappointments are real tough," he said. "You just have to smile and forget it and just keep your chin up and learn from it. You have to keep saying, 'This is all part of the process,' and you have to keep it all in perspective. If you get too upset by it, you'll never really make it."

Hill advises aspiring songwriters who are thinking about moving to Nashville to plan the move carefully and be prepared to make a long-term commitment.

"You've got to plan," said Hill. "You've got to figure out where your money will come from. To stay in Nashville and keep writing, you've got to survive, so usually another job is necessary. The biggest artist can record your song tomorrow, and you may not see any royalties for a year and a half. Don't expect anything to happen overnight."

—*Tyler Cox*

Music: Mostly rock and pop. Recently released *Encounter*, (by Daniel McGlynn), recorded by Fantasy Band on Sheperd (LP).

SIRE RECORDS, 3 East 54 St., New York NY 10022. (212)832-0950. A&R Assistant: Shirley Divers. Record company.
How to Contact: Prefers cassette and lyric sheet. Does not accept unsolicited material. Reports in 1 month.
Music: All types. Recently released *Learning to Crawl*, by The Pretenders (rock LP); and *Speaking in Tongues*, by The Talking Heads.

SKYLIGHT RECORDS, 939 Felix Ave. (lwr.), Windsor, Ontario N9C 3LZ Canada. (519)256-6604. Labels include JLT Records. President: Jim Thomson II. Record company, record producer and music publisher (On the Wing Music Publishing Co./PROCAN). Releases 2 singles and 2 albums/year. Works with songwriters on contract. Works with composers. Pays statutory rate to publishers for each record sold or first recording will be negotiable.
How to Contact: Arrange personal interview. Prefers cassette or ½" VHS or ¾" U-matic videocassette with 4 songs, lyric sheet and biography; "submit at least 2 of each style; if submitting more than 1 style, prefer 3 songs." Does not return unsolicited material. Reports in 2 weeks "but only if interested due to volume."
Music: Mostly gospel and children's; also bluegrass, blues, church/religious, classical, country, easy listening, folk, jazz, MOR, progressive, rock, Spanish, R&B, soul and top 40 pop. Recently released "Mountain Climbing," "Oh Lord," and *Raw*, all by Preflyte (gospel).
Tips: "I work with artists and songwriters who have a sense of purpose other than just music behind what they do. Send bio outlining motivations, convictions and goals, and we may end up working together."

SLASH RECORDS, Box 48888, Los Angeles CA 90048. (213)937-4660. Labels include Ruby, Big International, Slash and Warner. A&R Director: Anna Statman. Record company and music publisher. Releases 5 singles and 6-10 albums/year. Works with artists on contract. Pays negotiable royalty to artists on contract; statutory rate to publishers for each record sold.
How to Contact: Write first and obtain permission to submit. Prefers cassette with 3-5 songs on demo. Does not return unsolicited material. Reports in 1 month.
Music: Country, R&B, rock, soul, top 40/pop, rockabilly, new wave and punk. Recently released "Hallowed Ground," by The Violent Femmes; and "Long Gone Dead," by Rank & File.

SOLID RECORDS, Apt. M, 10101 Woodlake Dr., Cockeysville MD 21030. A&R Director: George Brigman. Record company, music publisher and record producer (Sone Songs/BMI). Labels include Bonafide Records. Releases 1 single, 1-2 EPs, and 1-2 albums/year. Works with musicians on salary; artists and songwriters on contract. Pays 5-20% royalty to artists on contract; standard royalty to songwriters on contract; statutory rate to publishers for each record sold.
How to Contact: Write first to learn if we're accepting new material. Submit 7½ ips reel-to-reel with 1-6 songs and lyric sheet. No cassettes. Does not return unsolicited material. SASE. Reports in 3 weeks.
Music: Mostly hard rock, heavy metal and progressive rock; also blues and jazz. Recently released "Silent Bones," by George Brigman/Split (hard/progressive rock EP); *The Train to Disaster*, by various artists (hard rock LP); and *The New Jersey Teens*, by various artists (60s rock LP). Other artists include The Left, and Allan Marcum.

***SONATA RECORDS**, 4304 Del Monte Ave., San Diego CA 92107. (714)222-3346. President: Paul DiLella. Record company and music publisher. Member RIAA. Works with artists and songwriters on contract. Pays 5% royalty to artists on contract; 2¢/record to songwriters on contract.
How to Contact: Prefers 7½ ips reel-to-reel or cassette with 6-12 songs or lead sheet. SASE. Reports in 1 month.
Music: Church/religious, classical, country, dance, easy listening, gospel, MOR, rock and top 40/pop. Recently released "My Tropic Isle," by Cathy Foy (Hawaiian single). Other artists include Paul Dante.

SONIC WAVE RECORDS, Box 256577, Chicago IL 60625. (312)399-5535. President: Tom Petreli. Record company. Releases 5-10 singles and 2-5 albums/year. Works with artists on contract. Pays statutory rate.
How to Contact: Prefers cassette or videocassette with 2-4 songs and lyric sheet. SASE. Reports in 1 month.
Music: New wave. Recently released "80's," by Understrain (new wave single).

SOS RECORD PRODUCTIONS, INC., 7th Floor, 16 E. 41st St., New York NY 10017. (212)822-7769. Co-President: Joe Ferry. Record company and record producer. Releases 6 singles and 6 albums/

year. Works with songwriters on royalty contract. Pays 5-15% royalty to artists on contract.
How to Contact: Prefers cassette or VHS videocassette with 2-4 songs and lyric sheet. Prefers studio produced demos. SASE. "Do not call or visit." Reports in 6-8 weeks.
Music: Mostly dance; also R&B and jazz-fusion. Recently released "In the Middle of the Room," by Al Caldwell (R&B single); "Love Is Conditional," by John Tummolo (dance single); and "Let Me Touch You," by Revelation (R&B single). Other artists include Jeff Kline, Marty Campion, Sally Fox, Inez Brown, Eugene Ruffolo, and Book of Lies.
Tips: "Do not call to see if we've reviewed your tape. We review tapes constantly and answer all that include SASE. If we hear something we like we'll call you."

*SOUL SOUNDS UNLIMITED RECORDING CO., Box 24240, Cincinnati OH 45224. President: Alvin Don Chico Pettijohn. Record company and music publisher. Works with artists and songwriters on contract. Pays negotiable royalty to artists and songwriters on contract. Charges for some services. "If we feel that a writer or musician is best suited for our needs in the recording field, we will offer a recording contract."
How to Contact: Prefers 15 ips reel-to-reel or cassette. SASE. "All tapes will become the property of Soul Sounds if return postage is not included."
Music: Dance and soul.

SOUND IMAGE RECORDS, 6556 Wilkinson, North Hollywood CA 91606. (818)762-8881. Labels include Sound Image and Harmony. President: Martin J. Eberhardt. Vice President Sales & Studio Manager: Chuck Kopp. Vice President and General Manager: David Chatfield. Record company, record producer, music publisher (Sound Image Publishing), 24 track recording studio and video company. Member NARAS. Releases 12 singles and 6 albums/year. Works with artists and songwriters on contract; musicians on salary for in-house studio work. Pays 5-12% royalty to artists; statutory rate to publishers for each record sold.
How to Contact: Prefers cassette with 3-6 songs and lyric sheet. Include photo and bio. SASE. Prefers studio produced demos. Reports in 1 month.
Music: Mostly AOR, R&B and pop; also dance-oriented, top 40 and techno-pop. Recently released *George Faber & Stronghold*, (R&B/pop LP); *Mark Fosson*, (LP); and *Saint*, by Saint (AOR/pop LP).

SOUNDS OF WINCHESTER, Box 574, Winchester VA 22601. (703)667-9379. Labels include Alear, Winchester and Real McCoy Records. Contact: Jim or Bertha McCoy. Record company, music publisher (Jim McCoy Music, Alear Music and New Edition Music/BMI) and recording studio. Releases 20 singles and 10 albums/year. Works with artists and songwriters on contract; musicians on salary for in-house studio work. Pays 2% royalty to artists and songwriters on contract; statutory rate to publishers for each record sold.
How to Contact: Arrange personal interview. Prefers 7¹/₂ ips reel-to-reel with 4-12 songs. Does not return unsolicited material. Reports in 1 month.
Music: Bluegrass, country, country rock, gospel, and top 40/pop. Recently released "One More Time," by Earl Howard (country single); *Thank You Jesus*, by Jubilee Travelers (gospel LP); and "String Along," by Dave Elliott (country single). Other artists include Jim McCoy, Carroll County Ramblers and Alvin Kesner.

*THE SOURCE UNLTD., 331 E. 9th St., New York NY 10003. (312)473-7833. Vice-President: S. Mollica. Record company. Releases 2 singles/year and 2 LPs/year. Works with musicians on salary for in-house studio work.
How to Contact: Submit demo tape.

*SOUTHLAND RECORDS, INC., Box 1547, Arlington TX 76010. (817)461-3280. President: Steve Reed. Record company, music publisher and record producer. Releases 6-8 singles/year and 2-4 LP's/year. Works with musicians/artists and songwriters on contract; musicians on salary for in-house studio work. Pays negotiable royalty to artists on contract.
How to Contact: Prefers cassette with 4 songs and lyric or lead sheet. SASE. Reports in 6-8 weeks. "Demos should be 3 minutes and under in length."
Music: Mostly country, pop/rock and adult contemporary; also jazz. Recently released *The Rausch Touch*, recorded by Leon Rausch on Southland (country LP); "Rt. 66" (by Bobby Troup), and "Going Away Party," (by Cindy Walker) recorded by Leon Rausch on Southland (country singles). Other artists include Waldo "The Country Sax" Weathers.

*SPINNING GOLD INC., Box 2632, Austin TX 78768. (512)474-7355. Administrator: Bob Rhino. Labels include SG Records and Sunshine. Record company, music publisher and record producer. Releases 20 singles/year and 8 LP's/year. Works with musicians/artists and songwriters on contract;

musicians on salary for in-house studio work. Pays negotiable royalty to artists on contract.
How to Contact: Prefers cassette. SASE. Reports in 15 weeks.
Music: Mostly MOR, country and rock. Recently released *Devotion*, and *Ambrosia*, by O. Cessana (MOR LPs); and "First Love Feeling," by Glen Barber (country single).

SPRING RECORDS, 161 W. 54th St., New York NY 10019. (212)581-5398. Contact: A&R Department. Record company. Works with artists and songwriters on contract; musicians on salary for in-house studio work.
How to Contact: Submit demo tape and lyric sheet. Prefers masters.
Music: Dance and R&B. Recently released *Hard Times*, by Millie Jackson (R&B LP); and *Is This the Future?*, by Fatback Band (R&B LP).

THE STACY-LEE LABEL, Box 711, Hackensack NJ 07602. (201)488-5211. Labels include Banana, Inner Circle, Joy, Lions Den, Lotus, Lybra, Riot, Vanishing Point, S.A.M. Record company, record producer and music publisher (Miracle-Joy/BMI). Works with artists and songwriters on contract; musicians on salary for in-house studio work.
How to Contact: Prefers cassette with 1-6 songs and lyric sheet. SASE. Reports in 3 weeks.
Music: Children's, church/religious, country, easy listening, folk, gospel and MOR.

STAR RECORD CO., Suite 1700, 521 Fifth Ave., New York NY 10017. (212)682-5844. Record company, record producer and music publisher (McRon Music Co. and The Main Floor). Releases average 2-6 albums/year. Works with songwriters on royalty contract. Pays statutory rate to publishers for each record sold.

*STARBLEND RECORDS LIMITED, 31 Lingfield Rd., Wimblendon, London SW19 England. (01)879-1222. Assistant A&R Director: Carol Cook. Venom Records. Record company, music publisher (Solitaire Music) and TV Marketing firm. Releases 15 LP's/year. Works with musicians/artists on contract; musicians on salary for in-house studio work.
How to Contact: Prefers cassette. Does not return unsolicited material.
Music: MOR, country and rock.

STARBORN RECORDS, Box 2950, Hollywood CA 90078. Producer: Brian Ross. Record company, record producer, music publisher (Brian Ross Music/BMI, Thrush Music/BMI, IMC Music/ASCAP, Ian Anothony Ross Music, and New High Music /ASCAP); and worldwide record promotion, distribution, marketing and merchandising firm. Member AFM, AFTRA, AIMP, CCC, NARAS and NARM. Releases 25-50 singles and 15-25 albums/year. Works with artists and songwriters on contract. Pays 50% "of all money earned by Starborn Records to artists and songwriters on contract"; statutory rate to publishers for each record sold.
How to Contact: Prefers cassette or ¹/₂" VHS videocassette with 2-4 songs and lyric sheet. "Print your name and address clearly on tape box *and* cassette. Include photo and short biography." SASE. Does not assume responsibility for materials damaged or lost in the mail. Reports in 1 week.
Music: Mostly new wave, technopop and top 40/pop contemporary "with great hooks and good melodies and chord changes;" also all other types. Recently released "Jam The Box," by Jamtrak; "Second Chance," by Scapeboat; and "Take Some Time," by Pilot.
Tips: "This international record label specializes in releasing masters from foreign countries. Currently accepting finished masters for consideration as well as new song material. Starborn Records maintains licensing operations in over 35 countries outside of North America. Will give feedback as soon as possible, no calls please. Submit your product in 'easy-open' envelopes, do not use staples on your packages. Please enclose photo and short biography of yourself, your musical background, education, credits (if any) and be clear as to what you are looking for, i.e., a publishing deal, a record contract, both, or work as a writer in television and motion pictures."

STARCREST PRODUCTIONS, INC., 209 Circle Hills Dr., Grand Forks ND 58201. (701)772-6831. Labels include Meadowlark and Minn-Dak Records. President: George J. Hastings. Record company, management firm and booking agency. Releases 2-6 singles and 1-2 albums/year. Works with artists and songwriters on contract. Payment negotiable to artists on contract; statutory rate to publishers for each record sold.
How to Contact: Write first. Prefers cassette with 1-6 songs and lead sheet. SASE. Reports in 1 month.
Music: Country and top 40/pop. Recently released "A Good Yellow Rose," by Gene Wylos (country single); and "Holding Back Teardrops" and "Gypsy I Am," by Mary Joyce (country singles).

STARGEM RECORDS, INC., 43 Music Square East, Nashville TN 37203. (615)244-1025. President and A&R Director: Wayne Hodge. Record company, record producer and music publisher (Newwriters

Music/BMI and Timestar Music/ASCAP). Works with artists and songwriters on contract; musicians on salary for in-house studio work. Pays 5-15% royalty to artists on contract; statutory rate to publishers for each record sold.
How to Contact: Write first. Prefers cassette with 1-4 songs and lyric sheet. "Have clear recording and use new tape." SASE.
Music: Gospel (all styles).

STARK RECORDS & TAPE CO., 628 South St., Mount Airy NC 27030. (919)786-2865. Labels include Stark, Hello, Pilot and Sugarbear. Contact: Paul E. Johnson. Record company and music publisher (Tompaul Music Company/BMI). Releases 80 singles and 45 albums/year. Works with artists and songwriters on contract. Works with composers and teams collaborators. Pays 50% royalty to artists on contract; statutory rate to publishers for each record sold.
How to Contact: Prefers 7¹/₂ ips reel-to-reel or cassette with 3-5 songs and lead sheet. SASE. "Our return address should be on your SASE. Reports in 1 month.
Music: Mostly country, bluegrass and gospel; also church/religious, folk, country rock and top 40/pop. Recently released "Would You Walk With Jesus," and "Liquor by the Drink," and Carl P. Tolbert (country gospel singles); and "His Grace Is Sufficient," by Ellen Fiedler (pop gospel single). Other artists include Bruce Evans, Jim Hodges, Eddie Johnson, Paul E. Johnson, Alan Westmoreland, Bobby L. Atkins, Randy Scott, Ralph E. Hill and Johnny Long.

STARTIME MUSIC, Box 643, LaQuinta CA 92253. (714)564-4823. President: Fred Rice. Record company and music publisher (Yo Yo Music/BMI). ASCAP. Releases 2 singles and 2 albums/year. Pays standard royalty.
How to Contact: Prefers cassette with 1-2 songs and lead sheet. SASE. Reports in 6 weeks.
Music: Mostly novelty, country and top 40/pop; also rock. Recently released "My Palm Springs," by Mary Gramm Turner (pop/contemporary single) and "Palm Springs Party" by G. Whittaker and R. Miller (pop/contemporary); and "Mini-Van" by Vantastics (top 40).
Tips: "A song has to be built of 'flesh and blood'—the rhythm is the skeleton, the musical theme is the flesh and the lyrics are the blood (the soul). Don't write a song, write a record! Must have *provocative* title, *repetitive* musical theme with *simple* word phrase lyrics, *identifiable* melody line, and lastly should have a *different sound.*"

*STATUE RECORDS, 11818 Felton Ave., Hawthorne CA 92050. (213)978-8830. A&R Director: Sandor D. Padilla II. Record company. Releases 5-10 singles and 5-10 LPs/year. Works with musicians/artists and songwriters on contract. Pays 1-10% or negotiable royalty to artists on contract.
How to Contact: Prefers (in order of preference) Beta Hi-Fi videocassette, "high quality" cassette or 7¹/₂ or 15 ips reel-to-reel with 3-5 songs and lyric sheet. Does not return unsolicited material. Reports in 3-4 weeks; "large backlog. Please include glossy photo(s) if you are a group looking for a recording deal and include business card with all submissions."
Music: Mostly "up-tempo rock (no ballads), heavy metal with *strong* hooks and new wave/artistic punk; also comedy music (e.g. Weird Al Yankovic)." Recently released *England*, written and recorded by Geoffrey England on Statue (rock LP); "Strangest Love," (by Eddie Miller), recorded by England on Statue (rock single); and "Gotta Break," (by Jim Alfoma), recorded by Insomnia on Statue (comedy single). Other artists include Infra-Red, Veodream, Blue Network, and Krakatoa.

STONEDOG RECORDS, 1819 W. Thorne, Chicago IL 60660. President: Stoney Phillips. Record company, record producer and music publisher (Hannan/Phillips Music). Member RIAA and BMI. Releases 2 singles and 1 album/year. Works with artists and songwriters on contract. Pays 5-6% royalty to artists on contract; statutory rate to publishers for each record sold.
How to Contact: Prefers (in order of preference) Beta Hi-Fi videocassette, "high quality" cassette or 7¹/₂ or 15 ips reel-to-reel with 3-5 songs and lyric sheet. Does not return unsolicited material. Reports in
Music: Mostly crossover, pop and country; also easy listening, MOR and rock. Recently released "This Time," "Baby Please Stay," and "Sometimes," by R. Rice (crossover and pop singles).

STREETLIGHT RECORDS, 236¹/₂ Lasky Dr., Beverly Hills CA 90212. Labels include Koster, Snugglebush and Snugglebug Records. A&R Vice President: Bobby Joe Watson. Record company, record producer and music publisher (Snugglebush Music Company). Estab. 1984. Releases 20 singles and 5 albums/year. Works with artists and songwriters on contract. Pays 5-12% royalty to artists on contract; statutory rate or "if applicable, higher" rate to publishers for each record sold.
How to Contact: Prefers cassette or videocassette with 2 songs and lyric sheet. "If material is to be returned, send in SASE." Reports in 2 weeks.
Music: Mostly pop and R&B; also dance-oriented, easy listening, MOR, rock, soul and top 40.

*SUITE BEAT MUSIC, 1201 Olympic Blvd., Santa Monica CA 90404. (213)452-5949. President: Bob Marin. Labels include Rhino, Epitaph, Acid Reign. Record company. Releases 5-10 singles and 10-20 LPs/year. Works with musicians/artists on contract. Pays negotiable royalty to artists on contract.
How to Contact: Prefers cassette or ¹/₂" VHS videocassette with maximum 3 songs and lyric sheet. SASE. Reports in 4-6 weeks.
Music: Mostly rock/pop and modern new punk; also psychedelic and jazz. Recently released *Back to the Know*, recorded by Bad Religion on Epitaph (modern punk); "Acid Bath," recorded by Alien Sex Fiend on Epitaph (psychedelic/punk); and *The Olympic Sideburns*, recorded by The Olympic Sideburns on Epitaph (punk rock/soul).

SUN INTERNATIONAL CORP., 3106 Belmont Blvd., Nashville TN 37212. (615)385-1960. Labels include Plantation Records and SSS International Records. Professional Manager: Shelby Singleton. Record company, record producer and music publisher (Shelby Singleton Music, Prize Music). Member RIAA and NARAS. Releases 30 singles and 25 albums/year. Works with artists and songwriters on contract. Pays 8-15% royalty to artists on contract; statutory rate to publishers for each record sold.
How to Contact: Prefers cassette with 1-3 songs and lyric sheet. SASE. Reports in 1 month.
Music: Country, easy listening, MOR, easy rock and top 40/pop. Artists include Rita Remington, Patti Page and Charlie Walker.
Tips: "Present professional demo along with lyrics and explanation of career-goals. Artists should have a working band."

SUNNY DAY PRODUCTIONS, 1931 SE Morrison, Portland OR 97214. (800)547-5547 or (503)238-4525 in Oregon. Labels include Cricket, New Day and Rexius. President: Russell E. Gorsline. Record company, record producer and music publisher (Klickitat Music). Releases 4-8 singles and 2-5 albums/year. Works with artists and songwriters on contract. Pays negotiable royalty to artists on contract; statutory rate to publishers for each record sold.
How to Contact: Write or call first. Send submissions to Gary Perman, A&R Director. Prefers cassette with 2-5 songs and lyric sheet. SASE. Reports in 2 weeks.
Music: Mostly contemporary Christian, pop, MOR and jazz; also choral, church/religious, dance-oriented, gospel, MOR and pop/rock. Recently released *Fantasy*, by David O'Brian (pop/MOR LP); "She Ain't No Saint," by Helen Westin (novelty single); and "Shining Star," by Pamela Cansler (contemporary Christian single). Other artists include the Staples Brothers.

SUN-RAY RECORDS, 1662 Wyatt Pkwy., Lexington KY 40505. (606)254-7474. Labels include Sun-Ray and Sky-Vue Records. President: James T. Price. Record company and music publisher (Jimmy Price Music Publisher/BMI). Releases 9 singles/year. Works with songwriters on contract; musicians on salary for in-house studio work. Pays statutory rate to publishers for each record sold.
How to Contact: Prefers 7¹/₂ ips reel-to-reel with 2-6 songs and lead sheet. SASE. Reports in 3 weeks.
Music: Bluegrass (sacred or country), church/religious, country and gospel. Recently released "Truck Driver's Rock," by Virgil Vickers (single); "All Them Wives," by Harold Montgomery (single); and "Flat Top Box," by Tommy Jackson (single). Other artists include James Mailicote, Charles Hall and Kenny Wade.
Tips: "We need songs with a good story along with rhyme and meter."

*SUNSHINE RECORDS, 800 S. 4th St., Philadelphia PA 19147. (215)755-7000. Director of A&R: Walter Kahn. Labels include Sunshine, Moonshine and Lattitude. Record company and music publisher (Scully/Orange Bear Music Co.). Releases 10 singles/year and 2 LP's/year. Works with musicians/artists on contract.
How to Contact: Prefers cassette or VHS videocassette with 3-4 songs and lyric sheet. SASE. "Include an 8x10 photo, if available."
Music: Mostly R&B/dance, pop and rock; also rap and new wave. Recently released "Dr. Jam," (by Miller/Loris), recorded by Men at Play on Sunshine (rap single); "Hot for You," (by Walter Kahn), recorded by Karen Young on Sunshine (pop single); and "Dirty Looks," (by Karras/Kaplan), recorded by Dick Tracey on Sunshine (rock EP). Other artists include Juliet and David St. George.

SURPRIZE RECORDS, INC., 421 W. Ellet St., Philadelphia PA 19119. (215)276-8861. President: Gilda C. Woods. Vice President: W. Lloyd Lucas. Record company, record producer, music publisher (In the Woods) and artist management. Member ASCAP, BMI and SRS. Works with artists and songwriters on record contract. Pays 6-10% royalty to artists on contract; statutory rate to publishers for each record sold.
How to Contact: Write or call first. Prefers cassette with 1-5 songs and lyric sheet. SASE. "Do not send certified mail." Reports in 4 weeks.
Music: R&B, soul, top 40/pop, dance and MOR. Recently released "This Could Be the Night," by

Karla Garrison (dance single); "Pledging My Love," by Bill Lucas (single); and "You're Unforgettable," by Dave James (single). Other artists include Mimi Lopez, Darryl Lucas and Richie Merritt.

*SURESHOT RECORDS, Box 2236, Largo FL 33540. (813)595-5115. Contact: Alan Redstone. Record company and music publisher (Magic, Message Music). Releases 1 single/year and 1 LP/year.
How to Contact: Prefers cassette. SASE. Reports in 2 weeks.
Music: Mostly pop, country and adult contemporary; also rock. Recently released "Cold Hands and Wet Feet," (country rock single); and "Magic Message," (adult contemporary single), both written and recorded by Alan Redstone on Sureshot.

SUSAN RECORDS, Box 4740, Nashville TN 37216. (615)865-4740. Labels include Denco Records. A&R Director: Russ Edwards. Record company and music publisher. Releases 2-20 singles and 1-5 albums/year. Works with artists and songwriters on contract. Pays 6¢/record to artists on contract. Buys some material outright; payment varies.
How to Contact: Prefers 7¹/₂ ips reel-to-reel with 1-6 songs and lead sheet. SASE. Reports in 2 weeks.
Music: Blues, country, dance, easy listening, folk, gospel, jazz, MOR, rock, soul and top 40/pop.

T.C. RECORDS, (formerly Venture), 121 Meadowbrook Dr., Somerville NJ 08876. (201)359-5110. Labels include Venture. Coordinator: Marsha Terrill. Record company, record producer and music publisher (Etude, Barcam). Releases 50 singles and 10 albums/year. Works with artists and songwriters on contract; musicians on salary for in-house studio work. Pays negotiable royalty to artists on contract; negotiable rate to publishers for each record sold.
How to Contact: Prefers reel-to-reel or cassette with maximum 3 songs and lyric sheet. SASE. Reports in 1 month.
Music: R&B, rock, soul and top 40/pop. Soon to release music from The Fifth Dimension and a sound track form the movie *Stitches*.

T.M. INTERNATIONAL RECORDS OF MILWAUKEE, Box 16608, Milwaukee WI 53216. (414)461-0602. Contact: Odell or Cardell Tillman. Record company, music publisher (Famous Door Publishing Co.) and record producer. Releases 5 singles and 3 albums/year. Works with artists on contract; musicians on salary for in-house studio work. Pays statutory rate to publishers for each record sold.
How to Contact: Prefers cassette with 4 songs and lyric or lead sheet. SASE. Reports in 3 weeks.
Music: Mostly soul; also bluegrass, gospel, jazz and R&B. Recently released *Sorceress*, by Joanne Tardy (R&B LP); *Crazy Love* and *Music Makes Me High*, by Joanne Tardy (bluegrass LPs). Other artists include Kent Allen.

TAKE HOME TUNES, Box 10051, Beverly Hills CA 90213-3051. (818)761-2646. Labels include Broadway Baby and Original Cast Records. Contact: Doris Chu. Branch office: Box 1314, Englewood Cliffs NJ 07632. Record company and music publisher (The Chu Yeko Musical Foundation/BMI, Broadway/Hollywood International Music Publishers/ASCAP). Releases 8-10 albums/year. Works with artists and songwriters on contract. Royalty payment varies for artists on contract; pays 5-10% royalty to songwriters on contract.
How to Contact: Prefers cassette. SASE. Reports in 1 month.
Music: Mostly Broadway-type show tunes; also pop, rock, R&B, country and MOR. Recently released *King of Hearts*, by Millicent Martin and Don Scardino; *Bring Back Birdie*, by Donald O'Connor and Chita Rivera; *81 Proof* and *Housewives Cantata*, by the Original cast (musical LPs).
Tips: "A produced original musical singer or group appearing in Los Angeles area with financial backing would increase an artist's or songwriter's chance of working with us."

TELESON-AMERICA, 62 Fairfax St., Somerville MA 02144. (617)776-2146. Labels include Grand Orgue, Motette-Ursina and Solist. Record company. Releases 20-30 albums/year. Works with artists on contract.
How to Contact: Write first. Prefers 7¹/₂ or 15 ips reel-to-reel. SASE. Reports in 4 months.
Music: Pipe organ and religious choral (classical). Artists include Pierre Labric, Marie-Andree Morisset-Balier, Heinz Bernhard Orlinski, Jean Langlais, Almut Rossler, Michel Morisset, Gunther Kaunzinger, Marie-Louise Jacquet-Langlais, Gaston Litaize, Hermann Harrassowitz, Johannes Ricken, Rosalinde Haas, Daniel Roth, Jean-Jacques Grunenwald and Paul Wisskirchen.

TEROCK RECORDS, Box 4740, Nashville TN 37216. (615)865-4740. Labels include Terock, Susan, Denco, Rock-A-Nash-A-Billy. Manager: S.D. Neal. Record company, record producer, and music publisher (Heavy Jamin' Music/ASCAP). "We also lease masters." Member ASCAP, BMI. Releases 4 singles and 3 albums/year. Works with artists and songwriters on contract. Pays 5-8% royalty to artists on contract; standard royalty to songwriters on contract.

How to Contact: Prefers 7¹/₂ ips reel-to-reel or cassette with 3-6 songs and lyric sheet. SASE. Reports in 3 weeks.

Music: Mostly country and rockabilly; also bluegrass, blues, easy listening, folk, gospel, jazz, MOR, progressive, Spanish, R&B, rock, soul and top 40/pop. Recently released "That's Why I Love You," by Dixie Dee (country); "Born to Bum Around," by Curt Flemons (country); and "Big Heavy," by the Rhythm Rockers (rock).

3 G'S INDUSTRIES, 5500 Troost, Kansas City MO 64110. (816)361-8455. Labels include NMI, Cory, 3 G's and Chris C's Records. General Manager: Eugene Gold. Record company, record producer and music publisher (Eugene Gold Music and Gid-Gad Music). Releases 4 singles and 3 albums/year. Works with artists and songwriters on contract; musicians on salary for in-house studio work. Pays 4-6% royalty to artists on contract; statutory rate to publishers for each record sold.

How to Contact: Prefers cassette or videocassette with 4-8 songs and lyric sheet. SASE. Reports in 1 month.

Music: Mostly R&B and jazz; also church/religious, gospel and soul. Recently released "Baby We Can Make It" and "You Left Me at a Bad, Bad Time," by Ronnie and Vicky (R&B EP); and "Diamond Feather," by Bad News Band (R&B single). Other artists include Suspension, L. Washington, Thrust's, Jeff Lucas, James "Fuzzy" West, Cal Green and L.S. Movement Band.

TITAN INTERNATIONAL PRODUCTIONS, LTD., 185A, Newmarket Rd., Norwich, Norfolk, NR4 6AP, England. 44-0603-51139. Labels include Esquire, Starlite and Titan. Director: Peter Newbrook. Record company and music publisher (Esquire Music Co.). Releases 3 singles and 10 albums/year. Works with artists on contract. Pays negotiable royalty to artists on contract; 6¹/₄% to publishers for each record sold. Royalties paid to US songwriters and artists through US publishing or recording affiliate. Has not yet, but would listen to material from US songwriters and artists.

How to Contact: Write first. Prefers cassette. SAE and IRC. Reports in 1 month.

Music: Mostly jazz; also MOR and R&B. Artists include Cleo Laine, Teddy Wilson, John Dankworth and Mary Lou Williams.

TNA RECORDS, 10 George St., Box 57, Wallingford CT 06492. (203)269-4465. A&R Director: Rudolf Szlavi. Record company, record producer, music publisher (Rohm Music, QVQ Music, Linesider Music, BIG Music) and personal management. Releases 1-3 singles and 2-5 albums/year. Works with artists and songwriters on contract. Pays 12-75% royalty to artists on contract; statutory rate to publishers for each record sold.

How to Contact: Prefers cassette or videocassette with 1-3 songs and lyric sheet. Include statement of goals and purposes. SASE. Reports in 2 weeks.

Music: Mostly rock, R&B and top 40/pop; also blues and dance-oriented. Recently released *Best of Friends*," by Bob Mel (pop LP); *Charmaine*, by Christine Ohlman/Rebel Montez (rock LP); and *American Dream*, by the Cub Koda Band (rock LP).

Tips: "Artists and songwriters should have high code of ethics coupled with enthusiasm. Being in Connecticut area helps with communication in management and direction."

*TOMMY BOY, 1747 First Ave., New York NY 10128. (212)722-2211. A&R/Promotion Manager: Joseph Gardner. Labels include Body Rock. Record company, music publisher (T-Boy/T-Girl) and record producer. Releases 20-25 singles and 5-7 albums/year. Works with musicians/artists on contract; musicians on salary for in-house studio work. Pays varying royalty to artists on contract.

How to Contact: Call first and obtain permission to submit. Prefers cassette with 1-3 songs and lyric sheet. SASE. "When submitting a demo, please do not call to see if we are going to use it. If we are going to, you will be the first to know. We accept calls on Fridays only."

Music: Mostly R&B/rap, soul and R&B/dance. "No pop." Recently released "Forgive Me Girl," written and recorded by Force M.D.'s on Tommy Boy (R&B single); "He's Got the Beat," (by S. Knutson, M.Lynch), recorded by Whiz Kid on Tommy Boy (R&B/dance single); and "Celebrate," written and recorded by G.L.O.B.E. and Pow Wow on Tommy Boy (rap single). Other artists include Afrika Bambaataa, Rock Squad, Hiko & the Great Peso, Tuff Inc., Soul Sonic Force, TKA and The Golden Girls.

TOP DOG RECORDS, (formerly Full Sail Records), Top Dog Productions, 71 Boylston St., Brookline MA 02147. (617)739-2010. President: Fred Berk. Record company and music publisher. (Topdog Music/BMI). Releases 10 singles and 3 albums/year. Works with artists and songwriters on contract. Pays 5-7% royalty to artists on contract; standard royalties to songwriters on contract; statutory rate to publishers for each record sold.

How to Contact: Prefers cassette with 1-10 songs.

Music: Country, rockabilly, rock, soul and top 40/pop.

TOUCHE RECORDS, Box 96, El Cerrito CA 94530. Executive Vice President: James Bronson, Jr. Record company, record producer (Mom and Pop Productions, Inc.) and music publisher (Toulouse Music Co./BMI). Member AIMP. Works with artists and songwriters on contract; musicians on salary for in-house studio work. Pays statutory rate to publishers for each record sold.
How to Contact: Prefers cassette with 2-4 songs and lyric sheet. SASE. Reports in 1 month.
Music: Bluegrass, gospel, jazz, R&B and soul. Artists include Les Oublies du Jazz Ensemble.

*TREND RECORDS, Box 201, Smyrna GA 30081. (404)432-2454. Labels include Trendsetter, Atlanta and Stepping Stone Records. President: Tom Hodges. Record company, music publisher, record producer and management firm. Releases 6-10 singles and 2-8 albums/year. Works with artists on contract. Pays 5-7% royalty to artists on contract: standard royalty to songwriters on contract.
How to Contact: Prefers cassette with 3-6 songs and lead sheet. SASE. Reports in 3 weeks.
Music: Bluegrass, country, gospel, MOR, rock and soul. Recently released *Feet*, by Jim Single (country single and LP), "Sugar Daddy," by Frank Brannon (country single); and "Kennesaw Get Your Guns." Other artists include Jo Anne Johnson.

*TRIX RECORDS, INC., Drawer AB, Rosendale NY 12472. (914)687-9573. Contact: Peter B. Lowry. Labels include Ghetto Farms Records. Record company, music pubilsher (Baby Tate Music Corp.) and record producer (Katward Ho Productions). Releases 1-2 LPs/year. Works with musicians/ artists on contract. Pays standard royalty to artists on contract.
How to Contact: Prefers cassette. Does not return unsolicited material.
Music: Mostly blues, jazz and rock; also folk. Recently released *Does 12*, by Robert Jr. Lockwood on Trix (blues LP); *Get Outta Town Man*, by Maurice Reedus-El on Trix (jazz LP); and *I've Been Around*, by David "Honeyboy" Edwards on Trix (blues LP). Other artists include Roy Dunn, Dan Del Santo, Frank Edwards, Eddie Kirkland, Homesick James, and John Cephas.

TRUE NORTH RECORDS, The Finkelstein Management Co. Ltd., Suite 2B, 98 Queen St. E, Toronto, Ontario M5C 1S6 Canada. (416)364-6040. Contact: Jehanne Languedoc. Record company, management company, record producer, music publisher (Mummy Dust Music) and production company. Member CIRPA, CMPA, PROCAN, CAPAC. Releases approximately 18 singles and 6 albums/year. Works with artists on contract. Pays negotiable royalty to artists on contract; negotiable rate to publishers for each record sold.
How to Contact: Call first and obtain permission to submit. Prefers cassette with 2-4 songs. Include bio. Does not return unsolicited material. Prefers studio produced demos. Reports in 1 month but demo tape will not be returned.
Music: Top 40/pop and CMR/AOR. Recently released "If I Had a Rocket Launcher," and "Lovers in a Dangerous Time," by Bruce Cockburn (pop singles); and "Never Did Like That Train," by Murray McLauchlan (country single). Other artists includes Rough Trade, Tony Kosinec, and Johnny MacLead.

TRUSTY RECORDS, Rt. 1, Box 100, Nebo KY 42441. (502)249-3194. President: Elsie Childers. Record company and music publisher (Trusty Publications/BMI). Member NSAI, CMA. Releases 2-3 singles and 1 album/year. Works with artists and songwriters on contract. Pays 2% royalty to artists on contract; statutory rate to publishers for each record sold.
How to Contact: Prefers 7¹/₂ ips reel-to-reel or cassette with 2-4 songs and lead sheet. SASE. Reports in 1 month.
Music: Mostly country; also blues, church/religious, dance, easy listening, folk, gospel, MOR, soul and top 40/pop.
Tips: "Writer-artists and people with road tours are given top consideration."

*ULTRAZEN RECORD COMPANY, Box 50634, Dallas TX 75250. (214)747-5370. Producer: James Stearns. Record company, music publisher, record producer and promotion and distribution firm. Releases 2 singles/year and 2 LP's/year. Works with musicians/artists and songwriters on contract; musicians on salary for in-house studio work. Pays 5-11% royalty to artists on contract; statutory rate to publishers for each record sold.
How to Contact: Prefers cassette or VHS videocassette with 5 or more songs and lyric sheet. SASE. Reports in 12 weeks. "Include list of recording equipment used to make demo."
Music: Mostly "new music," rock and alternative music; also urban contemporary, modern country and international. Recently released "Give Love a Try," (by Tony Rosario), recorded by Coupe Studios on Ultrazen (rock single); "Cut Off Jeans," (by Jimmy Mack), recorded by Rudy Wilson on Jah (R&B soul novelty single); and "Spiral Shadows," (by Will Wesch), recorded by Ultrazen on Ultrazen (rock single).

*UMBRELLA ORGANISATION PTY. LTD., Box 2089, Sydney 2001, Australia. (2)233-5577. Contact: Manager. Music publisher, record company and record producer.

How to Contact: Prefers cassette or VHS (PAL) videocassette. Does not return unsolicited material. Reports in 6 weeks.
Music: Mostly contemporary pop/rock, film soundtracks and country.

UNIVERSAL ARTIST'S RECORDS, Box 1128 College Branch, Madison TN 37116-1128. (615)865-8692. Labels include Delta Record Co. Contact: Ken Galloway. Record company and record producer. Releases "several" singles/year. Works with artists and songwriters on contract. Pays statutory rate to publishers for each record sold.
How to Contact: Submit demo tape or arrange personal interview. Prefers 7½ ips reel-to-reel, cassette or videocassette with 6-10 songs and lyric sheet. SASE. Reports in 1 month.
Music: Mostly country. Recently released "Glad I Waited," by Lori Robin Smith (easy listening single); and "Work On It Baby," by Bob Money (country single).

UNIVERSAL-ATHENA RECORDS, Box 3615, Peoria IL 61614. (309)673-5755. A&R Director: Jerry Hanlon. Record company and music publisher (Jerjoy Music/BMI). Works with artists and songwriters on contract; musicians on salary for in-house studio work. Pays statutory rate to publishers for each record sold.
How to Contact: Prefers cassette with 4-8 songs and lyric sheet. SASE. Reports in 2 weeks.
Music: Country. Recently released *Memories,* by Jerry Hanlon (country LP). Other artists include Robby Hull.

UNREGULATED RECORD CO., INC., Box 81485, Fairbanks AK 99708. (907)456-3419. Labels include Lift Records. President: Michael States. Record company, record producer and music publisher (Unregulated Music/BMI). Releases 3 singles and 3 albums/year. Works with artists and songwriters on contract. Pays negotiable royalty to artists on contract; statutory rate to publishers for each record sold.
How to Contact: Prefers cassette with 2-5 songs and lyric sheet.
Music: Gospel (avant garde, soul, reggae). Recently released *Beat the Cynics,* by Cynics (new wave gospel LP); and *Christmas with Jesus,* by Lily of the Valley Choir (new wave/black gospel LP). Other artists include Marty Beggs, Paul Porter, Spoon, Pat Fitzgerald, Robyn Hood, Richard Jesse and the Movement.

URBAN ROCK RECORDS, Suite 3W, 40 W. 56th St., New York NY 10019. (212)315-0540. Record company, record producer and music publisher (Cousin Ice). Releases 4 singles and 2 albums/year. Works with artists on contract. Pays negotiable royalty to artists on contract; statutory rate to publishers for each record sold.
How to Contact: Prefers cassette with 3-4 songs and lyric sheet. Prefers studio produced demos. SASE. Reports in 1 month.
Music: Mostly soul; also dance-oriented and R&B soul. Recently released "Fire Fly," by Cousin Ice (R&B single); "Night People," by Prestige (dance single); and "Hands Off," by Jocelyn Brown (R&B single). Other artists include Diva Gray.
Tips: "Submit a feeling, not just a formula. Use high quality cassettes."

VANGUARD RECORDING SOCIETY, 71 W. 23rd St., New York NY 10010. (212)255-7732. A&R Director: Jeff Zaraya. Record company and music publisher (Silkie Music Publishers/BMI). Works with artists on contract.
How to Contact: Prefers cassette with 2-4 songs and lyric sheet. SASE. Reports in 1 month.
Music: Mostly dance-oriented; also progressive and mainstream rock, soul and top 40/pop. Recently released "Electric Kingdom," by Twilight 22 (R&B/dance single); "All Night Passion," by Alisha (pop/dance single); and *Juke Box,* by Flirts (pop/dance/rock single and LP). Other artists include Real Eyes.

VIC RECORDS, 1327 Cobb St., Kalamazoo MI 49007. (616)342-5328. Contact: Vic LaVal. Record company and record producer. Releases 50 singles and 20 albums/year. Pays statutory rate to publishers for each record sold.
How to Contact: Prefers reel-to-reel or cassette with 2-10 songs and lyric sheet. SASE. Reports in 3 weeks.
Music: Country and country rock. Recently released *Letter to My Ex Wife,* by Eddie Vispa (country LP); and *Stoop Down Baby,* by Chick Willis (R&B LP). Other artists include Val Vegas, Cold Fire, Kathleen Hill, Frisco, Hot Nuts and The R.A.R.S.

VOKES MUSIC PUBLISHING & RECORD CO., Box 12, New Kensington PA 15068. (412)335-2775. Labels include Vokes and Country Boy Records. President: Howard Vokes. Record company, booking agency and music publisher. Releases 8 singles and 5 albums/year. Works with artists and songwriters on contract. Pays 2½-4½¢/song royalty to artists and songwriters on contract.

How to Contact: Submit cassette only and lead sheet. SASE. Reports in 2 weeks.
Music: Bluegrass, country and gospel. Recently released *Songs of Broken Love Affairs* and *Tears at the Grand Ole Op'ry*, by Howard Vokes; *Hank Williams Isn't Dead*, by Denver Duke and Jeffery Null; *Ballad of Johnny Horton*, by Hank King, Jimmy Parker, Larry Dale and Rudy Thacker; and *Billy Wallace Sings His Hits*, by Billy Wallace.

*WALK ON WATER RECORDS, Rt. 2, Box 566-H, New Braunfels TX 78130. (512)629-4396. Producer/Manager: Brian C. Carr. Record company, music publisher, record prducer and recording studio. Releases 2 singles/year and 1 LP/year. Works with musicians/artists and songwriters on contract. Pays 7-11% royalty to artists on contract.
How to Contact: Write first and obtain permission to submit. Prefers cassette, 7¹/₂ ips reel-to-reel or VHS videocassette with 2-3 songs and lyric sheet. Does not return unsolicited material. Reports in 4-6 weeks. "Include SASE for reply."
Music: Mostly AOR-pop/rock, new music and country. Recently released *Every Ones a Spy*, (by Morgan/Stirm), recorded by Secrets on Walk on Water (rock LP); *Salute to San Antonio*, written and recorded by Rusty Lawrence on Walk on Water (country LP); and "Jamacian Beaches," written and recorded by Norm Allen on Walk on Water (rock single). Other artists incude Tommy Thompson, Dennis Peek, Howard Yeargan and Tim Catron.

WALTNER ENTERPRISES, 14702 Canterbury, Tustin CA 92680. (714)731-2981. Labels include Calico and Daisy. President: Steve Waltner. Record company and music publisher (Early Bird Music/BMI). Releases 2-5 singles and 1 album/year. Works with musicians and songwriters on contract. Pays 5-10% royalty to artists on contract; standard royalty to songwriters on contract; pays statutory rate to publishers for each record sold.
How to Contact: Prefers cassette or videocassette with 2-4 songs and lead sheet. SASE. Reports in 3 weeks.
Music: Country, easy listening, MOR and top 40/pop. Recently released "Will You Be Here in the Morning," by Jason Chase (country/pop single); "Country's Here to Stay," by Steve Shelby (country single); and "Slim & Lefty," by Lester Cash (country novelty single).

WARNER BROTHERS RECORDS, INC., 3300 Warner Blvd., Burbank CA 91510. (818)846-9090. Contact: A&R Coordinator. Record company. Works with artists and songwriters on contract.
How to Contact: Write first. Prefers cassette or videocassette. Does not accept unsolicited material. Reports in 8 weeks.
Music: Country, disco, easy listening, folk, jazz, progressive, R&B, rock, soul and top 40/pop.

WATTS CITY RECORDS, 11211 Wilmington Ave., Los Angeles CA 90059. (213)566-9982. Labels include Watts City and Melatone. President/Producers: Joe Fornnis. Record company, record producer and music publisher (Watts City Productions/ASCAP). Releases 5 singles and 2 albums/year. Works with artists and songwriters on contract. Pays 6% royalty to artists on contract; statutory rate to publishers for each record sold.
How to Contact: Prefers cassette with 4-12 songs and lyric sheet. SASE. Reports in 3 weeks.
Music: R&B, soul and top 40/pop.

WEA MUSIC OF CANADA, LTD., 1810 Birchmount Rd., Scarborough, Ontario M1P 2J1, Canada. (416)291-2515. Labels include Warner Bros., Elektra, Atlantic, Reprise, Sire, Bearsville, ECM, Geffen, Qwest, Asylum, Nonesuch, Solar, Atco, Mirage, Rolling Stones, Swan Song and WEA. A&R Manager: Bob Roper. Record company and music publisher (Don Valley Music, Home Cooked Music). Member CRIA, CARAS. Releases 250 singles and 300 albums/year. Works with artists on contract. Pays negotiable royalty to artists on contract; negotiable rate to publishers for each record sold.
How to Contact: Currently interested in Canadian artists only. Prefers cassette or videocassette with 4-6 songs and lyric sheet. Include photos, bio and any other pertinent information. SASE. Reports in 1 month.
Music: Mostly rock and top 40/pop; also classical, country, dance-oriented, easy listening, folk, jazz, MOR, progressive, R&B and soul. Recently released *No Jacket Required*, by Phil Collins (rock LP); *Agent Provocateur*, by Foreigner (rock LP); and *Honeymoon Suite*, by Honeymoon Suite (rock LP).

WEBCO RECORDS & RECORDING STUDIO, 8705 Deanna Dr., Gaithersburg MD 20879. (301)253-5962 or 251-1285. President: Wayne E. Busbice. Record company, record producer and music publisher (Old Home Place Music). Member CMA. Releases 4-6 singles and 8 albums/year. Works with artists and songwriters on contract. Pays 40% royalty (after costs) to artists on contract; statutory rate to publishers for each record sold.
How to Contact: Write first and obtain permission to submit. Prefers cassette with 3-5 songs. SASE. Reports in 1 month.

Music: Mostly bluegrass; also country. Recently released "Shenandoah Grass, Yesterday & Today," by Jim Eanes (bluegrass LP); *Carl Nelson & His Fiddle on Pine Lake*, by Carl Nelson (fiddle & bluegrass LP); and *The Bluegrass Sounds of Buzz Busby*, by B. Busby (bluegrass LP). Other artists include Darrell Sanders, Blackthorn Stick, The Grass Reflection, Bill Rouse & The Uptown Grass Band, Brooke Johns, Jack Fincham & The Dixie Grass, The Overland Express, Bobby Atkins & The Countrymen, Joe Boucher, Hobbs & Partners, and D.J. & The C.B. Pickers.

W/G PUBLISHING AND RECORD CO., 991 Oak St., West Barnstable MA 02668. (617)362-4908. Labels include Welchy Grape Records. President: Mike Welch. Record company, record producer and music publisher (WelchyGrape Publishing). Releases 2 singles and 1 album/year. Works with songwriters on contract.
How to Contact: Write first. Prefers cassette or records (LP or single) with 10 songs and lyric sheet. SASE. Reports in 1 month.
Music: Country, easy listening, folk/rock, MOR, rock (country and hard) and top 40/pop. Recently released *Renovations*, by Mike Welch (MOR LP); *Resurgence*, (MOR/rock LP); "Everybody Knows," (MOR single); and "Turning Point," (rock single) all by Mike Welch and Renovations Band.
Tips: "Looking for more established artists. Prefer local artists."

WHITE ROCK RECORDS, INC., 401 Wintermantle Ave., Scranton PA 18505. (717)343-6718. President: Phil Ladd. Record company, music publisher and record producer. Releases 4-16 singles and 2-4 albums/year.
How to Contact: Query. Prefers cassette with minimum 2 songs and lead sheet. SASE. Reports in 3 weeks.
Music: Children's, country, easy listening, R&B, rock and top 40/pop. Recently released "Drummer," by Frantic Freddy (rock single); and "Ain't Misbehavin'," by Evra Bailey (MOR single).

*WISHBONE RECORDS, Weiherstr. 21, 4630 Bochum 1, West Germany (0234)37031, 37032. Contact: Ferdinand Kother. Labels include Backbone Records. Record company, record producer and distributor. Releases 5-10 LPs/year. Works with musicians/artists on contract. Pays varying royalty to artists on contract.
How to Contact: Prefers cassette or VHS videocassette with 5-10 songs. Does not return unsolicited material. Reports in 4-8 weeks.
Music: Mostly heavy metal, new wave/psychobilly and punk; also mainstream rock and oldies (re-releases). Recently released *Laughter in the Wings*, written and recorded by No More on Wishbone (new wave LP); *Prayers of Steel*, written and recorded by Avenger on Wishbone (heavy metal LP); and *Taken by Storm*, written and recorded by Stormwind on Wishbone (heavy metal LP). Other artists include Darxon, Metal Sword and Der Riss.

*WOODRICH RECORDS, Box 38, Lexington AL 35648. (205)247-3983. President: Woody Richardson. Record company and music publisher (Woodrich Publishing Co.) and record producer (Woody Richardson). Releases 6 singles/year and 6 LP's/year. Pays standard royalty to artists on contract.
How to Contact: Prefers cassette with 4 songs and lyric sheet. SASE. Reports in 2 weeks. "We prefer a good studio demo."
Music: Mostly country, gospel and bluegrass; also rock and jazz. Recently released "I'm Calling You," (by Rex Elliott), recorded by Bitter Creek on Woodrich (country single); *Sinner Man*, (by Gus James), recorded by Rocket City Harmmonizers on Woodrich (black gospel album); and *Serving God*, (by Dorothy Scott), recorded by Rocket City Harmonizers on Woodrich (black gospel album). Other artists include Wayne Yocom, The Hobson Family and The Ellison Family.

*WORLD ARTIST, Box 63, Orinda CA 94563. (415)937-6469. A&R Representative: J. Malcom Baird. Record company, music publisher (Hansen Music Company), record producer (Geoffrey Hansen Enterprises) and personal management firm. Releases varying number of singles and LP's/year. Works with musicians/artists and songwriters on contract; musicians on salary for in-house studio work. Pays negotiable royalty to artists on contract.
How to Contact: Prefers cassette or videocassette and lyric sheet or lead sheet. SASE. Reports in 4-6 weeks. "We do not want the same material that you are sending to other companies. We are looking for the 50s and 60s style rock and doo-wop vocal harmony plus artists with star quality."
Music: Mostly top 40/MOR, rock-a-billy and country-rock; also blues, French and Spanish. Recently released "This is Hilo, Hawaii, (by B. Friel), *Surf Rock Guitar*, (by C. Trouten), and *Hawaii Rock 85*, (by B. Friel), all recorded by Bert Friel on World Artist (Hawaiian LPs). Others include assorted artists in Hawaii, Japan, Philippines, Korea and Latin America, etc.

WOULD'N SHOE/L'ORIENT, Box H, Harvard MA 01451. (617)456-8111. Labels include Would'n Shoe, L'Orient, Greenpeace, New Moon. A&R Coordinator: Joshua Green. Record company and music

publisher (Bullet Management, It's A Hit Productions). Releases 2-5 singles and 2-3 albums/year. Works with artists and songwriters on contract. Pays minimum of 2% royalty to artists on contract; statutory rate to publishers for each record sold.
How to Contact: Write first. Prefers 7¹/₂ ips reel-to-reel or cassette with 3-8 songs and lyric sheet. Does not return unsolicited material. Reports in 1 month.
Music: Mostly pop rock and country rock; also country and MOR. Recently released "Are Your Afraid of Falling?," by Estes Boys; "Hold Onto Love," by the Secrets; and "Keep on Singing," by Dean Adrien. Recently distributed "Save the Whales," by Allen Estes and "Inside the Storm," by D. Adrien (all pop singles).
Tips: Looking for "professionalism, hook, structure and presentation."

ZONE RECORD CO., 2674 Steele, Memphis TN 38127. (901)357-0064. Owner: Marshall E. Ellis. Record company, music publisher and record producer. Works with songwriters on contract. Pays 4¢/record royalty to artists on contract; statutory royalties to songwriters on contract.
How to Contact: Prefers cassette with 4 songs. "Be sure the words are clear. Don't try to make a master—just a good clean tape." SASE. Reports in 2 weeks.
Music: Country and country/pop. Recently released "Was It All That Bad? ," by Patti Faith (country-rock single); "Words Softly Spoken," by the Wrane Show (country single); and "Baby You Don't Love Me Anymore," by J. Pullman (country single).

ZZYZX RECORDS, Box 23, Sun Valley CA 91353. (213)982-2174. Contact: J. Eric Freedner. Record company and music producer (Boss Tweed Music). Releases 1 single and 1 album/year. Pays statutory rate to publishers for each record sold.
How to Contact: Write first. Prefers 7¹/₂ ips reel-to-reel or cassettes with 1-3 songs. SASE.
Music: Folk, rock, humorous and novelty. Recently released *Tooloose Latric*, by J. Eric Freedner and Larry Treadwell (novelty LP).

Geographic Index

The US section of this handy geographic index will quickly give you the names of record companies located in the music centers of Los Angeles, Nashville and New York. The International section lists, geographically, markets for your songs in Australia, Canada, Germany, The United Kingdom and New Zealand.

Find the names of companies in this index, and then check listings within the Record Companies section for addresses, phone numbers and submission details.

UNITED STATES

LOS ANGELES

A&M Records, Inc.
Alfie Records
Atlantic Recording Corp.
Azra Records
Baywest Records
Blue Gem Records
Boyce & Powers Music
Broadway/Hollywood Productions
Cambria Records & Publishing
Capitol Records, Inc.
Carousel Records, Inc.
Chattahoochee Records
The Chu Yeko Musical Foundation
Command Records
Cowgirl Records
D-Town Records (of California) Inc.
Dupuy Records/Produc-

tions/Publishing, Inc.
Eagle Records
Emkay Records
Grass Roots Record & Tape/ LMI Records
Gule Records Inc.
Hollyrock Records
Jet Records
L.M.I. (Lee Magid, Inc.)
Light Records
Longhorn Records
Manquin
Modern Records, Inc.
Mystic Records, Inc.
Paris Records
Pausa Records
Penthouse Records
Princess Productions Ltd.
O.L. Records Inc.
Original Cast Records
Quinto Productions/Records
RCA Records

Rockin! Records
Rogue Records
Rollin' Rock Records
Shaolin Records
Slash Records
Sound Image Records
Starborn Records
Statue Records
Streetlight Records
Suite Beat Music
Take Home Tunes
Warner Brothers Records, Inc.
Watts City Records
ZZYZX Records

NASHVILLE

Angelsong Records/Masterstouch Record Production
Asa Records
Black Rose Records
The Calvary Music Group

Carrie Records Co.
Charta Records
Country International
Curtiss Records
F&L Records
50 States Records & Tapes
Landmark (Audio of
　Nashville)
MCA Records
Melodee Records
Nashboro Records
Stargem Records, Inc.
Sun International Corp.
Susan Records
Terock Records

NEW YORK
A&M Records Inc.
Ambient Sound Records

Apexton Records Mfg.
　Corp.
Apon Record Company, Inc.
Big Mike Music/Bildo Music
Buddah Records, Inc.
Cargo Records
Courrier Records
Deuce Records
Dragon Records, Inc.
EMI America/Liberty Re-
　cords
Factory Beat Records, Inc.
HME Records
Manhattan Records
Maria Records
Monotone Records
Mustevic Sound, Inc.
On Time Records, Inc.
Orange Records

Pentagramm Records
Personal Records
PolyGram Records
The Prescription Co.
Ra-Jo International
Ripsaw Record Co.
Roperry Records
RSO Records
Sire Records
SOS Record Productions,
　Inc.
The Source Unltd.
Spring Records
Star Record Co.
Tommy Boy
Urban Rock Records
Vanguard Recording Soci-
　ety

INTERNATIONAL

AUSTRALIA
Laser Records
Mushroom Records Pty.
　Ltd.
Umbrella Organisation Pty.
　Ltd.

CANADA
A&M Records of Canada,
　Ltd.
Anthem Records of Canada
Aquarius Records
Attic Records Ltd.
Berandol Records
Boot Records, Ltd.
The Creation Co.
The Master's Collection
　Limited

Monticana Records
Numbers
PCRL/Disques Fleur, Inc.
Production Connection Inc.
Skylight Records
True North Records
WEA Music of Canada, Ltd.

ENGLAND
Arista/Ariola Records
Bam-Caruso Records
BGS Productions Ltd.
Big Bear Records
Creole Records Ltd.
Dansan Records
Heavy Metal Records
Le Matt Music Ltd.
Mawson and Wareham (Mu-

　sic) Ltd.
Outlet Recording Co. Ltd.
Rutland Records
Sain (Recordiau) CYF
Starblend Records Limited
Titan International Produc-
　tions, Ltd.

WEST GERMANY
Ariola-Eurodisc GmbH
Arminia Musikproduktion-
　Erich Storz
Autogram & Folk Records
Bella Musica Tontraeger
　GmbH
Comma Records & Tapes
Playbones Records
Wishbone Records

Record Producers

Independent record producers are the true entrepreneurs of the music business. They invest their own time and money in songs and artists they think will provide a good return on their investment when the finished master recording is sold or leased to a record company.

Several advantages exist for the songwriter who has been signed by, or whose material has been picked up by a record producer. Because most record producers were either artists or recording engineers before they were producers, they often have extensive contact networks of important industry executives that they can utilize to help market your music. In addition many producers will take a very genuine, personal interest in your music and will help you develop it to its maximum hit potential. Their livelihood depends on it.

Record producers often make good business partners for those songwriters and artists whose material is thought of as being outside the popular music mainstream. They are usually more receptive to the more innovative and experimental use of different types of musical instruments and recording techniques. For the "avant garde" songwriter, marketing your music through a record producer can provide a kind of freedom and flexibility unavailable in other arrangements.

Each listing that follows outlines what type of music each producer is looking for, what records and artists he's recently produced and what other artists he produces on a regular basis. Study the listings carefully noting the names of artists he's producing and consider if any of your songs might fit a particular artist's style. Athough most publishers are open to a wide variety of material they will most probably be concentrating on the styles of music that satisfy their artists' immediate recording needs. For a weekly update on who's producing what and whom, refer to the trade music charts within *Billboard* and *Cash Box* magazines.

ABERDEEN PRODUCTIONS, (A.K.A. Scott Turner Productions), 524 Doral Country Dr., Nashville TN 37221. President: Scott Turner. Record producer and music publisher (Buried Treasure/ ASCAP, Captain Kidd/BMI). Deals with artists and songwriters. Works with 30 new songwriters/year. Produces varied number of singles and 15-20 albums/year. Fee derived from sales royalty and production fee.
How to Contact: Prefers cassette with maximum 4 songs and lead sheet. SASE. Reports in 2 weeks.
Music: Mostly country, MOR and rock; also top 40/pop. Recently produced "Just a Dream," written and recorded by Jimmy Clanton (pop single); "I've Been Down," (by D. Travis/D. Owens), recorded by Don Malena (country single); and "I'm Not Tough Enough (to Fall in Love Again)," (by D. Ramsey), recorded by D. Malena (country single). Other artists include Sim Whitman, Nilsson, Jonathan Edwards, Del Reeves, David Grossman and Jerry Wallace.
Tips: "Be unique. A great song doesn't care who sings it."

ACCENT RECORDS, 71906 Highway 111, Rancho Mirage CA 92270. (619)346-0075. President: Scott Seely. Record producer and music publisher (S&R Music). Deals with artists. Produces 10 singles and 5 albums/year. Fee derived from sales royalty.
How to Contact: Prefers cassette with any number of songs and lyric sheet. SASE.
Music: Mostly AC, country and MOR; also all types. Recently produced *Armendares*, by J. Armendares (contemporary gospel, JRA Records); *Along the Line*, by Richard Christopher (pop, Accent Records); and *Classics in Rythmn*, by Buddy Merrill. Other artists include Chante, Kirby Hamilton, Eddie Rose, Don Malena, The Last Live Band, Jeri Sullivan and Jeffer.

*ACE ADAMS PRODUCTION CO., 100-19 Alcott Pl., Bronx NY 10475. (212)379-2593. Producer: Joe Adams. Record producer. Deals with artists and songwriters. Produces 10 singles/year and 3 albums/year. Fee derived from sales royalty.
How to Contact: Call first and obtain permission to submit. Prefers cassette. SASE. Reports in 2 weeks.
Music: Mostly pop and blues.

ALHART MUSIC PUBLISHING CO., Box 1593, Lakeside CA 92040. (619)443-2170. A&R: RueAnna Roland. Record producer, music publisher, record company and promoter. Deals with artists,

songwriters and producers. Works with 18-25 new songwriters/year. Prefers studio produced demos. Fee derived from sales royalty.
How to Contact: Prefers cassette with 1-3 songs and lyric sheet. Reports "if a song is placed."
Music: Mostly country and MOR; also bluegrass. Recently produced "You'll Be My Baby Tonight" and "Party For One," by Diane Michaels (C&W singles, Alhart Records); and "Don't Turn My Gold to Blue," by D. Michaels (MOR single, Oak Records).

ALLEN & MARTIN PRODUCTIONS, 9701 Taylorsville Rd., Louisville KY 40299. (502)267-9658. Producer: J.D. Miller. Major productions include national and regional jingles and exclusive song demo production for Falls City Music. Deals with artists, songwriters and singers. Fee derived from sales royalty or by outright fee from songwriter/artist or record company.
How to Contact: Prefers 7½ ips reel-to-reel or cassette with 3-5 songs and lyric sheet. Does not return unsolicited material. Reports in 2 weeks.
Music: Mostly country crossover rock; also bluegrass, jazz, progressive and top 40/pop. Recently produced "Bondarz Superstarz," by Al Bondar (top 40, Starsongz Records); *Walker, Pietius & Kays*, by Walker, Pietius & Kays (jazz vocal, Bridges Records); and "Remaining Faithful," by Monks of St. Meinrad (religious, Abbey Press Records). Other artists include Free Fall, Bill Owens and Quick Draw.

*ALX, INC., Box 427, 145 N. Narberth Ave., Narberth PA 19072. (215)668-9302. President: Alexander Murphy. Record producer and publishing company.
How to Contact: Write first about your interest. Prefers cassette with 1-3 songs and lyric sheet. "Include background information and reviews, if any." SASE. Reports in 1 month.
Music: Easy listening, jazz, MOR, progressive, rock (country and mainstream) and top 40/pop. Works primarily with bands, solo performers and songwriters.

*AMERICAN COMMUNICATION ENTERPRISES, 25128 Blanche Ct., Flat Rock MI 48134. (313)782-4973. Producer: John D. Lollio. Record producer and music publisher (Lo Pine Music). Deals with artists and songwriters. Produces 10 singles/year and 2 albums/year. Fee derived from sales royalty.
How to Contat: Prefers cassette and lyric sheet or lead sheet. SASE. Reports in 2 weeks.
Music: Mostly country and gospel. Recently produced *Sweetest Words*, *Change in Love*, and *After the Pain*, by Johni Dee (country LPs and singles on ACE). Other artists include Marty Damler, David Atkins and Le Moine.

JOE ANDERSON PRODUCTIONS, 792 W. Main, Hendersonville TN 37075. (615)822-5087. Professional Manager: Laura Allen. Record producer, music publisher (Natasha Dawn Music Publ. Co./ BMI) and record company. Deals with artists, songwriters and musicians. Produces 50 singles and 16 albums/year.
How to Contact: Prefers cassette with 1-3 songs and lyric sheet. SASE. Reports in 3 weeks.
Music: Mostly country; also gospel, country rock and country crossover. Recently produced "Fire and the Wine," by Loretta Pierre (country single/Natasha Dawn Records); "Country Fever," by Kimberly Dawn (country single/Natasha Dawn Records); and "Let's All Get Crazy Tonite," by Kevin McCrea (country crossover single/Natasha Dawn Records). Other artists include Cal Meece, Grant Ray, C.D. McDaniel, Darlene Michaels and Kenneth King.

APON RECORD COMPANY, INC., Box 3082, Steinway Station, Long Island City NY 11103. (212)721-5599. Manager: Don Zemann. Record producer and music publisher (Apon Publishing). Deals with artists and songwriters. Produces 20 albums/year. Fee derived from outright fee from record company.
How to Contact: Prefers cassette with 2-6 songs and lyric sheet. SASE. Reports in 1 month.
Music: Classical, folk, Spanish, Slavic, polkas, and Hungarian gypsy. Recently produced *Czech Polka Festival* and *Polka Fever*, by Kunst (polka LPs, Apon Records); and *Holiday in Spain*, by Yavaloyas Orchestra (songs and dances LP, Apon Records).

APPROPRIATE PRODUCTIONS, #406, 1800 N. Argyle, Hollywood CA 90028. (213)463-8400. Producer: Ben Brooks. Record producer, music publisher (DGO/ASCAP and DudGor/BMI), and promoter. Deals with artists and songwriters. Produces 2 singles/year. Fee derived from sales royalty or outright fee from record company.
How to Contact: Prefers cassette with 1-3 songs and lyric sheet. Prefers studio produced demos. SASE. Reports in 3 weeks.
Music: Rock and R&B; also country and MOR. Recently produced "Conscience of Man," "Back Up to Zero," "Access" and "Hands Off," by Oskar Scotti (rock singles). Other songwriters include K.A. Parker and T.M. Kenefick.
Tips: "Be professional. Learn the business and music well enough to create for the market place."

*ARCHER PRODUCTIONS, INC., Box 1118, Pompano Beach FL 33061. (305)781-9901. President: Peter Archer. Record producer and TV and radio programming company. Deals with artists and songwriters. Produces 2-4 albums/year. Fee derived from sales royalty or program syndication fees.
How to Contact: Prefers cassette, 15 ips reel-to-reel or ½" VHS videocassette with 8-10 songs and lyric sheet or lead sheet. "Submit pro quality." Does not return unsolicited material. Reports in 6-8 weeks.
Music: Mostly electronic music, soundtracks and new music; also instrumental rock, pop and jazz. Recently produced *Zodiac*, by Zodiac (soundtrack LP, API); *The Robotz*, by The Robotz (pop music video LP, API); and *E-Gram*, by Electrogram (electronic music LP, API).
Tips: "Artists should have completed music videos; songwriter's should have master tapes."

ARPCO PRODUCTIONS LTD./BURNT OUT MUSIC, 126 Frederick, Bellwood IL 60104. (312)544-0848. Chairman: Donald Burnside. President: Archie Russell. Record producer and music publisher (Eichra Music, Burnt Out Music). Deals with artists and songwriters. Produces 4 singles and 4 albums/year. Fee derived from sales royalty.
How to Contact: Write first and obtain permission to submit. Prefers cassette with 4-6 songs. Prefers studio produced demos. SASE. Reports in 3 weeks.
Music: Dance, R&B, soul and top 40/pop. Recently produced "Lucy," (by Lionel Richie and Gene Chandler), recorded by Fast Fire (pop ballad single); "Telephone," (by G. Cooper and D. Burnside), recorded by Essence (pop ballad single, Elektra Records); and "Chocolate Lover," by Dorelle (funk dance single, MCA Records). Other artists include Superior Movement and The Chi-Lites.

ARZEE, ARCADE AND CLYMAX RECORDS, 3010 N. Front St., Philadelphia PA 19133. (215)426-5682. Production Manager: Lucky Taylor. Record producer and music publisher (Rex Zario Music/BMI, Seabreeze Music/BMI, Jack Howard Publishing/BMI, Arcarde Music Co./ASCAP, Valley Brook Publishing/ASCAP). Deals with artists and songwriters. Produces 8-12 singles and 1-3 albums/year. Fee derived from sales royalty.
How to Contact: Prefers 7½ ips reel-to-reel or cassette with 4-6 songs and lyric sheet. SASE. Reports in 1 month.
Music: Mostly country; also bluegrass, MOR and rock. Recently produced "Ten Gallon Stetson," by Bill Haley (country, Arzee Records); "This World of Mine," by Shorty Long (country, Arzee Records); and "Blues on the Block," by Charlie Stone (MOR, Arzee Records). Other artists include Dick Thomas, Rusty Wellington, Al Taber, Ben Taber, Willis Meyers, James E. Myers, Al Rex, Frank Marshall, Ray Coleman, Ray Hatcher, Bob Saver, Tex Carson, Eddie Thompson, Dallas Turner, Tommy Carr, Bob Dean, Jimmy Collett and Rex Zario.

*A/S PRODUCTIONS, 5414 W. Sheridan, Chicago IL 60649. (312)878-7121. Vice President: Jerome Metcalfe. President: Sylvester Ames, Jr. Record producer and music publisher (Amse Publishing). Deals with artists and songwriters. Fee is derived from sales royalty or production deal with record company.
How to Contact: Prefers cassette. SASE. Reports in 4 weeks.
Music: Mostly gospel (contemporary). Recently produced *Fountain of Life Church*, by Fountain of Life Baptist Church (gospel LP on Gospel Root). Other artists include Voices of Original Gospel Choir.

AZURE RECORDS, 1450 Terrell, Beaumont TX 77701. (409)832-0748. President: Don Gilbert. Record producer and music publisher (Don Gilbert Music/BMI) and record company. Deals with artists and songwriters. Produces 10 singles/year. Fee derived from sales royalty.
How to Contact: Prefers 7½ ips reel-to-reel with 2-10 songs and lyric sheet. SASE. Reports in 1 month.
Music: Religious music only. Recently produced "Sweet and Simple," by Randy McClain (country MOR single, Azure Records); "Take Your Memories Too," by Sherry Black (country MOR single, Gold Guitar Records); and "Cajun Lullaby," by Jesse Stuart (country MOR single, Gold Guitar Records). Other artists include Silver Strings and Don Gilbert.

B.C. ENTERPRISES OF MEMPHIS, INC., 726 E. McLemore Ave., Memphis TN 38106. (901)947-2553. Administrative Assistant: Nat Engleberg. Record producer and music publisher (Colca Music, Epitome Music, Insight Music/BMI). Deals with artists and songwriters. Produces 2 singles and 1 album/year. Fee derived from sales royalty.
How to Contact: Prefers cassette with 1-3 songs and lyric sheet. SASE. Reports in 1 week.
Music: Mostly R&B and pure blues; also gospel and soul. Recently produced "Where Are We Headed," by Rev. David Lawrence (LP); "Love Me At Own Risk," by Curtis Davis (R&B single, Brian Manor Records); and "You Must Be Gravity," and "Self Rising Flour," by Sir Henry Ivy. Other artists include Calvin Leavy and the Larry Gibson Group.

BAG LADY PRODUCTIONS, Suite 602, 928 Broadway, New York NY 10010. (212)505-7332. Contact: Alan Zwirn. Record producer and music publisher. Listens to finished masters. Works with artists and songwriters on contract.
How to Contact: Send cassette with maximum 3 songs and lyric sheet. ("If master, include photo, bio and we'll listen to entire project.") SASE. Reports within 1 month.
Music: Soul, dance, pop/rock.
Tips: Looking for "potential hit single material only."

BAL RECORDS, Box 369, LaCanada CA 91011. (818)952-1242. President: Adriam Bal. Record producer and music publisher (Bal & Bal Music). Deals with artists and songwriters. Produces 1-4 singles/year. Fee derived from sales royalty or outright fee from artist/songwriter or record company.
How to Contact: Prefers cassette with 3 songs and lyric sheet. SASE. Reports in 1 month.
Music: Blues, church/religious, country, easy listening, jazz, MOR, R&B, rock, soul and top 40/pop. Recently produced "Los Angeles," by Rich Martin (ballad, Bal Records); and "Song of the Pasadena Rose Parade," by Jack Heindenrich (swing, Bal Records). Produces musicians in local area.

JOHN BAUERS MUSIC PRODUCTIONS, 1200 Park Ave., Hoboken NJ 07030. Creative Department: John Bauers and Tim Dobel. Record producer and music publisher. Deals with artists and songwriters. Produces 4-6 singles and 2-3 albums/year. Fee derived from sales royalty.
How to Contact: Prefers cassette with 1-3 songs and lyric sheet. SASE. Reports in 1 month.
Music: Mostly R&B, dance and rock; also children's, country, MOR, progressive, soul and top 40/pop. Recently produced "I Need a Lover Tonight," (by Dobel-Bauers), recorded by Phyllis Harris (dance/pop single, Turbo Records-Europe); "Higher," (by Bauers), recorded by Cindy Valentine (dance); and "Invasion of My Privacy," (by Hahn-Bauers), recorded by Carol Hahn (dance/R&B single, Heavyweight Records). Other artists include Sister & Brother and Karl Anthony.

*BAYWEST PRODUCTIONS, Suite #398, 2554 Lincoln Blvd., Marina del Rey CA 90292. (213)822-7629. President: Ron Patton. Record producer and music publisher (Free & Show Music/ASCAP, Honeymaker Music/BMI). Deals with artists and songwriters. Produces 3 singles/year and 1 album/year. Fee derived from sales royalty.
How to Contact: Write first and obtain permission to submit. Prefers cassette or videocassette with 3-5 songs and lyric sheet or lead sheet. "Submit master tapes only. No Demos." SASE. Reports in 4 weeks.
Music: Mostly R&B, dance and pop/rock; also country/pop, gospel and jazz. Recently produced "Don't Blame Me," by Michael Peyser (top 40/pop/rock single on Baywest); "Midnight Fantasies," by Lizz Fiedora (top 40/pop single on Satin Sounds); and *Your Key Fits*, by Laurie Roberts (pop/R&B/dance LP on Baywest). Other artists include Gene Gizzi, Patton's Army and Leroy "Ace" Miller.
Tips: "Submit photo and biography. Be sure they are pro quality."

*BELIEVE'N PRODUCTIONS, Box 120204, Nashville TN 37212. (615)385-9408. President: Lanny E. Smith. Record producer and music publisher. Deals with artists and songwriters. Fee derived from sales royalty or special projects.
How to Contact: Write or call first and obtain permission to submit. Prefers cassette with 3 songs and lyric sheet. SASE. Reports in 3 weeks.
Music: Mostly country, country rock and pop; also R&B and new age. Recently produced "Believe'n in Your Love," by Donna Anderson (adult contemporary single, Windy Hill); and "Your Love Will Pull Me Thru," by Lanny Smith (adult contemporary single, Windy Hill).

HAL BERNARD ENTERPRISES, INC., 2181 Victory Parkway, Cincinnati OH 45206. (513)861-1500. President: Stan Hertzmann. Record producer and music publisher (Sunnyslope Music Inc., Bumpershoot Music Inc.). Deals with artists and songwriters. Produces 5 singles and 3-4 albums/year. Fee derived from sales royalty.
How to Contact: Prefers cassette with 1-3 songs and lyric sheet. SASE. Reports in 1 month.
Music: Recently produced *Twang Bar King*, by Adrian Belew (rock LP, Island Records); *The Raisins*, by The Raisins (rock LP, Strugglebaby Records); and *Ladies and Gentlemen . . .*, by The Adults (rock LP, Strugglebaby Records). Other artists include The Young Invaders and Charlie Fletcher.

BIG BEAR, 190 Monument Rd., Birmingham, B16 8UU, England. 44-021-454-7020. Managing Director: Christine Morley. Record producer, music publisher (Bearsongs) and record company (Big Bear Records). Works with lyricists and composers and teams collaborators. Produces 15 singles and 10 albums/year. Fee derived from sales royalty.
How to Contact: Write first about your interest, then submit demo tape and lyric sheet. Reports in 2 weeks.
Music: Blues, jazz, R&B and soul.

*BLACK DIAMOND MUSIC PUBLISHING & PRODUCTION GROUP, 726 Cypress Ave., Box 467, Lansdown PA 19050. (215)623-1549. President: Allen Gabriel. Record producer and publisher. Deals with artists, songwriters, producers, record companies and musicians. Fee derived from product sales. Administrative service charge to contractor.
How to Contact: Write first. Prefers cassette or VHS or Beta videocassette with 2 songs and lyric sheet. "All demos must be of good quality and all lyric sheets must be clearly printed." Does not return unsolicited material. Reports in 4-6 weeks.
Music: Mostly children's, gospel, jazz, R&B, soft rock, reggae and commercial jingles ("various, product oriented"); also dance, Hispanic, progressive, soul, rock and top 40/pop.

*DAVID BLUEFIELD, Box 726, Hollywood CA 90028. (213)463-SONG (7664). Contact: President. Record producer, music publisher and recording studio. Deals with artists and songwriters. Produces 5 singles/year and 3 albums/year. Fee derived from outright fee from songwriter/artist or studio rental.
How to Contact: Write or call first to arrange personal interview. Prefers cassette or VHS videocassette with 5 songs. Does not return unsolicited material. Reports in 4 weeks.
Music: Mostly pop, rock and R&B. Recently produced "Kick It In," by Virg L. Beckham (country crossover single, Dblue); and "Everybody Likes Rock 'n' Roll, by Pop Signal (pop R&B single, Dblue).

*CARSTEN BOHN/LINGO MUSIC, 314 W. 53rd St., New York NY 10019. (212)582-8800. Producer: Carsten Bohn. Record producer and music publisher. Deals with artists and songwriters. Produces 5 albums/year.
How to Contact: Prefers cassette or Beta videocassette with 3-5 songs and lyric or lead sheet. "Include photo and resume if possible." SASE. Reports in 3-4 weeks.
Music: Mostly rock, pop, R&B, gospel and jazz; also soundtracks. Recently produced *CB Radio*, by Carsten Bohn (rock/pop/R&B LP, Intercord); "I Feel Great," by C.B. and D.J. Holly (R&B/rap single, Polygram/Mer); and *It Is*, by Living Proof (R&B/pop/rock LP, Phonogram).

BOUQUET-ORCHID ENTERPRISES, Box 18284, Shreveport LA 71138. (318)686-7362. President: Bill Bohannon. Record producer and music publisher (Orchid Publishing). Deals with artists and songwriters. Produces 5 singles/year. Fee derived from sales royalty.
How to Contact: Prefers cassette with 3-5 songs and lyric sheet. "Include brief background information. Make lyrics clear and the demos as strong as possible." SASE. Reports in 1 month.
Music: Country, contemporary gospel and top 40/pop. Recently produced "Freeborn Man," by Bill Bohannan; and "A Little More Like You," by Adam Day (country singles, Bouquet Records).

BOBBY BOYD PRODUCTIONS, 2609 NW. 36th St., Oklahoma City OK 73112. (405)942-0462. Producer: Bobby Boyd. Record producer (Boyd Records) and music publisher (Watonga Publishing/ASCAP and Catalpa Publishing/BMI). Deals with artists and songwriters. Produces 10 singles/year.
How to Contact: Prefers 7½ ips reel-to-reel or record with 3-12 songs and lyric sheet. Does not return unsolicited material. Reports in 2 weeks "if interested."
Music: Country, R&B, rock, soul and top 40/pop. Recently produced *Trucking Truth*, by Marvin Ray (country LP, Boyd Records). Artists include Dale Greear.

BROADWAY PRODUCTIONS, INC., 1307 Broadway St., Box 551, Sheffield AL 35660. (205)381-1833. President: David Johnson. Vice President of Publishing: Cal Freeman. Record producer and music publisher (Love House Music/ASCAP, Tired Iron Publishing/BMI). Deals with artists and songwriters. Produces 10 singles and 4 albums/year. Works with 5-6 new songwriters/year. Teams collaborators. Fee derived from sales royalty or outright fee from record company.
How to Contact: Prefers 7½ ips reel-to-reel or cassette with 1-3 songs and lyric sheet. SASE. Reports in 2 weeks.
Music: Mostly R&B and country; also rock, soul and top 40/pop. Recently produced "(It's So Good to Be) Wanted Again," (by Tony Joe White), recorded by Percy Sledge (country/R&B single); *It's So Nice To Be With You Again*, recorded by Jimmy Gold (country pop LP); and *Suite Dreams*, written and recorded by Ruben Romero (Spanish/classical LP, RPM Records). Other artists include James Govan, Sonny Swift, Alton Thrasher, Jack Denton & Dixie, and the Debow Brothers.

BROTHER LOVE PRODUCTIONS, Box 852, Beverly Hills CA 90213. (818)980-3812. Producer: Jeremy McClain. Secretary: S. Roshay. Record producer and music publisher (Pratt & McClain Music/ASCAP, Happy Days Music/BMI). Deals with artists and songwriters. Produces 20 singles and 2 albums/year. Works with 3-5 new songwriters/year. Fee derived from sales royalty.
How to Contact: Query with letter of introduction or arrange personal interview. Prefers cassette with 4 songs and lead sheet. Prefers studio produced demos. SASE. Reports in 3 weeks.

Music: Mostly top 40; also country, dance, easy listening, MOR, rock pop and religious music. Recently produced "Summertime in the City," and "California Cowboy," by Pratt (rock singles, Warner Bros.); and "Hallelejah Child," by J. McClain (religious single, Brother Love Records). Other artists include Ocean (Warner Bros. Records, MCA Records, and Songbird Records).

RON BROWN MANAGEMENT, Box 15375, Pittsburgh PA 15237. (412)486-7740. Producer: Ron Brown. Record producer, music publisher (Etna Music/BMI) and record company (Brown Bear Records). Produces 5-15 singles and 3 albums/year. Deals with artists and songwriters. Fee derived from sales royalty or outright fee from record company.
How to Contact: "Submit only cassette tapes and lead sheet. Reel-to-reel and 8 track tapes will not be accepted." SASE. Reports in 2 weeks.
Music: Mostly R&B, dance and soul; also blues, dance, easy listening, MOR, progressive, rock and top 40/pop. Recently produced "Funky Fun for Everyone," and *It's Rocker Time*, written and recorded by Rocker Band/Brown Bear Records (dance); and "Its My Heart," (by Terry Guadagni), recorded by Shaker/Brown Bear Record. Other artists include Hytek, Fresh and Herb Fame.

BULLDOG RECORDS, 8 Mark Lane, New City NY 10956. (212)687-2299. Vice President: Howard Kruger. Record producer and music publisher (Songs for Today, Inc./SESAC). Deals with artists, songwriters and foreign publishers. Produces 10 singles and 20-30 albums/year. Fee derived from sales royalty.
How to Contact: Prefers cassette with 1-4 songs and lyric sheet. Does not return unsolicited material. Reports in 2 weeks.
Music: MOR, R&B and soul. Recently produced *Live, In Concert*, by Glen Campbell (MOR LP, RCA Records); and *Me and My Friends*, by David Soul (MOR LP, Energy Records). Other artists include Going Straight, Simon Spiro, Diane Solomon and Dave Martin.

BILL BYRON PRODUCTIONS, 1727 Elm St., Bethlehem PA 18017. (215)865-1083. Project Coordinator: Heather Lynne. Record producer and record company (Mystic Oak Records). Deals with artists. Produces 10 singles and 12 albums/year. Works with 4-6 new songwriters/year. Fee derived from sales royalty.
How to Contact: Write first and obtain permission to submit. Prefers cassette or videocassette with 3-9 songs. SASE. Reports in 2 months.
Music: Mostly synthesized rock; also new wave and experimentals. Recently produced *Dreams*, by Office Toys (dance rock LP, Mystic Oak Records); *I Don't Lie*, by the Polygraphs (comedy LP, Mystic Oak Records); and "Heather," by Bill Byron (ballad single, Mystic Oak Records). Other artists include Even Stephen, Ego, Trendsetter, Psychic Warriors, the BBC, Steve Brosky and Wall to Wall.
Tips: "We are looking for artists with both good studio ability and a good live show. Inform us of any performance dates you might have in the northeast region."

THE CALVARY MUSIC GROUP, 142 8th Ave. N, Nashville TN 37203. (615)244-8800. Artist Development: Nelson S. Parkerson Jr. Record producer and music publisher. Deals with artists and songwriters. Produces 10 singles and 12 albums/year. Fee derived from sales royalty or outright fee from songwriter/artist.
How to Contact: Prefers cassette or videocassette with 1-3 songs and lyric sheet. Reports in 1 month "if SASE is included."
Music: Mostly gospel; also choral and church/religious.

CAROLINA PRIDE PRODUCTIONS, Box 99, Rougemont NC 27572. (919)477-4077. Manager: Freddie Roberts. Record producer, music publisher (Freddie Roberts Music/BMI) and management and booking agency. Deals with artists, songwriters and session musicians. Produces 7 singles and 2 albums/year. Fee derived from sales royalty.
How to Contact: Call or write first. Prefers 7½ ips reel-to-reel or cassette with 1-5 songs and lyric sheet. SASE. Reports in 3 weeks.
Music: Mostly country, MOR and top 40/pop; also bluegrass, church/religious, gospel and country rock. Recently produced *Forever Yours*, by Freddie Roberts (country LP, CA Records); "Gone, Gone," by Rodney Hutchins (southern rock single, Bull City Records); and "Forget Me," by Brenda Roberts (pop single, Bull City Records). Other artists include Sleepy Creek, Eldorado, Billy McKellar, Les Howard, Lacey and Doug McElroy.

DON CASALE MUSIC, INC., 377 Plainfield St., Westbury NY 11590. (516)333-7898. President: Don Casale.
How to Contact: Call or write (include SASE) *before* submitting.

*DAVID CASE ARTIST PRODUCTIONS, Box 132, Station B, Sudbury, Ontario P3E 4N5 Canada. Producer: David Case. Record producer and music publisher. Deals with artists and songwriters. Produces 4-5 singles/year and 1 album/year. Fee derived from sales royalty.
How to Contact: Prefers cassette with 4 songs and lyric sheet and lead sheet. SAE and IRC. Reports in 2 weeks.
Music: Mostly pop, R&B and rock; also country. Recently released "Don't Stop Me," and "Thing Called Love," by Mainstreet (MOR singles, Mainstreet); and "Technicolor," by David Case (R&B single, Case of Gold Records).
Tips: "Be original and confident."

CATALPA PUBLISHING CO., 2609 NW. 36th St., Oklahoma City OK 73112. (405)942-0462. Manager: Bobby Boyd. Record producer and music publisher. Deals with artists and songwriters. Produces 12 singles and 4 albums/year.
How to Contact: Prefers cassette with minimum 4 songs and lyric sheet. Does not return unsolicited material. Reports in 3 weeks.
Music: Mostly country; also dance-oriented and rock.
Tips: "Know who the song might be good for."

*CATERO PRODUCTIONS, 1301 Chestnut St., San Carlos CA 94070. (415)592-2072. Producer/Engineer: Fred Catero. Record producer and record company. Deals with artists. Produces 2 singles/year and 10 albums/year. Fee derived from sales royalty or outright fee from songwriter/artist or record company; "depends on the deal."
How to Contact: Call first and obtain permission to submit. Prefers cassette and lyric sheet. "Keep demo clean and short with lyrics up front." Does not return unsolicited material.
Music: Mostly jazz, new age and contemporary pop; also R&B and classical. Recently produced *Sweet & Lovely*, by Di Hindman (jazz trio LP on Catero); *Messenger of the Son*, by C. Verdeaux (new age LP on Catero); and *Sarah's Samba*, by Mel Martin (jazz LP on Catero).

CHA CHA RECORDS, (formerly Donald L. Delucia), 15041 Wabash Ave., South Holland IL 60473. (312)339-0307. President: Donald DeLucia. Record producer and music publisher (Don-Del Music and Don-De Music). Deals with artists. Produces 3 singles and 2 albums/year. Fee derived from sales royalty.
How to Contact: Prefers 15 ips reel-to-reel with 4-6 songs and lyric sheet. SASE. Reports in 1 week.
Music: Country, rock and top 40/pop.

LOU CICCHETTI, 211 Birchwood Ave., Upper Nyack NY 10960. (914)358-0861. Contact: Lou Cicchetti. Record producer and music publisher (Cousins Music). Deals with artists and songwriters. Produces 2 singles/year. Works with 3-4 new songwriters/year. Works with composers. Fee derived from sales royalty.
How to Contact: Prefers 7½ or 15 ips reel-to-reel or cassette with any number songs and lyric sheet. SASE. Reports in 3 weeks.
Music: Country and rock. Recently produced "Your Honor," by Koko (country single, Daisy Records); "Runaway," by Apostle (rock single); and "Special Lady," by Joe Amato (country single, Daisy Records).
Tips: "We produce mostly demos (8- or 16-track) and try to find major labels who will sign the acts directly. But, if all else fails, we will release on our own labels."

CLAY PIGEON PRODUCTIONS, Box 20346, Chicago IL 60620. A&R Director: V. Beleska. Record producer. Deals with artists and songwriters. Produces 10-25 singles and 5-15 albums/year. Fee derived from sales royalty or outright fee from record company.
How to Contact: "We cannot consider any material without a written inquiry first, describing self and material in some depth. Do not phone." Prefers 7½ ips reel-to-reel or cassette with 1-5 songs. SASE. Reports in 2-8 weeks.
Music: Bluegrass, blues, children's, choral, church/religious, classical, country, dance, easy listening, folk, gospel, jazz, MOR, progressive, rock, soul, top 40/pop, avant-garde and punk rock. Recently produced "All for You," by Christopher (MOR single, Clay Pigeon International Records); "Disco People," by Roto Applicators (punk rock single, Broken Records); and *Active Music for Children*, by William Hooper (children's rock LP).
Tips: "Cover letter should explain songwriter's background, type of songs written and why songs are unique enough to be listened to."

CLOUDBURST RECORDS, Box 31, Edmonton KY 42129. (502)432-3183. President: W. Junior Lawson. Record producer, music publisher (Holy Spirit Music) and record company. Deals with artists and songwriters. Produces 3 singles and 4 albums/year. Fee derived from sales royalty.

How to Contact: Prefers 7½ ips reel-to-reel or cassette and lyric sheet. SASE. Reports in 3 weeks.

Music: Mostly southern gospel; also MOR. Recently produced "I Went to Jesus," by the Servants; "Don't Let the Ship Sail Without You," by the New Apostles; and "When I See the Great King," by the Helmsmen (all southern gospel singles, Cloudburst Records).

Tips: "Be honest. Submit material with less volume on instruments and more volume on voices."

CODEX INTERNATIONAL, Box 37156, Cincinnati OH 45222. Branch: 11211 Wilmington, Los Angeles CA 90059. Contact: Steve Halper. Record producer and music publisher (Saul Avenue Publishing Co.). Deals with artists and songwriters. Produces 2 singles/year. Fee derived from sales royalty.

How to Contact: Write first about your interest. Prefers cassette with 2-4 songs. SASE. Reports in 2 weeks.

Music: Bluegrass, blues, country, gospel, R&B and rock.

COUNTRY STAR PRODUCTIONS, 439 Wiley Ave., Franklin PA 16323. (814)432-4633. President: Norman Kelly. Record producer and music publisher (Country Star Music/ASCAP, Kelly Music/BMI and Process Music/BMI). Deals with artists and songwriters. Produces 8-10 singles and 2-3 albums/year. Works with 3-4 new songwriters/year. Works with lyricists and composers and teams collaborators. Fee derived from outright fee from artist/songwriter or record company.

How to Contact: Prefers 7½ ips reel-to-reel or cassette with 2-4 songs and lyric sheet. SASE. Reports in 2 weeks.

Music: Mostly country; also bluegrass, easy listening, folk, gospel, MOR, rock and top 40/pop. Recently produced "Bella Bella Mia," (by Daniel Cershel), recorded by Sal Rainore/Process (MOR single); "Hidden Beauty," (by Edna Garham), recorded by Kopperfield/Country Star (country single); and "The Holiday Waltz," (by Stetzer), recorded by Junie Lou/Country Star (country single). Other artists include Bonnie Baldwin, Denver Bill, Virge Brown and Debbie Sue.

Tips: "Submit only your best efforts."

COUSINS MUSIC, 211 Birchwood Ave., Upper Nyack NY 10960. President: Lou Cicchetti. Record producer. Produces 2 singles/year. Works with 2-3 new songwriters/year. Works with composers. Fee derived from sales royalty.

How to Contact: Prefers 7½ or 15 ips reel-to-reel or cassette with minimum 2 songs. SASE. Reports in 2 weeks.

Music: Country (any) and rock. Recently produced "Wall Between Us," by the Earls (soul/rock, Dakar Records); "One More Heartache," by CoCo (country, Daisy Records); and "Spend the Weekend," by Joe Amato (country single, Daisy Records).

COWBOY JUNCTION PUBLISHING CO., Hwy. 44 W., Lecanto FL 32661. (904)746-4754. Contact: Elizabeth Thomson. Record producer and music publisher (Cowboy Junction). Deals with artists and songwriters. Produces 3 singles and 2 albums/year. Works with 6 new songwriters/year. Works with lyricists and composers and teams collaborators. Fee derived from sales royalty.

How to Contact: Prefers 7½ ips reel-to-reel or cassette with 1-4 songs and lyric sheet. SASE. Reports ASAP.

Music: Mostly country, gospel and bluegrass. Recently produced "Hang My Guitar on the Wall," (by Boris Max Pastuch), recorded by Buddy Max (country single, Cowboy Junction Records); "Thank You Lord," written and recorded by Wally Jones (country gospel single, Cowboy Junction Records); and "The Stompin Greek Stomp," written and recorded by Lloyd Stevens (bluegrass fiddle single, Cowboy Junction Records).

THE CREATION CO., 939 Felix Ave. Lwr, Windsor, Ontario N9C 3L2 Canada. (519)256-6604. President: Jim Thomson II. Record producer, music publisher (On the Wing Music) and record company. Deals with artists and songwriters. Produces 3 singles and 2 albums/year. Publishes 6-10 new songwriters/year. Fee derived from sales royalty or outright fee from songwriter/artist or record company.

How to Contact: Prefers cassette or videocassette with 4-6 songs and lyric sheet. Does not return unsolicited material. "No report unless interested."

Music: Mostly rock, new music, top 40/pop and gospel; also bluegrass, children's, church/religious, easy listening, folk, jazz, progressive, R&B and soul. Recently produced "Eden," "Baby I'm Gone," and "Old Gypsy Moon," by Jim Thomson II/JLT Records (top 40). Other artists include Brian Panter Band and Legion of Honour.

Tips: "I work with artists who have convictions about things other than just music. Music alone is not enough motivation to keep an artist going in the down times. Generally every musical statement must be fused with sense of responsibility to the listener."

Close-up

Danny Tate
Songwriter/Performer
Nashville, Tennessee

"I'm kind of a misfit in a town that's known predominately for country music," says Nashville rocker Danny Tate. Tate, an Arkansas native and son of a Baptist minister, decided that even though Music City was known as the capital of country music, it was a good place to settle down and concentrate on his career. "At the time I had been on the road for two years doing about 600 assembly programs at high schools. Although it was very tiring it gave me an incredible amount of performing experience. In these shows I incorporated about 50% of my own material and as time went on I realized that the kids were relating to my original tunes more and more and eventually they became the most popular songs in the show.

"I think the real thing that drew me to Nashville was the success of hit songwriter Randy Goodrum ("Bluer Than Blue," "You Needed Me," "Before My Heart Finds Out"). He is from Arkansas too, and he was having such tremendous success as a pop writer living in Nashville and I had always heard that Nashville was a real writer's town, so I decided that it was a good place to start."

It was only after several years of working in studios (in addition to working as a waiter to make ends meet) and with the help of some engineer friends that Tate eventually saw success. "One of the projects I recorded during that time was a song that was originally titled 'Superman,' which I tried to shop on my own for about a year without much success. My co-writer on the song, Blaise Tosti, a writer for Dolly Parton at the time, always thought that this song would be great for Australian star Rick Springfield." After several vain attempts at trying to get the song to Springfield's management, they finally succeeded by catching the elusive star at the Hollywood Palace after the debut of one of his

videos. "Blaise knew a girl who was working with the video company that had produced Rick's video and she agreed to get him inside the Palace. He went there armed with a cassette of the song, kept an eye on Springfield and eventually followed him into the men's room and gave him the cassette. About a month later the phone rang and it was Springfield's manager telling us that Rick had rewritten the chorus and lyrics and wanted to record it as 'Affair Of The Heart.' Quite a jolt for a guy who to that point had gotten absolutely nowhere! It became the first single from Springfield's album *Living in Oz* and gave me the platform to shop for a publishing deal. I went on to record an album myself, *Sex Will Sell*, which was released on an independent label. It did very well locally but wasn't picked up by any major labels." Tate says the controversial title was merely his comment on today's society and its use of sex to sell a commercial product.

As for his style of writing, Tate sees himself as one who isn't afraid to follow trends. "I'm pretty much a formula writer but I like to incorporate fresh new sounds, new melodic ideas and lyrical approaches into my music. These are the kinds of things that I count on to help separate me from the crowd.

"I'm a commercially oriented writer," says Tate. "I was raised on the radio and I think my writing just tends to reflect the times."

*MAL DAVIS, 730 S. Harvey, Oak Park IL 60304. (312)386-7355 or 653-1919. Producer: Mal Davis. Record company. Deals with artists and songwriters. Produces 2-4 albums/year. Fee derived from sales royalty or outright fee from songwriter/artist or record company. (Engineering services also available.)
How to Contact: Prefers cassette, 7½ or 15 ips reel-to-reel or VHS videocassette with 2-6 songs and lyric sheet or lead sheet. Does not return unsolicited material. Reports in 4 weeks.
Music: Mostly contemporary gospel, MOR rock and progressive rock and jazz; also country. Recently produced *Foretaste*, by Russ Daughtry (gospel-contemporary LP on Russong); *Patiently Waiting*, by Changes (contemporary gospel LP on Pressin' On); and *Let the Music Move Me*, by Stephen Alexander-sen (contemporary gospel LP on White Horse). Other artists include Phil Keaggy and James Ward.

DAWN PRODUCTIONS, 2338 Fruitville Rd., Lancaster PA 17601. President: Joey Welz. Record producer, music publisher and record company. Deals with artists, songwriters and producers. Produces 6-8 singles and 2 albums/year. Works with 2-4 new songwriters/year. Teams collaborators. Fee derived from outright fee from record company or percentage of sales.
How to Contact: Prefers cassette with 3-6 songs and lyric sheet. Does not return unsolicited material. "We hold submissions for consideration."
Music: Mostly pop, rock and country; also dance, easy listening, folk, MOR and top 40/pop. Recently produced "No More Nightmares," "Heavy Metal Kids," and *American Made Country Roll*, by Joey Welz (Caprice).

DENNY MUSIC GROUP, 39 Music Square E., Nashville TN 37203. (615)255-6535. President: John E. Denny. Record producer, music publisher and production company. Deals with artists and songwriters. Fee derived from sales royalty, production, publishing and management.
How to Contact: Prefers cassette with 2 songs and lead or lyric sheet. SASE. Reports in 6 weeks.
Music: Bluegrass, country, gospel and MOR.

DESTINY PRODUCTIONS, INC., 117 W. Rockland Rd., Box 615, Libertyville IL 60048. (312)362-4060. Vice President: Rick Johnson. Record producer and music publisher (Amalgamated Tulip Corp.). Deals with artists and songwriters. Produces 4 singles and 2 albums/year. Works with 5 new songwriters/year. Fee derived from sales royalty.
How to Contact: Write first. Prefers cassette with 3-5 songs and lyric sheet. SASE. Reports in 1 month.
Music: Mostly rock, top 40 and country; also top 100, MOR, hard rock, Spanish rock and blues. Recently published *Conrad Black*, by Conrad Black (rock/R&B LP, Dharma Records); *Dancexercise*, by Johnson & Poole (exercise LP, Homexercise Records); and "Walkin In a Straight Line," by Nouvea Riche (pop rock).

*DIAMOND JIM PRODUCTIONS, 5929 Hillview Park Ave., Van Nuys CA 91401. (818)988-4969. President: James Hilton. Record producer and music video/producer director. Deals with artists and songwriters. Produces 20 singles/year and 5 albums/year. Fee derived from sales royalty or advance against royalties; video fee from outright fee from record company.
How to Contact: Prefers cassette or VHS videocassette and lyric sheet or lead sheet. SASE.
Music: Mostly rock, rock MOR-AOR and R&B; also country and jazz. Recently produced *Dream Babies Go Hollywood*, and *Bombs Away Dream Babies*, by John Stewart (rock LPs on RSO); and "Dark Glasses," by Dick St. John (rock single on RCA Japan). Other artists include Blue Eye's.

DOOR KNOB RECORDS, 2125 8th Ave. S, Nashville TN 37204. (615)383-6002. Labels include Society Records. President: Gene Kennedy. Vice President: Karen Jeglum. Director of Promotions: Butch Paulson. Record producer, music publisher, distributor and promotor. Deals with artists and songwriters. Fee derived from sales royalty and/or service fees.
How to Contact: Call first about your interest. Prefers 7½ ips reel-to-reel or cassette with maximum 4 songs and lyric sheet. SASE. Reports in 1-3 weeks.
Music: Country, gospel and MOR. Recently released "Ladies' Man," by Bonnie Nelson (country single); "New Tradition," by Bobby G. Rice (country single); and *A New Beginning*, by B.G. Rice (LP). Other artists include Wayne Kemp, Mullins Brothers, and Bill Anderson.

*MIKE DOUGLAS & ASSOCIATES, 4747 Central Ave., St. Petersburg FL 33713. (813)321-8649. A&R: Lee C. Bevilacqua. Record producer, music publisher (Lisa's Theme Music, Inc.) and record company (First Dynasty Records, Inc.). Deals with artists and songwriters. Produces 12 singles/year and 12 albums/year. Fee derived from sales royalty.
How to Contact: Prefers cassette or 7½ ips reel-to-reel with 4 songs and lyric sheet. SASE.
Music: Mostly contemporary Christian, gospel music and country gospel. Recently produced "Neath the Shadow of His Wings," and "Life Without You," by Mike Rudasill (country gospel singles on First

Dynasty Records, Inc.); and "Fig Tree," by The Joint-Heirs (contemporary gospel single on First Dynasty Records, Inc.).
Tips: "We are searching for new writers/artists. We are exclusively into gospel music."

DRAGON RECORDS, INC., 872 Morris Park Ave., Bronx NY 10462. (212)792-2198. Vice President: Mr. "G". Record producer and music publisher (Vin-Joy Publishing). Deals with artists and songwriters. Produces varying number of singles and 3-4 albums/year. Fee derived from sales royalty.
How to Contact: Write first about your interest. Prefers cassette with 2-4 songs. SASE. Reports in 1 month.
Music: Easy listening, MOR and top 40/pop.

PETE DRAKE PRODUCTIONS, INC., 809 18th Ave. S, Nashville TN 37203. (615)327-3211. Producer: Pete Drake. Record producer and music publisher (The Drake Music Group, Window Music Publishing Co., Inc.). Deals with artists and songwriters. Produces 6-10 singles and 3 albums/year. Fee derived from sales royalty.
How to Contact: Call or write first. Prefers cassette with 2-4 songs. SASE. Reports in 3 weeks.
Music: Mostly country and MOR; also church/religious, easy listening, gospel and top 40/pop. Recently produced "The Man I Used to Be," by Box Car Willie. Other artists include Bobbie Vinton, Allen Frizzell and Ronny Robbins.
Tips: "Submit only your best material and only for the artists we handle."

DUANE MUSIC, INC., 382 Clarence Ave., Sunnyvale CA 94086. (408)739-6133. President: Garrie Thompson. Record producer and music publisher. Deals with artists and songwriters. Fee derived from sales royalty.
How to Contact: Prefers cassette with 1-3 songs. SASE. Reports in 1 month.
Music: Blues, country, rock, soul, and top 40/pop. Recently produced "Wichita," (country single, Hush Records); and "Syndicate of Sound," (rock single, Buddah Records).

DUPUY RECORDS/PRODUCTIONS/PUBLISHING, INC., Suite 200, 10960 Ventura Blvd., Studio City CA 91604. (818)980-6412). President: Pedro Dupuy. Record producer and music publisher (Dupuy Publishing, Inc./ASCAP). Deals with artists, songwriters, music arrangers, copyists, musicians, background vocalists, singers and recording engineers. Produces 5 singles and 5 albums/year. Fee derived from sales royalty; differs with each artist.
How to Contact: Write or call first or arrange personal interview. Prefers cassette with 2-4 songs and lyric sheet. SASE. Reports in 1 month.
Music: Easy listening, jazz, MOR, R&B, soul and top 40/pop. Artists include Gordon Gilman, David Loeb, Michael Gruwell and Robert Buttera.
Tips: "Artists and songwriters should have strong songs, versatility, and open minds."

DYNAMIC ARTISTS PRODUCTION COMPANY, Box 25654, Richmond VA 23228. (804)288-3939. Producer: Joe Carter. Record producer, music publisher (Hot Gold Music Publishing Co.) and record company (Dynamic Artists Records, Legacy Records). Deals with artists and songwriters. Produces 20 singles and 2 albums/year. Fee derived from sales royalty.
How to Contact: Prefers cassette with 3-5 songs and lyric sheet. Does not return unsolicited material. Reports in 1 month.
Music: Mostly top 40/pop, R&B and soul; also gospel and jazz. Recently produced "Without You Tonight," by Waller Family (ballad single, Dynamic Artists Records); "I Believe in You," by Waller Family (ballad single, MCA Records); and "Let Me Lay My Funk on You," by Poison (dance/funk single, Roulette Records). Other artists include Legacy.

KENNY EARL, #307, 1300 Division, Nashville TN 37203. (615)242-4314. Producer: Kenny Earl. Record producer, music publisher (Eagle Association), independent lable and management firm. Deals with artists and songwriters. Fee derived from sales royalty or outright fee from songwriter/artist or record company.
How to Contact: Write or call first and obtain permission to submit. Prefers cassette or ¾" videocassette with maximum 3 songs and/or lyric sheet or lead sheet. Does not return unsolicited material. Reports in 4 weeks.
Music: Mostly rock, pop and jazz; also 50's rock, big band and country. Recently produced *Impressions of Christmas*, by Jay Patton (jazz LP on Celebration); *Canvas*, by Jerry Tachow (jazz LP on Aviata); and *Turned on Swing*, by Bob Davis and Prime Time Orchestra (swing/pop LP on Eagle).

EARTH RECORDS CO., Rt. 3, Box 57, Troy AL 36081. (205)566-7932. Record producer and music publisher (Rashone Music/BMI). Deals with artists and songwriters. Produces 4 singles/year. Fee de-

rived from sales royalty or outright fee from record company.
How to Contact: Call first about your interest. Prefers cassette with 2-4 songs. SASE. Reports in 2-3 weeks.
Music: Blues, children's, country, gospel, progressive, R&B, rock and soul. Recently produced "Need Your Loving," by Tim Toney (soul single, Earth Records).

ECHO RECORDS, 824 83rd St., Miami Beach FL 33141. (305)865-8960. President: Walter Dana. Record producer and music publisher (Dana Publishing). Deals with artists. Produces 2 singles and 1 album/year.
How to Contact: Write first about your interest. Prefers 7½ or 15 ips reel-to-reel or cassette. SASE.
Music: Classical and Polish. Recently produced "God's Children," by Don Bennett; "We Want God," by Regina Kujawa (religious singles, Echo Records); *Chor Dana*, by Chor Dana (Polish pop LP, Echo Records); *Polish Dances Opus 40, 41, 43, 44*, by Walter Dana (piano solo and classical form of Polish dances); and "Come Back Lost Day," by Stas Jaworski (Polish pop single, Echo Records).

EN POINTE PRODUCTIONS, Box 1451, Beverly Hills CA 90213. (805)497-1584. President: Jeff Weber. Record producer. Deals with artists. Produces 2 singles and 3-7 albums/year. Works with 5-8 new songwriters/year. Works with lyricists and composers and teams collaborators. Fee derived from sales royalty, by outright fee from record company or royalty advance from labels or private companies.
How to Contact: Write first. Prefers cassette with 2-4 songs. "Record on the best tape available utilizing the best means available." SASE. Reports in 2 weeks "or less."
Music: Bluegrass, classical, jazz, R&B, rock, soul, and top 40/pop. Recently produced *It's About Time*, by McCoy Tyner (LP on Blue Note Records); *More Than You Know*, by Toni Tennille (LP, Mirage/Atlantic Records); and *Target*, by Tom Scott (LP, Atlantic Records).
Tips: "My work is primarily involved with audiophile recording techniques (i.e., direct to disc, digital and live to two track). My recordings accentuate artistry and, above all else, emotional involvement."

EPOCH UNIVERSAL PUBLICATIONS, INC., 10802 N. 23rd Ave., Phoenix AZ 85029. (602)864-1980. President: Raymond P. Bruno. Record producer and music publisher. Affiliate: North American Liturgy Resources. Deals with artists, songwriters and authors. Produces 12 albums/year. Fee derived from sales royalty or outright fee paid by artist/songwriter or record company.
How to Contact: Prefers 15 or 30 ips reel-to-reel, cassette or videocassette with minimum 6 songs and lyric sheet. SASE. Reports in 1 month.
Music: Mostly liturgical; also children's, choral, church/religious, and gospel. Other artists include Rev. Carey Landry, Fr. Lucien Deiss and the St. Louis Jesuits.
Tips: "Songs should be written to be sung by a congregation."

ESQUIRE INTERNATIONAL, Box 6032, Station B, Miami FL 33123. (305)547-1424. President: Jeb Stuart. Record producer, music publisher and management firm. Deals with artists and record labels. Produces 5 singles/year. Fee derived from sales royalty or independent leasing of masters and placing songs.
How to Contact: Write or call first. Prefers cassette or disc with 2-4 songs and lead sheet. SASE. Reports in 1 month.
Music: Blues, church/religious, country, dance, gospel, jazz, rock, soul and top 40/pop. Recently produced "Can't Count the Days," (R&B single, Kent Records); "Sitba," (R&B single, King Records); and "Hung Up on Your Love," (disco single, Esquire Records), all by Jeb Stuart.

EXCALIBUR PRODUCTIONS, Box 3860, Kingsport TN 37664. (615)246-3845. Contact: Tilford A. Salyer. Record producer. Estab. 1984. Deals with artists. Produces 20 singles/year and 16 albums/year. Fee derived from outright fee from record company.
How to Contact: Prefers cassette. Does not return unsolicited material. Reports in 6 weeks.
Music: Mostly southern gospel and contemporary Christian; also secular music and country. Recently produced *Follow Me*, by Ellason (contemporary Christian single and LP on Trinity); *Premiere Issue*, by Barry Gregory (contemporary Christian single and LP on Trinity); and *Memories Live On*, by Philip Myers (contemporary secular LP on Excalibur). Other artists include Ray Branham Family, Lewis Harrah, Brotherhood, Royalmen, and Dumplin Valley Boys.
Tips: "Be what you are—don't imitate."

*EXTRATERRESTRIAL SOUND, 40 Hitching Post Lane, Glen Cove, NY 11542. (516)759-9396. Producer: Gregg Winter. Record producer and music publisher (G X Music Co.). Deals with artists and songwriters. Produces 2 singles/year and 2-3 albums/year. Fee derived from outright fee from record company.

How to Contact: Prefers cassette or VHS videocassette with 1-2 songs and lyric sheet. Does not return unsolicited material. Reports in 4-6 weeks.
Music: Mostly rock; also pop. Recently produced *Mood Swing*, by The Nails (rock LP on RCA); and "Der Kommissar," by After The Fire (rock single on Epic).

FACTORY BEAT RECORDS, INC., 521 5th Ave., New York NY 10175. (212)757-3638. Record producer and music publisher (Ren-Maur Music/BMI). Produces 6 singles and 2 albums/year. Fee derived from sales royalty.
How to Contact: Prefers cassette with 2-4 songs and lyric sheet only. SASE. Reports in 3 weeks.
Music: R&B, rock, soul and top 40/pop. Recently produced "Let's Slip Away" and "Everybody's Doin' It," by Charles T. Hudson (R&B/funk singles, Factory Beat Records); "I Love Your Beat" and "Dance It Off," by Rena (dance singles, Factory Beat Records); "Do It to Me and I'll Do It to You," by Rena Romano; and "Get Fresh," by P.C. Crew (breakdance).
Tips: "Have a finished product, ready to master and press for commercial use."

*FAHL PRODUCTIONS, Johnston CO 80534. Producer: Stever Fahl. Record producer. Deals with artists and songwriters. Produces 4 singles/year and 2 albums/year. Fee derived from outright fee from songwriter/artist or record company.
How to Contact: Write first to arrange a personal interview. Prefers cassette with 2-3 songs and lyric sheet. "Send letter describing your ambitions." SASE. Reports in 4 weeks.
Music: Mostly pop, country and soft rock. Recently produced *Apples/Live*, and *Cowboy Songs*, by Starlite Ramblers (country LPs on RPI); and *David Lyon*, by David Lyon (soft rock LP on Mountain Lyon).
Tips: "Rework your lyrics. Be sure your choice of words is best."

*CHARLIE FIELDS, 44 Music Sq. E., Nashville TN 37203. (615)255-2175. President: Charlie Fields. Record producer and music publisher (Charta Records). Deals with artists and songwriters. Produces 10 singles/year and 6-8 albums/year. Fee derived from sales royalty or outright fee from songwriter/artist.
How to Contact: Prefers cassette or reel-to-reel with 2-3 songs and lyric sheet. SASE. Reports in 2-3 weeks.
Music: Mostly MOR, blues and country; also gospel. Recently produced "Country Man Country Lady," by Steve & Debby Brown (MOR single on Charta); "You Touched Me Country," by Jim Passion (country single on Sun Rize); and "One, Two Three Love," by The Marshall (MOR single, De Lux.). Other artists include Marge & Debby Rhoads, David Walsh and Donna, Darlene and Jack Elliott.

FUTURE 1 PRODUCTIONS, 808 S. Pantamo Rd., Tucson AZ 85710. (602)885-5931. Producers: James M. Gasper and Thomas M. Dukes. Record producer and music publisher (Myko Music/BMI). Deals with artists and songwriters. Produces 2 singles and 2 albums/year. Fee derived from sales royalty.
How to Contact: Call first. Prefers 7½ ips reel-to-reel or cassette with 3-5 songs and lyric sheet. Does not return unsolicited material. SASE. Reports in 1 month.
Music: Mostly R&B, pop and rock; also easy listening and pop-rock. Recently produced "Good Clean Fun," written and recorded by Silent Partners ("surfabilly" single, Ariana Records); "Wait," (by Ruben Ruiz/Tom Privett), recorded by Mobile Cubes (pop-ska single, Ariana Records); and "Lonely Eyes," (by Gasper Dukes), recorded by 2 of a Dind (pop ballad single, Ariana Records).

FUTURE STEP SIRKLE, Box 2095, Philadelphia PA 19103. (215)844-8736. Vice President: S. Deane Henderson. Record producer, music publisher and promoter (Communication Concept). Deals with artists and songwriters. Produces 3 albums/year. Fee derived from sales royalty.
How to Contact: Prefers cassette or VHS videocassette with 4 songs and lyric sheet. Does not return unsolicited material. Reports in 3 weeks.
Music: Mostly heavy metal; also church/religious, gospel, hard rock and top 40/pop. Recently produced "Delirious," by Molecules of Force, (Future Step Sirkle Records); "Live by Faith," by Verdell Colbert and Off Spring Gospel Singers (gospel single, Future Step Sirkle Records); and "Just Hurry On Up," by Molecules of Force (new wave/R&B single, Future Step Sirkle Records). Others artists include Dean Morrow, The Racers, Krun Vallatine and Shonee.

FYDAQ PRODUCTIONS, 240 E. Radcliffe Dr., Claremont CA 91711. (714)624-0677. President: Gary K. Buckley. Record producer. Deals with artists, songwriters and record companies. Produces 2-5 singles and 4-5 albums/year. Fee derived from sales royalty, outright fee from record company, or outright fee from songwriter/artist.
How to Contact: Write first. Prefers cassette with 1-4 songs and lead sheet. SASE. Reports in 3 weeks.
Music: Country, easy listening, folk, gospel, MOR, rock, soul and top 40/pop. Recently produced

"Touch Me Now," by Borderline (top 40/single, Majega Records); *Sky's the Limit*, by Michael Noll (top 40/pop LP, Gottabehit Records); and *My Simple Song*, by Debbie Norheim (gospel LP, DNC Records).

*MICHAEL GALE ENTERTAINMENT, 29 S. Erie, Toledo OH 43602. (419)244-8599. Vice President: Michael Drew Shaw. Record producer and music publisher. Deals with artists and songwriters. Produces 5-10 singles/year and 1-5 albums/year. Fee derived from sales royalty.
How to Contact: Prefers cassette or videocassette with 3 songs and lyric sheet. Does not return unsolicited material. Reports in 6 weeks.
Music: Mostly country, jazz and rock; also MOR. Recently produced "Ring-a-Ding," and "Helluva Nite," by Hotlix (MOR singles, MDS); and "A Place to Hide," by Mikki Walsh (MOR single, Jamestune). Other artists include Nate Gurdey, Lori Le Fevre and Nevada Flatts.

*ARNOLD GARCIA, 1236 S. Staples, Corpus Christi TX 78404. (512)882-7066. Producer: Arnold Garcia. Record company, music publisher (Dark Heart Music) and record company. Deals with artists and songwriters. Produces 20-100 singles/year and 5-20 albums/year. Fee varies depending on artist or writer.
How to Contact: Prefers cassette. Include full address and home and work phone numbers. Does not return unsolicited material. Reporting time varies.
Music: Mostly rock, Spanish and country; also gospel. Recently produced *Ready as Hell*, by Black Oak Arkansas (rock LP and single, Hacienda); *It's Magic*, by Pio Trevino (Spanish LP and single, Hacienda); and *El Bro*, by Steve Jordan (Spanish LP and single, Hacienda). Other artists include Romance, Hot Sauce, and Steve Borth.
Tips: "Be prepared to perform and/or travel."

GCS PRODUCTIONS, Suite 206, 1508 Harlem, Memphis TN 38114. (901)274-2726. Producer: Reginald Eskridge. Record producer. Deals with artists and songwriters. Produces 20 singles and 7 albums/year. Fee derived from sales royalty or outright fee from record company.
How to Contact: Prefers 7^1/$_2$ ips or 15 ips reel-to-reel with 3-7 songs and lyric sheet. SASE. Reports in 6 weeks.
Music: Mostly top 40/pop, R&B and gospel; also blues and soul. Recently produced "Early Morning Man," by Cheryl Fox (top 40/pop single, GCS Records); "I'm a Rover," by Eddie Mayberry (blues/R&B single, Blue Town Records); and "Rainbow Love," by Howard Everett (soul single, Blue Town Records).

GERVASI RECORD & PUBLISHING CO., Box 4547, Redding CA 96099. (916)222-1401. Executive Producer: James A. Gervasi. Record producer and music publisher. Deals with artists and songwriters. Produces 4 singles and 1 album/year. Fee derived from sales royalty.
How to Contact: Prefers cassette with 3-5 songs and lyric sheet. SASE. Reports in 2 weeks.
Music: Mostly country; also country rock. Recently produced "Hungry Man's Dream," "High Time," and "The Look of a Lovin' Lady," by Wyvon Alexander (country singles, Gervasi Records).
Tips: "Lyric sheets are always helpful. Keeping in contact by phone is also helpful."

GET RICH MUSIC/STAY RICH MUSIC, Box 314, New York NY 10037. Record producer and music publisher (Get Rich Music/BMI, Stay Rich Music/ASCAP). Deals with artists, songwriters, staff writers and producers. Produces 12 singles and 6 albums/year. Works with 10 new songwriters/year. Fee derived from sales royalty.
How to Contact: Write about your interest. Prefers 7^1/$_2$ ips reel-to-reel, cassette or videocassette with 1-3 songs and lyric sheet. Prefers studio produced demos. SASE. Reports in 6 weeks.
Music: Mostly dance, up-tempo funky music and urban contemporary for radio formats; also R&B, soul and rap. Recently produced "Happiness" and "Take Your Time," by The Conservatives (dance singles, On Time Records); "Reality," by The Bangie Boys (rap single, On Time Records) and "Nothing Ever Changes," by The All-Stars (rap single).
Tips: "Be commercial, professional, organized and neat."

GMT PRODUCTIONS, Box 25141, Honolulu HI 96825. (808)737-7059. President: Gil M. Tanaka. Record producer and music publisher (Music Publishers of Hawaii). Deals with artists and songwriters. Produces 6 singles and 6 albums/year. Fee derived from sales royalty.
How to Contact: Prefers cassette and lyric sheet. SASE. Reports in 1 month.
Music: Mostly top 40/pop; also country, easy listening, jazz, R&B, rock and soul. Recently produced *Kevin I.*, by Kevin I. (top 40/pop LP, GMT Records); *Morning Light*, by Paul Flynn (top 40/pop LP, GMT Records); and *Music Magic*, by Music Magic (jazz LP, GMT Records).

*MORRIS D. GOLODNER, 8946 Ellis Ave., Los Angeles CA 90034. (213)836-4028. Executive Producer: Morris D. Golodner. Record producer and music publisher (Super Sound Productions). Deals with artists and songwriters. Produces 6 singles/year and 2-4 albums/year. Fee derived from sales royalty or outright fee from record company.
How to Contact: Prefers cassette, 7½ ips reel-to-reel or videocassette with maximum 10 songs. SASE. Reports in 12 weeks.
Music: Mostly pop/rock, rock and AOR; also country, jazz and gospel. Recently produced "The Distance," by Lawyers (pop single, Super Sound Records); "Lightning, Lightning," by Rumors (AOR single, Super Sound Records); and "In My World," by Rashaameen (country single, M.D.G. Records). Other artists include The Limelighters, Gypsy Queen, Eddy Morgan, and Jerry Snow.
Tips: "Good songs and concepts are always welcome."

*GOPHER BAROQUE PRODUCTIONS, 7560 Garden Grove Blvd., Westminster CA 92683. (714)893-3457. Contact: Michael Mikucka. Record producer, music publisher (More Baroque Music/ BMI) and recording studio. Deals with artists and songwriters. Produces varying number of singles and albums/year. Fee negotiable.
How to Contact: Prefers cassette or 7½ ips reel-to-reel with 2-4 songs. "Artists should include 8x10 black & white photo." Reports in 2-3 weeks.
Music: Mostly pop/rock, new music and country; also R&B, dance and rock. Recently produced *Play w/Boys*, by Exude (pop/new music LP on A&M); "Talk to Me," by Private I (pop/new music single on 37 Records); and "Give My Love," by Jeff Pearson (country single on Baroque).
Tips: Looking for "songs that we can sing along with by the time we get to last chorus."

GRASSROOTS PROJECTS UNLIMITED, Box 4689, San Francisco CA 94101. Contact: James L. Heisterkamp. Record producer and music publisher (Grassroots Projects Unlimited/BMI). Fee derived from sales royalty.
How to Contact: Write first. "We are really not looking for new talent at this time. We have an in-house operation and use San Francisco talent when needed." SASE.
Music: Ragtime, songs about San Francisco by San Francisco writers, and gospel by Bay area talent. Recently produced *Never a White Christmas*, by Weslia Whitfield; and "Taraval Street Rag," by Frank Levin (ragtime).
Tips: "Believe in yourself and your material. Be prepared to invest in your own projects should that become necessary. No one would give me a chance to have my songs published or recorded, so I did it myself. That is how I got started in the business. I now try to help set up that first rung on the ladder of success to those with whom I have personal contact."

*DOBIE GRAY PRODUCTIONS, Suite N-101, 210 25th Ave. N., Nashville TN 37203. Record producer and music publisher (Simonton). Deals with artists and songwriters. Produces 2 albums/year.
How to Contact: Write first and obtain permission to submit. Prefers cassette with 2 songs and lyric sheet. SASE.
Music: Mostly country, pop and rock. Recently produced *Offer I Couldn't Refuse*, by Kathleen Baker (country LP), *Dark Side of Town*, and *Something We Won't Lose*, by Dobie Gray (country LPs, Capitol).

MILES GRAYSON PRODUCTIONS, 1159 S. LaJolla Ave., Los Angeles CA 90035. (213)938-3531. Musical Director: Robert Riley. Record producer. Deals with artists and songwriters. Fee derived from sales royalty.
How to Contact: Prefers cassette with 2-4 songs and lyric sheet. SASE. Reports in 2 weeks and "sometimes minutes."
Music: Dance, country, R&B, soul and top 40/pop. Recently produced *Let's Take a Chance*, by Sandra Minx (LP, RCA Victor Records); and *Shopping Upstairs*, by Mojo (LP, Mercury/Phonogram Records). Other artists include Michael Jackson, Kenny Rogers, Sister Sledge, Hall & Oates, Pointer Sisters and Lionel Richie.
Tips: "Interested in good, contemporary country music."

GREAT LAKES PRODUCTIONS, INC., 15855 Wyoming, Detroit MI 48238. (313)861-2363. Manager: Will Davis. Record producer, music publisher (Groovesville Productions, Inc.) and recording studio (United Sound Systems, Inc.). Deals with artists, songwriters and producers. Produces 10-12 singles and 4-5 albums/year. Fee derived from sales royalty.
How to Contact: Prefers cassette with 2-4 songs and lyric sheet. SASE. Reports in 6 weeks.
Music: Mostly rock, soul, R&B and dance-oriented; also easy listening, MOR, progressive and top 40/ pop. Recently produced "Shake It to Me Baby," by Slang (dance-oriented single, Reliant Records); "Love Bandit," by Otis Clay (blues single, Reliant Records); and "I'm Here Again," by the Four Tops (R&B single, Reliant Records). Other artists include Johnnie Taylor, Tyrone Davis and Dramatics.

*BILL GREEN, 10452 Sentinel, San Antonio TX 78217-3824. (512)654-8773. Contact: Bill Green. Record producer and music publisher. Deals with artists and songwriters. Produces 20 singles/year and 3 albums/year. Fee derived from outright fee from songwriter/artists or record company.
How to Contact: Prefers cassette with 1-4 songs and lyric sheet. SASE. Reports in 4-8 weeks.
Music: Mostly contemporary country and traditional country. Recently produced "Blackjack Whiskey," by Bobby Jenkins (country single on Zone 7); "Fool #1, by Jack Young (country single on BGM); and "Me & Margarita," by Bobby Jenkins (country single on Zone 7). Other artists include Diana Hart and David Price.

GST MUSIC PRODUCTIONS, 17 Ponca Trail, St. Louis MO 63122. (314)821-2741. Producer: Gregory Trampe. Record producer and music publisher (Tragrey Music Publishing/BMI). Deals with artists and songwriters. Produces 8-12 singles and 2 albums/year. Works with 6-10 new songwriters/year. Works with lyricists and teams collaborators. Fee derived from sales royalty or outright fee from record company.
How to Contact: Write or call first or arrange personal interview. Prefers 7½ ips reel-to-reel or cassette with 2-4 songs and lyric sheet. SASE. Reports in 1 month.
Music: Mostly top 40, rock, country and contemporary gospel.

*GEORGE GUESS PRODUCTIONS, 2250 Bryn Mawr Ave., Philadelphia PA 19131. (215)477-7122. A&R Director: Ted Brown. Record producer. Deals with artists and songwriters. Produces 3-5 singles and 2-3 albums/year. Fee derived from sales royalty, outright fee from artists or record company.
How to Contact: Query with letter of introduction. Prefers 7½ ips reel-to-reel or cassette with 5 songs. SASE. Reports in 3 weeks.
Music: Dance, soul, and top 40/pop. Recently produced "Turnin' Me Out," by the Lambchops (R&B single, Pearl Harbor); and "Love Tonight," by David Simmons (R&B single, Pearl Harbor). Other artists include Day One and George Guess.
Tips: "If a writer, be consistent with creativity of original compositions. Stay on top of what's musically happening."

JIM HALL & GIDGET STARR PRODUCTIONS, 5 Aldon Circle, West Caldwell NJ 07006. Contact: Jim Hall. Record producer and music publisher (Cactus Music, Gidget Publishing and Jimmy Allison Music). Deals with artists and songwriters. Produces 1-2 singles and 1-2 albums/year. Fee derived from sales royalty.
How to Contact: Write first. Prefers 7½ ips reel-to-reel, cassette or 8-track with 4-5 songs. Does not return unsolicited material. Reports in 3 weeks.
Music: Mostly blues, rock, country and gospel; also bluegrass, church/religious, country, easy listening, folk, jazz, R&B, soul and top 40/pop. Recently produced "Back to the Mountains," by J.C. Davis (bluegrass single, Tar Heel Records); and "I'm a Winner" and "Gamblin' Daddy," by Tune Twisters (Dynamite Records). Other artists include Jim Hall, Gidget Starr, Charlie Bailey and Sal Franco.

HALNAT PUBLISHING CO., Box 37156, Cincinnati OH 45222. (513)891-2300, 2301; 531-7605. Contact: Saul Halper. Record producer and music publisher (Halnat). Works with artists and songwriters. Produces 4 singles/year. Fee derived from sales royalty.
How to Contact: Prefers cassette with 4-5 songs and lyric sheet. SASE. Reports in 2 weeks.
Music: Bluegrass, blues, gospel, R&B and soul.

R L HAMMEL ASSOCIATES, Box 531, Alexandria IN 46001-0531. Contact: Randal L. Hammel. Record producer, music publisher (Ladnar Music/ASCAP) and consultants. Deals with artists and songwriters. Produces 3-4 singles and 10 albums/year. Fee derived from sales royalty, outright fee from artist/songwriter or record company, or negotiable fee per project.
How to Contact: Write first and obtain permission to submit and include brief resume (including experience, age, goal). Prefers cassette with 3 songs maximum. "Lyrics (preferably typed) *must* accompany tapes!" SASE. Reports as soon as possible.
Music: Blues, church/religious, country, dance, easy listening, gospel, MOR, progressive, R&B, rock (usually country), soul and top 40/pop. Recently produced *Companions on the Journey*, by Carey Landry (NALR); *Indiana Lady*, by Carlton-Taylor Band (Independent); and *Lately*, by Morris Chapman (Word Records). Other artists include Overeasy and Heigh-Liters.
Tips: "Though there are certain stigmas that go along with being from the Midwest, we still maintain that quality work can be done, and our good reputation with the 'biggies' in Chicago, Los Angeles, Nashville, etc. will bear us out. Only those who have a full knowledge of the sacrifice involved with this industry (or those willing to hear it) should consider contacting this office. We will shoot straight, and it is *always* explained that our observations are just that—'ours', and another company/production team/ etc., will present a different opinion. Always get a second opinion (or more)."

HAM-SEM RECORDS, INC., 541 S. Spring St., Los Angeles CA 90013. (213)627-0557. A&R Director: Dianna Green. Record producer (Four Buddies/ASCAP). Deals with artists and songwriters. Produces 4 singles and 1 album/year. Fee derived from sales royalty or outright fee from artist/songwriter.
How to Contact: Call first about your interest. Prefers cassette with 4-10 songs. Does not return unsolicited material. Reports in 1 month.
Music: Church/religious, gospel (contemporary), MOR, rap, R&B and top 40/pop. Recently produced *Secret Love*, by Charles Scott (disco LP, Ham-Sem Records); and "Share Your Love," by C. Scott (ballad single, Ham-Sem Records).

*GEOFFREY HANSEN ENTS. LTD., Box 63, Orinda CA 94563. (415)937-6469. A&R Representative: J. Malcom Baird. Record producer, music publisher, record company, personal management, and production firm. Produces varying number of singles and albums/year. Fee derived from sales royalty, outright fee from songwriter/artist or record company or contract.
How to Contact: "Do not call in advance. It's a waste of time to call prior to hearing material." Prefers cassette, ¾" or VHS videocassette and lyric sheet or lead sheet. "Send a neat and clean package. We are looking for talent with star quality." SASE. Reports in 4-6 weeks.
Music: Mostly top 40/MOR, rock-a-billy and country rock; also blues, French and Spanish. "We are looking for 50's and 60's style rock 'n roll and do-wop vocal harmony tunes plus TV motion pictures and theatrical music." Recently produced *Race to Lace*, (motion picture soundtrack LP on EMI); *Tenko*, by Tenko Orchestra (motion picture soundtrack LP on RCA/NIPPON); and *Burning Desire*, by Touring Company Cast (theatrical show LP on MCA).
Tips: "We do not read form letters. Do not send the same thing to us that you send to other companies."

*RICK HANSON PRODUCTIONS, %Ric Rac Inc., Box 712, Nashville IN 47448. (812)837-9569. Executive Producer: Rick Hanson. Record Producer. Estab. 1984. Deals with artists. Fee derived from sales royalty, outright fee from record company, or fees from spec and custom clients.
How to Contact: Write first and obtain permission to submit. Prefers cassette with 1-4 songs and lyric sheet or lead sheet. "Do not make phone inquiries as to status of material submitted." SASE. Reports in 6-8 weeks.
Music: Mostly country, rock and easy listening (MOR). Recently produced "Lonesome Town," by Barry Johnson (country single on Ric Rac); "The Country Bump,' by Debby Lane (country single on Country Bump); and "Laced with Love," by Rick Hanson (country single on Ric Rac). Other artists include Jack Lawles.
Tips: "Have a good understanding of the music business overall."

HARD HAT PRODUCTIONS, 519 N. Halifax Ave., Daytona Beach FL 32018. (904)252-0381. President/producer: Bobby Lee Cude. Record producer and music publisher (Cude & Pickens Publishing). Deals with artists and songwriters. Produces 12 singles and 6 albums/year. Works with lyricists and composers and teams collaborators. Fee derived from outright fee from songwriter/artist.
How to Contact: "Write first telling me about yourself—what type artist etc." Prefers cassette or videocassette with 1-6 songs. SASE. Reports as soon as possible.
Music: Mostly country; also easy listening, gospel, MOR, top 40/pop and Broadway show. Recently produced "Los Angeles Town," (by Cude & Pickens), recorded by National Hall of Fame Marching Band (march single on Hard Hat Records); "Come to the Islands of the Caribbean," (by Cude & Pickens), recorded by Caribbean Knights (ballad single, Hard Hat Records); and "Heard You Married Him Today," (by Cude & Pickens), recorded by Blue Bandana Country Band (country single, Hard Hat Records). Other artists include City Falls Country Band.

HARD-BOILED RECORDS (PHIL PHILLIPS-PRODUCER), 484 Lake Park Ave., Box 6, Oakland CA 94610. (415)482-4854. A&R Director: Dan Orth. Record producer and music publisher (Dynamo Publishing Co./BMI). Deals with artists, songwriters and musicians. Produces 1 single/year. Works with 6 new songwriters/year. Fee derived from sales royalty.
How to Contact: Write or call first. Prefers cassette with 1-3 songs and lyric sheet. SASE. Reports in 1 month.
Music: Mostly pop, rock and new wave; also country, easy listening, folk and R&B. Recently produced "Cruisin' the Strip" (hard rock single, Hard-Boiled Records); and "It Takes More," by Phil Phillips (pop rock single, Hard-Boiled Records).

*JOHN HARVEY ENTERPRISES, (formerly John Daniels Publishing Co.), Box 245, Encinal TX 78019. President: John Harvey. Record producer and music publisher (John Harvey Publishing Co./BMI). Deals with artists and songwriters. Produces 6 singles and 6 albums/year. Works with 2 new songwriters/year. Fee derived from sales royalty.

How to Contact: Prefers cassette with 3-6 songs and lyric sheets. Will accept 7½ ips reel-to-reel. "Include letter giving brief resume of artist/songwriter with submission." SASE. Reports in 2 weeks.
Music: Mostly Latin, polka and country; also children's, gospel, easy listening and folk. Recently produced "La Untouchable," written and recorded by John Harvey (polka single, Mundial Records); "El Pato," (by Jesus Garza), recorded by El Chico (Latin single, Mundial Records); and "Muchachita Linda," written and recorded by Oscar Gonzalez (Latin single, Sol-5 Records).

*HIS HEAD IS WEDGED PRODUCTIONS, 115 Corinth St., Warner Robins GA 31093. (912)923-5507. President: David Norman. Record producer, record studio and local radio show. Deals with artists. Produces 12 singles/year and 5 albums/year. Fee derived from sales royalty or outright fee from record company.
How to Contact: Prefers cassette with 3 songs. SASE. Reports in 2 weeks.
Music: Mostly funk, new wave and rock; also punk. Recently produced *City Lights*, by Circle (funk LP on PCR); "Meow," by K.I.T.T.E.N. (new wave EP on Amethyst); and "12 Noon," by Playmates (funk new wave EP on Amethyst). Other artists include AC Black & The Mean Kate, Controversey, Tracy Carothers, and Virgin Boys.
Tips: "Have an open attitude and desire to work hard."

*HOGAR MUSICAL PRODUCTIONS, 4225 Palm St., Baton Rouge LA 70808. (504)383-7885. President; Barrie Edgar. Record producer and music publisher (Silverfoot). Deals with artists and songwriters. Produces 0-5 singles/year and 0-2 albums/year. Fee derived from outright fee from record company.
How to Contact: Prefers cassette with maximum 4 songs and lyric sheet. SASE.
Music: Mostly rock, blues ("not soul") and country. Recently produced "Louisiana's Basin Child," by Top Secret (rock single, Gulfstream).

HOLY SPIRIT PRODUCTIONS, INC., 27335 Penn St., Inkster MI 48141. President: Elder Otis G. Johnson. Record producer and music publisher (God's World/SESAC, Manfield Music/BMI, Stephen Enoch Johnson Music/ASCAP). Deals with artists and songwriters. Produces 5 singles and 2 albums/year. Works with 6 new songwriters/year. Works with lyricists and composers. Fee derived from sales royalty.
How to Contact: Write first. Prefers 7½ ips reel-to-reel or cassette with 3 songs and lyric first. SASE. Reports in 1 month.
Music: Church/religious, country, easy listening and gospel. Recently produced "More Sad Good-Byes," by Diana Warden (country single, God's World Records); "And To Be With You," by Valorie Jean Rema and Otis G. Johnson; "Dream Girl," (by Robert Lou), recorded by Annexus; and "Storm of Life," written and recorded by O.G. Johnson (all easy listening singles, Aspro Records).

HOMESTEAD PRODUCTIONS, Box 256577, Chicago IL 60625. (312)399-5535. President: Tom Petreli. Record producer. Deals with artists and songwriters. Produces 8-15 singles and 2-5 albums/year. Fee derived from sales royalty.
How to Contact: Prefers cassette or videocassette with 2-4 songs and lyric sheet. SASE. Reports in 1 month.
Music: Mostly country; also bluegrass, church/religious, gospel and Spanish. Recently produced "Arizonia," by Arizonia Country (country single). Other artists include Tom Petrei, Tempe and Messa.

*HRS PRODUCTIONS, 1119 W. German Ave., Garland TX 75040. Contact: Gene Huddleston. Record producer. Deals with artists and songwriters. Produces 2 singles/year and 4 albums/year. Fee derived from sales royalty.
How to Contact: Prefers cassette and lyric sheet. SASE. Reports in 2 weeks.
Music: Mostly country, Christian and pop. Recently produced "Tend to the Mendin'," by Gene Huddleston (country single, Puzzle); *Nashville Star*, by Don Ferguson (country LP, Puzzle); and "Slow Song," by Mary Craig (country single, Puzzle). Other artists include Terry Yates.
Tips: "write new material and submit on regular basis."

*HUMDINGER PRODUCTIONS, 607 Piney Point Rd., Yorktown VA 23692. (804)898-8155/595-4191. Professional Managers: Lana Puckett and Kim Person. Record producer, music publisher (Hot Knobs Music) and recording studio. Estab. 1984. Produces 5 singles/year and 2 albums/year. Fee derived from outright fee from songwriter/artist or record company.
How to Contact: Write first and obtain permission to submit. Prefers cassette or Beta videocassette with 1-5 songs and lyric sheet. "Material must be presented on a decent demo—whatever it takes to get song across." SASE. Reports in 3 weeks.
Music: Mostly country, easy listening and pop; also bluegrass, gospel and children's music. Recently

produced *Heart of Glass*, by Rich Follett (easy listening/contemporary country LP, Unicorn); "Love Ain't What It Seems," by Lana Puckett (top 40 single, Cimirron/Rainbird); and "Hard Habit to Break," by L. Puckett (country single, Cimirron/Rainbird).
Tips: "Artist must have a professional attitude and be willing to work hard."

*HUTCHINSON PRODUCTIONS, INC., 56-44 142nd St., Flushing NY 11367. (718)762-2295. Producer: Clay Hutchinson. Record producer and music publisher. Estab. 1984. Deals with artists and songwriters. Fee derived from sales royalty, or outright fee from songwriter/artist or record company.
How to Contact: Call first and obtain permission to submit. Prefers cassette and lyric sheet. SASE. Reports in 4-6 weeks.
Music: Mostly pop/rock and pop/R&B. Recently produced *Behind Enemy Lines*, by Spys (pop/rock LP on EMI).

IEA/INTERNATIONAL ENTERTAINMENT ASSOCIATES, (formerly American Creative Entertainment), Suite 818, 1616 Pacific Ave., Atlantic City NJ 08401. (609)347-0484. President: Danny Luciano. Associate Producer: Armand Cucinotti. Record producer and music publisher (Donna Marie Music/ASCAP). Deals with artists and songwriters. Produces 2 singles and 1 album/year. Fee derived from sales royalty.
How to Contact: Prefers 7½ ips reel-to-reel or cassette with 4-8 songs and lyric sheet. "No 8 track." SASE. Reports in 6 weeks.
Music: MOR, R&B, rock (all types), soul and top 40/pop. Recently produced "Ting-A-Ling Doubleplay," by Larry Bowa and Dave Cash of the Philadelphia Phillies (top 40 single, Molly Records).

IF PRODUCTIONS, INC., Omnipop Enterprises, Suite 225, 223 Jericho Tpke., Mineola NY 11501. (516)248-4019. Branch: 22240 Schoenborn St., Canoga Park CA 91304. (213)883-4865. New York Contact: Tom Ingegno. California Contact: Mike Frenchik. Record producer and music publisher (Beautiful Day Music). Works with artists. Producers 3-5 singles and 2 albums/year. Fee derived from sales royalty or outright fee from record company.
How to Contact: Prefers cassette with minumum 3 songs and lyric sheet. SASE. Reports in 3 weeks.
Music: R&R and top 40/pop. Recently produced "First Thrills," "Front Page News," and "Thrills Three," by Thrills (rock singles, G&P Records).

*IN ACTION, 3530 Kensington Ave., Philadelphia PA 19134. (215)288-4750. Vice President: Dave Wilson. Record producer and music publisher (Sulzer Music). Deals with artists and songwriters. Produces 50 singles/year and 10 albums/year. Fee derived from sales royalty.
How to Contact: Prefers cassette. SASE. Reports in 3 weeks.
Music: Mostly country, top 40 and rock; also all others. Recently produced "The Lonely Road," by Paul Christopher (MOR single on In Action); "Danny Boy," by Joe Porter (Irish single on In Action); and "Bluesy Basie," by Vincent Lopez (big band single on In Action). Other artists include Tom Borneman, Dusty Roads and Joanne Petrevitch.

INNOCENT LUST PRODUCTIONS, Box 333, Evanston IL 60204. (312)274-9126. President: Graham Carlton. Record producer, music publisher (Graham Carlton Music Co.) and record company. Deals with artists and songwriters. Produces 130 singles and 40 albums/year. Fee negotiated.
How to Contact: Prefers cassette or videocassette with 1-5 songs and lyric sheet. SASE. Also send biographical material and photos. Reports as soon as possible.
Music: Bluegrass, blues, country, dance-oriented, easy listening, folk, jazz, MOR, progressive, R&B, rock, soul, top 40/pop and humorous. Recently produced *Mr. Love*, by Shackle (punk LP, Hybrid Records); *Quitting Time*, by Dawn Martin (country LP, Hybrid Records); and *Tomorrow*, by Sue Stassen (R&B LP, Hybrid Records). Other artists include Down Home Band, Eddie Wilson and Bob Barton.

*INSIGHT OUT PRODUCTIONS, Box 5509, Mill Valley CA 94942. (415)388-8107. Chief Executive Officer/Producer: Jay A. Leibovitz. Record producer and recording production and distribution company. Estab. 1985. Deals with artists and songwriters. Produces 3-4 albums/year. Fee derived from sales royalty. "We seek collaborative ventures with other book, video and record/tape publishing companies."
How to Contact: Prefers cassette or VHS videocassette "preferably of performance" with 1-10 songs and lyric sheet and lead sheet "if available. We produce primarily acoustic music for children, 'nature lovers,' and storytellers. Other submissions will be accepted. Contact by mail or phone before submitting, if desired." SASE. Reports in 4 weeks.
Music: Mostly music appropriate for children's audiences (all ages), storytellers and folk/traditional; also music for relaxation/stress recreation, folk/contemporary and "nature/environmental" music. Recently produced *For the Child in Us All*, by Jay Leibovitz (children's LP, Insight Out Productions); and

Were Goin' to the Zoo Tomorrow, an anthology (children's LP, Insight Out Productions). Other artists include Redmond O'Connell and Cindy Barnett (storyteller).
Tips: "We wll consider re-release of previously published materials, and include material in anthologies. Submit 1 song, even if you feel it's the only one ready at the time."

*ITS A HIT PRODUCTIONS, Box H, Harvard MA 01451. (617)456-8111. Chief Executive Officer: Stephen Bond Garvan. Record producer, music publisher (Down to Earth) and management firm (Bullet Management). Deals with artists and songwriters. Produces 2-5 singles/year and 1-2 albums/year. Fee derived from sales royalty or outright fee from songwriter/artist or record company.
How to Contact: Prefers cassette. SASE.
Music: Mostly rock, pop and country. Recently produced "Into Another Life," by Dean Adrien (pop single on Wouldn Shoe); "Hearts Overflowing," by AMA (pop single on Wouldn Shoe); and "Once They're Gone," by Allen Estes (pop rock single on Greenpeace). Other artists include Secrets.

*J & J MUSICAL ENTERPRISES, Suite 404, 150 Fifth Ave., New York NY 10011. (212)691-5630. General Manager: Jude St. George. Record producer and music publisher (Jeneane & Jude Music). Deals with artists. Fee derived from outright fee from songwriter/artist.
How to Contact: Write first and obtain permission to submit. Prefers cassette with 4 songs and lyric sheet. "Typewritten letters preferred." Does not return unsolicited material. Reports in 3-4 weeks.
Music: Mostly progressive, jazz and blues. Recently produced "Freeway Fusion," by Freeway Fusion (progressive EP on J & J Musical Enterprises).

J.C.W. MUSIC ENTERPRISES, INC., Box 22805, Highland Heights Station, Memphis TN 38122. Contact: Music Consultant. Record producer. Estab. 1984. Deals with artists and songwriters. Produces 10 singles and 4 albums/year. Works with 6-10 new songwriters/year. Fee derived from sales royalty or outright fee from artist/songwriter or record company.
How to Contact: Prefers cassette or 7½ ips reel-to-reel with minimum 4 songs and lyric sheet. SASE. Reports in 1 month.
Music: Mostly country, gospel and R&B; also soul.

*J.P. PRODUCTIONS, 414 Vanderbilt Ave., Brooklyn NY 11238. (718)622-7524. Contact: John A. Pergamo. Record producer and record company (ACE Records). Deals with artists and songwriters. Produces 12 singles/year and 4 albums/year. Fee derived from sales royalty, or outright fee from songwriter/artist or record company; "depending on negotiations."
How to Contact: Write first to arrange a personal interview. Prefers cassette, 15 ips reel-to-reel or VHS videocassette with 3-5 songs and lyric sheet or lead sheet. SAE. Reports in 1 week.
Music: Mostly heavy metal, pop/funk and reggae; also blues, 50s, country and new wave. Recently produced *Ground Zero*, by Nu-Clear Energy (reggae LP, ACE); "Longlive Rock," by Big Boys (rock single, ACE); and "Face the Music," by Superdude 1984 (techno pop single, ACE). Other artists include Zappha Brothers, Buddy Bowser, King Bee, Jackie Blue, and Black Skull.
Tips: "Send clear quality sound recording and cover letter explaining exactly what you want to do."

JOHN & KARIN, Bente Record, 382 Central Park W, New York NY 10025. (212)749-2267. President: Karin Mann. Record producer and music publisher (Jorin Music). Deals with artists. Fee derived from sales royalty.
How to Contact: Prefers cassette with 3-5 songs and lyric sheet. SASE. Reports in 1 month.
Music: R&B and soul.

LITTLE RICHIE JOHNSON PRODUCTIONS, Box 3, 1700 Plunket, Belen NM 87002. (505)864-7441. President: Little Richie Johnson. Record producer and music publisher (Little Richie Johnson Music/BMI and Little Cowboy Music/ASCAP). Deals with artists and songwriters. Produces 10 singles and 4 albums/year. Works with new songwriters, lyricists and composers. Fee derived from sales royalty.
How to Contact: Call first. Prefers 7½ ips reel-to-reel with 4-8 songs. SASE. Reports in 2 weeks.
Music: Country, gospel and Spanish. Recently produced "I Could Never Be Ashamed of You," by Ronnie Smith (single, Little Ritchie Records); and "Statue of a Fool," by Barbie Phillips (country single).

*JUNE PRODUCTIONS LTD., Toftrees Church Rd., Weldingham, Surrey, England. Managing Director: David Mackay. Record producer.
How to Contact: Prefers cassette with 1-4 songs and lyric sheet. SAE and IRC. Reports in 2 weeks.
Music: MOR, rock and top 40/pop. Recently produced "Its A Heartache," by Bonnie Tyler (top 40/rock single, RCA Records); "I'd Like to Teach the World to Sing," by The New Seekers (MOR single, Elektra Records); and "Look What You've Done to My Song, Ma," by The New Seekers (MOR/pop single, Elektra Records).

BUTCH KELLY PRODUCTION, 11 Shady Oak Trail, Charlotte NC 28210. (704)554-1162. Executive Director: Butch Kelly. Record producer and music publisher. Deals with artists and songwriters. Produces 2 singles and 2 albums/year. Fee derived from sales royalty.
How to Contact: Prefers cassette or videocassette with 3 songs and picture and lyric sheet. SASE. Reports in 1 month.
Music: Mostly pop and R&B; also dance-oriented, jazz, gospel, soul and top 40. Recently produced "13 Years," and "Super Star," (by Dennis Jones), recorded by LA Stars (Executive Records); and "Fantasy II," (by Butch Kelly), recorded by Melisa Kelly Montgomery (pop single, Executive Records). Other artists include VIP Express, Will Wylie, and Lebo Blackmon.

KENCO PRODUCTIONS, INC., 3784 Realty, Dallas TX 75244. (214)241-7854. President: K.J. Hughes. Record producer, music publisher (Luvco Music/BMI) and 24-track recording studio. Deals with artists and songwriters. Produces 12-15 singles and 8-12 albums/year. Fee derived from sales royalty.
How to Contact: Prefers cassette with 1-3 songs and lyric sheet. SASE. Reports in 1 month.
Music: Most country and novelty; also bluegrass, R&B and top 40/pop. Recently produced *I Don't Mean to Sound Obscene*, by Bullit and The Buffaloes (novelty LP, Merit Records); "Dallas Does It," by Nancy Allyson Parrish (MOR single, Luv Records); and "Dolly Parton for President," by Roger Howell (Luv Records).

GENE KENNEDY ENTERPRISES, INC., 2125 8th Ave. S., Nashville TN 37204. (615)383-6002. President: Gene Kennedy. Vice President: Karen Jeglum. Director of Promotion for Door Knob Records: Butch Paulson. Record producer, independent distribution and promotion firm and music publisher (Chip 'N' Dale Music Publishers, Inc./ASCAP, Door Knob Music Publishing, Inc./BMI and Lodestar Music/SESAC). Deals with artists and songwriters. Produces 40-50 singles and 3-5 albums/year. Fee derived from outright fee from artist or record company.
How to Contact: Submit demo tape or arrange for personal interview. Prefers 7 ½ ips reel-to-reel or cassette with up to 4 songs and lyric sheet. SASE. Reports in 1-3 weeks.
Music: Country, easy listening and MOR. Recently produced *A New Beginning*, by Bobby G. Rice (LP).
Tips: "We are looking for hit songs and good talent."

KEYNOTE PRODUCTIONS, 4322 Mahoning Ave., Youngstown OH 44515. (216)793-7295. Executive Producer: Richard Hahn. Record producer and music publisher (Al-Kris Music/BMI). Deals with artists and songwriters. Produces 5 singles and 2 albums/year. Fee derived from sales royalty or outright fee from songwriter/artist.
How to Contact: Query by mail first. Prefers cassette with 3-5 songs and "neat" lyric sheet. SASE. Reports in 3 weeks.
Music: Country, gospel, MOR and top 40/pop. Produced "Here Come the Browns," by Kardiak Kids (MOR single, Keynote Records); "Help Me I'm Falling," by Kirsti Manna (MOR single, Genuine Records); "Teach Me Lovely Lady," by Jim Stack (country single, Peppermint Records); and "The San Francisco 49er's Fight Song" and "Prom Night," by the B-Minors (MOR singles). Other artists include Leigh Fisher and Gary Kekel.
Tips: "The artist or writer should be willing to compromise on creative decisions by the producer to achieve the best possible product."

KIDERIAN RECORDS PRODUCTIONS, 4926 W. Gunnison, Chicago IL 60630. (312)899-5535. President: Raymond Peck. Record producer. Deals with artists and songwriters. Fee derived from sales royalty and outright fee from record company.
How to Contact: Prefers cassette with 4-6 songs and lyric sheet. SASE. Reports in 1 month.
Music: Blues, country, dance, MOR, new wave, power pop, R&B, hard rock, soul and top 40/pop. Recently produced "Oh That Man," by Nadine Herman (new wave single, Stang Records); and "Tribute to John Lennon," by Torn Orphan (rock single, Kiderian Records). Other artists include Boyz, Mammoth, Destiny, Poppetteer, Alicja, Ted Wika, Lucy Guess and Deceivor.

*KINGSPORT CREEK MUSIC, Box 6085, Burbank CA 91510. Contact: Vice President. Record producer and music publisher. Deals with artists and songwriters.
How to Contact: Prefers cassette or videocassette. Does not return unsolicited material.
Music: Mostly country and gospel. Recently produced "Tennessee Cowgirl," "Wash Your Hands," and "Only Life I Know," by Melvena Kaye (country/gospel singles on Cowgirl).

KNOWN ARTIST PRODUCTIONS, 1219 Kerlin Ave., Brewton AL 36426. (205)867-2228. President: Roy Edwards. Record producer and music publisher (Cheavoria Music Co./BMI and Baitstring

Music/ASCAP). Deals with artists and songwriters. Produces 12 singles and 3 albums/year. Fee derived from sales royalty or outright fee from record company.
How to Contact: Write first about your interest. Prefers cassette with 3-5 songs and lyric sheet. SASE. Reports in 1 month.
Music: Country, easy listening, MOR, R&B and soul. Recently produced "Music Inside," by Roy Edwards (MOR single, Bolivia Records); "Make Me Forget," by Bobby Roberson; and "Always and Forever," by Jim Portwood (country singles, Bolivia Records).
Tips: "Write a good song that tells a good story."

FREDDIE KOBER PRODUCTIONS, Box 11967, Houston TX 77016. (713)694-2971. President: Freddie Kober. Record producer and music publisher (Anode Music/BMI and Clauda Bee Music/ASCAP). Deals with songwriters. Produces 4 singles/year. Fee derived from sales royalty.
How to Contact: Prefers cassette with 1-3 songs and lyric sheet. SASE. Reports in 2 weeks.
Music: Gospel and soul. Recently produced "Life Can Be Beautiful," "I Feel You, I Feel Me," and "Take This Love," by Rue Davis.

IREN KOSTER PRODUCTIONS, 236½ Lasky Dr., Beverly Hills CA 90212. A&R Director: Bobby Joe Watson. Record producer and music publisher (Snugglebush Music Company). Deals with artists and songwriters. Produces 5 singles and 10 albums/year. Fee derived from sales royalty.
How to Contact: Prefers cassette or videocassette with 2 songs and lyric sheet. SASE. Reports in 2 weeks.
Music: Mostly top 40/pop; also country, dance-oriented, easy listening, MOR, R&B, rock and soul.

PERRY LA MARCA/NOATZ PRODUCTIONS, Suite L-106, 12200 Montecito, Rossmoor CA 90740. President: Perry LaMarca. Record producer. Produces 4-5 singles/year and 2-3 albums/year. Fee derived from sales royalty or outright fee from record company.
How to Contact: Prefers cassette or 7½ ips reel-to-reel with 1-5 songs and lyric sheet or lead sheet. Does not return unsolicited material. Reports in 3-4 weeks.
Music: Mostly adult contemporary, top 40 and easy listening; European (non-English) pop/MOR. Recently produced "Beside Me," by Westwind (top 40 single on Sunset); and "A Little Latin Dancing," by Silvia Montebello (European pop single on Sunset). Other artists include The Perry La Marca singers.

LADD & ASSOCIATES, 401 Wintermantle Ave., Scranton PA 18505. (717)343-6718. President: Phil Ladd. Record producer and music publisher (Ladd Music Co.). Deals with artists, songwriters and other producers. Produces 6 singles and 1 album/year. Fee derived from sales royalty.
How to Contact: Prefers cassette or videocassette with 4-12 songs and lyric sheet. SASE. Reports in 3 weeks.
Music: Mostly top 40/pop; also children's, country, easy listening, MOR, R&B and rock. Recently produced "Lovin'," by Bobby Brant (MOR single, Whiterock Records). Other artists include Clyde Stacy, Kaye Kalls and Mitch Cord.

LAMON RECORDS/PANHANDEL RECORDS, Box 25371, Charlotte NC 28212. (704)537-0133. President: Dwight Moody. A&R: Carlton Moody. Record producer and music publisher (Laymond Publishing Co. and CDT Productions). Deals with artists, songwriters and publishers. Produces 25 singles and 12 albums/year. Fee derived from sales royalty.
How to Contact: Write first and obtain permission to submit. Prefers cassette with minimum 2 songs. Does not return unsolicited material. Reports in 1 month.
Music: All types. Recently produced "Slow Shag," by Billy Scott (beach single, Lamon Records); "All My Yesterdays," by Charlie Harris (country single, Lamon Records); and "Sweet Country Music," by Jim Snyder (square dance single, Panhandel Records). Other artists include Carlton Moody.

LANDMARK AUDIO OF NASHVILLE, (formerly The Berkley Music Group), 1106 18th Ave. S, Nashville TN 37212. (615)868-3407. Producers: Bill Anderson, Jr. or D.D. Morris. Record producer, music publisher (Newcreature Music/BMI) and TV/radio syndication. Deals with artists and songwriters. Produces 4 singles and 4 albums/year. Works with 1 new songwriter/year. Works with lyricists and composers and teams collaborators. Fee derived from sales royalty.
How to Contact: Prefers 7½ ips reel-to-reel, cassette or videocassette with 4-10 songs and lyric sheet. SASE. Reports in 1 month.
Music: Mostly country crossover; also blues, country, gospel, jazz, rock and top 40/pop. Recently produced *Sincerely, Rhona*, by Rhonda Ingle (MOR LP, Phonorama Records); and *The Traditional Continues*, by Vernon Oxford (country LP, Audiograph Records). Other artists include De Fox and Wayne Oldham.

LAS VEGAS RECORDING STUDIO, INC., 3977 Vegas Valley Dr., Las Vegas NV 89121. (702)457-4365. Vice President: Wally Jones. Producer: Raul DiBiano. Record producer, music publisher, management firm and record company. Deals with artists and songwriters. Fee derived from sales royalty, outright fee from record company, or outright fee from songwriter/artist. "We do not charge songwriters for their demos, but we do ask for publishing if we place the material."
How to Contact: Prefers cassette and lyric and lead sheets. SASE. Reports ASAP.
Music: Bluegrass, blues, church/religious, country, easy listening, folk, gospel, jazz, MOR, progressive, rock, soul, top 40/pop, and instrumental. Recently produced Ronnie Fuller, Joy Britton, JoAnna Neal and Terry Richards for ECR Records.
Tips: "Send all correspondence to: 4318 Hayes Place, Las Vegas NV 89107."

LAZER RECORDS, 7330 Sycamore Ave., Philadelphia PA 19126. (215)635-2878. President: A. Gravatt. Record producer and music publisher (Lazer Music/BMI). Deals with artists and songwriters. Produces variable number singles and albums/year. Fee derived from sales royalty or outright fee from artist/songwriter.
How to Contact: Write first and obtain permission to submit, then submit cassette with limit of 1 song and lyric sheet. SASE.
Music: Dance-oriented, jazz, MOR, progressive, R&B, rock, soul and top 40/pop. Recently produced "Tight Money," by CE Rock (R&B/pop single, Lazer Records); and "I Want You (So Bad)," by Latita (pop single, Lazer Records).

OVERTON LEE, 10051 Green Leaf, Santa Fe Springs CA 90670. (213)946-1524. President: Overton Lee. Record producer and music publisher (Boggy Depot, Overton Lee Music). Deals with artists and songwriters. Produces 6 singles and 2 albums/year. Fee derived from sales royalty.
How to Contact: Prefers cassette with 1-3 songs and lyric sheet. SASE. Reports in 4 months.
Music: Mostly country; also bluegrass, blues, country and gospel. Recently produced *Hard On the Heart* and *Some Where in Houston*, both by Johnny Blankenship (Overton Lee Records); and *May You Never Be Alone*, by Overton Lee (Overton Lee Records). Other artists include Alan Lee Blackwell, Gene Davis, Eddie Marie, The Bonner Family, Carmen Wilder and Darvy Traylor.

ROOSEVELT LEE INTERNATIONAL RECORDS, 3966 Standish Ave., Cincinnati OH 45213. (513)793-8191. President: Roosevelt Lee. Record producer and music publisher (Citiy Music). Deals with artists and songwriters. Produces 4 singles and 2 albums/year. Fee derived from sales royalty.
How to Contact: Prefers cassette with 4 songs and lyric sheet. SASE. Reports in 1 month.
Music: Country, R&B and soul. Recently produced "Love City," by Larry Daby (soul single, Wes World Records); and "Come Home to Me," by Mike Ellis (country single, Wes World Records).

LEGEND RECORDS AND PROMOTIONS, 1102 Virginia St. SW, Lenoir NC 28645. (704)758-4170. President: Mike McCoy. Record producer and music publisher (Nancy Jane Publishing/BMI). Works with artists and songwriters. Produces 2 singles/year. Works with composers. Fee derived from sales royalty.
How to Contact: Prefers cassette with 1-4 songs and lyric sheet. SASE. Reports in 1 month.
Music: Mostly country, rock and rockabilly; also soft rock, church/religious, gospel, R&B and outlaw country. Recently produced "My Baby Loves Old Rock and Roll," and "Rock and Roll Outlaw," by Mike McCoy (rock and roll singles, Legend Records); and "From My Land to Graceland," by M. McCoy (country crossover single, Legend Records).

*LEMON SQUARE PRODUCTIONS, Box 31819, Dallas TX 75231. (214)750-0720. A&R: Mike Anthony. Record producer, music publisher and record label. Deals with artists and songwriters. Produces 20 singles/year and 2 albums/year. Fee derived from sales royalty.
How to Contact: Write first and obtain permission to submit. Prefers cassette and lyric sheet or lead sheet. Does not return unsolicited material. Reports in 6-8 weeks.
Music: Mostly country and gospel. Other artists include Christy Hedges, Glen Baily and Audie Henry.

LIFESINGER PRODUCTIONS, Suite #902, 50 Music Square W., Nashville TN 37203. (615)329-2278. President: Bobby Fischer. Record producer, music publisher (Bobby Fischer Music Group), record company (F&L Records) and distribution and promotion firm. Deals with artists and songwriters. Produces 10 singles and variable number of albums/year. Fee derived from record company.
How to Contact: Prefers cassette with 2-3 songs and lyric sheet. SASE. Reports "when time permits."
Music: Country and progressive. Recently produced "An Afternoon of Love," by Clifford Russell and Mary Lou Turner (love song single, Sugartree Records); "Cheater's Last Chance," by Larry Riley (love song single, F&L Records); and "Somebody's Darlin', Somebody's Wife," by Dottsy (love song single, Tanglewood Records).

LIFETIME RECORDINGS, 314 S. Goodman St., Rochester NY 14607. (716)244-7526. Contact: Lester W. Osband. Record producer.
How to Contact: Prefers cassette and lyric sheet. SASE. Reports in 1 month.
Music: "Any kind."

LI'L WALLY MUSIC PRODUCTIONS, 35 NE 62nd St., Miami FL 33138. (305)258-0000. President: Walter Jagiello. Record producer and music publisher (Jay Jay Publishing/BMI). Deals with songwriters. Produces 8 singles and 8 albums/year. Works with lyricists and composers and teams collaborators. Fee derived from sales royalty.
How to Contact: Prefers cassette with 2-6 songs and lyric sheet. SASE. Reports in 1 month.
Music: Mostly polkas, love songs, waltzes and country; also easy listening. Recently produced "Little Lost Angel," by Eddie Howard (pop single, A Great Variety Records); "How Can I Love Somebody Else," by Li'l Wally (pop single, Bonfire Records); and "Best of Your Days," by Toni Ardeen (pop single, A Great Variety Records).

LITTLE GIANT ENTERPRISES, Box 205, White Lake NY 12786. (914)583-4471. President: Mickey Barnett. Record producer and music publisher (Karjan Music Publishing Co./SESAC). Deals with artists and songwriters. Produces 3 singles and 5 albums/year. Fee derived from outright fee from artist/songwriter.
How to Contact: Prefers cassette with 1-3 songs and lyric sheet. SASE. Reports in 3 weeks.
Music: Blues, country, easy listening, MOR, R&B and top 40/pop. Recently produced *Country Songs and Dreams*, by Chuck Wilson (country LP, Killer Records); *Valley View House Presents*, by T. Barry Kaminski (MOR LP, Little Giant Records); and *Young and Polish*, by Kenny Adams (comedy single, Killer Records). Other artists include Jayson Ross, The Third Edition, Mickey Barnett and The Little Giants.

LONSONG MUSIC INC., Suite 600, 1055 Wilson Ave., Toronto, Ontario M3K 1Y9, Canada. (416)630-2973. President: Frank Longo. Record producer and music publisher (Lonsong Music, Inc./ CAPAC). Deals with artists and songwriters. Produces 4 singles and 1 album/year. Works with 2 new songwriters/year. Works with lyricists and composers and teams collaborators. Fee derived from sales royalty.
How to Contact: Prefers cassette with 1-3 songs and lyric sheet. SAE and IRC. Reports in 2 weeks.
Music: Mostly R&B and MOR; also dance-oriented, easy listening and top 40/pop. Recently produced "Don't Change," by Patti Janetto (MOR ballad single); "Manhattan," by the Longo Brothers (crossover single); and "I'm Ready for Your Love," by P. Janetto (adult contemporary single).

HAROLD LUICK & ASSOCIATES, 110 Garfield St., Box B, Carlisle IA 50047. (515)989-3679. Record producer and music publisher. Deals with artists and songwriters. Produces 30 singles and 12 albums/year. Fee derived from sales royalty, outright fee from artist/songwriter or record company, and from retainer fees.
How to Contact: Call or write first. Prefers cassette with 3-5 songs and lyric sheet. SASE. Reports in 3 weeks.
Music: Bluegrass, country, dance-oriented, easy listening, gospel, MOR, R&B, rock and top 40/pop. Recently produced "House of Memories," by Bob Schirmer (country single, RDS Records); "What You Do to Me," by Linda Cooper (pop single, LC Records); and *Proud to be a Mother*, by June Murphy (country LP, Jay/Bee Records). Other artists include Ray Faubus and the Kenny Hofer Orchestra.
Tips: "Producers are becoming more and more independent (this means not having to rely on a big record company) and they can be more creative. This means they have use for more song material than ever before. Keep writing commercial material that has possibilities, let the producer work the 'probabilities.' Don't 'hype' a producer about your song. This is one of the biggest turnoffs that amateurs use."

***LUST ENTERPRISES**, 8769 Sharmead Way, Fair Oaks CA 95628. (916)966-1437. Executive Producer: Gary Koekoek. Record producer and promoter. Deals with artists and songwriters. Fee derived from sales royalty or outright fee from record company.
How to Contact: Prefers cassette, 15 ips reel-to-reel or VHS videocassette with 1-5 songs and lyric sheet. "Lyric sheets, basic rhythm track and vocals encouraged." SASE. Reports in 4 weeks.
Music: Mostly heavy metal and top 40. Recently produced *Livin' in Sin*, by Vincent Michael (rock LP, Lust); and "Windsong," by V. Michael (MOR single, 4-Star International).

***M.D.M. PRODUCTIONS**, 117 W. 8th, Hays KS 67601. (913)625-9634. President: Mark Meckel. Record producer, music publisher (Street Singer Music) and record company. Deals with artists and songwriters. Produces 12 singles/year and 15 albums/year. Fee derived from outright fee from songwriter/artist.

How to Contact: Prefers cassette with 2 songs and lyric or lead sheet. SASE. Reports in 2 weeks.
Music: Mostly R&B, country and gospel; also rock/Christian, country R&B and 50s rock. Recently produced *Into His Courts*, by Bill Sanchez (Christian LP on MDM); and *One Way Ticket*, by Mark Selby (rock/country LP on Black Dolpin). Other artists include Rusty Bush, Kim Haiger and Galen Schmidtberger.

LEE MAGID PRODUCTIONS, Box 532, Malibu CA 90265. (213)858-7282. President: Lee Magid. Record producer and music publisher (Alexis Music, Inc./ASCAP, Marvelle Music Co./BMI). Deals with artists, songwriters and producers. Produces 20 singles and 8 albums/year. Publishes 10-15 new songwriters/year. Works with lyricists and composers and teams collaborators. Fee derived from sales royalty and "advance fee against royalties"; sometimes pays a flat outright sum.
How to Contact: Write first about your interest giving address and phone number; include SASE. Prefers cassette or videocassette with 3-6 songs and lyric sheet. SASE. Reports "as soon as we can after listening."
Music: Mostly country, rock, jazz, and pop; also bluegrass, church/religious, easy listening, folk, blues, MOR, progressive, soul, instrumental and top 40. Recently produced *Have Horns, Will Travel*, recorded by Russ Gary Big Band Express (jazz LP); "It's a Blue World," (by C. Wright/B. Forrest), recorded by Four Freshmen (pop/jazz single); and "Snowbound," (by Frank Hunter/Larry O'Brien), recorded by Big Band Express (instrumental single). Other artists include Papa John Creach, Nan Brennan, and Becky Bishop.
Tips: "The visual effect is just as important as the audio. An act should have theatrical as well as musical ability."

MAINROADS PRODUCTIONS, INC., 100 Huntley St., Toronto, Ontario, Canada M4Y 2L1. (416)961-8001. Manager: Paul Kelly. Record producer, music publisher (Mainroads Publishing/CAPAC, Bruce W. Stacey Publishing/PRO). Deals with artists and songwriters. Produces 3 albums/year. Fee derived from sales royalty.
How to Contact: Write first about your interest. Prefers cassette with 3 songs. SAE and IRC. Reports in 1 month.
Music: Children's, choral, church/religious and gospel.

PETE MARTIN/VAAM MUSIC PRODUCTIONS, Suite C-114, 3740 Evans St., Los Angeles CA 90027. (213)664-7765. President: Pete Martin. Record producer and music publisher (Vaam Music/BMI, Pete Martin Music/ASCAP). Deals with artists and songwriters. Produces 5-10 singles and 2-8 albums/year. Fee derived from sales royalty.
How to Contact: Prefers 7 1/2 ips reel-to-reel or cassette with 1-4 songs and lyric sheet. SASE. Reports in 1 month.
Music: Country, easy listening, MOR, rock (general), soul and top 40/pop. Recently produced "Secrets Are for Telling," by Meza (rock single, Blue Gem Records); "Shattered, Tattered & Battered," by Joe Ward (country single, Blue Gem Records); "Here Is Happiness," by Reynolds & Nalani (pop single, Hi-Lute Records); *I've Got the Country in Me*, by Kamie Redell (country LP, Blue Gem Records). Other artists include P.S. Lambert, Flashback and Wayne Allen Anderson.

MASTER SOUND PRODUCTIONS INC., Kaufman Astoria Studios, 34-12 36th St., Astoria NY 11106. (516)354-3374. President: Ben Rizzi. Vice President: Maxine Chrein. Record producer, audio recording facility and (limited) video post production. Deals with artists, record companies, songwriters, film scorers and producers. Payment is "negotiable."
How to Contact: Prefers 7 1/2 or 15 ips reel-to-reel or cassette with 1 song and lyric sheet. Does not return unsolicited material. "We prefer to file tapes and contact person when warranted." Reports if interested.
Music: Mostly adult contemporary and pop rock; also dance-oriented, easy listening, MOR, rock and top 40/pop.

MASTERSOURCE PRODUCTIONS, 704 N. Wells, Chicago IL 60610. (312)922-0375. Executive Producer: Charles Thomas. Music producer. Deals with artists and songwriters. Produces 8-10 singles/year. Fee derived from sales royalty. "We desire long-term artist relationships."
How to Contact: Query. Prefers cassette with 3 songs and lyric and lead sheets. Does not return unsolicited material. Reports in 3 weeks.
Music: Top 40, AOR, adult contemporary and contemporary Christian. Recently produced *Gift of Gladness*, by Chris Christensen (contemporary Christian LP, World Christen Records); *Sold*, by Jim Miller (contemporary Christian LP, World Christen Records); and "Modern Motion," by Stan Hickerson (top 40 single, Mega Media Records).

MASTERVIEW MUSIC PUBLISHING CORP., Ridge Rd. and Butler Lane, Perkasie PA 18944. (215)257-9616. General Manager: Thomas Fausto. President: John Wolf. Record producer, music

publisher (Masterview Music/BMI), record company and management firm. Deals with artists and songwriters. Produces 12 singles and 3-4 albums/year. Fee derived from sales royalty.
How to Contact: Arrange personal interview. Prefers 7¹/₂ or 15 ips reel-to-reel with 2-6 songs and lead sheet. SASE. Reports in 2 weeks.
Music: Folk and gospel. Recently produced "Up North to Bluegrass," by Country Boys (bluegrass); "I Am Happen," by El Botteon (Rheta Records); and "Footprints," by Charles Newman (religious single, Masterview Records). Other artists include Sugarcane.

DAVID MATHES PRODUCTIONS, Box 22653, Nashville TN 37202. (615)822-6119. President: David W. Mathes. Record producer. Deals with artists and songwriters. Produces 5-10 singles and 3-6 albums/year. Fee derived from sales royalty.
How to Contact: Prefers 7¹/₂ or 15 ips reel-to-reel, cassette or videocassette with 2-4 songs and lyric sheet. "Enclose correctly stamped envelope for demo return." Reports as soon as possible.
Music: Mostly country and gospel; also bluegrass, R&B and top 40/pop. Recently produced *Silver Eagle Band*, by Silver Eagle Band (MOR-country LP, Sapphire Records); and "Singing His Praises," by G. Anderson (gospel LP, Heirborn Records). Other artists include DeAnna, Johnny Newman and Nashville Sidemen and Singers.
Tips: "We look for professional material and presentations."

MCP/DAVISOUND, Bypass 76/Sunset, Box 521, Newberry SC 29108. (803)276-0639. Studio Manager: Teresa Massey. Producer/Director: Hayne Davis. Record producer, music publisher and production company. Deals with artists and songwriters. Produces 5-6 singles and 2-3 albums/year. Fee derived from sales royalty, outright fee from record company, or outright fee from songwriter/artist. Charges for some services: "In special cases, where the songwriter/artist is simply booking our studio facilities, there is a charge. Also, if an artist/writer wishes us to produce him with himself as co-producer, we share profits on a 50/50 basis but at the same time, expenses of production are also shared 50/50."
How to Contact: Prefers 7¹/₂ ips reel-to-reel or cassette with 4-8 songs. SASE. Reports in 2 weeks.
Music: Country (contemporary), dance, easy listening, MOR, rock (all) and top 40/pop (all). Recently produced "Sheila," by James Meadows (country/rock single, Mother Cleo Records); "Too Far Gone," by Curt Bradford (country/rock single, Mother Cleo Records); and "Brainwasher," by J. Teal Band (rock single, Mother Cleo Records). Other artists include Raw Material and Sugar & Spice.

MERCANTILE MUSIC, Box 2271, Palm Springs CA 92263. (619)320-4848. President: Kent Fox. Record producer and music publisher (Mercantile Music/BMI and Blueford Music/ASCAP). Deals with artists and songwriters. Fee derived from sales royalty.
How to Contact: Prefers cassette with 3-5 songs and lyric sheet. SASE. Reports in 1 month.
Music: Country, easy listening and top 40/pop. Recently produced "Keeping the Tradition Alive," and "Heart."

*MIGHTY "T" PRODUCTIONS, Box 1869, Hollywood CA 90078. (213)564-1008. Producer: Kent Washburn. Record producer, music publisher (Highest Praise Publishing) and record company. Deals with artists and songwriters. Produces 5 albums/year. Fee derived from sales royalty.
How to Contact: Prefers cassette with 4 songs and lyric sheet. Prefers studio produced demos. SASE. Reports in 8 weeks.
Music: Mostly gospel, R&B and pop. Recently produced *Words Can't Express*, and *Dedicated*, by Nicholas; and *This Is My Story*, by Vernessa Mitchell (all contemporary gospel LPs on Command).

JAY MILLER PRODUCTIONS, 413 N. Parkerson Ave., Crowley LA 70526. (318)783-1601 or 788-0773. Contact: Jay Miller. Manager: Mark Miller. Record producer and music publisher. Deals with artists and songwriters. Produces 50 singles and 10 albums/year. Fee derived from sales royalty.
How to Contact: Arrange personal interview. Prefers 7¹/₂ ips reel-to-reel or cassette for audition. SASE. Reports in 1 month.
Music: Blues, country, Cajun, disco, folk, gospel, MOR, rock, top 40/pop, and comedy. Recently produced *Introduces Pierre and the Squirely Squirrels*, by Camey Doucet; *Cajun Fiddlin*, by Hadley Castille; and *Singing Now and Tomorrow*, by Leroy Broussard and the Lagniappe Gang.
Tips: "Inquiries are invited."

Market conditions are constantly changing! If this is 1987 or later, buy the newest edition of *Songwriter's Market* at your favorite bookstore or order directly from Writer's Digest Books.

*MULTIPRISES, 500 West End Ave., New York NY 10024. (212)874-6440. President: Toby Bryon. Record producer and music publisher. Produces 1 album/year. Fee derived from sales royalty.
How to Contact: Write first and obtain permission to submit. Prefers cassette or videocassette. Does not return unsolicited material.
Music: Mostly rock, pop and R&B. Recently produced *Bloomfield*, by Michael Bloomfield (rock LP on CBS).

*CHUCK MYMIT PRODUCTIONS, 98-40 64th Ave., Forest Hills NY 11375. (516)783-8800. Director of A&R: Chuck Mymit. Record producer, music publisher (Chargo Music) and arranger. Deals with artists and songwriters. Produces 3-5 singles/year and 2-3 albums/year. Fee derived from sales royalty.
How to Contact: Prefers cassette with 3-5 songs and lyric sheet or lead sheet. "Send short bio of artist/songwriter and picture if possible." SASE. Reports in 2-4 weeks.
Music: Mostly MOR, rock and country; also jazz, instrumentals and ballads. Recently produced *Tony Spatano Love*, (MOR LP on Colla Voce); *On My Own*, by Vinny Oppido (rock/country LP on VR); and "Here I Go Again," by We Three (pop ballad single on Roma). Other artists include the Topnotes.

*NARADA PRODUCTIONS, 1845 N. Farwell, Milwaukee WI 53202. (414)272-6700. Contact: A&R Department. Record producer. Deals with artists and songwriters. Produces 30 albums/year.
How to Contact: Prefers cassette. Does not return unsolicited material.
Music: Mostly instrumental new age music.
Tips: Considers only instrumental music.

NERVOUS MUSIC, 4/36 Dabbs Hill Lane, Northolt, Middlesex, London England. 44-01-422-3462. Managing Director: Roy Williams. Record producer, music publishing (Nervous Publishing) and record company (Nervous Records). Works with artists. Produces 3 singles and 10 albums/year. Works with 20 new songwriters/year. Fee derived from sales royalty.
How to Contact: Prefers cassette with 3-10 songs and lyric sheet. "Include photo and a letter giving your age and career goals." SAE and IRC. Reports in 2 weeks.
Music: Mostly rockabilly; also blues, country, R&B and 50s R&R. Recently produced *Do You Feel Restless*, by (Ben Coorer/Marie Harman), recorded by Restless (rockabilly LP); and "Hall of Mirrors," (by Whitenhouse/Pepler/Brand), recorded by Frenzy (psychobilly single).

NEW DAWN PRODUCTIONS/SOUTH BOUND PRODUCTIONS, Box 186, Cedarburg WI 53012. (414)284-7058. Producer: Robert Wiegert. Record producer and music publisher (RobJen Music, Trinity Music and Great Northern Lights Music). Works with artists and songwriters. Fee derived from sales royalty.
How to Contact: Prefers 7½ ips reel-to-reel or cassette with 3 songs and lyric sheet. Does not return unsolicited material. Reports in 1 month.
Music: "Any and all types of commercial music." Recently produced "I Believed In You," by Cathy Bemis (MOR/pop single, Abacus Records); "I Think It's Gonna Rain," by Stills & Scott (country rock single, Abacus Records); and "Far Far Cry," by Gregg Scott (MOR/pop single, Abacus Records). Other artists include Katie McGivin.
Tips: "If we feel a song is a hit, we do everything possble to get it cut. But writers must be self critical and write, write, write."

*BILLY NICHOLS, 521 5th Ave., New York NY 10175. (212)757-3638. Producer/President: Rena L. Feeney. Record producer and music publisher (Bill-Lee Music). Deals with artists and songwriters. Produces 2-3 singles/year and 2-3 albums/year. Fee derived from sales royalty.
How to Contact: Prefers cassette and lead sheet.

*NIGHTHAWK RECORDS PRODUCTIONS, Box 15856, St. Louis MO 63114. (314)576-1569. Contact: Robert Schoenfeld. Record producer and music publisher (Blackheart Music). Deals with artists and songwriters. Produces 2-4 singles/year and 3-5 albums/year. Fee negotiable.
How to Contact: Prefers cassette with 4-6 songs and lyric sheet. SASE. Reports in 3 weeks.
Music: Mostly reggae, blues and R&B. Recently produced *Serious Thing*, by Gladiators (reggae LP on Nighthawk); *Give Me Power*, by Itals (reggae LP on Nighthawk); and *Travel with Love*, by J.H. & Dominoes (reggae LP on Nighthawk).
Tips: Looking for "gutsy original tunes with character and a message."

*NIGHTWORK RECORDS, 355 W. Potter Dr., Anchorage AK 99502. (907)562-3754. Contact: Kurt Reimann. Record producer and music licensor (electronic). Produces 10 albums/year. Fee derived from licensing fee.
How to Contact: Prefers cassette or 15 ips reel-to-reel with 1-3 songs. "Send jingles and songs on separate reels." Does not return unsolicited material. Reports in 4 weeks.
Music: Mostly electronic and electronic jingles. Recently produced *Nightworks*, by Kurt Reimann (electronic LP on Innovative Communication); and *Wizard of Oz*, by K. Reimann (electronic LP on Nightwork). Other artists include most Alaskan artists and independent producers.

NISE PRODUCTIONS, INC., Suite 101, 413 Cooper St., Camden NJ 08102. (215)276-0100. President: Michael Nise. Record producer and music publisher. Affiliates: Logo III Records, Wordan Records and Power VP Records. Deals with artists and songwriters. Produces 10 singles and 10 albums/year. Fee derived from sales royalty.
How to Contact: Prefers cassette with 1-3 songs and lyric sheet. SASE. Reports in 1 month.
Music: Children's, church/religious, country, dance-oriented, easy listening, folk, gospel, jazz, R&B, rock, soul and top 40/pop.
Tips: "Record label seeking masters—send cassette."

NMI RECORDS, 5500 Troost, Kansas City MO 64110. (816)361-8455. President: Eugene Gold. Record producer and music publisher (Eugene Gold Music/BMI). Deals with artists and songwriters. Produces 6 singles and 2 albums/year. Fee derived from sales royalty.
How to Contact: Call first and obtain permission to submit. Prefers cassette with 4-6 songs. SASE. Reports in 1 month.
Music: Church/religious, gospel, jazz, R&B and soul. Recently produced "Diamond Feather," by Bad New Band (R&B single, NMI Records); "Give Into the Power of Love," by the Committee (R&B single); and *He's Worthy to be Praised*, by Mt. Vernon Inspirational Choir (gospel LP). Other artists include LaVerne Washington, Ronnie and Vicky, Paula Lucas, Jeff Lucas, Supension, Bump and the Soul Stomper, and Barbara White and the Wing of Grace.

NORTH AMERICAN LITURGY RESOURCES, 10802 N. 23rd Ave., Phoenix AZ 85029. (602)864-1980. Record Producer: Paul Quinlan. Music Editor: Henry Papale. Record producer and music publisher. Deals with artists and songwriters and arrangers/conductors. Produces 10 albums/year. Fee derived from sales royalty.
How to Contact: Prefers cassette with 5-12 songs and lyric sheet. SASE. Reports in 1 month.
Music: Children's, choral, church/religious and liturgical. Recently produced "Lord of Light," by St. Louis Jesuits; "Color the World with Song," by Rev. Carey Landry; "Path of Life," and "Reflections," by the Dameans; and "Awaken My Heart/The Dawn of Day," by Lucien Deiss (all NALR Records). Other artists include Al Valverde, Victor Cabrera, Tom Kendzia, Michael Joncas, Daniel Consiglio, Joe Pinson, Jack Miffleton, Paul Contio, Timothy Crawley, Jerry Goebel and Marcy Tinger.
Tips: "Be familiar with our recordings. Free catalogs and brochures are supplied on request."

*NORTHERN COMFORT PRODUCTIONS, 10 Erica Ave., Toronto, Ontario M3H 3H2 Canada. (416)923-5717. President: J. Allan Vogel. Record producer and music publisher (Northern Comfort Music/CAPAC and Sacro-Iliac Music/PROCAN). Deals with artists and songwriters. Produces 4 singles and 1 album/year. Fee derived from sales royalty.
How to Contact: Prefers 7½ ips reel-to-reel or cassette with 3-5 songs and lyric sheet. SAE and IRC. Reports in 3 weeks.
Music: Mostly pop, rock and top 40; also R&B and soul. Recently produced *Flux*, by Flux (NCP Records).
Tips: "Write honest, hook-laden songs about city life!"

*RICHARD O'CONNOR, Box 387, Hollywood CA 90078. (213)372-9126. Producer: Richard O'Connor. Record producer and music publisher (Shaolin Music). Estab. 1984. Deals with artists and songwriters. Produces 4 singles/year and 3 albums/year. Fee derived from sales royalty or outright fee from songwriter/artist or record company.
How to Contact: Prefers cassette or Beta videocassette and lyric sheet. "Include bios, photos and reviews." SASE. Reports in 4 weeks.
Music: Mostly rock, pop and blues. Recently produced *Temptation, Coyote in a Graveyard*, and "Out of My Mind," by Richard O'Connor (rock LPs and single on Shaolin). Other artists include The Streethearts, The Rich and Second Chance.

OLD HAT RECORDS/THE WIND MILL, 3442 Nies, Ft. Worth TX 76111. (817)834-3879. President: J. Taylor. Record producer and music publisher (Royal T. Music/ASCAP). Deals with artists and

songwriters. Produces 2 singles and 1 album/year. Fee derived from sales royalty.
How to Contact: Prefers cassette and lyric sheet. SASE. Reports in 1 month.
Music: Children's, choral, country, easy listening, folk, MOR, rock (all kinds) and top 40/pop. Recently produced *(Texas) Water Under the Bridge*, by Texas Water (country pop LP, Old Hat Records); "Memories Don't Grow Old," by James Michael (country single, Old Hat Records); and "One More," by Texas Water (country single, Old Hat Records). Other artists include Peggy Souix.

*ON TIME RECORDS, LTD., Box 314, New York NY 10037. Contact: Producer. Record producer. Deals with artists and songwriters. Produces 12 singles/year and 6 albums/year. Fee derived from sales royalty or outright fee from record company.
How to Contact: Prefers cassette, reel-to-reel or videocassette with 3 songs and lyric sheet or lead sheet. SASE. Reports in 6-8 weeks.
Music: Mostly urban dance, R&B dance and R&B funk. Recently produced "Spicy (You're So Shady)," by Cherokee (urban dance single on On Time); and "Pushin' the Nation," by Majestic MC's (R&B dance rap on On Time). Other artists include Jumar Starr, First Rate, T.N.T., and The Budda Boys.

100 GRAND RECORDS, 11 Norton St., Newburgh NY 12550. (914)561-4483. President: Gregg Bauer. Record producer and music publisher. Deals with artists and songwriters. Produces 5 singles and 2 albums/year. Works with 2 new songwriters/year. Fee derived from sales royalty or outright fee from record company.
How to Contact: Prefers cassette or videocassette with 3-5 songs and lyric sheet. SASE. Reports in 1 month.
Music: Mostly rock, dance and jazz; also choral, easy listening, folk, soul and top 40/pop. Recently produced "One of the Girls," (by P. Otero, G. Bauer, D. Baker); "Another Stroke," and "Heart in Distress," (by P. Otero); all recorded by Art Nouveau (all rock singles, 100 Grand Records).

OZARK OPRY RECORDS INC., Box 242, Osage Beach MO 65065. (314)348-3383. A&R/Producer: Jim Phinney. Record, jingle and commercial producer. Deals with artists and songwriters. Fee derived from sales royalty.
How to Contact: Prefers 7½ ips reel-to-reel or cassette with 1-3 songs and lyric sheet. "Please include cover letter, explaining general information about material." SASE. Reports in 2-4 weeks.
Music: Bluegrass, blues, children's, church/religious, country, dance, easy listening, gospel, jazz, MOR, progressive, R&B, rock, soul and top 40/pop. Recently produced "Waylon, Sing to Mama," by Darrell Thomas (country single, Ozark Opry Records); "Untanglin' My Mind," by Larry Heaberlin (country single, Hoedown U.S.A. Records); and "Don't Say No to Me Tonight," by Mark Sexton (pop/country single, Son De Mar Records). Other artists include Robbie Wittkowski and Lee Mace's Ozark Opry.

PABLO & ASSOCIATES, INC., Suite B, 3505 E. Livingston, Columbus OH 43227. President: William Davis. Record producer and music publisher (Noir Music Publishing, Uno Music).
How to Contact: Write first about your interest. Submit cassette "only."
Music: R&B and pop. Current artists include "Griffin," and Radiance.

PACIFIC CHALLENGER PRODUCTIONS, 2940 E. Miraloma Ave., Anaheim CA 92806. (714)992-6820. President: Chuck Whittington. Record producer and music publisher (Moonridge). Deals with artists and songwriters. Produces 8 singles and 4 albums/year. Fee derived from sales royalty.
How to Contact: Prefers cassette with 1-4 songs and lyric sheet. Does not return unsolicited material. Reports in 1 month.
Music: Mostly country; also gospel and top 40/pop. Recently published *Waltzes & Western Swing* and "Big Tulsa Tillie," (by Donnie Rohrs); and "Building Up to A Letdown," (by Robert Lee Smith), all recorded by Donnie Rohrs/Pacific Challenger Music.

PAD RECORDS AND DEMO STUDIO, Rt #2, Box 219, Myrtle MS 38650. Publisher: Glenn Summers. Record producer. Estab. 1984. Deals with artists, songwriters and "people who want to make tapes for demo purposes." Produces 2 singles/year. Fee derived from sales and airplay royalties.
How to Contact: Write first. Prefers cassette or 8-track with 1-2 songs. SASE. Reports in 1 month.
Music: Mostly country; also bluegrass, blues, gospel, jazz and R&B. Recently produced "45 Rainbow Rd.," "Thinking about You" and "Delta-Town" all by Carlton Azlin (country ballad singles, Rainbow Road records).

*MICHAEL PANEPENTO, #811, 225 Oxmoor Circle, Birmingham AL 35209. (205)942-3222. President: Michael Panepento. Record producer, music publisher (Weedhopper Music) and recording studio/record label. Deals with artists and songwriters. Produces 5 singles/year and 5 albums/year. **Fee**

derived from sales royalty or outright fee from record company.

How to Contact: Write first and obtain permission to submit or arrange personal interview. Prefers cassette or 15 ips reel-to-reel with 3 songs and lyric sheet. SASE. Reports in 3 weeks.

Music: Mostly rock, AOR and jazz/R&B; also country, jazz/straight and classical. Recently produced *Scotti*, by Scott McDavid (AOR LP, Polymusic); *Assault*, by Assault (heavy metal LP, Polymusic); and *Dancin in the Wrong Shoes*, by Jan Hunter (rock/R&B LP, Polymusic). Other artists include K.D. Ryzee Band and Patchwork.

PANIO BROTHERS LABEL, Box 99, Montmartre, Saskatchewan S0G 3M0, Canada. Executive Director: John Panio, Jr. Record producer. Deals with artists and songwriters. Produces 1 single and 1 album/year. Works with lyricists and composers and teams collaborators. Fee derived from sales royalty or outright fee from artist/songwriter or record company.

How to Contact: Prefers cassette with any number of songs and lyric sheet. Does not return unsolicited material. Reports in 1 month.

Music: Country, dance-oriented, easy listening and Ukrainian. Recently produced "Christmas Is Near," by the Panio Brothers Band (Christmas single); and "Celebrate Saskatchewan," by Panio Brothers (Ukrainian).

PARASOUND COMMUNICATIONS, 2631 Clay St., San Francisco CA 94115. (415)563-0202. President: Bernie Krause. Record producer and music publisher (Parasound Publishing, Wild Sanctuary Music). Deals with artists and songwriters. Produces 1 album/year. Fee derived from sales royalty.

How to Contact: Write about your interest. Prefers cassette with 2-4 songs. SASE. Reports in 3 months.

Music: Mostly electronic new wave. Recently produced *Citadels of Mystery*, by Bernie Krause (electronic jazz LP, Mobile Fidelity Sound Labs Records); and *The New Nonesuch Guide to Electronic Music*, by Bernie Krause (electronic LP, Nonesuch Records).

Tips: "We write our own music. However, we would be open to listening to other people's music. We're very interested in lyrics and soon will get into more record production of other artists."

THE PASHA MUSIC ORG., INC., 5615 Melrose Ave., Hollywood CA 90038. (213)466-3507. General Manager: Carol Peters. Record production and music publisher. Custom label distributed by CBS. Deals with artists and songwriters. Fee derived by sales royalty.

How to Contact: Write first. Prefers cassette with 1-3 songs. SASE. Reports in 3 weeks.

Music: Progressive, rock and top 40/pop.

DAVE PATON, Suite 170, 14116 E. Whittier, Whittier CA 90605. Contact: Dave Paton. Record producer and music publisher (Heaven Songs/BMI). Deals with artists and songwriters. Produces 20 singles and 3-5 albums/year. Fee negotiable.

How to Contact: Write first. Prefers 7½ ips reel-to-reel or cassette with 3-6 songs and lyric sheet. SASE. Reports in 2 weeks.

Music: Country, dance-oriented, easy listening, jazz, MOR, progressive, R&B, rock, top 40/pop and comedy.

PENTAGRAMM PRODUCTIONS, 116 Wendy Dr., Box 384, Holtsville NY 11742. President: Arthur Poppe. Record producer and music publisher (Little Wizard). Deals with artists and songwriters. Produces 5 singles and 10 albums/year. Fee derived from sales royalty.

How to Contact: Write first about your interest. "Don't phone." Prefers cassette or videocassette with 1-3 songs. SASE. Reports in 3 weeks.

Music: Country, dance-oriented, easy listening, MOR, R&B, rock, soul and top 40/pop.

*GORDON PERRY, 11260 Goodnight Lane, Dallas TX 75229. (214)241-5182. President: Gordon Perry. Record producer and music publisher (Three Hearts Music). Deals with artists and songwriters. Produces 4 singles/year and 2 albums/year. Fee derived from sales royalty or outright fee from record company.

How to Contact: Prefers cassette or 15 ips reel-to-reel with 4 songs. SASE. Reports in 4 weeks.

Music: Mostly pop/rock and R&B. Recently produced *Face to Face*, by Face to Face (rock LP on Epic); *Cat Dancer*, by Sandy Stewart (rock LP on Modern); and "Wild Heart," by Stevie Nicks (pop/rock single on Modern). Other artists include Automatic and Marc Beeno.

*PAUL PETERSON CREATIVE MANAGEMENT, 6335 W. 50th St., Mission KS 66202. (913)362-5804. Contact: Paul Peterson. Record producer, music publisher and personal management firm. Deals with artists and songwriters. Produces 2 albums/year. Fee derived from sales royalty, outright fee from songwriter/artist or record company.

How to Contact: Prefers cassette and lyric sheet. SASE. Reports in 4 weeks.
Music: Mostly rock, pop and jazz; also country. Recently produced *Lost Cabin Session*, by Ozark Mountain Daredevils (country rock LP on Legend); and *Dogs?*, by Dogs? (rock EP on Dogs). Other artists include KC Jazz artists.

***MICHAEL ROBERT PHILLIPS/CYNTHIA PRODUCTIONS**, Box 606, Orinda CA 94563. (415)254-2000. Producer: Michael Robert Phillips. Record producer and video company. Deals with artists and songwriters. Produces 10-20 albums/year. Fee derived from sales royalty or outright fee from record company and advance.
How to Contact: Prefers cassette or ½" videocassette and lyric sheet or lead sheet. Does not return unsolicited material. Reports in 8 weeks.
Music: Mostly rock, pop rock and pop.

***FRANK PIERCE PRODUCTIONS**, 148 Winthrop, Columbus OH 43214. (614)262-4518. President: Frank Pierce. Record producer, music publisher (No Boos Publishing) and jingle producer. Deals with artists and songwriters. Produces 2 singles/year and 2 albums/year. Fee derived from sales royalty or outright fee from record company.
How to Contact: Prefers cassette with 3 songs and lyric sheet. "Submit songs with strong hooks!" SASE. Reports in 2-3 weeks.
Music: Mostly pop rock, dance rock and dance funk; also pop ballads. Recently produced *Snapshot*, by Julie Ivary (pop rock LP and single on America); *Kelly Crum*, (pop rock LP and single on Leo); and *Spittin Image* by K. Crum (rock LP and single on MCA). Other artists include Mimi Rousseau, Sally Fingerette, and Dan Green.
Tips: "Keep songs simple, melodic and rhythmically interesting."

***PLATINUM SOUND PRODUCTIONS**, #21, 1605 N. Martel, Hollywood CA 90046-3515. (213)851-9418. President: Kenneth H. Smith. Record producer, music publisher (Keristene Music, Ltd.) and video production firm. Deals with artists. Produces 3 singles/year and 2 albums/year. Fee derived from sales or outright fee from record company.
How to Contact: Write or call first and obtain permission to submit. Prefers cassette or VHS videocassette with maximum 3 songs and lyric sheet. Does not return unsolicited material. Reports in 6-8 weeks.
Music: Mostly heavy metal, rock and dance; also urban rock, country and R&B. Recently produced *Some Of Them Escaped*, by Merrell Fankhauser (surf rock LP and single on D-Town); *The Kind*, by Broken Toys (dance floor LP and single on Platinum Sound); and "Midnight Fantasy," by Debby Clinton (urban rock single on Platinum Sound). Other artists include Lee Rogers, Cindy Bandes, Diane Anderson, Cardella Dimilo, and Bernadette Bascom.
Tips: "We are looking for finished product and polished acts."

***PLUM PRODUCTIONS**, 5988 Silvery Lane, Dearborn Heights MI 48127. (313)277-0082. Producer: D.J. Radko. Record producer and studio recording label. Deals with artists and songwriters. Produces 12 singles/year and 3 albums/year. Fee derived from sales royalty or outright fee from songwriter/artist or record company.
How to Contact: Prefers cassette or VHS videocassette with 4 songs and lyric sheet or lead sheet. SASE. Reports in 12 weeks.
Music: Mostly top 40, rock and R&B; also urban contemporary, country and gospel. Recently produced *Mystery of The Myth*, by Vic Lainwyn (rock LP and single on Plum); *Again*, by Maintain (top 40 LP on Plum); and *Talk to Me*, by June (rock LP). Other artists include Tom Trip and C&R.

POSITIVE PRODUCTIONS, Box 1405, Highland Park NJ 08904. Contact: J. Vincenzo. Record producer and music publisher. Produces 5 singles/year. Deals with songwriters. Payment negotiable.
How to Contact: Prefers 7½ ips reel-to-reel with 2-4 songs and lyric sheet. SASE. Reports in 1 month.
Music: Children's, easy listening, and MOR. Recently produced "Waiting for the Sunshine," and "Think of Me," by J. Remington (MOR).

PRAISE INDUSTRIES CORP., 7802 Express St., Burnaby, British Columbia V5A 1T4, Canada. (604)421-3441. Manager: Paul Yaroshuk. Record producer. Deals with artists. Produces 30 singles and 24 albums/year. Fee derived from sales royalty.
How to Contact: Prefers cassette with 1-12 songs and lyric sheet. SAE and IRC. Reports in 2 weeks.
Music: Bluegrass, children's, choral, church/religious, country, folk, gospel and gospel/rock.

***PRELUDE MANAGEMENT CO.**, Rt 7, Box 683W, Canyon Lake TX 78130. (512)899-7474. Contact: Donald L. Nunley. Record producer and music publisher (Nunley Publishing Co.). Deals with artists and songwriters. Fee derived from sales royalty or percentage for management.

How to Contact: Write or call first and obtain permission to submit. Prefers cassette and lyric sheet or lead sheet. "Make sure cassette is labeled with name, address, song title and phone number." SASE. Reports in 10 weeks.
Music: Mostly country, blues and rock. Recently produced "Hey Little Girl," and "Sink or Swim," by Gayle Smith (MOR singles on Tama).

THE PRESCRIPTION CO., 70 Murray Ave., Port Washington NY 10050. (516)767-1929. President: David F. Gasman. Record producer, record company, and music publisher (Prescription Co./ BMI). Deals with artists and songwriters. Fee derived from sales royalty or outright fee from record company.
How to Contact: Write or call first about your interest then submit demo. Prefers cassette with any number songs and lyric sheet. Does not return unsolicited material. Reports in 1 month. "Send all submissions to Mitch Vidur, General Manager with SASE or no returns."
Music: Bluegrass, blues, children's, country, dance-oriented, easy listening, jazz, MOR, progressive, R&B, rock, soul and top 40/pop. Recently produced "You Came In" and "Rock 'n' Roll Blues," by Medicine Mike (pop singles, Prescription Records); and *Just What the Doctor Ordered*, by Medicine Mike (LP, not yet released, Prescription Records).
Tips: "We want quality—fads mean nothing to us. Familiarity with the artist's material helps too."

PRITCHETT PUBLICATIONS, 38603 Sage Tree St., Palmdale CA 93550. Branch: 171 Pine Haven Dr., Daytona Beach FL 32014. (904)252-4849. President: Leroy Pritchett (California). A&R Director: Charles Vickers (Florida). Record producer and music publisher (BMI). Deals with artists and songwriters. Produces 1 album and 1 single/year. Works with 2-3 new songwriters/year. Works with composers and teams collaborators. Fee derived from sales royalty.
How to Contact: Submit lead sheet only first. SASE. Reports in 1 month.
Music: Church/religious, gospel and country. Recently produced *Heaven Is Just Over the Hill*, *The Magic of Gospel*, (gospel LPs); and "Let Your Light Shine," (gospel single), by Charles Vickers.

PRODUCTION CONNECTION, 1422 McGill College, Montreal, Quebec H3A 1Z6 Canada. (514)287-9574. President: Yves Godin. Vice President: Alaen Deland. Record producer and music publisher (Les Editions la Bobine). Deals with artists and songwriters. Produces 15 singles/year. Fee derived from sales royalty.
How to Contact: Prefers cassette with minimum 5 songs and lyric sheet. SAE and IRC. Reports in 2 weeks.
Music: Mostly pop and dance; also easy listening and rock. Recently produced "If You Can Count," by Cesarez (electro pop single, Bobinason Records); "Snap," by Beau Flash (electro rock single, Focus Records); and "SOS Anonyme," by Dwight Druick (pop rock single, Bobinason Records).

QL RECORDS, INC., 314 Romano Ave., Coral Gables FL 33134. (305)446-2477. President: Rob Burr. Record producer and music publisher (QL Music, Inc.). Deals with artists and songwriters. Produces 2 singles and 2 albums/year. Fee derived from sales royalty.
How to Contact: Call first and obtain permission to submit. Prefers metal bias cassette with 2-10 songs. SASE. Reports in 2 months.
Music: Mostly progressive new wave rock; also classical, dance-oriented, folk, jazz, progressive, rock and reggae. Recently produced "The Sleep of Reason" and "Shelters Are Melting," by O. Herrera (new wave rock singles, QL Records); and "Stranger in My Room," by T. Rusch (new wave rock single, QL Records). Other artists include Einstein's Riceboys and Rogers-Lyon.
Tips: Artists "must be *good* in a live performance."

QUINTO RECORDS, Box 2388, Toluca Lake CA 91602. (818)985-8284. Producer: Quint Benedetti. Produces 1-2 singles and 2 albums/year. Deals with artists and songwriters on speculation only. Fee derived from sales royalty.
How to Contact: Prefers cassette with 2-4 songs and lead sheet. SASE. Reports in 1 month.
Music: Seasonal and Christmas songs only. Recently produced "Christmas Is for Children" and "Christmas Presents," (Quinto Records).

R.E.F. RECORDS, 404 Bluegrass Ave., Madison TN 37115. (615)865-6380. President: Bob Frick. Manager: Shawn Frick. A&R Director: Scott Frick. Record producer and music publisher (Frick Music Publishing Co./BMI). Deals with artists, songwriters and producers. Produces 10 albums/year. Fee derived from sales royalty.
How to Contact: Write or call first and obtain permission to submit, then submit 7½ ips reel-to-reel or cassette with 2-10 songs and lyric sheet. SASE. Reports in 1 month.
Music: Country, gospel, rock and top 40/pop. Recently produced *Imgenes*, by Francisco Morales (gos-

pel LP, R.E.F. Records); *Live in Nashville*, by Larry Ahlborn (gospel LP, Love Notes Records); and *I Can't Help Myself*, by Bob Scott and Family (gospel LP, R.E.F. Records).

RADIO MAGIC/BSO RECORDS, Via Carmine Modestino, 64, Paternopoli AV 83052 Italy. (0827)71073 or 71033. President: Sal Barbieri. Record producer and music publisher (Conypol Music/BMI). Deals with artists and songwriters. Produces 10 singles and 4 albums/year. Works with 4 new songwriters/year. Fee derived from outright fee from artist/songwriter.
How to Contact: Prefers cassette and lyric sheet. Prefers studio produced demos. SAE and IRC. Reports in 1 month.
Music: Mostly dance and top 40/pop; also country, easy listening, MOR, progressive, R&B, rock and soul. Recently produced "In the Name of Love," by S. Barbieri (dance single, BSO Europe Records); "Coming Up," by Sigfrida (top 40 single, BSO Europe Records); and "Heavy Stuff," by S. Barbieri (top 40 single, BSO Records).

RAINA PRODUCTIONS CO., 1818 E. Ardmore Dr., Phoenix AZ 85040. (602)276-2039. Vice President: Odessa M. Payton. Record producer and music publisher (La-Nai). Deals with artists and songwriters. Produces 6 singles/year. Fee derived from sales royalty.
How to Contact: Prefers cassette with 4 or more songs and lyric sheet. SASE. Reports in 3 weeks.
Music: Country, gospel, jazz and R&B. Recently produced "Love Knows," by Lawrence Carroll (jazz single, Raina Records); "I'm at the Crossroads," by Bobby Barnes (R&B single, Raina Records); and "Imitations," by The Johnson Family (gospel single, Raina Records).

*RAINBOW COLLECTION LTD., #806, 50 Music Sq. W, Nashville TN 37203. (615)320-1177. Executive Producer: Richard O'Bitts. Record producer, music publisher (Rocker Music, Happy Man Music) and management firm. Deals with artists and songwriters. Produces 10 singles/year and 4 albums/year.
How to Contact: Prefers cassette with 4 songs and lyric sheet. SASE.
Music: "All types." Artists include Don McLean, Janis Ian and Tony Byrd.

RAINBOW RECORDING STUDIOS, 2322 S. 64th Ave., Omaha NE 68106 (402)554-0123. Producer: Lars Erickson. Record producer and music publisher (Nils Erickson Publishing/BMI). Deals with artists, songwriters in production of "commercial jingles." Produces 5 singles and 5 albums/year. Works with 5 new songwriters/year and works with composers. Fee derived from outright fee from client, record company or songwriter/artist.
How to Contact: Query. Prefers 7½ ips reel-to-reel or cassette with maximum 4 songs and lyric sheet. SASE. Reports in 1 month.
Music: Any style acceptable. Recently produced *Dark Nights*, by Dark Nights (new music LP); *Tom Ware*, by T. Ware (techno-jazz LP); and "It's No Accident," by Hit 'N' Run (rock single).

RAINFIRE MUSIC PRODUCTION, 15217 Otsego St., Sherman Oaks CA 91403. (213)784-0388. A&R Director: Lou Penta. Record producer and music publisher (Rainfire Music/BMI). Deals with artists and songwriters. Produces 3 singles and 2 albums/year. Fee derived from sales royalty.
How to Contact: Prefers cassette with 3-5 songs and lyric sheet. SASE. Reports in 1 week.
Music: Mostly pop and rock; also country, dance-oriented, MOR and R&B. Artists include Rita Jenrette and Rhonda Silver.

RA-JO INTERNATIONAL RECORDS & TAPES, Box 214, Co. Op. City Station, Bronx NY 10475. (212)379-2593. Executive Producers: Joe or Ace Adams. Record producer and music publisher (Ace Adams Music, Adam Puertas Music, Bill Ace Music). Deals with artists and songwriters. Produces 5 singles and 2 albums/year. Fee derived from sales royalty or outright fee from artist/songwriter or record company.
How to Contact: Call or write first. Prefers cassette with 4-8 songs and lyric sheet. SASE. Reports in 2 weeks.
Music: Mostly R&B, country and dance; also children's, progressive, soul, top 40/pop and punk. Recently produced "Zoot Zoot Zoot," by Tiny Tim (children's Christmas single, Ra-Jo Records); and "Honky Tonk," by Bill Doget (dance single, King Records).

RANDALL PRODUCTIONS, Box 11960, Chicago IL 60611. (312)561-0027. President: Mary Freeman. Record producer, video producer and music publisher; total music services (Billetdoux Music/BMI). Deals with artists and songwriters. Produces 5 singles and 2 albums/year. Fee derived from sales royalty.
How to Contact: Prefers cassette with 3-6 songs and lyric sheet. SASE. Reports in 1 month.
Music: Gospel, jazz, MOR, R&B, rock, soul and top 40/pop. Recently produced *Made in USA*, by

Stutz (hard rock LP); "Crossroads," by by Randy Terry (country/rock/pop single, Grandville Records); and *Journey to Beyond*, by Duncan Pryce Kirk (AOR LP, Grandville Records). Other artists include Larry Caballero, Steve Hepler & Dynaglide.

REALITY RECORDS/PRODUCTIONS, 19 Roxborough Place, Willingboro NJ 08046. (609)877-7653. Producer: "Hank" Strasser. Record producer and record company. Deals with artists. Produces 1-2 albums/year. Fee derived from sales royalty.
How to Contact: Prefers cassette with 3-5 songs. Include biographical material. "At the moment, I am only interested in jazz." SASE. Reports in 1 month.
Music: Jazz only. Recently produced *Antigua*, by Rio Clemente (jazz LP, Reality Records).

REDBUD RECORDS, A Division of CAE Inc., 611 Empire Mill Rd., Bloomington IN 47401. (812)824-2400. General Manager: Rick Heinsohn. Record producer. Deals with artists, songwriters and bands. Produces 1 single and 4 albums/year. Payment negotiated.
How to Contact: Call first about your interest. Prefers cassette with 2-10 songs. SASE. Reports in 1 month.
Music: Mostly folk and jazz; also bluegrass, choral, church/religious, classical, and easy listening. "We'll listen to anything!" Recently produced *Chicago Style*, by Friedlander and Hall (swing LP, RedBud Records); *Solo Guitar*, by Royce Campbell (jazz LP, RedBud Records); and *Buffalo Gal*, by Leftwich and Higginbotham (folk LP, RedBud Records). Other artists include Eric Rosser, Jan Henshaw, High Ground, Kiether-Lowrie Duet and Bill Wilson.
Tips: "Perform a lot and be willing to sell records at your gigs. Have a professional approach to the business end of things. Play your music well—with taste and humor."

BOBBY RICH, Box 1128, College Branch, Madison TN 37116-1128. (615)868-0559. Contact: Bobby Rich. Record producer and music publisher (Bo-Rich Publishing). Deals with artists and songwriters. Produces 6-10 singles/year. Fee derived from sales royalty.
How to Contact: Prefers 7½ ips reel-to-reel, cassette or videocassette with 6-10 songs and lyric sheet. SASE. Reports in 1 month.
Music: Bluegrass, blues, classical, country, easy listening, folk, gospel, jazz, MOR, R&B, country (hard), soul and top 40/pop. Recently produced "Make Me Your Woman," by Lori-Robin Smith (easy listening single, Universal Artists Records); and "Good Times Come Easy," by Bob Money (country single, Universal Artists Records).

RICHMAR PRODUCTIONS, 23 Darby Ln., Cherry Hill NJ 08002. (609)779-9111. President: Richard DeMarco. Record producer and music publisher (Brigantine Music/BMI). Deals with artists and songwriters. Produces 2 singles and 1 album/year. Fee derived from sales royalty.
How to Contact: Prefers 7½ or 15 ips reel-to-reel, cassette or videocassette with 1-6 songs and lead sheet. SASE. Reports in 1 month.
Music: Country, R&B, rock (all types), soul and top 40/pop.

*RM AUDIO PRODUCTIONS, 2528 Chamblee-Tucker Rd., Chamblee GA 30341. (404)458-6000. Executive Producer: W. Louis Simmons, Jr. Record producer and music publisher. Deals with artists and songwriters. Produces 5 singles/year and 2 albums/year. Fee negotiable.
How to Contact: Prefers cassette. "Submissions should be melodic rock/pop material; humor-oriented OK." Does not return unsolicited material. Reports in 4 weeks.
Music: Mostly rock/pop, novelty/humor and jazz. Recently produced *Live at Moonshadow*, by Heartfixers (blue wave LP on Landslide); *Glenn Phillips Live*, by Glenn Phillips Band (rock instrumental LP on Showstar); and *Sinister Angel*, by Sinister Angel (metal rock EP on S.A. Productions). Other artists include Spies of Life, Curtis Middlebrook, John Scully and Roger Smith.

RMS TRIAD PRODUCTIONS, 6267 Potomac Circle, West Bloomfield MI 48033. (313)661-5167 or (313)585-2552 (Branch). Contact: Bob Szajner. A&R Manager: Laura Holliday. Record producer, record company and music publisher (RMS Triad Publishing/ASCAP). Deals with artists and songwriters (instrumental). Produces 3 albums/year. Fee derived from outright fee from artist/songwriter or record company for services.
How to Contact: Write first about your interest. Prefers cassette with 1-3 songs. SASE. Reports in 3 weeks.
Music: Jazz and instrumental. Recently produced *Jazz Opus 20/40*, *Detroit Jazz Center* and *1981 Montreaux/Detroit Live*, by Triad (jazz instrumental LPs, RMS Records); *Are You Glad to Be in America*, by James "Blood" Ulmer; and *Where Flamingos Fly*, by Gil Evans (jazz instrumental LPs, Artist's House Records). Other artists include Frank Isola and Roy Brooks.

*ROCKLAND PRODUCTS, 117 W. Rockland Rd., Libertyville IL 60048. (312)362-4060. President: Perry Johnson. Record producer and music publisher (Rockland Music). Deals with artists and songwriters. Produces 5 singles/year and 2 albums/year. Fee derived from sales royalty.
How to Contact: Prefers cassette with 1-5 songs and lyric sheet. SASE. Reports in 8 weeks.
Music: Mostly top 40/pop, rock and country. Recently produced *Animation*, by Animation (pop/rock LP); *Taxi*, by Taxi (hard rock LP); and *Nightbeat*, by Oh Boy (pop LP on Rockland Records). Other artists include Madelyn Brown, McCormick Sinclair, Linda Quick, and Slim Huston.
Tips: "Send single type songs, not album cuts."

*ROCKY MOUNTAIN HEARTLAND PRODUCTIONS, Box 6904, Denver CO 80206. (303)690-6904. Executive Producer: Steve Dyer. Record and video producer and advertising firm. Deals with artists and songwriters. Fee derived from sales royalty or outright fee from songwriter/artist or record company.
How to Contact: Write or call first and obtain permission to submit. Prefers cassette or videocassette with 3-5 songs and lyric sheet or lead sheet. Does not return unsolicited material. Reports in 4 weeks.
Music: Mostly gospel, top 40 and rock; also jazz and country. "Music open and not limited to these types." Recently produced *The Best Is Yet to Come*, by Kent Parry (big band and orchestra gospel LP on Record Harvest); *From Here to Kingdom Come*], by Heart Song (mild gospel/top 40 LP on Record Harvest); and *Going, Going, Gone*, by Heart Song (gospel rock LP on Record Harvest).
Tips: "We are investing in new, up and coming artists."

ANGELO ROMAN, Box 65134, Los Angeles CA 90065. Producer: Angelo Roman. Management/consultant. Primarily deals with singer-songwriters. Works with 5-10 new songwriters/year. Works with lyricists and composers and teams collaborators. Fee derived from "various arrangements with artists and production companies." Always negotiable.
How to Contact: Prefers cassette with 1-3 songs. SASE. Reports in 1 month.
Music: Mostly R&B/pop and top 40/rock; also jazz, MOR and soul. Recently produced "You Win," and "I Believe in Love," by Vennette Gloud (R&B pop single); and "Let's Talk It Over," by Debi Foster (pop single).

*ROPERRY, 645 Madison Ave., New York NY 10022. (212)308-2636. General Manager: Jane Lowy. Record producer, music publisher and record company. Deals with artists and songwriters. Produces approximately 3 singles and 1-2 albums/year. Fee depends on contract.
How to Contact: Call first. Prefers cassette with 1-3 songs and lyric sheet. "Send a picture, bio, lead sheets and SASE." Reports in 3 weeks.
Music: Mostly top 40/pop; also children's, dance-oriented, easy listening and MOR. Recently produced *Patsy*, by Patsy (pop LP, Roperry Records); "Single Again," by Joey Latini (pop single, Roperry Records); and "Just a Little Imagination," by Patsy (adult contemporary single, Roperry Records).
Tips: "Try to be professional—don't send lyrics we can't read or distorted tapes. Roperry is looking for growing talents."

ROSE HILL GROUP, 1326 Midland Ave., Syracuse NY 13205. (315)475-2936. A&R Director: Vincent Taft. Record producer and music publisher (Katch Nazar Music, Bleecker Street Music). Produces 5 singles and 2 albums/year. Fee derived from sales royalty or outright fee from artist/songwriter or record company.
How to Contact: Prefers cassette with 1-5 songs. SASE. Reports in 2 weeks.
Music: Mostly top 40/pop, rock, dance-oriented; also jazz and MOR. Recently produced *Taksim*, by Taksim (jazz LP, Star City Records); "Win Some, Lose Some," by Zarm (MOR single, Hill Records); and "Lifeline," by Manly Band (top 40/pop single, 2 Sided Records).

ROSEMARY MELODY LINE CO., 732 Montrose St., Vineland NJ 08360. (609)696-0943. Producer: Dennis Link. Record producer and recording studios. Deals with artists and songwriters. Produces 30 singles and 3-5 albums/year. Works with 20 new songwriters/year. Also works with lyricists. Fee derived from sales royalty or outright fee from artist/songwriter.
How to Contact: Write first. Prefers cassette or videocassette (Beta Hi-Fi) with 3-5 songs. SASE. Reports in 2 weeks.
Music: Mostly top 40/pop; also bluegrass, church/religious, gospel and rock. Recently produced "Lovish Hate," by Kenny Philage (pop single, Windrose Records); "Olivia," by Vanessa Beals (pop single, Private Records); and ""Complete Mysteries of the Rosary," (Beta videocassette).

ROSEWOOD PRODUCTIONS, 3½ Fern St., New Castle PA 16101. (412)654-3023. Contact: Wes Homner. Record producer. Deals with songwriters. Produces 3 singles/year and 2 albums/year. Fee derived from sales royalty.

How to Contact: Prefers cassette and lyric sheet. Does not return unsolicited material. Reports in 3 weeks.
Music: Mostly country, gospel and bluegrass; also easy listening. Recently produced "Amazing Love," by Steve and Dave (country gospel single, Rosewood); "Take Me Back," by Wes Homner (country single, Rosewood); and *New River Train*, by Larry Zarath (bluegrass LP, Oglala).
Tips: "Submit clean, positive love songs and gospel songs."

BRIAN ROSS PRODUCTIONS, Box 2950, Hollywood CA 90078. A&R Producer: Brian Ross. Record producer and music publisher (Brian Ross Music/BMI); also international music representation in all foreign countries. Deals with artists, songwriters, attorneys, agents and managers. Produces 25 singles and 25 albums/year. Fee derived from sales royalty.
How to Contact: Prefers cassette or ½" videocassette with 1-4 songs; also include photo and bio (if artist) "giving details about management, performances, etc. Be professional. Pick your 2-4 best songs, enclose SASE, and label clearly." Reports in 1 week, "24 hours if good." Does not assume responsibility for materials damaged or lost in the mail.
Music: Mostly top 40/pop, contemporary and MOR; also all types of music including techno-pop and new wave. "Foreign releases are our specialty." Recently produced "Talk Talk," by Music Machine (new wave single, Rhino Records); "I'm on Fire," by the Muglestons (pop ballad, Starborn Records); "I Wish You the Best," by Robert Jason (MOR ballad, Starborn Records); and "Cry Like a Baby," by Didi Anthony (R&B ballad, Starborn Records). Other artists include El Chicano, Lance Powers, Fire and Ice, Dick Gesswein, Dove, Squeezer, Great Western, Mouse, Jensen Interceptor (Canada), Chakra, The Light, Lance Powers, and Rain.
Tips: "For a copy of our free brochure, write to us with 'brochure' on the outside of the envelope. Please send SASE." Affiliated with International Music Commission USA."

*ROXY RECORDING STUDIO, 827 Meridian, Nashville TN 37207. (645)227-0920. Producer: Doug Waterman. Record producer. Deals with artists and songwriters. Produces 10 + singles/year and 4 + albums/year.
How to Contact: Prefers cassette or ¾" videocassette and lyric sheet. SASE. Reports in 1-6 weeks.
Music: Mostly country. Other artists include Clyde Moody, Carl & Pearl Butler, Bobby Bridge, and Jackie Frazier.
Tips: Looking for "talent, dedication, desire and the ability to listen."

*RSD PRODUCTIONS, 7459 Arroyo Vista Ave., Cucamonga CA 91730. (714)625-3288. Contact: Robert S. Dire. Record producer and recording studio. Deals with artists and songwriters. Produces 25 singles/year and 3-5 albums/year. Fee derived from outright fee from record company.
How to Contact: Prefers cassette or VHS videocassette with 3 songs and lyric sheet or lead sheet. "Also send resume and picture. Cassettes will not be returned—will be kept on file." Does not return unsolicited material. Reports in 8 weeks.
Music: Top 40/crossover, rock and country. "No heavy metal." Recently produced *Tonight*, by Candu (rock LP); *No Way Out*, by Exit (rock LP, Entrance); and "Mama," by Desperado Band (country single, Bandit Records).

*S G INC., 221 W. 6th St., Austin TX 78701. (512)474-7355. Administrator: Bob Rhino. Record producer and music publisher. Deals with artists and songwriters. Fee derived from sales royalty or outright fee from songwriter/artist or record company.
How to Cotact: Prefers cassette. Reports in 15 weeks.
Music: Mostly MOR, country and rock. Recently produced "Ambrosia," "Notes of Love," and "Velvet Touch," by OC (MOR cassettes). Other artists include Barber Houston, Hall Green, OC, Oak Ridge and Anderson.

SAMARAH PRODUCTIONS, INC., Box 2501, Columbia SC 29202. (803)754-3556. President: Daniel Hodge, Jr. Record producer, music publisher (Jemiah Publishing/BMI) and artist management. Deals with artists, songwriters and record companies. Produces minimum of 4 singles/year. Fee derived from sales royalty or outright fee from record company.
How to Contact: Prefers cassette with 1-3 songs, lyric sheet "and lead sheet if possible." SASE. Reports in 1 month.
Music: Church/religious, country, gospel, MOR, R&B, rock (top 40), soul and top 40/pop. Recently produced "I Who Have Nothing," by Midnight Blue (R&B/pop single, Motown Records); "Wishing" and "Feel It and Groove Together," by Midnight Blue (both R&B singles, Samarah Records).
Tips: "Rhythm tracks and vocals on tape must be tight. Before sending tape compare the *feel* of your song to the *feel* of a successful artist's song in the same market."

SANSU ENTERPRISES, 3809 Clematis Ave., New Orleans LA 70122. (504)949-8386. Contact: Clarence Toussaint. Record producer and music publisher (Marsaint Music, Inc./BMI, Rhinelander Music/BMI, Martu Music/ASCAP). Deals with artists. Produces 10 singles and 6 albums/year. Fee derived from sales royalty or outright fee from record company.
How to Contact: Prefers cassette with 3-5 songs and lyric sheet. SASE. Reports in 2 months.
Music: Blues, gospel, country, jazz, R&B, rock and soul. Recently produced *Touch of Silk*, by Eric Gale (jazz LP, Columbia Records); *Routes*, by Ramsey Lewis (jazz LP, Columbia Records); and *Released*, by Pat Labelle (soul LP, Epic Records). Other artists include Allen Toussaint, Lee Dorsey, Earl King and Ernie K. Doe.

STEVE SCHARF, Steven Scharf Productions, 61 Jane St., New York NY 10014. (212)929-2068. Contact: Steve Scharf. Record producer, music publisher (Weeze Music Co./BMI) and independent record producer. Produces 4 singles and 4 albums/year. Deals with artists and songwriters. Fee derived from sales royalty or outright fee from artist/songwriter or record company. Production fees charged for demos and records.
How to Contact: Call first. Prefers 7½ ips reel-to-reel or cassette with maximum 4 songs and lyric sheet. SASE.
Music: Mostly rock, pop and R&B; also adult contemporary and top 40. Recently produced "Frozen Tears," by Bob Halligan, Jr. (rock ballad single); "Baby Do," and "Stand Up," by American Dog (rock singles). Produces "local rock and pop bands developing in New York City."
Tips: "Songwriters must have great attitudes as people, then original hit material."

SEASUN EXPERIENCE MUSIC PRODUCTIONS, Box 1725, Daytona Beach FL 32015. (904)255-4891. Creative Manager: T. Patrick Brown. Record producer. Deals with songwriters and owners of master tapes. Produces 1 single and 1 album/year. Works with 10 new songwriters/year. Works with lyricists and composers. Fee derived from sales royalty or outright fee from record company.
How to Contact: Prefers cassette with 1-3 songs and lyric sheet. SASE. Reports in 3 months.
Music: Mostly contemporary soul, rap and crossover; also children's, classical, dance-oriented, easy listening, MOR, progressive, R&B and top 40/pop. Recently produced "It's Alright," and "It's Not Too Late," by T.P. Brown (rap singles, Raw Honey Records); and "Sailing," by Frank Fletcher (soul single, Raw Honey Records). Other artists include Flarre, Magic Band, James Smith, Rozlyn Walker and Derrick James.
Tips: "Send only songs with catchy melodies, harmonies and clear lyrics. Don't be too kinky or negative and aim for the heart of the market with a large amount of originality to boot."

SECOND SUN PRODUCTIONS, Rt. 4, Box 428, Vashon Island WA 98070. (206)463-2850. Producer: Robert Krinsky. Record producer and music publisher (Ferry Boat Music/ASCAP, Thea Music/BMI). Record labels include Second Sun and Pinup. Deals with artists and songwriters. Produces 2 singles and 3 albums/year. Fee derived from sales royalty.
How to Contact: Prefers cassette with 1-4 songs and lyric sheet. "Include cover letter stating whether you are submitting for artist or publishing consideration. Artists should be regionally located." Does not return unsolicited material.
Music: Blues, jazz, rock and top 40/pop. Recently published *Lonesome City Kings*, by the Lonesome City Kings (rock LP, First American Records); *Big Time Blues Man*, by Isaac Scott (blues LP, Music Is Medicine Records); and *Diane Schuur I and II*, by Diane Schuur (jazz vocal LP, First American Records).

SEIXAS MUSIC PRODUCTIONS, 913 Carmans Rd., Massapequa NY 11758. (516)798-8236. President: Ron Seixas. Record producer and record company (Cargo Records). Deals with artists and songwriters. Fee derived from sales royalty.
How to Contact: Prefers cassette with 2 songs and lyric sheet. Include photograph. SASE. Reports in 3 weeks.
Music: Mostly rock music with top-40 appeal; also new wave/dance. Recently produced "Tough Boy," by Seixas (dance rock single, Cargo Records); and "Theory," by Seixas (new wave single, Cargo Records). Other artists include Cynthia Marie.

*7TH RAY RECORDS, Box 3771, Hollywood CA 90028. (213)467-0611. President: Alan Ames. Associate Producer: R.A. "Bumps" Blackwell. Record producer and music publisher (Seventh Ray Publishing/ASCAP). Deals with artists and songwriters. Produces 3-5 singles and 3-5 albums/year. Fee derived from sales royalty.
How to Contact: Prefers cassette with 3-8 songs and lyric sheet. SASE. Reports in 1 month.
Music: Blues, easy listening, jazz, progressive, R&B, rock and top 40/pop. Recently produced "Seeds

of Peace," by Stephen Fiske (R&B/easy listening single, 7th Ray Records); "Nobody But You," by Gay Martin (top 40 single, 7th Ray Records); and "Peace on Earth," by Fantuzzi (reggae/rock/pop single, 7th Ray Records). Other artists include Sky Sulamyth, Voyager Orchestra and soundtracks for T.B.M. Productions.

*SIGHT AND SOUND ENTERTAINMENT MARKETING, Box 12752, Memphis TN 38182. (901)725-5387. A&R Director: Bill Lusk. Vice President/Entertainment: Don Von Maurer. Record producer and music publisher (Rocken Rythmn Publishing). Deals with artists, songwriters, producers and promoters. Fee derived from sales royalty or outright fee from artist/songwriter or record company.
How to Contact: Prefers cassette with 1-4 songs and lyric sheet. Specify the number of songs on the tape. SASE, but "we keep the tape on file and contact writer if interested."
Music: Mostly blues, top 40 and pop/R&B. Other artists include Blues Rambles.

SILVER BLUE PRODUCTIONS, Penthouse, 220 Central Park S, New York NY 10019. (212)586-3535. Contact: Joel Diamond. Record producer and music publisher. Deals with artists and songwriters. Fee derived from sales royalty.
How to Contact: Prefers cassette with 1-3 songs and lyric sheet. SASE.
Music: MOR, dance, easy listening, country, R&B, rock, soul and top 40/pop. Recently produced "I Am What I Am," by Gloria Gaynor (single); and "Where the Boys Are," by Lorna.

*SILVER BULLET PRODUCTIONS/TRULY FINE RECORDS, Box 423, Station F, Toronto, Ontario M4Y 2L8 Canada. Professional Manager: Allen Shechtman. Record producer and music publisher (Sidewalk Sailor Music/CAPAC, Scales of My Head Music/PROCAN, Etheric Polyphony/CAPAC, Cumulonimbus Music/PROCAN). Deals with artists, songwriters, labels, producers and publishers. Produces maximum 2 singles and 1 album/year. Fee derived from sales royalty or by outright fee from record company.
How to Contact: Write first about your interest. Prefers 7½ or 15 ips reel-to-reel or cassette with minimum 3 songs. Does not return unsolicited material. Reports in 3 months.
Music: Mostly crossover pop, country and R&B. Recently produced *Graeme Card*, by G. Card (LP, Truly Fine Records); *Saskatoon*, by Humphrey and Dumptrucks, (bluegrass LP, United Artists Records); and "Do Not Leave Us if You Love Us," by Mark Labelle (AOR/ballad single, Apex/InterDisc/MCA Records).

*SILVERLINING PRODUCTIONS, 373 Walnut St., Englewood NJ 07631. (201)567-6855. Producer: Vince Castellano. Record prducer, music publisher and management firm (Know Talent Management). Deals with artists and songwriters. Produces 8-10 singles/year and 4 albums/year. Fee derived from sales royalty.
How to Contact: Prefers cassette, 7½ or 15 ips reel-to-reel or VHS videocassette with 3 songs and lyric sheet. SASE. Reports in 3-6 weeks.
Music: Mostly rock (commercial), R&B (contemporary) and AOR; also heavy metal and pop. Artists include Ray Goodman & Brown (R&B), Connie Francis (pop); and Lonnie Young Blood (R&B).

*SO FAR SO GOOD PRODUCTIONS, 227 Brocket Pl., Stafford TX 77477. (713)774-0433. Executive Producer: Randy Soffar. Record producer and music publisher. Deals with artists and songwriters. Produces 1-4 singles/year and 1-2 albums/year. Fee negotiable.
How to Contact: Write or call first and obtain permission to submit. Prefers cassette, 15 ips reel-to-reel or VHS videocassette with 3-5 songs and lyric sheet. "Send promo material and pictures if available." SASE. Reports in 4-6 weeks.
Music: Mostly top 40/pop, rock and new wave; also techno pop and R&B. Recently produced "The Teacher's A Punk," by Z-Rocks (pop rock single, Red Hot Richy); "She Gets On My Nerves," by Airbath (rock single, Tub & Tile Records); and *The Way She Looks at Me*, by Z-Rocks (dance rock LP, Z-Records). Other artists include George Richard.

SOUND ARTS RECORDING STUDIO, 2036 Pasket, Houston TX 77092. (713)688-8067. President: Jeff Wells. Record producer and music publisher (Earthscream Music). Deals with artists and songwriters. Produces 15-20 singles and 3 albums/year. Fee derived from sales royalty.
How to Contact: Prefers cassette with 2-5 songs and lyric sheet. SASE. Reports in 1 month.
Music: Mostly rock; also top 40 pop.

SOUND COLUMN PRODUCTIONS, Division of Sound Column Companies, 46 E. Herbert Ave., Salt Lake City UT 84111. (801)355-5327. General Manager: Clive Romney. Record producer, music publisher (Ronarte Publications/ASCAP, Mountain Green Music/BMI and Macanudo Music/SESAC). Deals with artists. Produces 4 singles and 5 albums/year. Fee derived from sales royalty.

How to Contact: Write first. Prefers cassette with 1-3 songs. SASE. "We work mainly with staff writers at our affiliated publishing companies and other established publishers. Our demand fluctuates according to projects we're doing." Reports as soon as possible—"honestly we do get backed up, but you'll eventually be heard."
Music: Mostly pop and country crossover; also easy listening, gospel, MOR and top 40. Recently produced "Too Good to Be Through," by Dave Lemmon (country single, SCP Records); "Somethin' Wonderful," by Dave Compton (pop single, SCP Records); and "You Are the Reason Why," by Steve Eaton (adult contemporary single, LDS Records). Other artists include Brett Raymond and Heidi Magleby.

SOUND IMAGE PRODUCTIONS, 6556 Wilkinson, North Hollywood CA 91606. (818)762-8881. Vice President: David Chatfield. President: Martin John Eberhardt. Vice President Sales/Studio Manager: Chuck Kopp. Record producer, music publisher (Sound Image Publishing), record company and 24-track recording studio. Deals with artists, songwriters and producers. Produces 12 singles and 6 albums/year. Fee derived from sales royalty or outright fee from artist/songwriter or record company or by combination of the above.
How to Contact: Submit finished masters. Prefers cassette with 2-6 songs and lyric sheet. Does not return unsolicited material. Reports in 1 month.
Music: Dance-oriented, R&B, rock (mainstream) and top 40/pop. Recently produced *Saint*, by Saint (AOR/pop LP, Sound Image Records); "I Wanna Know," by Mark Fosson (country single, Image Records); and "Your Loss, My Gain," by George Faber (R&B/pop single, Image Records).

SOUNDS OF WINCHESTER, Box 574, Winchester VA 22601. (703)667-9379. Contact: Jim McCoy. Record producer and music publisher (New Edition Music, Jim McCoy Music and Alear Music/BMI). Deals with artists and songwriters. Produces 20 singles and 10 albums/year. Fee derived from sales royalty.
How to Contact: Prefers 7½ ips reel-to-reel or cassette with 4-10 songs and lead sheet. SASE. Reports in 1 month.
Music: Bluegrass, country, gospel, MOR and rock. Recently produced "One More Time," by Earl Howard (country single, Alear Records); and *Thank-You Jesus*, by Jubilee Travelers (gospel LP, Faith Records). Other artists include Dave Elliott, Alvin Kesner, Carroll County Ramblers, Jim McCoy, Al Hogan and Jimmie Rogers.

THE SOURCE UNLIMITED, 331 East 9th St., New York NY 10003. (212)473-7833. Vice President: S.J. Mollica. Record producer. Deals with songwriters. Produces 2 singles/year. Works with 2 new songwriters/year. Outright fee from record company.
How to Contact: Write first about your interest. Prefers cassette or VHS videocassette with 3-6 songs and lyric sheet. SASE. Reports in 1 month.
Music: Folk, gospel, jazz, progressive, R&B and rock. Recently produced *Music from the Street*, "Son of a Working Man" and "Never to Deliver," by Santo (Source Unimited Records).

SOUTHERN SOUND PRODUCTIONS, 100 Labon St., Tabor City NC 28463. (919)653-2546. President: Elson H. Stevens. Record producer, music publisher (Creekside Music/BMI) and record company. Deals with artists, songwriters and radio stations. Produces 15-20 singles and 4 albums/year. Fee derived from sales royalty.
How to Contact: Write first about your interest. Prefers cassette or 8-track tape with 1-3 songs and lyric sheets. SASE. Reports in 1 month.
Music: Mostly country; also bluegrass, gospel, rock (country and hard) and beach music. Recently produced "Nightime Lady," by T. Jay Jon; "Happy Endings," by Sheila Gore (both country singles, Seaside Records); and "Cheap Imitation," by J.C. Batchelor (country single, JCB Records). Other artists include Mitch Todd, Copper Creek and The Entertainers.
Tips: "Please make sure that all songs submitted have a very strong hook. Limit of 3 songs per submission."

*SOUTHLAND RECORD PRODUCTIONS, Box 1547, Arlington TX 76010. (817)461-3280. President: Steve Reed. Record producer and music publisher. Deals with artists and songwriters. Produces 6-8 singles/year and 2-4 albums/year. Fee negotiable.
How to Contact: Prefers cassette or videocassette with 4 songs and lyric sheet or lead sheet. No reel-to-reel. Reports in 6-8 weeks.
Music: Mostly country, pop/rock and adult contemporary; also jazz. Recently produced *Rausch Touch*, by Leon Rausch (country LP on Southland); "Rt.66," and "Going Away Party," by L. Rausch (country singles on Southland). Other artists include Waldo "The Country Sax" Weathers.

SPRING/POSSE RECORDS, 161 W. 54 St., New York NY 10019. (212)581-5398. President: Julie Rifkind. Vice President: Roy Rifkind. Treasurer: Steve Rifkind. Record producer and music publisher

(Possie Music Corp.). Deals with artists and songwriters. Produces 12 singles and 2-3 albums/year. Fee derived by sales royalty or outright fee from record company.

How to Contact: Prefers cassette with 2-4 songs and lyric sheet. "Masters only." SASE. Reports in 3 weeks.

Music: Mostly R&B; also gospel. Recently produced *Joe Simon's Greatest Hits*, by Joe Simon (R&B LP, Posse Records); *Hard Times*, by Millie Jackson (R&B LP, Spring Records); *Is This the Future?*, by Fatback Band (R&B LP, Spring Records); and *Lay My Burden Down*, by Jackie Verdell (gospel LP). Other artists include Fonda Rae and Joe Simon.

SSS INTERNATIONAL, 3106 Belmont Blvd., Nashville TN 37212. (615)385-1960. Producer: Billy Self. Record producer. Deals with artists and songwriters. Produces 8 singles and 6 albums/year. Fee derived from sales royalty or outright fee from songwriter/artist or record company.

How to Contact: Call about your interest. Prefers cassette with 1-3 songs and lyric sheet. Does not return unsolicited material. Reports in 1 month.

Music: Mostly country and MOR; also easy listening, gospel and top 40/pop. Recently produced "Bogalusa," by Jim Owen (country single, Sun Records); "Barbara's Daughter," by Patti Page (MOR/country single, Plantation Records); and *Double Winners*, by Ken Lowery (country LP, Plantation Records). Other artists include Paul Martin, Norris Treat, Rita Remington and Dave Dudley.

Tips: "We (the act and myself) must be in total agreement in our direction and have the utmost mutual trust in our abilities."

STAIRCASE PROMOTION, Box 211, E. Prairie MO 63845. (314)649-2211. Manager: Tommy Loomas. Record producer and music publisher. Deals with artists and songwriters.

How to Contact: Prefers cassette with 2-4 songs and lyric sheet. SASE. Reports in 1 month.

Music: Country, easy listening, MOR, country rock and top 40/pop. Recently produced "Yesterdays Teardrops," and "Round & Round," by The Burchetts (country singles, Capstan Records).

*STAR RECORD CO. PRODUCTIONS, INC., 521 5th Ave., New York NY 10017. (212)682-5844. Record producer and music publisher (McRon Music Co.). Produces 10-12 singles and 3-9 albumsyear. Deals with artists and songwriters. Pays royalty to artists on contract.

How to Contact: Call first about your interest. Prefers 15 ips reel-to-reel or cassette with 3 songs. Does not return unsolicited material. Reports in 3 weeks, "if solicited."

Music: Mostly church/religious, easy listening, MOR, R&B, rock and Jewish Klezmer Cantorial music; also children's, choral and folk. Recently produced *Silent No More*, by Theodore Bikel (ethnic LP, Star Records); and *The Art of Klezmer*, by Giora Fridman (Jewish Klezmer LP, Star Records).

STARGEM RECORD PRODUCTIONS, 43 Music Sq. E, Nashville TN 37203. (615)244-1025. President/A&R Director: Wayne Hodge. Record producer and music publisher (Newwriters Music/BMI and Timestar Music/ASCAP). Deals with artists and songwriters.

How to Contact: Call first about your interest. Prefers cassette with 1-4 songs and lyric sheet. SASE. Reports in 1 week.

Music: Country and MOR.

STARK RECORDS AND TAPE CO., 628 S. South St., Mount Airy NC 27030. (919)786-2865. Contact: Paul E. Johnson. Record producer and music publisher (TomPaul Music Company/BMI). Deals with artists, songwriters, publishers and recording companies. Produces 80 singles and 45 albums/year. Works with 100 new songwriters/year. Fee derived from outright fee from record company.

How to Contact: Prefers 7½ ips reel-to-reel or cassette with 4-6 songs and lyric sheet. SASE. "My return address should be on the SASE." Reports in 1 month.

Music: Mostly country, bluegrass, pop and gospel. Recently produced "Liquor by the Drink," written and recorded by Carl Tolbert (country single, Stark Records); "Lord Keep Me Humble," written and recorded by Earl Upchurch (country gospel single, Stark Records; and "Here I Am Lord," written and recorded by Ellen Fielder (gospel single, Stark Records). Other artists include Blue Ridge Mountain Boys, Sanford Teague, and Ella Mae Crabtree.

STARTIME MUSIC, Box 643, LaQuinta CA 92253. (714)564-4823. President: Fred Rice. Record producer, music publisher and record company. Produces 2 singles and 2 cassettes/year. Works with 8 new songwriters/year. Teams collaborators. Fee derived from sales royalty.

How to Contact: Submit demo tape or videocassette (if it dramatizes lyrics—no concert footage) and lead sheet. Cassette only with 1-2 songs on demo. SASE. Reports in 6 weeks.

Music: Mostly pop, country and novelty; also rock and top 40. Recently produced "My Palm Springs," and "Palm Springs Party," by Robin Miller (contemporary pop single); and "Mini-Van," by Vantastics (top 40 single).

Tips: "A song has to be built on 'flesh and blood'—the rhythm is the skeleton, the musical theme is the flesh and the lyrics are the blood (the soul). The song must have a *provocative* title, *repetitive* musical theme with *simple* word phrase lyrics, *identifiable* melody line, a *different* sound and always the proverbial 'hook'."

*JAMES STEARNS/ULTRAZEN RECORD CO., Box 50634, Dallas TX 75250. (214)747-5370. Producer: James Stearns. Record producer, music publisher, record company and promotion and distribution firm. Deals with artists and songwriters. Produces 2-3 singles/year and 2 albums/year. "Production delays have limited our output. Ideally we would like to release 4-5 new artists and LPs per year. We will hit that figure in 1985-86." Fee derived from sales of product and publishing.
How to Contact: Prefers cassette or VHS videocassette with 5 or more songs and lyric sheet. "Include a list of recording equipment used to make demo." SASE. Reports in 12 weeks.
Music: Mostly new music, rock and alternative music; also urban contemporary, modern country and international. Recently produced "Give Love a Try," by Tony Rosario (rock single on Ultrazen); "Cut Off Jeans," by Jimmy Mack (R&B/soul novelty single on JAH); and "Spiral Shadows," by Will Welch (rock EP on Ultrazen). Other artists include John Q Public (Michael Bishop).
Tips: "Know thy market, develop your style, be patient and persistent."

A. STEWART PRODUCTIONS, 22146 Lanark St., Canoga Park CA 91304. (818)704-0629. President: Art Stewart. Record producer and music publisher (Famosonda Music/BMI and Sonada/ASCAP). Deals with artists and songwriters. Produces 4 singles and 2 albums/year. Fee determined by sales royalty.
How to Contact: Prefers 7½ ips reel-to-reel or cassette with 1-4 songs and lyric sheet. SASE. Reports in 1 month.
Music: Soul. Recently produced "Eboni Band," by Eboni Band (Afro/American, Eboni Records); *Cherry*, by Platypus (soul LP, Casablanca Records); "Same Old Story," by Sai Whatt (soul single, Stache Records); "Got to Give It Up," by Marvin Gaye; "You and I," by Rich James, and "Lil' Suzy," by Ozone. Other artists include Charades and Randie Coulter.

STONEDOG PRODUCTIONS, 1819 W. Thome, Chicago IL 60660. (312)869-0175. Vice President: Stoney Phillips. Record producer and music publisher (Hannan-Phillips Music). Deals with artists and songwriters. Produces 2-4 singles and 1 album/year. Works with 3-4 new songwriters/year. Works with lyricists and composers and teams collaborators. Fee derived from sales royalty.
How to Contact: Prefers cassette with 1-3 songs and lyric sheet. SASE. Reports in 3 weeks.
Music: Mostly country and country pop; also country crossover, MOR and country rock. Recently produced "This Time," "Why Don't I See More of You" and "Baby Please Stay," by Ronnie Rice (country crossover and pop singles, Stonedog Records).

*STUDIO AMERICA PRODUCTIONS, INC., 50 N. Mentor, Pasadena CA 91106. (818)440-9919. Vice President: R. Gene Oropallo. Record producer and music publisher. Deals with artists and songwriters. Produces 20 singles/year and 4 albums/year. Fee "negotiated by deal."
How to Contact: Prefers cassette or 30 ips reel-to-reel with 3 songs and lyric sheet or lead sheet. Does not return unsolicited material. Reports in 6 weeks.
Music: Mostly country, jazz and gospel; also blues and rock. Recently produced *Perfect Stranger*, (rockabilly LP, Azra); *Connections*, by Sweat & Steel (Steel Drums Island Music LP); and *By Mandrill*, by Energize (jazz/blues LP). Other artists include Sharron Nulte, Danny Spanos, and Leisaa Zucari.

SUNBURST MUSIC PRODUCTIONS, Suite 203, 26949 Chagrin Blvd., Beachwood OH 44122. Executive Producer: Jim Quinn. Associate Producer: Otto F. Neuber. Record producer, music publisher (Solarium Music/ASCAP) and management firm. Deals with artists and songwriters. Produces 3-5 singles and 1-3 albums/year. Works with 2 new songwriters/year and teams collaborators. Fee derived from outright fee from record company and/or royalty on sales.
How to Contact: Prefers cassette only with 1-3 songs. SASE. Reports in 3 weeks.
Music: AOR and top 40/pop. Recently produced "Love Strikes," by Unknown Stranger (dance single, RCA Records); *Exotic Birds*, by Exotic Birds (new music LP, Saturn Records); "No Communication," by Exotic Birds (new music single and video, Saturn Records); and *Champion*, by Champion (AOR LP).

SUNNY DAY PRODUCTIONS, 1931 SE Morrison, Portland OR 97214. (503)238-4525. Producer: Gary W. Perman. Executive Producer: Russell E. Gorsline. Record producer and music publisher (Klickitat Music). Deals with artists and songwriters. Produces 3-5 singles and 3-5 albums/year. Fee derived from sales royalty.
How to Contact: Prefers cassette with 2-3 songs and lyric sheet. SASE. Reports in 1 month.

Music: Mostly pop/top 40 and rock. Recently produced "Shining Star," by Pamela Cansler (Christian single, Cricket Records); "Alone in the City," by P. Cansler (pop single, Cricket Records); and *Helen Westin*, by H. Westin (novelty LP, Rosetown Records).
Tips: Songwriter "must have tremendous potential as an artist or writer. Must be open to changes in material and very versatile."

SUNSET PRODUCTIONS, 15 Albert Crescent, Penarth, South Glamorgan, South Wales, United Kingdom. 44-0222-704279. Director: Paul Barrett. Record producer. Deals with artists and songwriters. Fee derived from sales royalty. Royalties paid directly to US songwriters and artists. Has not yet, but would listen to material from US songwriters and artists.
How to Contact: Prefers cassette and lyric sheet. SAE and IRC. Reports in 3 weeks.
Music: 50s rock only. Recently produced *Tiger*, by Shakin' Stevens and Sunsets (R&R LP); *Unleashed*, by Blue Caps (R&R LP); and *Greasy Kids Only*, by Johnny Storm and Sunsets (R&R LP). Other artists include Nervous Breakdown, Haley & The Hailstones, Rockin' Louie, Phil Fernando and Ben Hewitt.

SUNSET RECORDS, INC., 1577 Redwood Dr., Harvey LA 70058. (504)367-8501. President: George Leger. Record producer and music publisher (Country Legs Music/ASCAP and Golden Sunburst Music/BMI). Deals with artists and songwriters. Produces 5 singles and 1 album/year. Works with 15 new songwriters/year. Works with lyricists and teams collaborators. Fee derived by outright fee from record company.
How to Contact: Prefers cassette ("if very clear") with 3-5 songs and lyric and lead sheets. SASE. Reports in 1-2 months.
Music: Mostly country; also gospel, progressive country and R&B. Recently produced "Broken Homes," by Sonny Tears (country single, Sunset Records); and "I Don't Care," by Larry Maynard (country single, Sunburst Records).
Tips: "Always looking for new artists."

THE SUNSHINE GROUP, 800 S. 4th St., Philadelphia PA 19147. (215)755-7000. President: Walter Kahn. Publicity: Julie Carter. Record producer (Sunshine Records) and music publisher (Scully Music/ASCAP and Orange Bear Music/BMI). Works with artists and songwriters on contract. Produces 15 singles and 5 albums/year. Pays standard royalty.
How to Contact: Prefers 7½ ips reel-to-reel or cassette with 1-4 songs and lyric sheet. SASE. Reports in 1 month.
Music: Mostly pop, R&B and dance; also top 40 and rock. Recently recorded "Hot For You," by Karen Young (Sunshine Records); "Deetour," by K. Young; (Atlantic Records; and "The Flute," by Pipedream (CBS/Epic Records). Other artists include David St. George, Danny Paradise and Juliet.

SURPRIZE RECORDS, INC., 421 W. Elet St., Philadelphia PA 19119. (215)276-8861. President: Gilda C. Woods. Vice President: W. Lloyd Lucas. Record producer, music publisher (Delev Music Co./BMI, Sign of the Ram Music/ASCAP and In the Woods Music/BMI) and management firm. Deals with artists, songwriters and publishers. Produces 3 singles and 1 album/year. Fee derived from sales royalty.
How to Contact: Prefers cassette with 1-5 songs and lyric sheet. SASE. Reports in 1 month.
Music: R&B, soul, top 40/pop, dance-oriented and MOR; also rock and country. Recently produced "This Could Be the Night," by Karla Garrison (pop/dance-oriented single, United Artist Records); and "Pledging My Love," by Bill Lucas (single, Surprize Records).

SWORD & SHIELD RECORDS, Box 211, Arlington TX 76010. (817)572-4051. Contact: Calvin Wills. Record producer. Deals with artists. Produces 6 singles and 20 albums/year. Fee derived from outright fee from artist/songwriter.
How to Contact: Call first about your interest. Prefers cassette with 2-6 songs. Does not return unsolicited material. Reports in 1 month.
Music: Mostly southern gospel and contemporary Christian music.

*SYSTEM, Box 11301, Kansas City KS 66111. (913)287-3495. Executive Producer: Steve Vail. Record producer and management, book and film company. Deals with artists and songwriters. Produces 1 single/year and 2 albums/year. Fee derived from outright fee from songwriter/artist or record company.
How to Contact: Prefers cassette, 7½ ips reel-to-reel or ½" or ¾" videocassette with 1-10 songs and lyric sheet. Does not return unsolicited material. Reports in 6 weeks.
Music: Mostly progressive rock, jazz and art rock. Recently produced *Time Tales*, by Realm (art rock LP, system).

TABITHA PRODUCTIONS, 39 Cordery Road, St. Thomas, Exeter, Devon EX2 9DJ England. 44-0392-7991X. Producer: Graham Sclater. Record producer, music publisher (Tabitha Music, Ltd.) and record company (Tabitha/Willow Records). Works with artists and songwriters. Produces 6 singles and 2 albums/year. Works with 6 new songwriters/year and works with composers. Fee derived from sales royalty.
How to Contact: Prefers cassette with 2-6 songs and lyric sheet. SAE and IRC. Reports in 3 weeks.
Music: Mostly AOR, MOR and rock; also country, dance, soul and top 40/pop. Recently produced "No Love," written and recorded by Andy Ford (rock single, Tabitha Records); "Dance Your Body," (by John Artes and Alan Gradbury), recorded by Flic (disco single, Towerbell Records); and "Somebody," (by Adrian Hess), recorded by Obus (rock single, Capo Disco Records). Other artists include Beat the Heat, Colin Wilson, Alien, Bobby Arnot, The Smith, and Shoot to Kill.

*TAKE HOME TUNES! RECORD CO., Box 10051, Beverly Hills CA 90213. (818)761-2646. Branch: Box 1314, Englewood Cliffs NJ 07632. Messages: (201)567-5524. Box 1314, Englewood Cliffs NJ 07632. Messages: (201)567-5524. Producer: Doris Chu. Record producer and music publisher (The Chu Yeko Musical Foundation/BMI and Broadway/Hollywood International Music/ASCAP). Deals with artists and songwriters. Produces 8 albums/year. Fee derived from sales royalty.
How to Contact: Call first. Prefers cassette with any number songs and lyric sheet. SASE. Reports in 1 month.
Music: Children's, classical, country, easy listening, jazz, MOR, musicals, R&B and top 40/pop. Recently produced *King of Hearts*, by Millicent Martin and Don Scardino; *Lovesong*, by the original cast (musical LPs, Original Cast Records); *Ka-Boom!* and *Fly with Me*, by the original cast (musical LPs, Chu Yeko Musical Foundation Records); and *Christy (Playboy of the Western World)*, by the original cast (musical LP, Original Cast Records).
Tips: "We're interested in the 'top 10' pop types of songs; original cast musicals that had a production somewhere (preferably Los Angeles); and R&B songs sung by new singers, groups, etc. touring the Los Angeles area. Co-production possible with financial backing."

TEROCK RECORDS, Box 4740, Nashville TN 37216. President: Wade Curtiss. Record producer and music publisher. Deals with artists and songwriters. Fee derived from sales royalty.
How to Contact: Prefers 7½ ips reel-to-reel with 2-6 songs and lyric sheet. SASE. Reports in 3 weeks.
Music: Bluegrass, blues, country, dance, easy listening, folk, gospel, progressive, R&B, hard rock, soul and top 40/pop.

THREE G'S INDUSTRIES INC., 5500 Troost, Kansas MO 64110. (816)361-8455. A&R Directors: Eugene Gold and Chris King. Record producer and music publisher (Eugene Gold Music/BMI and Gil-Gad Music/ASCAP). Deals with artists and songwriters. Produces 6 singles and 5 albums/year. Fee derived from sales royalty.
How to Contact: Prefers cassette with 4-6 songs and lyric sheet. SASE. Reports in 1 month.
Music: Gospel, jazz, MOR, R&B and soul. Recently produced "Bootie Cutie" and "Party Tonight," by Robert Newsome (R&B singles, 3 G's Records); "You Left Me at a Bad Bad Time," by Ronnie & Vicky (R&B single, 3 G's Records); and "Magic," by Supension (R&B single, 3 G's Records).
Tips: "I like songs with a good beat, and a good storyline."

*ODELL TILLMAN, Box 16608, Milwaukee WI 53216. Producer: Odell Tillman. Record producer and music publisher (Famous Door Publishing Co.). Deals with artists and songwriters. Produces 4 singles/year and 3 albums/year. Fee derived from sales royalty.
How to Contact: Prefers cassette or reel-to-reel with lyric sheet or lead sheet. SASE. Reports in 3 weeks.
Music: Mostly soul, jazz and pop; also blues and gospel. Recently produced *Music Make Me High*, *You Pick Me Up*, and *Crazy Love*, by Joanne Tardy (LPs on T.M.). Other artists include Kent Allen.

RIK TINORY PRODUCTIONS, Box 311, Cohasset MA 02025. (617)383-9494. Artist Relations: Richard Tinory, Jr. Record producer and music publisher (Old Boston Publishing). Deals with artists. Produces 20 singles and 6 albums/year. Works with 1-2 new songwriters/year. Fee derived from sales royalty.
How to Contact: Call first and obtain permission to submit. Prefers cassette with 1-2 songs. Does not return unsolicited material.
Music: Recently produced "Here's to You, L.A.," by Rik Tinory (swing single, RTP Records).
Tips: "We are looking for master recordings with strong material ready for release."

TMC PRODUCTIONS, 3800 San Pedro Ave., San Antonio TX 78212. (512)735-3322. Producer: Joe Scates. Record producer, music publisher (Axbar Productions/BMI, Axe Handle Music/ASCAP) and record distributor. Deals with artists and songwriters. Produces 12-15 singles and 3-6 albums/year. Fee derived from sales royalty.

How to Contact: Prefers 7½ ips reel-to-reel or cassette with 1-5 songs and lyric sheet. SASE. Reports "as soon as possible, but don't rush us."

Music: Blues, country, comedy and rock (soft). Recently produced "Today Just Ain't the Day," by Mark Nesler (country single, Axbar Records); "Let's Make a Memory," (by David Loggins), recorded by Mark Chestnutt (country ballad); and "Talking About Big John," written and recorded by Carroll Gilley (up-tempo country rock). Other artists include Juni Moon, Rusty Button, Ray Sanders, and Wayne Carter.

Tips: "Send only your best shots. Average songs just don't make it anymore."

*LLOYD TOWNSEND, JR., 239-A E. Thach Ave., Auburn AL 36830. (205)821-JASS. Contact: Lloyd Townsend, Jr. Record producer and music publisher (Imaginary Music). Estab. 1985. Deals with artists and songwriters. Fee derived from sales royalty.

How to Contact: Prefers cassette or 7½ ips reel-to-reel with 4 songs and lyric sheet or lead sheet. SASE. Reports in 4 weeks.

Music: Mostly jazz, blues and rock. Recently produced "Fast Food Driver," by Tom & Rob (novelty rock single on Imaginary); *Serve & Protect*, by The Moderns (rock LP on Imaginary); and "Jagged Edges," by The Moderns (rock EP on Imaginary). Other artists include Logan Patton, Bob Richardson, J. Hatch, Jeff Graves, Cathy Bell, Brother Atkins, Steve Armour, David Evans, Judy Roderick, Somtow Sucharitkol and David Peters.

TREND PRODUCTIONS, Box 201, Smyrna GA 30080. (404)432-2454. Manager: Tom Hodges. Record producer, music publisher and artist manager. Deals with artists, songwriters and musicians. Fee derived from sales royalty.

How to Contact: Prefers cassette with 3-10 songs and lyric sheet. SASE. Reports in 3 weeks.

Music: Bluegrass, blues, country, gospel, MOR, R&B, rock, soul and top 40/pop. Recently produced "Sugar Daddy Man," by Frank Brannon (country single); "To See the Kids," by Jo Ann Johnson (country single); and "Be Bop A Lula," by Dempsey (country single). Other artists include Terry Brand.

TRIBAL RECORDS, Box 6495, Buena Park CA 90620. (714)554-0851. Contact: Jerry Wood. Record producer. Deals with artists and songwriters. Fee derived from sales royalty or outright fee from record company.

How to Contact: Prefers 7½ ips reel-to-reel or cassette with 3 songs and lyric sheet. SASE. Reports in 2 weeks.

Music: Country, easy listening and MOR. Recently produced "Many Are the Colors," by Roy Dee (country single, Tribal Records); "99 Years," by Ron Hayden (country single, Tribal Records); and "Gold Plated Boy Scout Knife," by Jeanne Taylor (country single, Tribal Records).

TROD NOSSEL ARTISTS, 10 George St., Box 57, Wallingford CT 06492. (203)269-4465. Executive Director: Thomas 'Doc' Cavalier. Record producer, music publisher (Rohm Music, Linesider Music, BIG Music) and record company manager. Produces 3-5 singles and 2-5 albums/year. Fee derived from sales royalty.

How to Contact: Prefers cassette with 2-3 songs and lyric sheet. Include statement of goals and purposes. Prefers studio produced demos. Does not return unsolicited material. Reports in 6 weeks.

Music: Rock, R&B and pop. Recently produced "Best Of Friends," by Bob Mel (pop single, TNA Records); "Charmaine," (by Christine Ohlman), recorded by Rebel Montez (rock single, TNA Records); and "Go You Tigers, Go!," (by Cub Koda), recorded by The Cub Koda Band (theme song, Telestar Records).

TUMAC MUSIC, 2097 Vistadale Ct., Tucker GA 30084. (404)938-1210. Professional Manager: Phil McDaniel. Record company, music publisher and record producer. Produces 3 singles/year. Deals with artists and songwriters on contract.

How to Contact: Prefers cassette with 1-3 songs and lyric sheet. SASE. Reports in 3 weeks.

Music: Blues, country, easy listening, country jazz, MOR, R&B, country and soft rock and top 40/pop.

*TUTCH PRODUCTIONS, Box 163, West Redding CT 06896. (203)438-5366. President: Paul Hotchkiss. Record producer and music publisher. Deals with artists and songwriters. Produces 5 singles/year and 1 album/year. Fee derived from sales royalty.

How to Contact: Prefers cassette with 2 songs and lyric sheet. Include bio. SASE. Reports in 3 weeks.

Music: Mostly country and country/pop. Recently produced "Welcome to My World," by Paul Hotchkiss (country single on Bronco/Axbar); "Knocking," by Diana Hart (country pop single on BGM);

Close-up

Reesa Kay Jones
Performer/Songwriter
Ottumwa, Iowa

If you are convinced you'll never make it in the music business because you're from a small town, don't tell singer/songwriter Reesa Kay Jones. Jones, who hails from Ottumwa, Iowa is well on her way to proving you wrong.

Reesa Kay, whose varied background includes The Miss Teenage America Contest, graduation from nursing school and driving 18-wheelers cross country, has been involved in entertaining since the age of five. Her first experience with the music business came about when songwriter Jimmy Powers needed a girl singer to help out on a couple of duets he wrote. It was that first break that eventually led to a Nashville recording contract, opportunities to work with a number of country music stars including Jack Reno, The Statler Brothers, Lonzo & Oscar, Moe Bandy, Danny Davis, and an appearance on The Grand Ole Opry Stage with the Association of Country Entertainers show singing her idol Patsy Cline's "Crazy."

One of her greatest thrills, however, was how she learned of her nomination for The Country Music Association's 1984 Female Vocalist of the Year Award. "My mother called me at work and told me to turn on the radio, but wouldn't tell me why," she recalled, "when I turned it on and they announced that I had been nominated I almost died of shock!" Since then Jones has been busy touring the countryside playing numerous clubs, shows and fairs with her five piece band Prairie Fire.

Although Jones is a relative newcomer to the business she already has a number of records to her credit including a single ("First In A Long Line Of Fools"), a mini-album (*A Hurtin Memory*), and an LP entitled *Simply For You*. She's currently at work collaborating with her husband and fellow band member Jay Kincaid on some material destined for her next album.

As much as this might sound like another "local girl makes good" story, Reesa Kay realizes that the road to Nashville isn't always paved with gold. Like many other budding young stars, she at first thought that moving to Nashville was the key to success, but soon discovered that there is more to the music business than meets the eye. "I don't think it's wise to go to Nashville to try and get a start. I moved to Nashville when I got out of nursing school and just wasn't prepared for what I found. There are people in the business that give the business a bad name. You have to be able to tell which people to believe and which ones to ignore and that's tough to do if you haven't been around the business very long. You have to have friends you can count on.

Although her many other trips to Nashville have been both enjoyable and career enhancing, she does offer some sage advice which has been echoed by many in the entertainment business: "Beware of anyone who says they'll make you a star overnight."

and *Texas Honky Tonkin*, by Kathy Kane (country LP and single on GBS). Other artists include Gerry Malone, Hutcher Brothers, and T-Bone Stankus.

TWO STAR PRODUCTIONS, 15 King George's Dr., Toronto, Ontario M6M 2H1 Canada. (416)656-1566. Producer: Bob Johnston. Record producer. Deals with artists and songwriters. Produces 5 singles and 1 album/year. Works with 3-4 new songwriters/year. Works with lyricists and composers. Fee derived from outright fee from songwriter/artist.
How to Contact: Call or write first. Prefers cassette with 2-4 songs on demo. Does not return unsolicited material.
Music: Mostly country and country crossover; also easy listening, MOR and rock (commercial). Recently produced "For Loving You," (by Bob Johnston/Bret McNaul), recorded by B. McNaul (country crossover single, Young St. Records); "Nothing More We Can Do," (by Bob Johnston/Lili Zlamal), recorded by Donny Jerrett & Lilianne (country single, Young St. Records); and "I'm Holding Memories Tonight," (by B. McNaul/Doug Virgin), recorded by B. McNaul (country crossover single, Young St. Records). Other artists include Dusty Shelf.

VENTURE SOUND STUDIO PRODUCTIONS, 121 Meadowbrook Dr., Somerville NJ 08876. (201)359-5110. Producer: Tony Camillo. Record producer, music publisher and production company. Deals with artists and songwriters. Produces 21-25 singles and 5-8 albums/year. Fee derived from sales royalty or outright fee from record company.
How to Contact: Query. Prefers cassette with 2-5 songs and lead sheet. "Send as complete a package as possible." SASE. Reports in "1 month or longer depending on schedule."
Music: Dance, soul, MOR and top 40/pop; "excellent material only." Recently produced *Let's Burn*, by Clarence Carter; "Without You" and *Don't Make Me Eat*, by Pendullum; "Body Bait," by Symba (disco single); and "Once a Night," by Charlie English (single from the movie, *Hopscotch*).

CHARLES VICKERS MUSIC ASSOCIATION, 171 Pine Haven, Daytona Beach FL 32014. (904)252-4849. President/Producer: Dr. Charles H. Vickers D.M. Record producer and music publisher (Pritchett Publication/BMI and Alison Music/ASCAP). Deals with artists and songwriters. Produces 90 singles and 4 albums/year. Works with 3 new songwriters/year. Teams collaborators. Fee derived from sales royalty.
How to Contact: Write first. Prefers 7½ ips reel-to-reel or cassette with 1-6 songs. SASE. Reports in 1 week.
Music: Mostly gospel and hymns; also bluegrass, blues, church/religious, classical, country, easy listening, jazz, MOR, progressive, reggae (pop), R&B, rock, soul and top 40/pop. Recently produced "Let Your Light Shine" and "The Other Side of the Rainbow," by Charles Vickers (gospel singles, King of Kings Records); *If God Is for You Who Can Be Against You*, and *Heaven Is Just Over the Hill*, by King of Kings (gospel LPs, L.A. International Records).

VIDIOM MUSIC/MUSIC CONSULTANT, Suite 1403, 1115 Sherbrooke W., Montreal, Quebec H3A 1H3 Canada. (514)282-1414. President: Michel Zgarka. Record producer, music publisher (Simone Publishing/CAPAC, Mekia Publishing/PROCAN, Vidiom Music) and international music consultant. Deals with artists, songwriters, managers and independent producers in finding them international releases. Produces 5 singles and 1 album/year. Works with 10-15 new songwriters/year. Works with lyricists and teams collaborators. Fee derived from sales royalty and publishing advances.
How to Contact: Prefers 7½ ips reel-to-reel, cassette or videocassette with 2-8 songs and lyric sheet. Include bio and photo. SAE and IRC. Reports in 5 weeks.
Music: Mostly up-tempo instrumental, dance-oriented and R&B; also soul, top 40/pop and French. Recently produced "Apartment 3," (by Joel Ferron/Yves Decarie), recorded by Tess (top 40 single, Vidian Records); and "Jeans," by Bill Hill (top 40 single, Vidian Records).

VOICE BOX RECORDS, 5180 Park Ave., Memphis TN 38119. (901)761-5074. President: Mark Blackwood. Record producer and music publisher (Songs From The Box/BMI, Voice Of Paradise/ASCAP). Deals with artists and songwriters. Produces 10 singles and 6 albums/year. Fee derived from sales royalty.
How to Contact: Prefers cassette and lyric sheet. Does not return unsolicited material. Reports in 1 month.
Music: Gospel. "We are primarily interested in Christian MOR songs and artists." Recently produced "Second to None," by Blackwood Brothers; "We're in This Together," by Sparrow; and "Livin' for the Light," by Tony Pilcher.

WILLIAM F. WAGNER, Suite 218, 14343 Addison St., Sherman Oaks CA 91423. Contact: Bill Wagner. Record producer. Deals with artists and songwriters. Produces 6-8 singles and 2-5 albums/year.

Works with 25 new songwriters/year. Fee derived from sales royalty.
How to Contact: Prefers 7½ ips and cassette with 1-5 songs and lead sheet. SASE. Reports in 1 month.
Music: Mostly top 40, pop, gospel and jazz; also blues, choral, country, easy listening, MOR, progressive, rock, soul and pop. Recently produced *Billy May For President*, by Pat Longo (jazz/dance-oriented album, Town Hall Records); "Suspicion," by Burn With Passion (rock/jazz single); and "Hearts Aflame," written and recorded by Vicki McClure (top 40 single, VMC Records). Other artists include Rich Szabo, Robert Pollack, Art Monroe and Candace Bennett.

*WALK ON WATER PRODUCTIONS, Rt. 2, Box 566-H, New Braunfels TX 78130. (512)629-4396. Producer/Manager: Brian C. Carr. Record producer, music publisher and recording studio. Deals with artists and songwriters. Produces 2 singles/year and 1 album/year. Fee derived from sales royalty or specific contract negotiation.
How to Contact: Write or call first and obtain permission to submit. Prefers cassette, 7½ ips reel-to-reel or VHS videocassette with 2-3 songs and lyric sheet. Does not return unsolicited material. Reports in 4-6 weeks.
Music: Mostly AOR pop/rock, new music and country. Recently produced *Everyone's A Spy*, by Secrets (rock LP, Walk on Water); *Salute to San Antonio*, by Rusty Lawrence (country LP, Walk on Water); and "Jamaican Beaches," by Norm Allen (rock single, Walk on Water). Other artists include Tommy Thompson, Howard Yeargan, Dennis Peek, and Tim Catron.

*WARD MUSIC, 438 Vallejo St., San Francisco CA 94133. (415)398-7530. Publisher/Agent: Henry Ward. Record producer, music publisher (Mark VIII Music/Quantum Records) and management firm (Thin Man Talent Agency). Deals with artists and songwriters. Produces 10 singles/year and 5 albums/year. Fee derived from sales royalty.
How to Contact: Prefers cassette or videocassette with 1-3 songs and lyric sheet. "A chorded song is acceptable." SASE. Reports in 4 weeks.
Music: Mostly rock, pop, new wave; also blues, country, gospel and jazz. Recently produced *Sapphire*, by Saldate (fusion LP on Quantium); *Time Tales*, by Knufler (rock LP on Quantium); and "Light on Life," by Villon (folk rock).
Tips: "Be as professional as possible. Think out a good plan and do it!"

*JOE WATERS, 455 Massieville Rd., Chillicothe OH 45601. (614)663-4030. Manager: Willi Pack. Record producer and music publisher (Lantern Music). Deals with artists and songwriters. Fee "depends on individual situation."
How to Contact: Prefers cassette with 1-3 songs and lyric sheet. Does not return unsolicited material. Reports as soon as possible.
Music: Country, top 40 and R&B. Recently produced *All the Way*, by Southbound.

WATTS CITY RECORDS & PRODUCTION CO., 11211 Wilmington Ave., Los Angeles CA 90059. (213)566-9982. Executive Producer: Joe Fornis. Record producer and music publisher (Watts City Production/ASCAP). Deals with artists and songwriters. Produces 5 singles and 2 albums/year. Fee derived from sales royalty.
How to Contact: Prefers cassette with 4-12 songs and lyric sheet. SASE. Reports in 3 weeks.
Music: R&B, soul and top 40/pop.

THE WAXWORKS RECORDING STUDIO, Box 299, Albert St., St. Jacobs, Ontario, Canada N0B 2N0. (519)664-3311 or 3332. Producer: Mr. Jim Evans. Record producer and music publisher (Hot Wax Publishing and St. Jacobs Music Publishing. Deals with artists and songwriters. Produces 12 singles and 8 albums/year. Works with 3 new songwriters/year. Works with lyricists and composers and teams collaborators. Fee negotiable.
How to Contact: Prefers cassette with 3-5 songs and lyric sheet. "Send only the best material in the best form possible. Express the compositions in the best form of production available and be sure lyrics and melody are easily discernable." SAE and IRC. Reports in 3 months.
Music: Mostly MOR, pop, R&B and C&W; also dance-oriented, easy listening, gospel, and rock (all types). Recently produced *More Better Music*, by the Beirdo Brothers (novelty LP, Waxing Records); "Don't Leave Me Alone," by Terry Greenside (C&W single, Waxing Records); and *Much Too Young*, by Zip Zip Four (new wave LP, Breslan Records).

WEBCO RECORDS & RECORDING STUDIO, 8705 Deanna Dr., Gaithersburg MD 20879. (301)253-5962. President: Wayne E. Busbice. Record producer and music publisher (Old Home Place Music). Deals with artists and songwriters. Produces 4 singles and 8-10 albums/year. Fee dervied from sales royalty.
How to Contact: Write first and obtain permission to submit. Prefers cassette with 3-5 songs. "It helps

if an artist is referred to me by an already-known artist." SASE. Reports in 1 month.
Music: Mostly bluegrass; also country. Recently produced "Shenandoah Grass, Yesterday and Today," by Jim Eanes (bluegrass single, WEBCO Records). Other artists include Bill Rouse & The Up Town Grass Band, The Grass Reflection, the Busby Brothers, Jack Fincham and The Dixie Grass, Buzz Busby, The Overland Express, Bobby Atkins & The Countrymen, Al Jones & Frank Necessary, Joe Boucher, Hobbs & Partners, and D.J. & The C.B. Pickers.
Tips: "Be referred by established artist."

THE WEISMAN PRODUCTION GROUP, 449 N. Vista St., Los Angeles CA 90036. (213)658-6417. Contact: Ben Weisman. Record producer and music publisher (Audio Music Publishers). Deals with artists and songwriters. Produces 30 singles/year. Fee derived from sales royalty.
How to Contact: Prefers cassette with 3-10 songs and lyric sheet. "Mention *Songwriter's Market*." SASE. Reports in 1 month.
Music: Mostly R&B, soul and top 40/pop; also all types of rock. Recently produced "Gangbanger," by Hakeem, recorded by Princess (rock single, Parliament Records); "Caught Between A Cold Place and A Fire," (pop single), and "Don't Overwork My Love," by Hakeem (R&B single, Parliament Records). Other artists include Traci Nelson, Max Badger and Jimmy Hodges.

WEST ALDEN PRODUCTIONS, 4637 Verdugo Rd., Los Angeles CA 90065. (213)257-0454. Producer: Mick Thompson. Record producer, music publisher (Town Line Music) and manager. Deals with artists. Produces 6 singles and 2 albums/year. Fee derived from sales royalty or outright fee from artist/songwriter.
How to Contact: Write first. Prefers cassette with maximum 4 songs and lyric sheet. SASE. Reports in 1 month.
Music: Mostly rock, top 40/pop, R&B and new wave.
Tips: "Send your best hit material that is competitive with what is on the charts. We're mostly interested in new music groups."

W/G RECORDS, 991 Oak St., West Barnstable MA 02668. (617)362-4908. President: Michael Welch. Record producer and music publisher (Welchy Grape Publishing). Deals with artists and songwriters. Produces 4 singles and 2 albums/year. Fee derived from sales royalty.
How to Contact: Submit records and promotional material or write first about your interest. Prefers cassette or record with 10 songs and lyric sheet. SASE. Reports in 1 month. Prefers studio produced demo.
Music: Country, easy listening, folk, MOR, rock (country/hard), heavy metal and top 40/pop. Recently produced "Don't Let the Sun," "Window Pain," and "Moon Ride," all by Mike Welch (W/G Records).

WHITEWAY PRODUCTIONS, INC., 65 W. 55th St., New York NY 10019. (212)757-4317. President: Eddie White. Vice President: Peter White. Record, play, film and concert producer. Deals with artists and actors. Fee derived from sales royalty.
How to Contact: Query or arrange personal interview. "We advertise or send out calls when we are doing a show." Does not return unsolicited material.
Music: Musical shows. Recently produced *Birmingham Rag* and *Dixieland Blues*, by Sunny Gale.

SHANE WILDER PRODUCTIONS, Box 3503, Hollywood CA 90078. (818)891-1185. President: Shane Wilder. Record producer and music publisher. Deals with artists and songwriters. Produces 25-30 singles and 10-15 albums/year. Fee derived from sales royalty plus production fee.
How to Contact: Prefers cassette with 6-8 songs and lyric sheet. SASE. Reports in 4 weeks.
Music: Country, rock and top 40/pop. Recently produced "Part Time Love," by Crystal Blue (disco single); and "Old Liars, Umpires and a Woman Who Knows," by Mike Franklin (country single, N.S.D. Records). Other artists include Priscilla Emerson, Laurie Loman (MCA recording artist) and Terry Brooks (rock artist, Jet Records).
Tips: "Looking for top country acts for record contract and management—acts must be highly commercial."

DON WILLIAMS MUSIC GROUP, Suite 809, 1888 Century Park E., Los Angeles CA 90067. (213)556-2458. Contact: Randall Rumage. Music publishing/administration and record production. Deals with artists and songwriters. Fee derived from sales royalty.
How to Contact: Prefers 2-3 songs and lyric sheet. List name, address and telephone number on package. SASE. Reports in 4-6 weeks.
Music: All types.

DAVE WILSON PRODUCTIONS, 3530 Kensington Ave., Philadelphia PA 19134. (215)288-4750. Vice President: Claire Mac. Record producer and music publisher (Arcade Music/ASCAP, Sulzer Music/BMI). Deals with artists and songwriters. Produces 5 singles and 1 album/year. Works with 30 new songwriters/year. Fee derived from sales royalty.

How to Contact: Prefers cassette with 2-6 songs and lyric sheet. SASE. Reports in 1 month.

Music: Country, pop and MOR. Recently produced "Price of Freedom," (by Joanne Petrevitch), recorded by Mel Moore (MOR single); "So Much in Love," (by Jackson/Williams/Straigs), recorded by Frank Langley (oldies single, Regime Records); and "Now It's Over," (by Gaston/Moschette), by Paul Christopher (country single, In Action Records). Other artists include Jacquie Lenning, Johnnie Mendell, and Mike Bennett.

WISHBONE, INC., Box 2631, Muscle Shoals AL 35662. (205)381-1455. President: Terry Woodford. Professional Manager: Richard Butler. Record producer, music publisher (I've Got The Music Co./ASCAP, Song Tailors Music Co./BMI, Terry Woodford Music/ASCAP and Creative Source Music/BMI) and video producer. Deals with artists and songwriters.

How to Contact: Prefers cassette with 2 songs and lyric sheet. SASE. Reports as soon as possible.

Music: Mostly top 40/pop and country; also dance-oriented, easy listening, MOR, progressive, R&B, rock and soul. Recently produced *Nothing But the Truth*, by Mac McAnally (top 40/pop/easy listening/rock LP, Geffen Records).

WORDS OF WISDOM PRODUCTION, 3403 N. Ralston Ave., Indianapolis IN 46218. (317)926-6271. Producer: Rickie Clark. Record producer and music publisher (Clark Publishing, Tyscot, Inc.). Deals with artists. Produces 4 singles and 2 albums/year. Fee derived from sales royalty or outright fee from record company.

How to Contact: Prefers cassette with 6 songs and lyric sheet. SASE. Reports in 1 month.

Music: Mostly soul, R&B and gospel; also church/religious, dance-oriented, jazz and top 40/pop. Recently produced "Hold Out," by Robert Turner (gospel single, Tyscot Records); "Flam," by Ricky Clark (soul single, Circle City records); and "Lady's Right," by R. Clark (soul single, Indy 5 Records). Other artists include Circle City Band, Truth & Devotion and Redd Hott.

BARRY YEARWOOD PRODUCTIONS, 100 Rutland Rd., Hempstead NY 11550. Vice President: Barry Yearwood. Record producer and music publisher (Mega-Star Music/BMI). Deals with artists and songwriters. Produces 2 singles/year. Fee derived from sales royalty. Does not return unsolicited material. Reports in 1 month.

Music: Mostly pop, dance and R&B; also rock, jazz and gospel. Recently produced *Cutie Pie*, by Conway and Temple (dance LP, Best Records); and *Tymes Are Tight*, by Jimmy Young (dance LP, Best Records).

YELLOW ROSE, Box 1010, Hendersonville TN 37077. (615)451-3920. General Manager: Dee Mullins. Record producer and music publisher (My Dee Dee Music, Mel Dee Music/BMI). Deals with artists and songwriters. Produces 10-20 singles and 20-30 albums/year. Works with 2-5 new songwriters/year. Fee derived from sales royalty.

How to Contact: Write or call first and obtain permission to submit, or arrange personal interview. Prefers 7½ ips reel-to-reel or cassette with 1-4 songs. Prefers studio produced demos. SASE. Reports in 1 month.

Music: Bluegrass, country, and MOR. Recently produced "There Lies the Difference," by Jerry McBee, recorded by Dee Mullins (country crossover single, Melodee Records); "Holdin On, Hangin On," by R.W. Anderson, recorded by Carlson Roberts & Kelly Harland (country crossover single, Melodee Records); and "Fire Out of Control," (by Gary Paxton), recorded by D. Mullins (country crossover single, Melodee Records). Other artists include Ronnie Osbahr, Joy Lewis and Hank Marshall.

Advertising Agencies

An excellent, but often overlooked market for the more accomplished songwriter exists in local and national advertising agencies. With the mushrooming use of music in broadcast advertising the need for songwriters and composers who can write effective, commercial music grows yearly.

When a company approaches an ad agency about a campaign for one of its products or services it places its trust, and very possibly the future of its product or product line, in the hands of that agency's creative staff. For this reason the agency must retain absolute control over each campaign.

An agency's creative department determines the thrust of the campaign and whether that campaign will include music. If it does, jingle writers whose work they know are contacted, or they may refer to a wide selection of demos they already have on file. They are searching for just the right sound, just the right hook that will make their ad, and their client's product or service, instantly recognizable.

Because advertising is a business strictly governed by time and money, an agency must be prepared to work and produce on very short notice and often with a predetermined, restrictive budget. To prepare for all eventualities agencies must work differently than do publishers, producers or record companies. For example, many agencies do not return submissions, but keep them on file for possible future use. In addition, most agencies pay by the job and buy all rights to your music. This permits both the agency and advertiser to use the music as many times as they wish without further payment to the songwriter. In this way the agency knows what portion of the ad's creative budget must go for music. Occasionally an agency will purchase one-time rights for a particular ad or campaign. Such rights are good for that one specified use and any further use must be renegotiated on a use-by-use basis.

When contacting ad agencies, keep in mind that they are looking for music that can capture and hold an audience's attention in a very short time span (usually 30 or 60 seconds). When submitting a demo to an agency don't forget to include samples of any previously aired work you may have. Your musical selections should fade in and fade out and include a variety of music styles to show your versatility. This is important because often agencies will produce several versions of an ad, each with its own particular style of music and target audience.

Sometimes knowing exactly what clients or types of clients a particular agency serves can be of use in preparing your submission. Many times a company which regularly uses music in its advertising will want to use that same basic style of music time and time again to help retain a certain identity for its product or service.

Each listing that follows will give you at least a general idea of what type of client each agency serves. For additional names, addresses and client lists of advertising agencies refer to the *Standard Directory of Advertising Agencies* (National Register Publishing Co.).

ADVERTISING COMMUNICATIONS, INC., Suite 715, 111 E. Third St., Davenport IA 52801. (319)326-4055. Broadcast Creative Director: Dean Teeselink. Advertising agency. Uses services of songwriters for jingles and background music. Commissions 3-5 lyricists and songwriters/year. Pays by the job. Buys all rights or one-time rights.
How to Contact: Submit demo tape of previous work. Prefers cassette with 4-10 songs. Reports if SAS postcard is provided; prefers to keep on file.
Music: "Music varies with each client and promotion."
Tips: "Be open to constructive criticism and change."

*ALDRICH & HELM ADVERTISING, 3302 Fourth Ave. N, Billings MT 59101. (406)259-1999. Broadcast Producer: Anne Gauer. Advertising agency. Clients include clothing, sporting goods, furniture, home electronics and automobile companies and banks. Pays $50 "per needle drop for background music, from record libraries." Buys one-time rights.
How to Contact: Prefers cassette, 7¹/₂ ips reel-to-reel or ³/₄" U-matic videocassette with 5-10 pieces

"Include brochure and rate card—interested in voices for voice-overs also." Does not return unsolicited material; prefers to keep on file. Reports "when services are needed."
Music: Wide variety. "We use lively, upbeat music more often than slow tempo for radio and TV commercial music beds. We use 30-second beds most often, 60-second beds occasionally. We rarely use full sing jingles."
Tips: "Any music for specific occasions is helpful, i.e., Christmas, St. Patrick's Day, 4th of July—or music appropriate for retail advertising. We would use existing material that was successful in other markets. Cost of original material is often too high."

AMVID COMMUNICATION SERVICES, INC., Box 577, Manhattan Beach CA 90266. (213)545-6691. Contact: Production Manager or Producer. Uses services of music houses for background music. Pays by the job.
How to Contact: Query with resume of credits or submit demo tape of previously aired work. Prefers 7¹/₂ ips reel-to-reel or cassette. SASE. Reports in 10 days.
Music: Background music written to convey specific moods.

BARRON HILLMAN & MELLNICK, INC., 80 Broad St., Boston MA 02110. (617)482-3883. Vice President/Creative Director: Capel States. Ad agency. Uses services of songwriters and lyricists for jingles. Commissions 3-4 songwriters/year and 2 lyricists/year. Payment negotiable. Buys all rights.
How to Contact: Query first or submit demo tape of previous work. Prefers reel-to-reel, cassette or video cassette with 5-10 songs. SASE, but prefers to keep material on file.
Tips: "Be updated at all times on trends in the marketplace—music styles in vogue, etc."

RON BERNS & ASSOCIATES, 520 N. Michigan Ave., Chicago IL 60611. (312)527-2800. President: Ron Berns. Ad agency. Uses services of independent songwriters for jingles. Pays by the job. Buys all rights.
How to Contact: Submit demo tape of previous work. Prefers reel-to-reel or cassette. Prefers studio produced demo. Does not return unsolicited material. Prefers to keep material on file. Reports when needed.

RALPH BING ADVERTISING CO., 16109 Selva Dr., San Diego CA 92128. (619)487-7444. President: Ralph S. Bing. Ad agency. Uses the services of lyricists and independent songwriters for jingles. Commissions 1 songwriter and 1 lyricist/year. Pays by the job as determined by the producer. Buys all rights.
How to Contact: Write first and obtain permission to submit. Prefers cassette with 3-6 songs. SASE, but prefers to keep on file.
Music: Easy listening.
Tips: "Go with current trends as they occur."

JOHN BORDEN ADVERTISING AGENCY, Suite 2, 2010 Marshall Ave., St. Paul MN 55104. (612)644-3443. Account Executive: John Borden. Serves small business, industrial, financial, medical, insurance and food manufacturing clients. Uses services of songwriters and lyricists for jingles and background music. Commissions 1-3 songwriters and 1-3 lyricists/year. Pay varies. Rights purchased vary.
How to Contact: Submit demo tape of previously aired work. Prefers cassette. Does not return unsolicited material. SASE, but prefers to keep material on file. Reports "when material fits need."
Tips: "Our specialty is small business advertising. Get product platform before writing."

SAL BUTERA ASSOCIATES ADVERTISING, 1824 Whipple Ave. NW, Canton OH 44708. Broadcast Services Supervisor/President: Sal Butera. Ad agency. Serves consumer clients. Uses jingles and background music for commercials. Commissions 5 pieces/year. Pays on a per-bid basis. Buys all rights or one-time rights.
How to Contact: Write first with resume of credits, submit demo tape of previously aired work or submit demo tape showing jingle/composition skills. Prefers 7¹/₂ ips reel-to-reel with 6-12 songs. Does not return unsolicited material. Reports in 1 month.

COLLE & McVOY ADVERTISING AGENCY, 1550 E. 78th St., Minneapolis MN 55423. Manager, Broadcast Production: Rose Chick. Ad agency. Uses services of jingle producers for jingles and background music. "Generally the same person who is hired to write the melody does the lyrics or he/she hires the lyricists." Commissions 2-6 songwriters/year. Payment negotiated. Buys various rights.
How to Contact: Write first with resume of credits or submit demo tape of previous work. Prefers 7¹/₂ ips reel-to-reel with 4-20 songs. SASE; but prefers to keep on file. "When need for music comes up we search our files for possible candidates, review tapes, then put work out for bid/estimate."

Music: "Most common need is for jingles for use on radio (some TV). Clients vary: financial institutions, agricultural products, retail, etc."
Tips: Looking for "good variety of styles on your demo and ability to provide full service—write, produce, arrange, etc."

CONRADI, JOHNSON AND ASSOCIATES, INC., Suite 1010, 7777 Bonhomme, St. Louis MO 63105. Media Director: Donna Vorhies. Creative Director: Don McKenna. Producer: Richard Ohms. Ad agency, public relations firm and marketing firm. Serves financial, automotive, industrial, hotel and retail clients. Uses services of songwriters and lyricists for jingles and background music for commercials. Commissions 2 songwriters/year. Payment negotiable. Buys all rights.
How to Contact: Submit resume of credits or submit demo tape showing jingle/composition skills. Prefers cassette with 4-5 songs. SASE, but prefers to keep material on file. "When the need arises, we'll phone."
Tips: "Basically, we look for music, and supply a good portion of the lyrics ourselves. Don't get so involved in the piece that you lose sight of what you're actually selling."

*COONS, CORKER & ASSOCIATES, 1614 W. Riverside Ave., Spokane WA 99201. Ad agency and public relations firm. Creative Director: Danita Petek. Serves industrial, retail, media, financial, public utility, real estate and automotive clients. Uses songwriters, lyricists, pre-marketed music and production houses for jingles and background music for commercials; uses lyricists for jingles—individual radio and TV spots. Commissions 2 songwriters and 2 lyricists/year. "Pay variable on project-by-project basis." Buys all rights.
How to Contact: Submit demo tape of previously aired work or submit demo tape showing jingle/composition skills and styles. Prefers 7^1/$_2$ ips reel-to-reel with 7-15 songs. *"The cost of submitted productions would be helpful."* Does not return unsolicited material. Reports "immediately, if we have a need."
Tips: "We're not interested in hearing from songwriters *per se*. We usually deal with music houses that are in the business of selling music for radio and TV commercials."

THE CRAMER-KRASSELT CO., 733 N. Van Buren, Milwaukee WI 53202. (414)276-3500. Contact: Creative Director. Serves consumer, financial and service accounts. Uses services of songwriters and music production companies for jingles and background music in commercials. Commissions 5-6 songwriters/year. Pays $2,500-14,000 per job. Usually buys all rights.
How to Contact: Send sample reel with cover letter; "everyone in the firm who would be a potential purchaser is made aware of it." Prefers 7^1/$_2$ ips reel-to-reel. Prefers to keep material on file. Responds as needed.

CREATIVE HOUSE ADVERTISING, INC., Suite 200, 24472 Northwestern Hwy., Southfield MI 48075. (313)353-3344. Vice President/Executive Creative Director: Robert G. Washburn. Ad agency and graphics studio. Serves commercial, retail, consumer, industrial, medical and financial clients. Uses services of songwriters and lyricists for jingles and background music for radio and TV commercials. Commissions 1 songwriter and 1 lyricist for 2 pieces/year. Pays $40-75/hour depending on job involvement. Buys all rights.
How to Contact: Query with resume of credits or submit tape demo showing jingle/composition skills. Submit cassette only with 6-12 songs. SASE, but would prefer to keep material on file. Reports in 1 month, if requested.
Music: "The type of music we need depends on clients. The range is multi, from contemporary, disco, rock, MOR and traditional."

CRESWELL, MUNSELL, FULTZ & ZIRBEL, INC., Box 2879, Cedar Rapids IA 52406. (319)395-6500. Executive Producer: Terry Taylor. Ad agency. Serves agricultural, consumer and industrial clients. Uses songwriters and music houses for jingles and background music in commercials and multi-image soundtracks. Commissions 7-8 songwriters for 15 pieces/year. Pays by the job. Buys rights on talent residuals.
How to Contact: Submit demo tape of previously aired work. Prefers 7^1/$_2$ or 15 ips reel-to-reel or cassette with 7-8 songs maximum. Does not return unsolicited material. Reports "when we want figures on a job."
Music: All types. Likes to hear a good range of music material. Will listen to anything from "small groups to full orchestration."
Tips: "Create unique, recognizable melodies."

JOHN CROWE ADVERTISING AGENCY, 1104 S. 2nd St., Springfield IL 62704. (217)528-1076. President: John F. Crowe. Ad agency. Clients include industrial, financial, commercial, aviation, retail,

state and federal agencies. Uses jingles and background music in commercials. Commissions 3-6 pieces/year. Pays $500-3,000/job. Buys all rights.
How to Contact: Submit demo tape of previously aired work. Prefers cassette with 2-4 songs. Does not return unsolicited material. Reports in 1 month.

D'ARCY-MacMANUS & MASIUS, INC., Gateway Tower, 1 Memorial Dr., St. Louis MO 63102. (314)342-8600. Contact: Director of Creative Services. Ad agency. Serves all types of clients. Uses staff for music, but occasionally uses outside material. Uses jingles and background music for commercials. Commissions 30 pieces/year.
How to Contact: Submit demo tape of previously aired work. Will listen to music done for someone else, but will *absolutely not* listen to anything done specifically for one of our clients."
Music: All types.

DE MARTINI ASSOCIATES, 414 4th Ave., Haddon Heights NJ 08035. President: Alfred De Martini. Ad agency. Serves industrial, consumer and food clients. Uses services of songwriters and lyricists for jingles, background music for commercials and educational filmstrips. Commissions 4 songwriters and 2 lyricists for 12-15 pieces/year. Pays $50-1,000/job. Buys all rights.
How to Contact: Query with resume of published credits. "Do not send tapes. They will be requested if we are interested."
Music: Background music for filmstrips and audiovisual purposes, and jingles. "Synthesizer music welcome."
Tips: "Be original. Have style. Be industrious. Be brief."

DELTA DESIGN GROUP, INC., 518 Central, Greenville MS 38701. (601)335-6148. President: Noel Workman. Ad agency. Serves industrial, financial, agricultural and retail commercial clients. Uses services of songwriters for jingles. Commissions 3-6 pieces/year. Pays $500-1,500/job. Buys "rights which vary geographically according to client. Some are all rights; others are rights for a specified market only."
How to Contact: Submit demo tape showing jingle/composition skills. Prefers 7 1/2 ips reel-to-reel with 3-6 songs. "Include typed sequence of cuts on tape on the outside of the reel box." SASE. Reports "when services are needed."
Music: Needs "30- and 60-second jingles for banks, savings and loans, home improvement centers, fertilizer manufacturers, auto dealers, furniture retailers and chambers of commerce."

*DISK PRODUCTIONS, 1100 Perkins Rd., Baton Rouge LA 70802. (504)343-5438. Director; Joey Decker. Jingle/production house. Clients include ad agencies, slide production houses and radio stations. Uses independent songwriters, lyricists and music houses for background music for commercials, jingles and albums. Commissions 3 songwriters/year and 3 lyricists/year.
How to Contact: Prefers cassette, 7 1/2 ips reel-to-reel or 1/2" videocassette and lyric sheet and lead sheet. Does not return unsolicited material, prefers to keep material on file. Reports in 1 week.
Music: Needs all types of music for jingles, music beds or background music for TV and radio etc.

*DALLAS C. DORT & COMPANY, 815 Citizens Bank Bldg., Flint MI 48502. (313)238-4677. Production Manager: Yvonne M. Penberthy. Ad agency. Clients include furniture, auto parts, health maintenance organizations, hospitals and insurance companies. Uses music houses for background music for commercials and jingles. Buys all rights or one-time rights.
How to Contact: Prefers cassette or 3/4" U-matic videocassette. Does not return unsolicited material; prefers to keep material on file. Reports in 2 weeks.

*DUNSKY ADVERTISING LTD., Suite 230, 1310 Green Ave., Montreal, Quebec H3Z 2B2, Canada. (514)937-4257. General Manager/Production: Reg Weiswall. Ad agency. Clients include automobile leasing, office furniture and highway transport firms. Uses independnet songwriters, lyricists and music houses for background music for commercials and jingles. Pays by the job. Buys all rights or one-time rights.
How to Contact: Prefers cassette. Does not return unsolicited material; prefers to keep material on file. Reports in 2 weeks.
Music: MOR for jingles, music beds or background music.

DUSENBURY & ALBANY INC., 5504 Chapel Hill Blvd., Durham NC 27707. (919)493-4455. Contact: Creative Director. Ad agency. Uses services of songwriters and lyricists for jingles. "I usually write a least a line and provide concept/musical approach, even sometimes providing entire lyrics myself." Commissions 6-9 songwriters and 3 lyricists/year. Payment "determined by budget for individual job." Negotiates rights.

How to Contact: Query with resume of credits or submit demo tape of previous work. Prefers cassette or videocassette with 4-10 songs. Does not return unsolicited material, prefers to keep on file. Reporting time varies.
Music: "Lots of adaptations to existing styles, rock 'n' roll—several instances where we'll write score to video."

EHRLICH-MANES & ASSOCIATES, 4901 Fairmont Ave., Bethesda MD 20814. (301)657-1800. Vice President, Creative Services: Lee Blom. Ad agency. Serves a wide variety of local, regional and national accounts. Uses jingles and background music for commercials. Commissions 5-10 pieces/year. Pays by the job. Rights purchased vary.
How to Contact: Query with resume, submit demo tape of previously aired work or submit demo tape showing jingle/composition skills. Prefers cassette. Does not return unsolicited material.

ESTEY-HOOVER, INC., Suite 225, 3300 Irvine Ave, Newport Beach CA 92660. (714)549-8651. Creative Director: Art Silver. Ad agency. Uses the services of songwriters for jingles and background music. Commissions 2 songwriters and 1 lyricist/year. Pays by the job. Buys all rights.
How to Contact: Query first; submit demo tape of previous work. Prefers cassette with 5-7 songs. SASE, but prefers to keep on file. Responds as need arises.
Music: "Depends upon the specific assignment. We have used, for example, heavy romantic schmaltz and also upbeat middle-of-the-road."
Tips: "Get samples on your reel ASAP. Sell yourself as a bargain when you're starting out just to build a reel. In time you'll make plenty of money if you're good."

EVANS & BARTHOLOMEW, INC., 2128 15th St., Denver CO 80202. (303)534-2343. Ad agency. Serves consumer, public service and financial clients. Uses music houses for jingles and background music in commercials. Commissions 4 pieces/year. Pays $2,500 minimum/job. Rights negotiable.
How to Contact: Submit demo tape of previously aired work. Prefers 7¹/₂ ips reel-to-reel. Does not return tape; prefers to keep on file.
Music: All types.

EVANS/CICCARONE, INC., 420 NW 42 Ave., Miami FL 33126. (305)445-1433. President: Peter Evans. Ad agency. Uses the services of songwriters and lyricists for jingles and background music. Commissions 3 songwriters and 1 lyricist/year. Payment negotiated. Buys all rights.
How to Contact: Query with resume of credits or submit demo tape of previous work. Prefers cassette with 3-6 songs. SASE, but prefers to keep on file. Responds as needs arise.
Music: All kinds.

FALLS/GARRETT ENTERPRISES, 3665 Cascade Road SW, Atlanta GA 30331. (404)691-3988. President: Ruby Grant Garrett. Ad agency. Estab. 1984. Uses services of songwriters for jingles, background music and video; lyricists for writing jingles. Commissions 1 songwriter/year and 1 lyricist/year. Pays $3,000-6,000/job. Buys all rights.
How to Contact: Query with resume of credits or submit demo tape of previous work. Prefers cassette or ³/₄ or ¹/₂" videocassette with 3 songs. SASE.

FAULKNER & ASSOCIATES, 1601 Broadway, Little Rock AR 72201. (501)375-6923. Broadcast Director: Cally Curtis. Copywriter: Gary Weidner. Ad agency. Uses the services of songwriters, lyricists and music production houses for jingles and background music. Commissions 1-3 songwriters and 1-3 lyricists/year. Pays $2,500-10,000/job. Buys all rights (30% of the time) or one-time rights (70% of the time).
How to Contact: Query first; submit demo tape of previous work and arrange a personal interview. Prefers 7¹/₂ ips reel-to-reel with 3-6 songs. Prefers studio produced demos. Does not return unsolicited material; prefers to keep on file. Responds "when the writer's product suits our needs."
Music: Suitable work for financial institutions (to project an image), fast food restaurants and retail merchants.
Tips: "Know your target market; be creative, but don't obscure your message with too much flash and dash. Also, be patient, be flexible, and keep prices realistic. Be honest about your musical opinions and respect the budget limitations of small agencies. If you can't produce a decent job for the money, say so. Buy-outs are preferable."

F/M FILM GROUP, (formerly T.F.C. Features), Suite 179, 8033 Sunset Blvd., Los Angeles CA 90046. (213)271-1012. Executive Vice President/Music Director: Chip Miller. Film and rock video production company. Uses services of songwriters and lyricists for jingles, background music and motion pictures. Commissions 2-4 songwriters and 8-10 lyricists/year. Pays by the job. Buys all rights.

How to Contact: Query with resume of credits. Prefers cassette or videocassette with 3 songs. SASE, but prefers to keep material on file.

JAN GARDNER AND ASSOCIATES, Suite 229, 3340 Poplar, Memphis TN 38111. (901)452-7328. Production Director: Mark Thompson. Ad agency. Uses services of songwriters and lyricists for jingles. Commissions 2 songwriters and 2 lyricists/year. Pays by the job. Buys all rights.
How to Contact: Submit demo tape of previous work. Prefers 7¹/₂ ips reel-to-reel with 3-12 songs. SASE, but prefers to keep material on file.
Music: "We have a wide range of clients and needs."

GARNER & ASSOCIATES, INC., Suite 350, 3721 Latrobe Dr., Charlotte NC 28211. (704)365-3455. Creative Director: John Garner. Copywriter: John W. Bell. Ad agency. Serves a wide range of clients; client list available upon request. Uses the services of songwriters for jingles. Pays by the job. Buys all rights.
How to Contact: Write first to arrange personal interview or submit demo tape of previous work. Prefers 7¹/₂ ips reel-to-reel "with enough songs to showcase your best work." Prefers studio produced demos. Does not return unsolicited material, but prefers to keep on file for possible future use.
Music: All types.
Tips: "Be flexible when it comes to price."

***GILBERT, WHITNEY & JOHNS, INC.**, 110 S. Jefferson Blvd., Whippany NJ 07981. (201)386-1776. Creative Administrative Assistant: Tricia McGinley. Ad agency. Clients include consumer package goods, service and industrial firms. Uses music houses for background music for commercials and jingles. Pays by the job. Buys all rights or one-time rights.
How to Contact: Write or call first to obtain permission to submit. Prefers cassette or ³/₄" videocassette. SASE.
Music: Various styles.

GILLHAM ADVERTISING, 5th Floor, Desert Plaza, 15 E. First S., Salt Lake City UT 84111. (801)328-0281. Producers: Katherine Gygi and Gary Woodhouse. Ad agency. Serves financial, real estate, fast food, mall and automobile dealer clients. Uses services of songwriters, composers and local production companies for jingles and background music in commercials and radio. Commissions 6 composers/year. Pays by the job.
How to Contact: Submit demo tape of previously aired work. Prefers 7¹/₂ ips reel-to-reel with 6-12 songs. Prefers studio produced demo. Does not return unsolicited material. Responds as needs arise.
Music: "Identity jingles for a variety of clients in a local market."
Tips: "Keep us up-to-date on your work with occasional demo tapes and inquiries about our needs. We may be looking for economical, quick turnaround on music for short term use."

GREY ADVERTISING, 1000 Midwest Plaza E., Minneapolis MN 55402. (612)341-2701. Contact: Creative Director. Serves retail department store, bookseller, jeweler, bedding, television, media, business, machine and airline clients. Uses songwriters and music houses for jingles and background music in commercials.
How to Contact: Submit demo tape of previous work or submit demo tape showing jingle/composition skills. Prefers 7¹/₂ ips reel-to-reel with 5-10 songs. SASE, prefers to keep on file.
Music: All types.

HERB GROSS & CO., 84 Edgerton St., Rochester NY 14607. (716)244-3711. President: Herb Gross. Consumer advertising specialist. Uses services of songwriters for jingles and movies. Commissions 3 songwriters/year. Pays $1,500-8,000/job; "depending on total authorized budget."
How to Contact: Submit demo tape of previous work. Prefers cassette with 3-6 songs. SASE, but prefers to keep material on file.
Music: Needs "60-second radio spots, 30- and 10-second TV spots. Uptempo, contemporary styles."

GROUP TWO ADVERTISING, 2002 Ludlow St., Philadelphia PA 19103. (215)561-2200. Senior Producer: Bobbi Helms. Ad agency. Serves industrial, entertainment, financial, real estate, hotel/motel and retail clients. Uses jingles. Commissions 1 songwriter/year. Pays $1,000-6,000/job. Buys one-time rights.
How to Contact: Submit demo tape of previously aired work. Prefers cassette with 5 songs minimum. Prefers studio produced demos. Does not return unsolicited material. "We prefer to keep material on file for future reference. We'll contact the person when a job comes up. A price list (no matter how general) is also helpful for us to keep on file."
Music: "Due to the variety of clients we handle, with various budgets, assignments can be of any nature."

HEALY-SCHUTTE & COMSTOCK ADVERTISING, 1207 Delaware Ave., Buffalo NY 14209. (716)884-2120. Broadcast Production Manager: Len Tobin. Ad agency. Uses services of jingle producers for jingles, background music and AV presentations. Commissions 3 songwriters and 3 lyricists/year. Pays $1,500-4,000/job. Buys all rights.
How to Contact: Submit demo tape of previous work. Prefers cassette with 6-12 songs. Prefers studio produced demos. Does not return unsolicited material; prefers to keep on file.

HEPWORTH ADVERTISING CO., 3403 McKinney Ave., Dallas TX 75204. (214)526-7785. President: S.W. Hepworth. Ad agency. Serves financial, industrial and food clients. Uses services of songwriters for jingles. Pays by the job. Buys all rights.
How to Contact: Call first and obtain permission to submit or submit demo tape of previously aired work. Prefers cassette. SASE. Reports as need arises.

THE JAYME ORGANIZATION, 23200 Chagrin Blvd., Cleveland OH 44122. (216)831-0110. Creative Supervisor: Merritt Johnquest. Ad agency. Uses the services of songwriters and lyricists for jingles and background music. Pays by the job. Buys all rights.
How to Contact: Query first; submit demo tape of previous work. Prefers cassette with 4-8 songs. SASE. Reponds by phone as needs arise.
Music: Jingles.

KETCHUM ADVERTISING, 4 Gateway Center, Pittsburgh PA 15222. (412)456-3500. Contact: Raymond Werner or Dick Sleeman. Ad agency. Serves consumer and business clients. Uses services of production houses for jingles, background music for commercials and "sometimes" films. Supplies lyricists with "basic strategic directions and background and often excellent lyrics as well." Commissions 10-15 songwriters and 10-15 lyricists for 15-20 pieces/year. Pays $500 minimum/job, "depends on markets." Buys all rights.
How to Contact: Query with resume of credits or submit demo showing jingle/composition skills. Prefers 7¹/₂ ips reel-to-reel with 7-15 songs. Does not return unsolicited material. "Material is kept on file in our creative department. Will respond only if writer calls."
Music: "We use a wide range of styles with memorable melodies and excellent production. Assignments are generally original, specific and with excellent lyrics supplied as a direction."
Tips: "Be simple. Be original. Be around."

*LA GRAVE KLIPFEL CLARKSON, INC., ADVERTISING, PUBLIC RELATIONS, MARKETING, 1707 High St., Des Moines IA 50309. (515)283-2297. Creative Director: Bob Harbert. Serves wide range of clients including financial, industrial and retail; client list available on request. Uses services of lyricists and jingle houses for jingles. Commissions 0-5 songwriters and lyricists/year. Pays $2,400-5,000/job. Rights negotiable.
How to Contact: "Telephone first then follow up with mailed information." Prefers reel-to-reel or cassette with any number songs. Does not return unsolicited material; prefers to keep material on file.
Music: Primarily interested in jingles.
Tips: "Don't rely on mailing demo—follow up. Have a good product; have a good track record; do free piano demos."

LANE & HUFF ADVERTISING, Suite 1200, 707 Broadway, San Diego CA 92101. (619)234-5101. Contact: Creative Director. Ad agency. Serves financial clients. Uses services of songwriters for jingles and background music in commercials. Commissions 4 songwriters and 4 lyricists/year. Pays $2,500-30,000/job. Buys all rights.
How to Contact: Submit demo tape of previously aired work. Prefers reel-to-reel with 8 pieces. Prefers to keep material on file. Reports in 1 month.
Music: Full lyric jingles.
Tips: "Include only your best work, even if it is only a few selections."

LD&A ADVERTISING CORP., 717 Main St., Batavia IL 60510. (312)879-2000. President: Leo Denz. Ad agency, public relations firm and audiovisual company. Serves consumer and industrial clients. Uses jingles and background music for commercials and audiovisual shows. Payment depends on use. Buys one-time rights or all rights.
How to Contact: Query with resume of credits or submit demo tape of previously aired work. Prefers cassettes. "Don't mix 'types' on a single cassette; for example, don't put jingles on the same tape as background music." SASE. "We'll keep material on file for client review. We like to let our clients have a hand in choosing talent for their commercials and films. Usually we select 3 and let them make the final choice."

Music: "Jingles: We will furnish the points to cover and their relative importance. Background: We will furnish the edited film with a description sheet of what the music is to accomplish."

AL PAUL LEFTON CO., 71 Vanderbilt Ave., New York NY 10169. (212)867-5100. Director of Broadcast: Joe Africano. Ad agency. Clients include financial, industrial and consumer products clients. Uses jingles and background music for commercials. Commissions 15 pieces/year. Buys all rights. **How to Contact:** Submit demo tape of previously aired work. Prefers 7^1/$_2$ ips reel-to-reel or cassette with 5 songs minimum. SASE. Reports in 3 weeks.

S.R. LEON COMPANY, INC., 111 Great Neck Rd., Great Neck NY 11021. (516)487-0500. Contact: Creative Director. Ad agency. Serves industrial, drug, automotive and dairy product clients. Uses jingles and background music for commercials. Commissions vary. Rights purchased are limited to use of music for commercials.
How to Contact: Submit demo tape of previously aired work. Prefers 7^1/$_2$ ips reel-to-reel with no length restrictions on demo.
Music: Uses all types.

LEWIS, GILMAN & KYNETTE, INC., 1700 Market St., Philadelphia PA 19103. (215)568-3775. Production Manager: Val Tursi. Ad agency. Serves industrial and consumer clients. Uses music houses for jingles and background music in commercials. Commissions 4 pieces/year. Pays creative fee asked by music houses.
How to Contact: Submit demo tape of previously aired work. "If songwriter has no previous work bought by ad agency, it's OK to submit samples of work." Prefers cassette. Will return with SASE if requested, but prefers to keep on file.
Music: All types.

LORD, SULLIVAN & YODER, INC., 196 S. Main St., Marion OH 43302. (614)387-8500. Ad agency. Serves industrial and consumer clients. Uses services of songwriters and music producers for jingles and background music for commercials plus scores for industrial films. Commissions 5-6 songwriters for 6-10 pieces/year. Pays $5,000-20,000/job. Buys all rights.
How to Contact: Write first with resume of credits, submit demo of previously aired work or submit demo tape of jingles/compositions for particular client. Prefers 7^1/$_2$ ips reel-to-reel with 6-12 songs. SASE. Reports "when job possibility arises."
Music: Jingles, TV post-scores, movie scores.
Tips: "Submit fresh, non-jingly ideas. Show an understanding of what commercial music should do. Stress strong enunciation in lyrics. We welcome and can sell totally new ideas as well as unusual adaptations of old forms and techniques. We don't welcome the jingle-mill sound. Nothing dull, nothing trite."

McCANN-ERICKSON/LOUISVILLE OFFICE, 1469 S. 4th St., Louisville KY 40208. (502)636-0441. Creative Director: Todd Hoon. Ad agency. Serves packaged goods, industrial, service, race track, etc. clients. Uses jingles and background music in commercials. Commissions about 12 pieces broadcast music/year. Buys rights on "13 week or yearly cycles according to AFM codes, etc."
How to Contact: Write first, then submit reel-to-reel or cassette with 3-4 songs. Reports in 1 week.

MCLEOD ADVERTISING CO., 8335 E. Jefferson Ave., Detroit MI 48214. (313)821-0120. Creative Director: Rick Trentacoste. Ad agency. Uses services of songwriters for jingles and background music.
How to Contact: Query with resume of credits or submit demo tape of previous work. "No phone calls, please." Prefers cassette with minimum 5 songs. Does not return unsolicited material. Prefers to keep material on file. Reports by phone or letter as need arises. Tapes kept 1 year.

MALLOF, ABRUZINO & NASH MARKETING, 477 E. Butterfield Rd., Lombard IL 60148. (312)964-7722. President: Ed Mallof. Ad agency. Uses services of songwriters, lyricists and production houses for jingles. Commissions 5 songwriters/year. Pays $600-3,500/job. Buys all rights.
How to Contact: Submit demo tape of previous work. Prefers cassette with 4-12 songs. SASE. Prefers to keep material on file. Reports "when we feel a need for their style." Works primarily with auto dealer jingles.
Tips: "Submit good driving music with clever lyrics."

MANDABACH & SIMMS, INC., Suite 3600, 20 N. Wacker Dr., Chicago IL 60606. (312)236-5333. Creative Director: Burt Bentkover. Copy Director: Linda Masterson. Ad agency. Serves industrial, financial and consumer clients. Uses jingles and background music for commercials. Commissions 5-10 songwriters/year. Pays union scale. "We normally work with complete production houses, not

individuals.'' Rights purchased dependent upon client's needs.
How to Contact: Submit demo tape of previously aired work. Prefers 7¹/2 ips reel-to-reel with minimum 6 songs. Does not return unsolicited material.
Music: All types for TV, radio and audiovisual presentations.
Tips: "Make sure tapes are labeled and dated. We normally don't acknowledge or comment on unsolicited material. We contact only if needed."

*MARKETAIDE INC., Box 500, Salina KS 67401. (913)825-7161. Advertising Production Manager: Dennis Katzenmeier. Advertising agency. Clients include agricultural, industrial, retail and commercial marketing. Uses music houses for background music for commercials and jingles. Pays by the job. Buys all rights or one-time rights.

MASLOW, GOLD & ROTHSCHILD, 1220 Statler Office Bldg., Boston MA 02116. (617)482-7700. Vice President/Creative: Alan Joseph. Ad agency. Uses the services of production companies for jingles.
How to Contact: Query with resume of credits; submit demo tape of previous work. Prefers 7¹/2 ips reel-to-reel or cassette with 7-12 songs. Does not return unsolicited material; prefers to keep on file. Responds by mail, "when I feel we can use the writer."
Music: "Types of needs vary by individual needs of client, account, etc."

METCALFE-COOK & SMITH, INC., 4701 Trousdale Dr., Nashville TN 37220. (615)834-6323. Contact: Betty Cook Sanders. Serves industrial and entertainment clients. Uses jingles and background music in commercials. Commissions 2 pieces/year. Payment depends on pre-determined budget.
How to Contact: Query first by mail. Prefers 7¹/2 ips reel-to-reel with minimum 3 songs. SASE. Reports in 2 weeks.

MOHAWK ADVERTISING CO., 1307 6th St. SW, Mason City IA 50401. (515)423-1354. Contact: Broadcast Production Manager. Ad agency. Serves financial and industrial clients, agricultural industries, fast food restaurants and insurance companies. Uses services of independent songwriters for jingles and background music in commercials, films and slide shows. Commissions 3-5 songwriters/year. Pays by the job. Prefers to buy one-time rights.
How to Contact: Submit demo tape of previously aired work or submit demo tape showing jingles/compositions for a particular client. Prefers 7¹/2 ips reel-to-reel or cassette with 5-10 songs. Material kept on file for reference.
Tips: "Follow up your demos with occasional notes/phonecalls. But be good first."

MUSICAL MESSAGES, INC., 354 Congress St., Boston MA 02210. (617)423-1117. Contact: Diane Cotman. Jingle producer. Uses services of songwriters, musicians and vocalists for jingles and background music; lyricists for jingles, songs and copy for ads and concepts. Commissions over 200 songwriters/year, over 200 lyricists/year. Pays $100-5,000/job.
How to Contact: Request Musical Message information sheet. Prefers cassette with 1-3 songs and lyric sheet. "We like strong repetitive hooks, clever lyrics, and sincere sentiments." Does not return unsolicited material, prefers to keep on file.
Music: Jazz, soft shoe, blues, swing, rock, or any variety of music.
Tips: "Learn all of the production angles of a piece of work and all of the cost considerations. Be aware of the concerns of all members of the production team—voice, producers, engineers, etc. Show a variety of your work. We give a chance to people who are different."

FRANK C. NAHSER, INC., 18th Floor, 10 S. Riverside Plaza, Chicago IL 60606. (312)845-5000. Contact: Milda Savage. Ad agency. Uses the services of songwriters for jingles and background music. Pays by the job. Buys all rights.
How to Contact: Submit demo tape of previous work. Prefers cassette as demo. Does not return unsolicited material; prefers to keep on file.

*NOBLE & ASSOCIATES, S.A., Constituyentes 908, Mexico City, D.F. 11950, Mexico. (5)259-2460. Contacts: Moisés Romero or Jorge Cantó. Ad agency. Clients include "all kinds of accounts. We are the biggest agency in Mexico." Uses independent songwriters and music houses for background music for commercials and jingles. Commissions 40-60 songwriters/year. Buys all rights.
How to Contact: Write first to obtain permission to submit. Submit demo tape of previously aired work. Prefers cassette or 15 ips reel-to-reel with 3-6 pieces. Does not return unsolicited material. Prefers to keep material on file. Reports in 3-5 weeks.
Music: "From classic to punk."

OGILVY & MATHER, INC., 735 Battery, San Francisco CA 94111. (415)981-0950. Contact: Creative Director. Ad agency. Serves financial, entertainment, outdoor apparel and consumer product

Close-up

Rebecca Richardson
Ad Agency President
Covington, Kentucky

"Look at a jingle as a marketing tool, but remember that it has to play an integral part in the entire marketing plan," advises Rebecca Richardson, president and founder of Richardson and Associates, one of the Greater Cincinnati area's fastest growing ad agencies.

Richardson, a former professional singer, started in advertising with political jingles for the now Governor of Kentucky, Martha Layne Collins. From there she began to approach small businesses in the area with finished jingles hoping to sell them on "spec" or speculation. (Meaning if the client liked it he'd probably buy it, if not he was under no obligation.)

She bases much of her success on maintaining personal interaction with all of her accounts and demanding the same of her staff. "All of our people are involved with every account we have. One thing that we stress here is total involvement and a total committment from everybody in the agency on *every* account." Richardson so believes in this approach that she continues to do most of the agency's jingle writing herself.

When writing she prefers to work at home where distractions can be kept to a minimum. "I like to develop a melody in my head first and the advertising message second, a method that is probably a result of my music background," says Richardson. After perfecting the melody and applying the appropriate lyrics or advertising message, she tests each jingle. "I step back from it for two or three days, then if I try to recall it and it's right there in my head, I know I've got something."

In addition to memorability, Richardson believes a jingle must also have "singability" meaning it can be easily sung by the average listener. "Listen to a lot of different music," she advises. "Get a good feel for styles and trends. Ask yourself what people are listening to today and apply it.

At the same time a writer should listen to what other agencies or jingle campaigns are doing, analyze their appeal and then determine if the same technique would be appropriate for what you're doing. Once you've developed a product you truly believe in don't be afraid to take a chance; put your work up and say here it is."

To help maintain a constant flow of new ideas Richardson likes to use freelance talent whenever she can. Freelancers "add a freshness to our creative pool and have the advantage of being able to fill in *when* and *as* we need them."

Although Richardson wants her agency to grow, she's determined to maintain the personal attention and flexibility a smaller, less structured agency allows. "There are a lot of businesses out there that really would like to do some advertising but can't afford to spend a lot. There are many inexpensive things that can be done effectively for the small businessman that just take a little bit of time and planning. I just don't think most large agencies are structured to be that flexible."

clients. Uses songwriters and music houses for jingles and background music in commercials. Commissions 20 pieces/year. Pays per job. Buys all rights.
How to Contact: Submit demo tape of previously aired work. Prefers 7¹/₂ ips reel-to-reel. Returns material if requested with SASE; prefers to keep tape on file.
Music: Usually sophisticated.

OGILVY & MATHER INC., 2 E. 48th St., New York NY 10017. (212)907-3400. Contact: Director of Music. Ad agency. Serves all types of clients. Uses services of songwriters for jingles and background music for commercials; uses services of lyricists for jingles. Commissions 20-30 songwriters and 5-10 lyricists for about 50 pieces/year. Pays by the job. "A nationally used jingle pays $5,000-10,000."
How to Contact: Send demo tape of previously aired work or demo tape showing jingle/composition skills to Director of Music. Do not include unsolicited jingles relating to clients because of possible legal implications. Prefers 7¹/₂ ips reel-to-reel with "bits of songs. Two minutes is enough and 10 pieces on a jingle demo is sufficient." Likes to file tapes for later review. Does not return unsolicited material. Reports "when something comes up."
Music: Uses all types.

*OMAR ADVERTISING, INC., 5525 N. Broadway, Chicago IL 60076. (312)271-2720. Creative Director: Paul Sierra. Ad agency. Clients include Jewel, Illinois Bell, Peoples Gas, Jay's Potato Chips, and WBBS-TV. Uses independent songwriters and music houses for background music for commercials and jingles. Commissions 2 songwriters/year and 2 lyricists/year. Pay negotiable. Buys all rights.
How to Contact: Prefers reel-to-reel or ³/₄" videocassette. Returns material if requested; material on file. Reports in 2 weeks.
Music: Music with Hispanic flavor for jingles, music beds or background music for TV, radio etc.
Tips: "We prefer light music—no heavy beat—and jingle-type music that can carry a voice over."

PEARSON, CLARKE & SAWYER ADVERTISING & PUBLIC RELATIONS, Suite 1000, 5401 W. Kennedy Blvd., Lincoln Center, Tampa FL 33609. (813)877-2425. Copywriters: Carol Meyer, John Schuh. Ad agency and public relations firm. Serves industrial, financial, fast food, shelter and packaged goods clients. Uses services of songwriters for jingles. Commissions 2 songwriters/year. Payment varies. Rights negotiated.
How to Contact: Submit demo tape of previously aired work. SASE, but prefers to keep material on file. Reports by phone or mail as needs arise.

*PHILADELPHIA MUSIC WORKS, INC., Box 947, Bryn Mawr PA 19010. (215)825-5656. President: Andy Mark. Jingle producers/music library producers. Deals with artists and songwriters.
How to Contact: Call first and obtain permission to submit. Prefers cassette. "We are looking for quality jingle tracks already produced, as well as instrumental pieces between 2 and 3 minutes in length for use in AV music library." Does not return unsolicited material. Reports in 4 weeks.
Music: All types.
Tips: Looking for "knowledge of the jingle business and what works as background music for audiovisual presentations, such as slide shows, video training films, etc."

PRINGLE DIXON PRINGLE, 3340 Peachtree Rd. NE, Atlanta GA 30026. (404)261-9542. Creative Director: Bill Aydlotte. Ad agency. Serves fashion, financial, fast food and industrial clients; client list available on request. Uses services of songwriters for jingles and background music. Pays by the job. Rights vary, depending on job.
How to Contact: Submit tape of previous work. Prefers 7¹/₂ ips reel-to-reel. SASE.
Music: All types.

PRO/CREATIVES, 25 W. Burda Place, Spring Valley NY 10977. President: David Rapp. Ad and promotion agency. Serves consumer products and services, sports and miscellaneous clients. Uses background music in TV and radio commercials. Payment negotiable.
How to Contact: Query with resume of credits. SASE.

RAMEY COMMUNICATIONS, 3008 Wilshire Blvd., Los Angeles CA 90010. (213)384-2700. Producer: Allen Williams. Ad agency. Uses services of songwriters for jingles and background music. "We have copywriters on staff." Commissions 5 songwriters/year. Pays by the job. Buys all rights.
How to Contact: Submit demo tape of previous work. Prefers reel to reel or cassette with 5-10 songs. Does not return unsolicited material, prefers to keep on file. Reports "when the need arises."
Music: "We have many broadcast accounts—each project has its own qualifications."

RICHARDSON & ASSOCIATES, Suite 315, Fifth Street Center, Covington KY 41011. Contact: Sherry Ryle. Clients include small to medium size retailers, and political candidates. Uses the services of songwriters for jingles.
How to Contact: Submit demo tape of previously aired work or tape showing composition skills. SASE. Reports in 3 months.
Music: All styles.

RIVES SMITH BALDWIN CARLBERG + Y&R, 5444 Westheimer, Houston TX 77056. (713)965-0764. Producer: Cindy Weddle. Ad agency. Serves primarily consumer, financial and industrial (oil-related) clients. Uses songwriters and music houses for jingles and background music in commercials; lyricists for jingle lyrics. Commissions 25 pieces/year. Pays by the job. Purchase of rights depends on job.
How to Contact: Submit demo tape of previously aired work. Prefers 7¹/2 ips reel-to-reel or cassette with 6-7 songs. Prefers studio produced demos. Returns video tapes with SASE; does not return radio tapes.
Music: All types.

ALBERT JAY ROSENTHAL & CO., 400 N. Michigan Ave., Chicago IL 606ll. (312)337-8070. Contact: Group Creative Director. Ad agency. Serves fashion, consumer foods, kitchen utensils, automotive repair and cosmetics clients. Uses jingles and background music for commercials and sales films. Commissions 15-20 pieces/year. Pays by the job. Buys all rights.
How to Contact: Submit demo tape of previously aired work. Prefers 7¹/2 ips reel-to-reel demo 3-5 minutes long. SASE, but prefers to keep material on file.
Music: Uses all types.

CHUCK RUHR ADVERTISING, INC., 1221 Nicollett Mall, Minneapolis MN 55403. (612)332-4565. Contact: Art Director. Ad agency. Serves consumer and industrial clients; client list available on request. Uses services of songwriters for jingles and background music. Commissions 5-10 songwriters and 2-5 lyricists/year. Initial fee negotiated, after that pays union scales. Pays residuals for subsequent use of material.
How to Contact: Submit demo tape of previous work. Prefers cassette. Reports "when needed."
Tips: "Be good and be flexible."

THE SAVAN COMPANY, INC., 6528 Clayton Rd., St. Louis MO 63117. (314)647-7777. Contact: Frank Oros. Ad agency. Uses services of songwriters for jingles and background music. Pays by the job. Buys all rights.
How to Contact: Query first; submit demo tape of previous work. Prefers cassette with 2 songs. Does not return unsolicited material; prefers to keep on file.

SHAFFER SHAFFER SHAFFER, INC., 226 Hanna Bldg., Cleveland OH 44115. (216)566-1188. President: Harry Gard Shaffer, Jr. Ad agency. Uses services of songwriters for jingles and background music. Commissions 4-5 songwriters/year. Pays $3,000-15,000/job. Buys all rights.
How to Contact: Query with resume of credits. Prefers 7¹/2 ips reel-to-reel with 6-12 songs. SASE, but prefers to keep on file. Responds as needs arise.

SIMONS ADVERTISING & ASSOCIATES, 23042 Commerce Dr., Farmington Hills MI 48024. (313)471-7000. Creative Director: Diana Zuppe. Ad agency. Serves retail clients. Uses jingles and background music for commercials. Pays $750 minimum/job. Buys all rights.
How to Contact: Query with resume or submit demo tape of previously aired work. Prefers 7¹/2 ips reel-to-reel.

STEVENS, INC., 809 Commerce Bldg., Grand Rapids MI 49502. (616)459-8175. Creative Director: Burl Robins. Ad agency. Uses jingles and background music for commercials. Commissions 1-3 pieces/year. Pays $2,000 minimum/job. Buys all rights.
How to Contact: Submit demo tape of previously aired work. Prefers cassette with 5 songs. SASE. Reports in 3 weeks.

*STRENGTH PRODUCTIONS, (formerly London & Associates), 5th Floor, 168 N. Michigan, Chicago IL 60601. Creative Director: Kaye Britt. Full service video production firm. Serves retail, consumer products and trade clients. Uses services of songwriters for jingles, audiovisual presentations and background music in commercials. Commissions 4 songwriters/year. Pays $200-3,000/finished job and by "straight buy out." Buys all rights.
How to Contact: Submit demo tape of previously aired work. Prefers cassette with 6-12 songs. Prefers studio produced demos. SASE, but prefers to keep material on file. Reports in 2 weeks.

Music: "We need highly identifiable music/jingles. The type depends on clients. Be willing to work on small budget for spec tape."
Tips: "Be willing to work on spec basis—small budget for spec. Be flexible. Don't give up."

TAL, INC., 3645 W. Lake Rd., Erie PA 16505. (814)838-4505. Audiovisual, Broadcast Production: Tim Ely. Ad agency. Uses services of songwriters and jingle houses for jingles and background music. "Lyrics usually are part of jingle package." Commissions 3-4 songwriters/year. Pays $1,500-7,500/job. Buys all rights.
How to Contact: Submit demo tape of previous work. Prefers 7¹/₂ ips reel-to-reel with 6-12 songs. Prefers studio produced demos. Does not return unsolicited material; prefers to keep material on file. Reports by phone when a project comes up.
Music: Needs stand-alone jingles for both TV and radio; also background music for TV, radio and AV shows.
Tips: "Be patient! Be persistent! Be productive! Show me something new. We tend to shy away from music that is too commercial. We need fresh, new approaches that fit the particular demographic profile and mood of our campaigns."

J. WALTER THOMPSON CO., 600 Renaissance Center, Detroit MI 48243. (313)568-3800. Executive Producer: Jerry Apoian. Ad agency. Serves industrial, recreational, banking, media clients and major car companies. Uses music houses and individual songwriters for jingles (often writes own lyrics) and background music in commercials. Commissions 30-40 pieces/year. Pays union rates. "If music is written for specific needs of client, buys all rights."
How to Contact: Call first about demo tape. Prefers 7¹/₂ ips reel-to-reel. Use best works. SASE.
Music: All types.

TRAVIS/WALZ & ASSOC., ADVERTISING, 8500 W. 63rd St., Shawnee Mission KS 66202. (913)384-3550. Associate Creative Director: Bev Bellinger. Ad agency. Uses services of songwriters and music production companies for jingles, background music and post scoring. Commissions 2-3 songwriters/year. Pays by the job. Buys all rights.
How to Contact: Submit demo tape of previous work. Prefers cassette with 3-10 songs. Prefers studio produced demos. SASE, but prefers to keep material on file. Reports "when a project suited to a specific songwriter's style comes along."
Music: Needs "jingle package (10-, 30- and 60-second versions with and without vocals) composing a pre-established theme line to music." Prefers experienced songwriters.
Tips: "Learn to create music that edits cleanly into 10 seconds segments to keep music versatile for ad use. Basically your demo sells you—make it as professional (and original, of course) as possible."

TULLY-MENARD, INC., 2207 S. Dale Mabry, Tampa FL 33629. (813)253-0447. Creative Director: David M. DiMaggio. Ad agency. Uses services of songwriters for jingles, background music and film and AV soundtracks. Commissions 2 songwriters/year. Payment negotiable, "dependent on project, budget and needs." Buys all rights.
How to Contact: Submit demo tape of previous work. Prefers 7¹/₂ ips reel-to-reel with 7-15 songs. SASE, but prefers to keep material on file. "We research our file at the onset of need to determine candidates and parameters, then obtain bids and demos."
Music: "Broadcast and off-line; jingles and music tracks."
Tips: "Show extreme versatility in style *and* production."

CALDWELL VAN RIPER, 1314 N. Meridian, Indianapolis IN 46202. (317)632-6501. Executive Creative Director: Jeffrey Leiendecker. Ad agency and public relations firm. Serves industrial, financial and consumer/trade clients. Uses jingles and background music for commercials. Commissions 25 pieces/year.
How to Contact: Submit demo tape of previously aired work or submit tape showing jingle/composition skills. Prefers 7¹/₂ ips reel-to-reel. SASE. Reports "as soon as possible."

VANDECAR, DEPORTE & JOHNSON, 255 Lark St., Albany NY 12210. (518)463-2153. Production Director: Marc W. Johnson. Ad agency. Serves financial, automotive, consumer and other clients. Uses services of lyricists and music houses for jingles, background music in commercials and filmtracks. Commissions 15 pieces/year. Pays by the job. Rights purchased vary.
How to Contact: Submit demo tape showing jingle/composition skills. Prefers 7¹/₂ ips reel-to-reel with minimum 3 songs. SASE, but prefers to keep material on file "but will dub off and send back if specified." Responds by phone when needs arise.
Music: Jingle work, music tracks, demo work, chart writing, conceptualization and assistance on assignments.

*WEAVER-SUTTON, INC., 1053 St. Gregory St., Cincinnati OH 45202. (513)241-0132. Copywriter: Joe Rosenberger. Ad agency. Clients include retail, medical products, insurance and manufacturing firms. Uses music houses for background music for commercials. Commissions 3-4 songwriters/year. Pays by the job or per hour. Buys all rights.
How to Contact: Prefers cassette, 7¹/₂ ips reel-to-reel, or ³/₄" videocassette. SASE. Prefers to keep material on file. Reports in 2 weeks.
Music: MOR "mostly for retail accounts", music beds and AV backgrounds.
Tips: "Songs must be very fresh with memorable music lines."

WEBER, COHN & RILEY, 444 N. Michigan Ave., Chicago IL 60611. (312)527-4260. Senior Creative Director: C. Welch. Ad agency. Serves real estate, financial and food clients. Uses jingles and background music for commercials. Commissions 3 pieces/year. Pays $500 minimum/job. Rights purchased vary.
How to Contact: Write a letter of introduction to creative director. SASE. "We listen to and keep a file of all submissions, but generally do not reply unless we have a specific job in mind."
Music: "We expect highly original, tight arrangements that contribute to the overall concept of the commercial. We do not work with songwriters who have little or no previous experience scoring and recording commercials."
Tips: "Don't aim too high to start. Establish credentials and get experience on small local work, then go after bigger accounts. Don't oversell when making contacts or claim the ability to produce any kind of 'sound.' Producers only believe what they hear on sample reels."

*WEITZMAN, DYM & ASSOCIATES, 4709 Montgomery Lane, Bethesda MD 20814. (301)652-7035. Chairman: Alan Weitzman. Ad agency. Clients include national, regional and local advertisers. Uses lyricists and music houses for jingles. Pays $5,000-15,000/job. Buys all rights.
How to Contact: Write first to obtain permission to submit. Prefers cassette. Does not return unsolicited material; prefers to keep material on file. Reports in 4 weeks.
Music: MOR, pop, rock for jingles, music beds or background music for TV, radio, etc.

WILDRICK & MILLER, INC., 350 5th Ave., New York NY 10118. President: Donald Wildrick. Ad agency. Serves industrial clients. Uses background music in commercials. "We have just begun to buy music." Pays by the job. Buys all rights.
How to Contact: Query. "We do not accept unsolicited material and we neither evaluate it nor return it."

WILK & BRICHTA ADVERTISING, 875 N. Michigan, John Hancock Center., Chicago IL 60611. (312)280-2800. Director of Broadcast Production: Mr. Clair Callihan. Ad agency. Uses services of songwriters for jingles, background music in commercials and longer films/filmstrips. Commissions 2-4 songwriters for 3-4 pieces/year. Pays by the job. Buys all rights.
How to Contact: Query by mail or phone, then submit by mail demonstration tape of previous work with cover letter. Will also review videocassettes and 16mm film but *call* before submitting. Prefers cassette. Prefers studio produced demos. Does not return unsolicited material. Reports "only if interested in specific material.".
Music: All types.

WOLKCAS ADVERTISING, 435 New Karner Rd., Albany NY 12205. (518)869-4846. Creative Director: Stewart Sacklow. Ad agency. Uses the services of songwriters and lyricists for jingles, background music and slide shows. Commissions 3-4 songwriters and 3-4 lyricists/year. Pays by the job and buy out. Buys all rights.
How to Contact: Submit demo tape of previous work. Prefers 7¹/₂ ips reel-to-reel with 3-5 songs. Prefers studio produced demos. Does not return unsolicited material; prefers to keep on file. Responds when needs arise.
Music: Various types depending on client—"from full string orchestra to hard rock and synthesizers."
Tips: "Keep submitting updated work; we are always looking for something new and fresh for our clients. Also, we need more short music to accompany IDs for TV."

WOMACK/CLAYPOOLE/GRIFFIN, Suite 125, 2997 LBJ Business Park, Dallas TX 75234. (214)643-1234. Contact: Bill Claypool. Ad agency. Serves petroleum, aviation, financial, insurance and retail clients. Uses services of songwriters for jingles and background music in commercials. Pays by the job. Buys all rights.
How to Contact: Submit demo tape of previous work. Prefers reel-to-reel. SASE, but prefers to keep on file.
Music: Radio spots and TV background.

Audiovisual Firms————

Audiovisual firms produce films, videotapes and slide presentations for a variety of uses. Sometimes the purpose is to instruct or inform as with educational or corporate training films. Other times a film or videotape is produced solely for its commercial entertainment value. Whatever the intended use, audiovisual producers realize the effectiveness of music. The visual portion of the production is employed to get an audience's attention while the audio portion is employed to maintain it.

Often the purpose of the production will dictate what style of music should or should not be used. For example, hard rock music would not generally be used for a sales training film. Concurrently the type of production often determines the length of music needed. Feature motion pictures obviously require longer pieces of music than do slide presentations.

When in need of music for a production audiovisual producers often turn to stock music houses for many projects simply because of time and budget considerations. Other times, when a new or particularly adventurous client is signed the AV producer will go in search of something fresh, original and unique; a situation from which competent and savvy songwriters can benefit. But the songwriter who wants to work in the audiovisual field must remember that most productions impart information visually and therefore the visual aspect of a production must take precedence over the audio aspect.

Audiovisual producers pay in a variety of ways. Some by the job, some by the hour and others by royalty. Rights purchased vary with the client and project.

Companies listed in this section include audiovisual producers as well as audio, video and motion picture production companies. All have expressed a willingness to hear fresh new material.

Additional names and addresses of audiovisual firms can be found in the *Audiovisual Marketplace* (R.R. Bowker).

ARZTCO PICTURES, INC., 15 E. 61st St., New York NY 10021. (212)753-1050. President/ Producer: Tony Arzt. Clients include industry, government and advertising agencies. "We're currently producing feature films." Uses services of music houses and songwriters for film scores. Commissions 20-50 pieces/year. Pay negotiable "depending on composer and the project." Buys all rights or one-time rights.
How to Contact: Submit demo tape of previously aired work or submit demo tape of composition skills. Prefers cassette with 6-12 songs. "We prefer to keep tapes on file, then review them when a project comes up." Reports "immediately, if appropriate for a job on hand."
Music: "We generally prefer small group sound—no large orchestras with too much brass and strings. Good beat and melody are important."

*AUDIO VISUAL ASSOCIATES, 1515 Old Bayshore, Burlingame CA 94010. Production Manager: Tamara Scott. Audiovisual firm, scoring service, motion picture production company and music/sound effects library. Clients include industrial firms. Uses the services of music houses, independent songwriters, lyricists and musicians for background music and scoring of film; jingles, commercials for radio and TV; and multi-image productions. Commissions 6-10 composers/year and 6-10 lyricists/year. Pays $150-1,000/job; $25-35/hour. Buys all rights or one-time rights.
How to Contact: Submit tape demonstrating composition skills, or query with resume of credits. Prefers cassette, reel-to-reel or videocassette. Does not return unsolicited material; prefers to keep on file.
Music: Commercial and all others.

*AUDIO-VISUAL ASSOCIATES, 334 E. 31st St., Kansas City MO 64108. (816)931-4102. Contact: Carl James. Clients include industrial firms. Uses services of songwriters for thematic scores in films and filmstrips. Payment negotiable. Buys all rights.
How to Contact: Query with demo tape of previously aired work. Prefers reel-to-reel or cassette. Keeps tapes on file.
Music: Broad range of musical styles for industrial, sales training and promotional shows.

THE AVTECH COMPANY, INC., 6023 N. Dixie Dr., Dayton OH 45414. (513)890-7600. Audio Director: M. Bruce Linebaugh. Audiovisual firm. Clients include business and industry. Uses services of music libraries for AV productions or audio tapes. "We have a very limited need for this. We have a musician/composer who does this type of work for us on a freelance basis." Commissions 1-2 composers/year. Pays $100-300/job. Buys all rights.
How to Contact: Submit demo tape of previous work. Prefers 7¹/₂ or 15 ips reel-to-reel with 4-6 songs. "Don't call us, we'll call you." Does not return unsolicited material. Reports in 2 weeks.
Music: Needs "industrial electronic scores, customized synthesized sound effects, etc."

*BALL COMMUNICATIONS, INC., 1101 N. Fulton Ave., Evansville IN 47710. (812)428-2300. President/Creative Director: Martin A. Ball. Audiovisual and television production and meeting production firm. Clients include Fortune 1000 firms. Uses the services of music houses and independent songwriters for background music for industrial video/multi-image; lyricists for jingles for TV and meeting presentations. Commissions 12 composers/year and 12 lyricists/year. Pays by the job or per hour. Buys all rights or one-time rights.
How to Contact: Prefers cassette, 7¹/₂ ips reel-to-reel or ¹/₂" videocassette. Does not return unsolicited material but prefers to keep on file. Reports in 2 weeks.
Music: All types.

*SAMUEL R. BLATE ASSOCIATES, 10331 Watkins Mill Dr., Gaithersburg MD 20879-2935. (301)840-2248. President: Samuel R. Blate. Audiovisual firm. Uses the services of music houses, independent songwriters and lyricists. Background music for slide/tape, filmstrip and video. Commissions 1-5 composers/year and 1 lyricist/year. Pay negotiated on a project need basis. Buys all rights or one-time rights. "Rights purchased generally depend client need—we usually try to buy one-time rights."
How to Contact: Query with resume of credits and sample tape. Prefers Dolby B or C cassette, 7.5 ips reel-to-reel or Beta videocassette with 5-10 pieces. "Submit resume with tape. We generally file both against future needs unless the composer desires to have the tape returned. SASE required. Due to volume of samples received, we usually do not respond until a need is identified. Please *label* submissions."
Music: "We use all types and styles of music and songs for AV presentations."
Tips: "Previous track record is not nearly as important as demonstrated artistry."

ROBERT BERNING-FILM PRODUCTIONS, 710 Papworth Ave., Metairie LA 70005. (504)834-8811. Audio Director: Jim Smith. Motion picture production company. Clients include advertising agencies, industrial firms and corporations. Uses services of music houses and songwriters for background music, musical scores in films, original songs for themes, music scoring, TV and radio commercials, international sales films, and safety/training films; uses lyricists for lyrics and themes. Commissions 10 composers and 4 lyricists/year for 10 pieces/year. Pays $1,000-10,000/job. Buys all rights or one-time rights.
How to Contact: Submit demo tape of previous work or query with resume of credits. Prefers 7¹/₂ ips reel-to-reel with minimum 4 songs. SASE. Reports in 1 month.
Music: Uses music for TV and radio commercials, multi-media productions and films.
Tips: "Submit examples of past work and work within budgetary range."

BURST/GOSA PRODUCTIONS, INC., Box 5354, Atlanta GA 30307. (404)523-8023. Vice President: Cheryl Gosa. Audiovisual firm and motion picture production company. Clients include business, industry, churches, schools, hospitals, government. Uses the services of music houses, songwriters and composers for musical backgrounds for filmstrips and slide shows, film scores and theme songs; and music with an international feel by country; rarely uses lyricists, but possibly for public service announcements. Commissions 10-20 composers/year. Pays $500 minimum/job. Buys all rights.
How to Contact: Query with resume of credits; submit demo tape of previous work. Prefers cassette with 5-10 songs. Does not return unsolicited material; "we like to keep material on file until a job requiring music arises."
Music: "Upbeat, light, industrial, contemporary, lyrical, sensitive, subtle and compassionate. Usually for 1-5 instruments. Rarely use lyrics. A typical filmstrip or slide show assignment would be 3-5 short (4 minutes) pieces of a genre, but each unique. Film tracks are more complex with needs according to individual films (14-90 minutes)."
Tips: "Be pleasantly available, i.e., check in periodically, but don't call every month. Exhibit flexibility and creativity in intuiting the musical needs of a script. Be open to changes—we rarely go with first drafts on anything."

CABSCOTT BROADCAST PRODUCTION, INC., 517 7th Ave., Lindenwold NJ 08021. President: Larry Scott. Audiovisual firm and audio video location and post production company. Clients include

business, industry and broadcast outlets (local and network). Uses services of music houses for "jingles for commercial music, bids in spots and industrial presentations and AV, video and film; lyricists for lyrics for jingles. Commissions 12-20 composers and 2-3 lyricists/year. Pays by the job. Buys all rights.
How to Contact: Query with resume of credits, submit demo tape of previous work or submit videocassette. Prefers 7¹/₂ or 15 ips reel-to-reel, cassette or videocassette with 3-10 songs on demo or 16mm or 35mm film. SASE. Reports in 1 month maximum.

*CANARY PRODUCTIONS, 145 Barcladen Rd., Rosemont PA 19010. (215)527-8812. President: Andy Mark. Music library. Uses services of music houses and independent songwriters for background music for AV use, jingles for all purposes, and commercials for radio. Commissions 15 composers/year. Pays 30% royalty, flat rate, or on consignment per composition.
How to Contact: Prefers cassette with 5-10 pieces. SASE. Reports in 2 weeks.
Music: All styles. "We pay cash for produced tracks of all styles and lengths. Production value is imperative. No scratch tracks accepted."

*ANTHONY CARDOZA ENTERPRISES, Box 4163, North Hollywood CA 91607. (818)985-5550. President: Anthony Cardoza. Motion picture producer. Scores for theatrical films. Commissions 1 composer/year and 1 lyricist/year. Pays by the job. Buys all rights.
How to Contact: Submit demo tape of previous work. Prefers cassette. Does not return unsolicited material; prefers to keep on file. Reports in 2 weeks.
Music: All types.

*CHAPPLE FILMS, INC., Rt. 198, Chaplin CT 06235. (203)455-9779. President: Wendy Wood. Audiovisual firm and motion picture production company. Clients include government, educational and industrial firms. Use the services of music houses, independent songwriters and lyricists. Pay "depends on budget."
How to Contact: Submit demo tape of previous work. Prefers cassette or 7¹/₂" or 15 ips reel-to-reel. SASE.
Music: Instrumental.

CINE DESIGN FILMS, 255 Washington St., Denver CO 80203. (303)777-4222. Producer: Jon Husband. Motion picture production company. Clients include business, industry and documentaries. Uses the services of music houses and songwriters. Commissions 7-12 composers and 2-3 lyricists/year. Pays by the job. Buys all rights or one-time rights.
How to Contact: Query with resume of credits; submit demo tape of previous work. Prefers 7¹/₂ ips reel-to-reel or cassette; finished, film or tape with 5-15 songs. Does not return unsolicited material.
Music: "Our needs could be from a full score to a spot jingle—depending on our needs at the time."
Tips: "Keep in touch and be flexible."

CINETUDES FILM PRODUCTIONS, 295 W. 4th St., New York City NY 10014. (212)966-4600. Producers: Christine Jurzykowski, Gale Goldberg. Motion picture production company. Clients include television. Uses services of songwriters for musical scores in films. Commissions variable number pieces/year. Pays by the job. Buys all rights.
How to Contact: Submit tape demonstrating composition skills. Prefers reel-to-reel with 2-4 songs. "Recommendations are helpful." SASE. Reports in 2 weeks.
Music: Film music.

*CLEARVUE, INC., 5711 N. Milwaukee, Chicago IL 60646. (312)775-9433. President: W. Mc-Dermed. Audiovisual firm. "We only produce for ourselves." Uses the services of independent songwriters. Pays one-time payment.

COMMUNICATION DESIGN ASSOCIATES, Suite 1250, 921 Walnut, Kansas City MO 64106. (816)472-5101. Producer: Bill Foard. Chief Engineer: Larry Johnson. Clients include business and promotional firms. Uses services of songwriters for music in radio and TV commercials. Payment negotiable. Rights purchased vary.
How to Contact: Submit demo tape of previously aired work. Prefers cassette with 4-5 songs. SASE. Reports in 1 week.

*COMMUNICATIONS CONCEPTS INC., Box 661, Cape Canaveral FL 32920. (305)783-5232. Manager: Jim Lewis. Audiovisual firm. Clients include resorts, developments and high tech industries. Uses the services of music houses, independent songwriters, lyricists and music libraries and services for scoring of TV shows and AV presentations, background music for AV programs, jingles for commercials and AV programs, and commercials for radio and TV. Commissions 2-3 composers/year and 1-2 lyricists/

year. Pays by the job. Buys all rights or one-time rights.
How to Contact: Prefers cassette. Does not return unsolicited material; prefers to keep on file.

*CREATIVE SUPPORT SERVICES, 1950 Riverside Dr., Los Angeles CA 90039. (213)666-7968. Contact: Michael M. Fuller. Audiovisual firm, scoring service and music/sound effects library. Clients include audiovisual production companies, ad agencies and broadcasters. Uses the services of independent songwriters and musicians for multi-image shows and videos, background music for AVs; jingles for "all of the above plus broadcasters" and commercials for radio and TV. Pay varies. Buys varying rights.
How to Contact: Write or call first to arrange personal interview. Prefers cassette "chrome or metal only," 7¹/₂ ips reel-to-reel or Beta videocassette with 3 or more pieces. Does not return unsolicited material; prefers to keep on file. Reports in 4 weeks. "Will call if interested."
Music: Uses "industrial music predominantly but all other kinds or types to lesser degree."
Tips: "Neatness counts. We judge sound quality as well as music especially if writer is the musician and recording engineer."

*CRYSTAL PROMOTIONS, Suite 24, 5130 Woodman Ave., Sherman Oaks CA 90025. (213)477-8561. Manager/Director: Rebecca Olivo. Artist management, music promotion firm (to music publishers) and music/sound effects library. Clients include music publishers, animation and independent music producers. Estab. 1984. Uses the services of music houses, independent songwriters and lyricists for scoring of animated features and children's market and commercials for radio. Pay negotiable. Buys all rights or one-time rights.
How to Contact: Submit tape demonstrating composition skills, submit manuscript showing music scoring skills, or query with resume of credits. "If demo is in regard to a particular ad, please specify." Prefers cassette or VHS videocassette with 4 pieces. Will return submissions "if we will not use the material."
Music: Country, pop, R&B, A/C and contemporary classical. "We encourage good Spanish ballads."

D.S.M. PRODUCERS, Suite #1204, 161 W. 54th St., New York NY 10019. (212)245-0006. Contact Suzan Bader. Scoring service, music/sound effects library and record production. Clients include industrial (Motorola), music publishers (song demos), groups (recording) and commercials (radio and TV). Uses the services of songwriters and lyricists for background music. Payment negotiable "as per agreement with D.S.M. producers." Rights purchased depends on client.
How to Contact: Submit demo tape of previous work. Prefers cassette or videocassette with 1-4 songs. SASE. Reports in 3 weeks.
Music: Mostly crossover; also pop, R&B, rock, country and jazz.

DCA FILM/VIDEO PRODUCTIONS, 424 Valley Rd., Warrington PA 18976. (215)343-2020. Executive Producer: Hal Fine. Audiovisual firm and motion picture production company. Clients include business, industry and advertising agencies. Uses services of music houses for musical scores in film, TV commercials, background music, etc. Commissions 3-4 pieces/year. Pays by the job. Rights vary, depending on job.
How to Contact: Submit demo tape of previous work or tape demonstrating composition skills. Prefers 7¹/₂ ips reel-to-reel. SASE. Reports in 3 weeks. Free catalog.

*DE MARTINI ASSOCIATES, 414 Fourth Ave., Haddon Heights NJ 08035. President: Alfred De Martini. Audiovisual firm. Clients include food, transport and clothing firms. Uses the services of music houses, songwriters and lyricists for scoring and background music. Commissions 5 composers/year and 4 lyricists/year. Pays $150-1,000/job or $50-100/hour. Buys all rights.
How to Contact: "Send resume only—we will contact you. Do not submit without invitation."
Music: Contemporary. "Synthesizers welcome."

*DIDIK TV PRODUCTIONS, Box 133, New York NY 11374. (718)843-6839. Contact: Creative Director. TV production company. Clients include government, ad agency, corporations. Uses the services of music houses, independent songwriters and lyricists for commercials for TV. Commissions 3 composers/year. Pays by the job. Buys variable rights.
How to Contact: Submit demo tape of previous work. Prefers cassette or videocassette. Does not return unsolicited material; prefers to keep on file. Reports in 3 weeks.

DUBOIS/RUDDY, 2145 Crooks, Troy MI 48084. (313)643-0320. Contact: Ms. C. Ruddy. Multi-image and animation production service. Clients include corporate communications. Uses services of music houses for background music, musical scores and jingles; lyricists for movie themes. Commissions 2-5 composers and lyricists/year. Pays by the job. Buys all rights.
How to Contact: Query with resume of credits, arrange personal interview, submit demo tape of

previous work, submit tape demonstrating composition skills. Prefers reel-to-reel, cassette or videocassette. SASE, but prefers to keep material on file. Reports in 1 month.
Music: "Original music and lyrics created for multi-image openings, closes, etc., or TV spots, film underscores, etc."
Tips: "Only interested in local suppliers."

THE DURASELL CORP., 16th Floor, 360 Lexington Ave., New York NY 10017. (212)687-1010. President: Albert A. Jacoby. Senior Producer/Acct. Services: Pat Jacoby. Audiovisual and video firm. Clients include package goods manufacturers, magazines, pharmaceutical, liquor, tobacco and food manufacturers. Uses the services of music houses and songwriters for background music for sales meetings, sound filmstrips, musical scores in films, originals songs for themes and music scoring; lyricists for writing lyrics for themes and other music. Pays by the job. Buys all rights on originals or one-time rights for existing tracks.
How to Contact: Query with resume of credits—"a letter is a *must*." Prefers cassette. Does not return unsolicited material.
Music: Upbeat, tuneful, show tune-oriented material for major sales meetings.

***EDUCATIONAL INSIGHTS**, 150 N. Carob, Compton CA 90220. (213)637-2131. Director of Development: Dennis J. Graham. Audiovisual firm. Clients include schools and parents of young children. Uses the services of music houses and independent songwriters for scoring of children's plays, learning programs and music education materials. Commissions 4 composers/year. Pays by the job or 5% royalty. Buys all rights.
How to Contact: Submit demo tape of previous work. Prefers cassette. SASE. Reports in 4 weeks.
Music: Needs "music for young children, especially educational in nature."

***DON ELLIOTT PRODUCTIONS**, 15 Bridge Rd., Weston CT 06883. (203)226-4209. Vice President in Charge of New Material: Doriane Elliott. Scoring service. Clients include advertising agencies, CBS Records, Arista Records. Uses the services of independent songwriters and lyricists for scoring of films and albums; background music for commercials; and jingles for radio and TV. Commissions for jingles only. Payment and rights purchased depend on the job.
How to Contact: Submit demo tape of previous work or tape demonstrating composition skills. Prefers cassette. Does not return unsolicited material; prefers to keep on file. Reports in 2 weeks.
Music: Looking for music for jingles or original music for possible albums.

***ENCORE VIDEO PRODUCTIONS INC.**, 933 Hwy 501, Myrtle Beach SC 29577. (803)448-9900. President: Rik Dickinson. Audiovisual firm and motion picture production company. Clients include broadcast and industrial companies. Uses the services of music houses for commercials for TV. Pays by the job. Buys one-time rights.
How to Contact: Submit demo tape of previous work. Prefers 3/4" U-matic videocassette. Does not return unsolicited material; prefers to keep on file.

***ENTERPRISES UNLIMITED**, 9F, 400 E. 59th St., New York NY 10022. (212)832-6659. Director: J.O. Walman. Audiovisual firm, motion picture production company and scoring service. Uses the services of music houses, independent songwriters and lyricists for scoring of films; background music for movies and TV; jingles for products and services; and commercials for radio and TV.
How to Contact: Query with resume of credits or call first to arrange personal interview. Prefers cassette. Does not return unsolicited material; prefers to keep on file. Reports in 10 weeks.
Music: All types.

ENTERTAINMENT PRODUCTIONS, INC., Box 554, Malibu CA 90265. (213)456-3143. Motion picture production company. President: Edward Coe. Clients include distributors/exhibitors. Uses services of music houses and songwriters for background and theme music for films and TV. Commissions/year vary. Pays scale/job. Rights purchased vary.
How to Contact: Query with resume of credits. Prefers reel-to-reel. Demo should show flexibility of composition skills. "Demo records/tapes sent at own risk—returned if SASE included." Reports in 1 month.
Tips: "Have resume on file."

***EXPANDING IMAGES**, Suite A-143, 14252 Culver Dr., Irvine CA 92714. (714)720-0864. President: Robert Denison. Audiovisual firm. Clients include industrial firms. Uses the services of music houses, independent songwriters and lyricists for background music for multi-media shows and commercials for TV. Pays by the job.
How to Contact: Prefers cassette. Does not return unsolicited material; prefers to keep on file.
Music: All types.

MARTIN EZRA & ASSOCIATES, 48 Garrett Rd., Upper Darby PA 19082. (215)352-9595 or 9596. Producer: Martin Ezra. Audiovisual firm and motion picture production company. Clients include business, industry and education. Uses services of music houses, songwriters and stock music for background music for sound filmstrips, musical scores in films, and original songs for themes; uses lyricists for movie themes. Commissions 5-6 compositions/year and 1-2 lyricists/year. Pays $100-2,000/job. Buys all rights or one-time rights.
How to Contact: Submit demo tape of previously published work. "We do not return tapes." Prefers cassette with 1-20 songs. Reports in 3 weeks.
Music: Uses music for film and audiovisual productions.

*FAST FORWARD PRODUCTIONS, 540 Brooklyn Mountain Rd., Hopatcong NJ 07843. (201)398-2536. President: Ms. Bree Jackson. Music/sound effects library. Estab. 1984. Clients include independent A/V producers, corporations, industry and institutions. Uses the services of songwriters for background music for sound filmstrips, film, slide, video presentation, and broadcast purposes such as radio or television commercials. Commissions a minimum of 10 pieces/year. Pays 25% minimum royalty. "Composers retain all rights to their work"
How to Contact: Query with resume of credits or submit demo tape of previous work. Prefers cassette with minimum 10 songs. "The individual songs should be from 1-3 minutes in length, and please put a 2-3 second pause between each song. Also submit a list of the names of each song in the order in which they appear on the cassette." SASE. Reports in 2 weeks.
Music: "Production music varies widely stylistically. It need not be all hi-tech electronic, or all jazz, or rock. It should however be interesting, bright and upbeat in its nature because it serves as the background to text and visuals that are designed to motivate, educate, or sell. It is important that the music is interesting but does not overpower the narrator or the visuals."

*FILM AMERICA, INC., 3132 Randolph Rd. NE, Atlanta GA 30345. (404)261-3718. President: Avrum Fine. Motion picture editing house. Clients include ad agencies, corporate audiovisual producers and film/tape producer. Uses the service of music houses and independent songwriters for scoring of industrial films/TV spots; lyricists for jingles for TV spots, commercials for TV and theater trailers. Commissions 3 composers/year and 3 lyricists/year. Pays by the job. Buys all rights.
How to Contact: Submit demo tape of previous work. Prefers cassette or VHS videocassette. Does not return unsolicited material; prefers to keep on file. Reports in 4 weeks.
Music: "All contemporary idioms."

PAUL FRENCH AND PARTNERS, Rt. 5, Box 285, LaGrange GA 30240. (404)882-5581. Contact: Ms. Gene Byrd. Audiovisual firm. Uses services of music houses and songwriters for musical scores in films and original songs for themes; lyricists for writing lyrics for themes. Commissions 20 composers and 20 lyricists/year. Pays minimum $500/job. Buys all rights.
How to Contact: Submit demo tape of previous work. Prefers reel-to-reel with 3-8 songs. SASE. Reports in 2 weeks.

FURMAN FILMS, INC., 3466 21st St., San Francisco CA 94110. (415)824-8500. Producer: Jan Davis. Motion picture production company. Clients include business, industry and education. Uses services of music houses and songwriters for "occasional use for original music and lyrics for motion pictures and background/theme music; rarely use lyricists." Payment varies according to budget. Buys all rights.
How to Contact: Query with resume of credits or submit demo tape of previous work. Prefers cassette with 5-10 songs. Does not return unsolicited material; "kept on file for reference."

*GLOBAL VIDEO COMMUNICATIONS CORP., 744 W. Church St., Orlando FL 32805. (305)423-8299. Creative Services Director: Bob Deistchle. Video duplication/production/post-production company. Clients include commercial, industrial, interactive disc/program firms. Uses the services of music houses for background music for various projects; jingles for station promos; and commercials for TV. Pays by the job. Buys all rights or one-time rights.
How to Contact: Submit demo tape of previous work or query with resume of credits. Prefers cassette. Does not return unsolicited material; prefers to keep on file. Reports in 4-6 weeks.
Music: Various types, "mood, background, low key, upbeat—depends on project."
Tips: "Looking for 'fresh' sounds—something more than 'library' pieces."

*THE GLYN GROUP, INC., 258 W. 4th St., New York NY 10014. (212)255-5156. Creative Director: Michael Glyn. Audiovisual firm and motion picture production company. Clients include major corporations. Uses the services of music houses, independent songwriters and lyricists for scoring of and background music for films and AV shows. Commissions 2 composers/year and 2 lyricists/year. Pays by the job. Buys all rights or one-time rights.

How to Contact: Prefers cassette, 7¹/₂ or 15 ips reel-to-reel or ³/₄" videocassette. Does not return unsolicited material; prefers to keep on file. Reports in 2-3 weeks.
Music: All types.

*GRAPHIC MEDIA, INC., 373 Route 46 W., Fairfield NJ 07006. (201)227-5000. Creative Director: Richard Peters. Audiovisual firm, scoring service and video production firm. Clients include business and industrial communications firms. Uses the services of audio producers for soundtracks for multi-image and video. Commissions 5 composers/year. Pays $500-1,000/job; "arranged on project basis." Buys rights "as project requires."
How to Contact: Submit tape demonstrating composition skills or music scoring skills; query with resume of credits; or write or call to arrange personal interview. Prefers cassette or ³/₄" U-matic videocassette. Does not return material; prefers to keep on file. Reports as necessary.
Music: "All styles and types—projects vary greatly."

*LENNY HAMBRO PRODUCTIONS INC., 1023 Oak Ave., Linwood NJ 08221. (609)653-6375. President: Lenny Hambro. Scoring service and music production. Clients include ad agencies and film houses. Uses the services of independent songwriters and lyricists for background music and scoring of commericals, films, industrials, etc.; jingles for ad agencies and commercials for radio and TV. Buys all rights.
How to Contact: Submit tape demonstrating composition skills or manuscript showing music scoring skills; query with resume of credits; or write first to arrange personal interview. Prefers cassette or 7¹/₂ ips reel-to-reel with 5-10 pieces. Does not return unsoclited material; prefers to keep on file. Reports in 2-6 weeks.
Music: "Send all styles to show versatility."

*HARTLEY FILM FOUNDATION, INC., Cat Rock Rd., Cos Cob CT 06807. (203)869-1818. Director: Elda Hartley. Audiovisual firm and motion picture production company. Clients include universities, hospitals, libraries, medical centers and individual organizations. Uses the services of independent songwriters and lyricists for background music for films and videos. Pay negotiable. Rights negotiable.
How to Contact: Write or call first to arrange personal interview or to obtain permission to submit; or submit demo tape of previous work; or tape demonstrating composition skills. Prefers cassette, reel-to-reel, or videocassette. SASE. Reports in 2-3 weeks.
Music: Instrumental, mood-evoking and environmental.

*HEAPING TEASPOON ANIMATION, 40002 19th St., San Francisco CA 94114. (415)626-1893. Creative Director: Chuck Eyler. Motion picture production company. Clients include large industrials and all types for TV spots. Uses the services of music houses and composers for instrumental scoring and synthesizer, scoring of industrial sequences and commercials for TV. Commissions 1 composer/year. Pay "dependent on client's budget." Buys varying rights.
How to Contact: Write or call first and obtain permission to submit; or submit tape demonstrating composition skills and sound effects. Prefers cassette or VHS videocassette. SASE. Reports in 3 weeks.
Music: "Needs vary with client preferences, but solid compositional basics usually required. Mostly short—30 seconds."

*IMAGE INTEGRATION, 2418 Stuart, Berkeley CA 94705. (415)841-8524. Producer: Vincent Casalaina. TV production company. Entertainment and industrial firms. Uses the services of music houses and independent songwriters for background music for sailing and industrial productions.

INDIANER MULTI-MEDIA, Suite 204, 16201 SW 95th Ave., Miami FL 33157. (305)235-6132. Vice President, Systems: David Gravel. President: Paul Indianer. Uses services of music houses and songwriters for video post-production scoring. Commissions 50-60 pieces/year. Pays $50/finished minute. Buys all rights or one-time rights.
How to Contact: Query with resume of credits or submit demo tape showing flexibility of composition skills. Prefers 7¹/₂ ips reel-to-reel with 5 songs minimum. SASE. Reports in 3 weeks.

INSIGHT! INC., 100 E. Ohio St., Chicago IL 60611. (312)467-4350. Audiovisual firm. Clients include business and industry. Uses the services of music houses, songwriters and lyricists. Commissions 20 composers and 15 lyricists/year. Pays by the job; "usually a bid figure—no set minimum." Buys all rights.
How to Contact: Submit demo tape of previous work or tape demonstrating composition skills. Prefers 7¹/₂ ips reel-to-reel or cassette. SASE.
Music: Film scores; industrial show music.

JACOBY/STORM PRODUCTIONS, INC., 22 Crescent Rd., Westport CT 06880. President: Doris Storm. Clients include schools, publishers, business and industrial firms. Uses services of music houses and songwriters for film scores, background music and an occasional theme song. Commissions 2-3 pieces/year. Payment negotiable. Buys all rights or one-time rights.
How to Contact: Write first with resume of credits or submit demo tape of previously aired work. "Don't send any material without writing first." Prefers 7¹/₂ or 15 ips reel-to-reel. SASE. Reports in 2 weeks.
Music: Needs songs and background music for films geared to elementary or high school students; also suitable for industrial and documentary films.

KEN-DEL PRODUCTIONS INC., 111 Valley Rd., Wilmington DE 19804-1397. (302)655-7488. A&R Director: Shirley Kay. General Manager: Ed Kennedy. Clients include publishers, schools, industrial firms and advertising agencies. Uses services of songwriters for film scores and title music. Pays by the job. Buys all rights.
How to Contact: Submit demo of previously aired work. Prefers acetate discs, but will accept tapes. SASE; "however, we prefer to keep tapes on file for possible future use." Reports in 2 weeks.

KIMBO EDUCATIONAL UNITED SOUND ARTS, INC., 10-16 N. 3rd Ave., Box 477, Long Branch NJ 07740. (201)229-4949. Producers: James Kimble or Amy Laufer. Audiovisual firm and manufacturer of educational material: records, cassettes and teacher manuals or guides. Clients include schools and stores selling teachers' supplies. Uses services of music houses, songwriters, and educators for original songs for special education, early childhood, music classes, physical education and pre-school children; lyricists for lyrics to describe children's activities centering on development of motor skills, language, fitness or related educational skills. Commissions 12-15 pieces and 12-15 lyricists/year. Pays by the job or royalty. Buys all rights.
How to Contact: Submit demo tape of previous work, tape demonstrating composition skills, manuscript showing music scoring skills or lead sheet with lyrics. Prefers 7¹/₂ or 15 ips reel-to-reel or cassette with 1-12 songs. "Upon receipt of a demo tape and/or written material, each property is previewed by our production staff. The same chances exist for any individual if the material is of high quality and we feel it meets the educational goals we are seeking." Reports in 1 month. Free catalog.
Music: "Contemporary sounds with limited instrumentation so as not to appear too sophisticated nor distracting for the young or special populations. Lyrics should be noncomplex and repetitive."

SID KLEINER MUSIC ENTERPRISES, 3701 25th Ave. SW, Naples FL 33964. (813)455-2693 or 455-2696. Managing Director: Sid Kleiner. Audiovisual firm. Clients include the music industry. Uses services of music houses, songwriters and inhouse writers for background music; lyricists for special material. Pays $25 minimum/job. Buys all rights.
How to Contact: Query with resume of credits or submit demo tape of previously aired work. Prefers cassette with 1-4 songs. SASE. Reports in 3-5 weeks.
Music: "We generally need soft background music, with some special lyrics to fit a particular project. We also assign country, pop, mystical and metaphysical."

LANE & JOHNSON, (formerly Origin, Inc.), 4466 Laclede, St. Louis MO 63108. (314)533-0010. Creative Director: George Johnson. Audiovisual firm, scoring service and music contractor. Clients include business, industry, government, agricultural conglomerates and hospitals. Uses services of songwriters and lyricists for music for conventions, industrial shows, films, video, etc. Payment negotiable. Rights purchased as requested by client.
How to Contact: Query with resume of credits; submit tape of previous work or tape demonstrating composition skills or manuscript showing music scoring skills. Prefers cassette with any number of songs. SASE. Reports in 2 weeks.
Music: Depends on client's needs.

WILLIAM V. LEVINE & ASSOCIATES, 31 E. 28th St., New York NY 10016. (212)683-7177. President: Bill Levine. Audiovisual firm. Clients include business and industry. Uses services of music houses, songwriters and lyricists. Commissions 6 lyricists/year. Pays by the job. Buys all rights.
How to Contact: Submit demo tape of previous work. Prefers reel-to-reel or cassette with 5-10 songs. SASE.
Music: "Needs simple melodies or embellishments on old and recent popular songs."

LONGBRANCH STUDIO, 6314 E. 13th St., Tulsa OK 74112. (918)832-7640. Manager: Greg Gardner. Scoring service and music/sound effects library. Clients include schools, producers, industry, business and advertising agencies. Uses services of songwriters, lyricists and inhouse writers to provide ideas or concepts; lyricists to provide ideas, concepts or musical content. Commissions 5 lyricists/year

for 20 pieces. Pays $100-800/job, or 50% royalty. Buys all rights or one-time rights.
How to Contact: Query with resume of credits and submit demo tape of previously aired work or submit demo tape showing flexibility of composition skills. Prefers 7¹/₂ or 15 ips reel-to-reel or cassette with 3-6 songs. SASE. Reports in 10 days.
Music: Needs vary with client's desires.

LYONS INC., 715 Orange St., The Market Place, Wilmington DE 19801. (302)654-6146. Producer, Audio Engineer: James Heffernan. Audiovisual firm and video production company. Clients include industrial, training and broadcast. Uses the services of music houses, songwriters; some in-house writing for background music (film, video, AV); and some jingle work (radio, TV); lyricists for industrial (live or canned) shows, or jingle lyrics. Commissions 10 composers and 1-2 lyricists/year. Pay "depends on budget and circumstances." Buys all rights, except demo and publicity use by songwriter.
How to Contact: Submit demo tape of previous work or tape demonstrating composition skills. Prefers cassette with 3-10 songs. SASE; returns material only "if requested." Reports as needs arise.
Music: Synthesizer, rhythmic, orchestral, piano/bass/drums. "Much of our music is either mysterious (mood-setting) or proud upbeat 'on the move' music."
Tips: "Learn to put visual suggestions into sound (think visually); and learn to take intense direction without letting your pride interfere."

LEE MAGID INC., Box 532, Malibu CA 90261. (213)858-7282. President: Lee Magid. Audiovisual firm, scoring service and motion picture production company. Clients include business, industry, theatrical and educational. Uses services of songwriters, lyricists and composer/arrangers—"depending on material and talent." Commissions 20-30 composers and lyricists/year. "All contracts are negotiable." Buys all rights or negotiates rights. Pays by royalty or "outright purchase."
How to Contact: Send resume of credits or submit tape demonstrating composition skills. Prefers cassette or videocassette with maximum 3 songs (or 3 minutes). "I would make direct contact with songwriter/composer and designate preference and style." SASE. Reports in 1 month.
Music: Mostly pop, rock and R&B; also jazz and country. Vocals and/or instrumental.
Tips: "Write your songs for visual and musical memory effect. Think commercial."

MARTIN/ARNOLD COLOR SYSTEMS, INC., 150 5th Ave., New York NY 10011. (212)675-7270. Contact: Martin Block. Audiovisual firm. Clients include schools, publishers, business and industry. Uses services of music houses for background music. Pays by the job. Rights purchased depend on assignment.
How to Contact: Query with resume of credits or submit demo tape of previously aired work. Prefers cassette. SASE. Reports in 2 weeks.

MEDIA DEPT., Box 1006, St. Charles IL 60174. (312)377-0005. General Manager: Bruce Meisner. Audiovisual firm. Clients include business and industry. Uses services of music houses and lyricists for backgrounds and themes for AV multi-image productions. Pays minimum $500/job. Buys all rights.
How to Contact: Query with resume of credits, submit demo tape of previous work or tape demonstrating composition skills. Prefers cassette with minimum 2 songs. SASE. Reports in 3 weeks.
Music: Uses "short 3-7 minute multi-image business presentations."

*****ARTHUR MERIWETHER INC.**, 1529 Brook Dr., Downers Grove IL 60515. (312)495-0600. Audiovisual firm. Clients include business, industry and advertising agencies. Uses the services of music houses and independent songwriters for background music for filmstrips, slides, audio tapes and videotapes and radio commercials. Buys all rights.
How to Contact: Submit demo tape of previous work, or query with resume of credits. Prefers cassette or 7¹/₂ ips reel-to-reel. Does not return unsolicited material; prefers to keep on file. Reports as soon as possible.

WARREN MILLER PRODUCTIONS, 505 Pier Ave., Hermosa Beach CA 90254. (213)376-2494. Production: Don Brolin. Clients include industrial, sports, resort and airline firms. Uses services of music houses for background music in films.
How to Contact: Submit demo tape of previously aired work. Prefers cassette with 1-10 songs on demo or disc. SASE.
Music: Needs action, outdoors, symphonic, soft rock and hard rock. "High energy music for action is our primary need."
Tips: "It is important to be in this area to score a film. The musician must work closely with the editor. Be adept at scoring several instruments. Instrumentals will be better for us than vocals."

MOTIVATION MEDIA, INC., 1245 Milwaukee Ave., Glenview IL 60025. (312)297-4740. Vice President Production Operations: Paul C. Snyder. Audiovisual firm, video, motion picture production

Close-up

J. Eric Schmidt
Musical Playwright
Los Angeles, California

J. Eric Schmidt entered the world of musical theatre in a roundabout way, by giving a dramatic play a musical score. Schmidt's unusual approach to breaking into the business, applying music to Marlowe's *The Jew Of Malta*, caused the *Los Angeles Times* to call him "a most promising composer."

Although musicals are his favorite mode of expression, Schmidt has composed for other entertainment media as well over the past seven years. He was music coordinator for the television series *Fame!* and has been commissioned by universities and performance societies to compose and conduct his many symphonies and concertos. He approaches the music business with dedication, developing new ideas from his experiences, his education and the daily exercise of his craft.

To help put some of those new ideas into practice, Schmidt, along with fellow playwrights Michael Ricciardi and David Holmes, co-founded *Musical Horizons* and *The Write Group*, two organizations dedicated to the creation of new theatrical musicals as well as new projects for motion pictures and television.

When writing songs for the theatre, Schmidt feels that both composer and lyricist must concentrate on being twice as visual than in any other medium. "All the special effects in the world will not conceal a weak score. Every song has to move the plot along, reveal some hidden emotion and remain faithful to the show's overall theme. If you've written a lyric which might not be crystal clear to the audience, revamp it," advises Schmidt. "If the song stops or impedes the story, get rid of it."

Because he feels success is 40% luck, with hard work and talent making up the balance, Schmidt sees musical theatre as being within the reach of many songwriters. *Big River* by Roger Miller, originally a West Coast production which saw later success on Broadway, has done a lot to encourage budding young playwrights outside the New York area. Like *Big River*, which chronicles life on the Mississippi River, "every musical should start with a story that the average theatre goer can both relate to and emotionally respond to."

To help up-and-coming musical playwrights weather some of the pitfalls, Schmidt advises, "Get your musical produced anywhere you can. Once you get someone to produce your musical you'll learn more about the strengths and weaknesses of your writing and composing than you could learn at any college. Stay involved in the rehearsal process and get a director who is just as excited about directing your work as you were about writing it."

In analyzing his own success, Schmidt sees each production as a learning opportunity to be applied to his next project. "Leave your audience wanting more, but always strive to understand what didn't work and *why*. The next time you'll know better."

company and business meeting planner. Clients include business and industry. Uses services of songwriters and composers "mostly for business meetings and multi-image production;" lyricists for writing lyrics for business meeting themes, audience motivation songs and promotional music for new product introduction. Commissions 6-10 lyricists and 6-10 songwriters/year. Pays minimum $500/job. Buys all rights.

How to Contact: Query with resume of credits; or submit demo tape of previous work. Prefers cassette with 5-7 songs. Does not return unsolicited material.

Music: Uses "up-beat contemporary music that motivates an audience of sales people."

Tips: "Keep in touch—let us know what new and exciting assignments you have undertaken."

OMNI COMMUNICATIONS, 12316 Brookshire Pkwy., Carmel IN 46032-3104. (317)844-8482. President: W. H. Long. Audiovisual firm. Clients include major corporations. Uses services of music houses and songwriters for scores for films and background music for voice overs; lyricists for original music and themes. Commissions varying number of composers and lyricists/year. Pays by the job. Buys all rights.

How to Contact: Query with resume of credits. Prefers reel-to-reel, cassette or videocassette. Does not return unsolicited material. Reports in 2 weeks.

SHELTON LEIGH PALMER & CO, INC., 360 E. 57th St., New York NY 10022. (212)980-3445. Contact: Mr. Shelly Palmer. Commercial music production house. Clients include consumer goods, communications industries, banks and automobile manufacturers. Uses services of staff writers. Uses services of songwriters for jingles and arrangements; lyricists for industrial or retail clients. Commissions 50+ composers and lyricists/year. Pays by the job. Buys all rights.

How to Contact: Submit demo tape or videocassette of previous work, tape demonstrating composition skills. Prefers 7½ or 15 ips reel-to-reel or cassette. Does not return unsolicited material. Reports in 1 week.

*PHOTO COMMUNICATION SERVICES, INC., 6410 Knapp NE, Ada MI 49301. (616)676-1499; 676-1454. President: M. Jackson. Audiovisual firm and motion picture production company. Clients include commercial, industrial and non-profit. Uses services of music houses, independent songwriters, and lyricists for scoring of multi-image, film and video, background music for multi-image, film and video, and jingles for multi-image, film and video. Negotiates pay. Buys all rights, or one-time rights.

How to Contact: Submit demo tape of previous work, tape demonstrating composition skills or query with resume of credits. Prefers cassette, 15 ips reel-to-reel or VHS videocassette. Does not return unsolicited material, but prefers to keep on file. Reports in 4-6 weeks.

Music: Uses mostly industrial, some mood.

POP INTERNATIONAL CORPORATION, Box 527, Closter NJ 07624. (201)768-2199. Producers: Arnold De Pasquale, G. Thomas Smith and Peter DeCaro. Motion picture production company. Clients include "political campaigns, commercial spots, business and industry concerns as a production service; feature films and documentaries as producers." Uses services of music houses and songwriters for "mood purposes only on documentary films. However, Pop International Productions does conceptualize major theatrical and/or album musical projects." Commissions commercial and soundtrack pieces for entertainment specials; commissions 2-3 lyricists/year. Pays $75-200/hour; minimum $500/job; 10% minimum royalty. Buys all rights and one-time rights.

How to Contact: Submit demo tape of previously aired work. Prefers cassette with 2-4 songs. "We review tapes on file, speak with agents and/or referrals, then interview writer. Once committee approves, we work *very* closely in pre-production." SASE. Reports in 3 weeks.

Music: Uses "mood music for documentaries, occasionally jingles for spots or promotional films or theme music/songs for dramatic projects (the latter by assignment only from producers or agencies). Some material is strictly mood, as in documentary work; some is informative as in promotional; some is motivating as in commercial; some is entertaining as in theatrical/TV."

Tips: "Be persistent and very patient. Try to get an agent, use demos and build a reputation for working very closely with scriptwriters/producers/directors."

PREMIER VIDEO, FILM AND RECORDING CORP., 3033 Locust St., St. Louis MO 63103. (314)531-3555. President: Wilson Dalzell. Secretary/Treasurer: Grace Dalzell. Audiovisual firm and motion picture production company. Uses services of songwriters for original background music and lyrics to reinforce scripts. Commissions 6-10 pieces and 5-10 lyricists/year. Pays according to the maximum contribution of the music to the total production. Buys all rights and "occasionally one-time rights with composer retaining title."

How to Contact: Query with resume of credits. Prefers 7½ or 15 ips reel-to-reel or cassette with any

number of songs. SASE. Reports "as soon as possible."
Tips: "Be sure a resume is direct, to-the-point and includes an honest review of past efforts."

*PRIMALUX VIDEO, 30 W. 26th St., New York NY 10010. Contact: Barbara Stumacher. Video production company. Clients include industrial, commercial, fashion and cable TV companies. Uses the services of music houses for background music for fashion and industrial productions and commercials for TV.
How to Contact: Call first and obtain permission to submit. Prefers cassette or videocassette. Does not return unsolicited material; prefers to keep on file.
Music: "Contemporary—for fashion and cable shows."

PROTESTANT RADIO & TV CENTER, INC., 1727 Clifton Rd. NE, Atlanta GA 30329. (404)634-3324. Chief Engineer: George Watts. Clients include denominational projects, local churches, schools and colleges (educational needs), and social service organizations. Uses services of songwriters for film scores, commercials and radio programs. Payment negotiable. Rights purchased vary.
How to Contact: Query or submit demo tape of previously aired work. Prefers $7^1/2$ or 15 ips reel-to-reel or cassette with 2-8 songs. Does not return unsolicited material. Reports in 1 month.
Music: Themes for radio, TV, film and audiovisual productions.

PULLIN PRODUCTIONS LTD., Suite 102, 617 11th Ave. SW, Calgary, Alberta T2R 0E1, Canada. (403)234-7885. Production Manager: Deke Rivers. Clients include business and industry. Uses the services of music houses, songwriters and lyricists for "original songs and themes for multi-image, motion picture and multi-media." Commissions 4 composers and 2 lyricists/year. Pays minimum $500/job. Buys all rights.
How to Contact: Submit demo tape or videocassette of previous work. Prefers reel-to-reel with 4-10 songs but "any format is OK." Does not return unsolicited material. "Contact is made only if interested."
Music: Looking for "strong themes for any number of instruments/vocals (single instrument to full orchestra). Requirements for each job are very carefully specified."

*DAVID RAPKIN AUDIO PRODUCTION, 473 West End Ave., New York NY 10024. (212)362-7236. Contact: Mr. Rapkin. Music/sound effects library and audio producer for all media. Clients include AV houses, animators, filmmakers, radio stations and industrial firms. Uses the services of music houses for scoring of soundtracks. Pay negotiable. Buys all rights or one-time rights.
How to Contact: Submit demo tape of previous work or tape demonstrating composition skills. Prefers $7^1/2$ ips reel-to-reel with 4-8 pieces. "Tapes should be $1/2$ track, if possible." Does not return unsolicited material; prefers to keep on file. Reports in 3 weeks.
Music: Uses mostly background music for industrial purposes.

*RECORDED SOUND LTD., 630 Fulton Bldg., Pittsburgh PA 15218. (412)288-9998. President: Jack Givens. Audiovisual firm and music/sound effects library. Clients include advertising agencies, retail firms, corporations and individuals. Uses the services of music houses for scoring of industrial slide shows, films, and video background music for industrial slide shows, films and commercials, retail jingles and commercials for radio and TV. Pays by the job.
How to Contact: Submit demo tape of previous work or query with resume of credits. Prefers cassette, 15 or $7^1/2$ ips reel-to-reel or videocassette. Does not return unsolicited material; prefers to keep on file.
Music: Music for jingles and film scores.

*RIVIERA PRODUCTIONS, 31628 Saddletree Dr., Westlake Village CA 91361. (818)889-5778. Contact: Will Zens. Motion picture production company and music/sound effects library. Uses the services of music houses and independent songwriters for scoring of films and background music for films. Pay negotiable.
How to Contact: Submit demo tape of previous work or tape demonstrating composition skills. Prefers cassette with any number of pieces. SASE.
Music: Uses non-synthesized, non-rock music.

*SHERIDAN ELSON COMMUNICATIONS, INC., 20 W. 37th St., New York NY 10018. (212)239-2000. Producer: Kathleen Held. Full service production company (film, tape, AV, radio VNR, etc.). Clients include corporate, commercial, public service, publishing, cosmetic, travel, etc. Uses services of music houses and independent songwriters for scoring of sound tracks, background music for films, AV shows, etc., jingles for commercials and commercials for radio and TV. Pays by the job. Buys varying rights.
How to Contact: "Write only and send resume of credits." Prefers cassette or $3/4$" or $1/2$" videocassette.

"Please don't call. Give information on any fees or mode of working, etc." Does not return unsolicited material, but prefers to keep on file.
Music: "Typically ranges from pretty, upbeat background music to heavy industrial, perhaps digital sound. Be willing to work on a 'by the job basis' with hopefully a recording situation suggested."

SILVER BURDETT COMPANY, 250 James St., CN 018, Morristown NJ 07960. (201)285-8002. Associate Music Editor: Donald Scafuri. Publisher of textbooks and records for kindergarten through 8th grade. "Our books and records are sold directly to schools and are evaluated and chosen for use according to the adoption procedures of a particular school district." Uses services of music houses, songwriters and lyricists for original songs for children K-8; lyricists for translating foreign lyrics into a singable English version and "writing original lyrics to a folk tune or a melody composed by someone else." Commissions 0-20 lyricists for 0-20 pieces/year. Pays $55 for lyrics and arrangements; $150 for original compositions (reprint rights plus statutory record royalty). Buys one-time rights.
How to Contact: Submit lead sheets of previous work. Prefers cassette. "If song is not copyrighted, author should write first to Music Editorial Department for Idea Submission Form to submit with song." SASE. Reports in 1 month. Free catalog.
Music: "We seek virtually any kind of song that is suitable both in words and music for children to sing. We are particularly interested in songs that are contemporary pop or folk-like in style. We are also interested in choral compositions for upper grades."
Tips: "Become acquainted with teachers and students in elementary or junior high classrooms. Find out what music they are presently using and what they would like to use."

***SOUND IMPRESSIONS, INC.**, 110 River Rd., Des Plaines IL 60016. (312)297-4360. Vice President: A.J. Holtane. Audiovisual firm and recording studio. Uses the services of independent songwriters and music libraries for scoring of multi-image shows and commercials for radio and TV.

STAGE 3 SOUND PRODUCTIONS, 1901 W. 43rd St., Kansas City KS 66103. (913)384-9111. President: Don Warnock. Audiovisual firm. Clients include business and advertising agencies. Uses services of songwriters for background music in productions. Pays AFTRA scale. Buys all rights.
How to Contact: Query. Prefers 7½ ips reel-to-reel or cassette. SASE. Reports "as soon as possible."

CARTER STEVENS STUDIOS, INC., 269 W. 25th St., New York NY 10001. President: Carter Stevens. Produces theatrical feature films and business documentaries. Uses services of music houses and songwriters for film scores. Commissions 40-60 pieces/year. Pays $250-1,000/job. Buys all rights or one-time rights.
How to Contact: Submit demo tape of previous work or query with resume of credits. "Do not call our office." Prefers cassette with 2-8 songs. SASE. Returns material if totally unusable; "we keep everything for future reference if we feel the writer has any potential. Send a sample of as many styles and moods of music as possible."
Tips: "There is a 3- to 6-month lag time on our projects, as we are working at least one to two films ahead at all times."

E.J. STEWART INC., 525 Mildred Ave., Primos PA 19018. (215)626-6500. General Manager: Robert Momyer. Audiovisual firm and video production company. Clients include broadcasting companies, cable TV, advertising agencies, schools, business, industry, government and the medical profession. Uses services of music houses and songwriters for background music for commercials and programs. Commissions 50 pieces and 5 lyricists/year. Payment negotiable by the job. Buys all rights.
How to Contact: Query with resume of credits or submit demo tape of previous work. Prefers reel-to-reel or cassette with any number of songs. SASE. Reports "when needed."

SUNSET FILMS, 625 Market St., San Francisco CA 94105. (415)495-4555. Executive Producer: Paul Fillinger. Motion picture and video production company. Clients include business and industry. Uses services of music houses and songwriters for background scores for films and TV. Commissions 15 pieces/year. Pays $5,000-20,000/movie. Buys all rights.
How to Contact: Query with resume of credits.
Music: "Sponsored films use a bouncy, up-beat flavor; the emotional qualities are secondary most of the time although they're what make films tick."
Tips: "It really is the personality mix that helps get your foot in the door as well as being a strong, confident musician."

TELECINE SERVICES & PRODUCTION LTD., 11 Ely Place, Dublin 2, Ireland. 353-01-763188. Telex 92309 PAVEL. Director: Anabella Jackson. Audiovisual firm and video productions. Clients

include advertising and commercial business. Uses services of songwriters and music houses for original songs for TV commercials and audiovisual and video programs; lyricists for writing lyrics for commercials and conference themes. Commissions 3 lyricists for 20 pieces/year. Pays $1,250 minimum/job. Buys all rights or rights within one country.
How to Contact: Query with resume of credits or submit tape demonstrating composition skills. Prefers 15 ips reel-to-reel or cassette with 3-10 songs. SASE. Reports in 1 month.

TELEMATION PRODUCTIONS, INC., 3210 W. West Lake, Glenview IL 60025. (312)729-5215. Producer: Jeanni McCormick. Video production house. Clients include advertising clients and industrial programs. Uses services of network and music libraries for jingles and background music for industrials; lyricists for jingles. Pays by the job. Buys all rights.
How to Contact: Submit demo tape of previous work, along with resume. Prefers cassette with 3-10 songs. SASE. "We return tapes if requested. However, we like to keep tapes on file for future reference." Reports in 3 weeks.
Music: Uses "up-tempo music that can be faded out smoothly to fit time alloted for commercials for industrial clients; some easy listening, mostly instrumental."

*TRANSLIGHT MEDIA ASSOCIATES, INC., 931 W. Liberty Dr., Wheaton IL 60187. (312)690-7780. Executive Vice President: Scott Davis. Audiovisual firm. Clients include industrial, religious and advertising firms. Uses the services of independent songwriters for scoring of original audiovisual soundtracks and jingles for sales meetings. Commissions 5 composers/year and 1 lyricist/year. Pays $2,500-10,000/job. Buys all rights. "Writer can use material for demonstration."
How to Contact: Prefers 15 ips reel-to-reel with 5-15 pieces. Does not return unsolicited material; prefers to keep on file. Reports in 2 weeks.
Music: "Industrial—for audiovisual presentations."

TULCHIN PRODUCTIONS, 240 E. 45th St., New York NY 10017. (212)986-8270. Executive Producer: Louis Georgaras. Motion picture production company. Clients include advertising agencies, business and industry. Uses services of music houses and songwriters for background music and musical scores for commercials and industrials, etc.; lyricists for writing lyrics for commercials. Pays by the job per agreement. Buys all rights.

*VIDEOFONICS, INC., 1101 Downtown Blvd., Raleigh NC 27603. (919)821-5614. Production Coordinator: Alex Bireline. Commercial production company. Clients include ad agencies, industrial firms. Uses the services of independent songwriters, lyricists and "occasionally" jingle writers and arrangers for commercials and video presentations. Commissions 3 composers/year and 4-5 lyricists/year. Pays by the job. Buys all rights.
How to Contact: Submit demo tape of previous work, or submit tape demonstrating composition skills. Prefers cassette or videocassette. Does not return unsolicited material; prefers to keep on file.
Tips: "Don't push! If you're doing good work and we have the need, we'll call."

*VIDEO COMMUNICATORS INTERNATIONAL, Suite R-307, 1830 16th St., Newport Beach CA 92663. (714)953-8097. President: Christopher Harwood. Audiovisual firm, motion picture production company and video/TV production company. Clients include business, education, government, ad agencies, broadcast and cable TV companies. Use the services of music houses, independent songwriters, lyricists and independent musicians for scoring of program themes, background music for documentaries and jingles for radio and TV commercials. Pays by the job. Buys all rights or one-time rights, "sometimes shares rights with composer."
How to Contact: Submit demo tape of previous work, or query with resume of credits. Prefers cassette or 3/4" videocassette. "Indicate in writing composer's/submitter's clear right to ownership and use." Does not return unsolicited material; prefers to keep on file. Reports in 3-4 weeks.
Music: Needs "contemporary music for program themes and/or scoring; rock/upbeat for commercials."

*VIDEO IMAGERY, 204 Calle De Anza, San Clemente CA 92672. (714)492-5082. Contact: Bob Fisher. Audiovisual firm. Clients include Apple Computer, AMF Inc., Potter & Brumfield and Scientific Drilling. Uses the services of music houses for background music for video productions. Pays by the job. Buys rights as required.
How to Contact: Submit tape demonstrating composition skills. Prefers cassette or 1/2" VHS videocassette. Does not return unsolicited material; prefers to keep on file. Reports in 3 weeks.

*WESTLAKE STUDIOS, #118, 31320 Via Colinas, Westlake Village CA 91362. (818)991-5452. Director, Project Development: Felix Girard. Audiovisual firm, motion picture production firm, scoring service and album/song producers. Clients include business, industry, entertainment, video and record companies. Uses the services of independent songwriters and lyricists for scoring of videos (entertainment and instructional), background music for industrials, jingles for radio and commercials. Commissions 6 composers/year and 3 lyricists/year. Pay negotiable by job. Buys all rights.

How to Contact: Call first and obtain permission to submit or query with resume of credits. Prefers cassette or ½" VHS or ¾" videocassette. Does not return unsolicited material, prefers to keep on file. Reports in 4 weeks.

Music: MOR, country, pop mainstream and original compositions for video scores.

Tips: "Songwriters and lyricists must be able to work well with artists and business people."

*WING PRODUCTIONS, 1600 Broadway, New York NY 10019. (212)265-5179. President: Jon Wing Lum. Clients include NBC and the New York State Education Department. Uses services of music houses, songwriters and lyricists for scores for films and tape, background music for sound filmstrips and original songs for themes. Commissions 20-40 lyricists for 20-40 pieces/year. Pays $500-5,000/job. Buys all rights.

How to Contact: Submit demo tape of previously aired work or submit tape showing flexibility of composition skills. Prefers 7½ or 15 ips reel-to-reel or cassette with 5 songs. SASE. Reporting time "depends on need." Free catalog.

Music: All types.

WREN ASSOCIATES, 208 Bunn Dr., Princeton NJ 08540. (609)924-8085. Production Manager: Debbie Schnur. Audiovisual firm. Clients include business and industry. Uses services of music houses and songwriters for "background music for multi-media presentations (slide, film, video and live talent) also, original scores and songs for the same." Commissions many composers and 1-2 lyricists/year. Pays $300-2,500/job.

How to Contact: Query with resume of credits, submit demo tape of previous work, or submit tape demonstrating composition skills. Prefers cassette or videocassette with minimum 5 songs. SASE. Reports in 1 month.

Music: Mostly motivational; also high tech.

Tips: "Have experience in producing soundtracks for slide, film and video presentations."

*ZELMAN STUDIOS, 623 Cortelyou Rd., Brooklyn NY 11218. (718)941-5500. Assistant Manager of Sound Services: Ann Shira. Audiovisual firm. Clients include schools, business and industry. Uses services of music houses and songwriters for background music and musical scores in films. Commissions 6-8 lyricists for 6-8 pieces/year. Pays $100-500/job. Buys one-time rights.

How to Contact: Submit demo tape of previous work. Prefers cassette with minimum 3 songs. SASE. Reports in 1 month.

ZM SQUARED, 903 Edgewood Lane, Box C-30, Cinnaminson NJ 08077. (609)786-0612. Clients include colleges, schools, businesses and AV producers. Uses services of songwriters "for themes for our no-needledrop music library and background for AV presentations. We prefer to work with composer/arranger/performer and use primarily background music." Commissions 4-5 albums with 10 cuts each/year; 1-2 lyricists/year. Pays 10-35% royalty. Buys all rights.

How to Contact: Submit demo tape of previous work. Prefers cassette with 4-6 songs. SASE. Reports in 3 weeks. Free catalog.

Music: "We require a variety of background music—educational and industrial for general use with audiovisual programs."

Tips: "Know what we want and be able to produce what you write."

Managers and Booking Agents————

For the songwriter who wants to perform his or her own material, the manager is probably the most valuable contact. A manager's expertise in the music business enables him to manage the sometimes complicated day-to-day business affairs of his clients while at the same time providing the guidance and encouragement necessary to advance their careers. Managers oversee many other functions as well, including security for the artist, contractual negotiations with record companies and publishers and—in cooperation with booking agents—most live performances.

In addition to managing the day-to-day affairs of his artists, the personal manager also plays an instrumental role in helping choose song material that is appropriate for their careers and individual styles. Most managers will listen to or review material from outside, unsolicited sources provided they are approached in a businesslike, professional manner. Most managers listed in this section indicate that they will review material for their acts free of charge.

When submitting a demo to a manager for review prepare your submission as you would for any other market listed in this book. Be sure to provide a fully labeled, cued-up, well recorded tape along with a neat (preferably typed) lyric or lead sheet and perhaps a brief biography.

If you are a songwriter/artist and are looking for a manager, you should also include a glossy photo, a list of songs that you perform (both covers and originals), a current itinerary, and any relevant press clippings. In the case of the songwriter/artist the demo should be one of you or your group in *live* performance rather than in the studio so the manager can appraise your performing talent as well as your songwriting. Submitting a videocassette demo, in which your visual stage presence as well as your musical ability can be judged is obviously something that should be seriously considered.

Most managers prefer to review material via the mail, although some indicate that they will meet with you for a personal interview provided you arrange it in advance. Because personal managers are often very busy handling the many details of their artists' careers, they often cannot accomodate unannounced visitors. The submitting songwriter or songwriter/artist should also be as patient as possible regarding response time on submissions. The nature of the manager's job dictates that his clients' interests and welfare come before all else.

ACE PRODUCTIONS, 3407 Green Ridge Dr., Nashville TN 37214. (615)883-3480. Contact: Jim Case. Management firm and booking agency. Represents artists, groups and songwriters; currently handles 12 acts. Receives 15-20% commission. Reviews material for acts.
How to Contact: Prefers cassette with 2-4 songs and lead sheet. SASE. Reports in 1 month.
Music: Mostly country; also rock (hard and country) and bluegrass. Works primarily with show, dance and bar bands. Current acts include Kevin and Joshua Moore, Johnny Patton, Debra Dare, Jerry Finley & Texas, Kathy Lynn Sacra, and Kathy Raye.

ACT "1" ENTERTAINMENT, Box 1079, New Haven CT 06504. (203)776-2847. President: Johnny Parris. Management firm, booking agency and record company. Represents artists, groups and songwriters; currently handles 20-25 acts. Reviews material for acts.
How to Contact: Query by mail or submit demo tape and lead sheet; arrange personal interview. Prefers cassette with 5-10 songs. SASE. Reports in 2 weeks.
Music: Mostly hard rock/top 40/pop, soul and R&B; also dance-oriented, easy listening, jazz, MOR and rock. Current acts include Bob Mel (top 40/pop); Half Moon (rock and top 40/pop); Splash (rock/top 40); Thin Ice (rock/top 40); Ricky Marz (top 40); Carl Barone (rock/top 40); Nick Fradiani (top 40/pop); All That Rhythm (swing/top 40); Trix (top 40/rock); Juicy (top 40/pop); and Clockwork (top 40/rock).
Tips: "I'm looking for people who are ethical and not into drugs."

ACTION TICKET AGENCY AND PROMOTIONS, 2609 NW 36th St., Oklahoma City OK 73112. (405)942-0462. Manager: Bobby Boyd. Management and booking agency and promotions firm. Represents individual artists from anywhere; currently handles 4 acts. Receives 25% minimum commission. Reviews material for acts.

How to Contact: Query by mail, then submit demo tape only. Prefers 7½ ips reel-to-reel with 3-12 songs. Does not return unsolicited material. Reports in 2 weeks.
Music: Country, R&B, rock and top 40/pop. Current acts include Dale Greear, Faye Haley and Bobby Barnett (all country acts).

ADORATION, INC., (aka The Tatom Agency), Suite 2-A, 6750 W. 75th St., Overland Park KS 66204. (913)384-1050. Vice-President: Betty Tatom. Management firm, booking agency and public relations company. Represents artists, groups and songwriters—"all are nationally known." Currently handles 8 acts. Receives "fee or love offering plus expenses." Reviews material for acts.
How to Contact: Write first and obtain permission to submit. Prefers cassette and lead sheet. Does not return unsolicited material. Reports "when various artists need material to record."
Music: Contemporary gospel, MOR gospel and country/pop gospel. Works primarily with gospel solos, quartets and groups. Current acts include Kathie Sullivan (gospel singer); The Lads (gospel quartet); Eternity (gospel group of 15); Johnny Hall (gospel singer); Bobby Jones & New Life (gospel group of 9); Jessy Dixon (gospel singer); and Rock City Boys (gospel trio).
Tips: "All material sent must be gospel."

ADVANCE PRODUCTIONS/FOUR SYSTEMS PUBLISHERS, 635 Cactus Lane, San Angelo TX 76903. (915)657-0038. Contact: J. Dendy. Management firm and booking agency. Represents artists and groups; currently handles 2 acts. "Writers retain writers' royalties and copyrights; we retain publishing." Reviews material for acts.
How to Contact: Write first. Prefers cassette with 2-4 songs and lyric sheet. SASE. Reports in 1 month.
Music: Progressive country, country and MOR. Works primarily with songwriters and dance bands. Current acts include Joe Moseley (country/progressive/MOR vocalist); and Stonecreek ((country/rock/blues dance band).

***ADVANCED MEDIA PRODUCTIONS**, Suite 101, 23611 Chagrin Blvd., Beachwood OH 44122. Co-owners: Ted Coombs and Vivek Bhargava. Management agency, booking agency and concert producer. Represents individual artists, groups and songwriters. Deals with artists from anywhere. Currently handles 15 acts. Receives 15-20% commission. Reviews material for acts (include SASE).
How to Contact: Prefers cassette or VHS videocassette with maximum 4 songs and lyric or lead sheet. SASE. Reports in 4 weeks.
Music: Mostly rock, folk and progressive; also country and classical. Works primarily with bar bands. Current acts include Quest and Rook.

THE AGENCY, Suite 200, 41 Britain St., Toronto, Ontario M5A 1R7, Canada. (416)365-7833. Vice President: Ed Smeall. Management firm and booking agency. Represents artists and groups; currently booking 93 attractions and managing 5 acts. Receives 10-20% commission. Reviews material for acts.
How to Contact: Write first. Prefers cassette with 2-5 songs and lyric sheet. Include photo. SAE and IRC. Reports in 1 month.
Music: Top 40/pop, dance and rock. Works with dance-oriented and top 40 vocalists. Current acts include Corey Hart (top 40); Spoons (dance); and Honeymoon Suite (rock).
Tips: "Label tape with information and phone number."

AJAYE ENTERTAINMENT CORP., 2181 Victory Pkwy., Box 6568, Cincinnati OH 45206. (513)221-2626. Artist Relations: Suzy Evans. Booking agency. Represents artists and groups; currently represents 33 acts. Receives 10-20% commission.
How to Contact: Submit demo tape and write or call to explain the purpose of submission. Prefers 7½ ips reel-to-reel or cassette with 3-6 songs. SASE. Reports in 1 week.
Music: Progressive, rock, soul and top 40/pop. Current acts include Bell Jar, The Raisins, The Young Invaders, CJSS, Prizoner, Elaine and the Biscaynes, Asher, Factor-S, Blitz, Michael Denton Group, The Twist, The Kids, Danny Morgan, The Cheaters, Merle Zimmerman Band, Free Reins, and Suzy & the Boulevard.

ALAMO TALENT AND PRODUCTIONS, 217 Arden Grove, San Antonio TX 78215. (512)225-6294. President: Carl Mertens. Management firm and booking agency. Represents artists and groups; currently handles 32 acts. Receives 15-25% commission. Reviews material for acts.
How to Contact: Query by mail. Prefers 7½ ips reel-to-reel or cassette with 3-5 songs. Does not return unsolicited material.
Music: Mostly country; also folk, MOR and Spanish. Works primarily with dance and club bands. Current acts include Lisa Lopez (Spanish artist); Janie C. Ramirez & Cactus Country; and American Express (C&W group).

No Doubt About It! band members from left to right are: Ron Gilbert, Jeff Shoemaker, Joe January, Patrice Kuni, Steve LaVoie.

Close-up

Patrice Kuni of No Doubt About It!
Songwriter/Performer
Denver, Colorado

When talented creative people decide it's time to shoot for the top, you'd better not get in their way and No Doubt About It! is one such group of people. After playing years of one-niters throughout the West and Midwest, the six band members have decided they've polished their craft and it's time to develop their careers. Rather than being "just another band from California," the group decided to settle in Denver. Patrice Kuni, lead singer and principal songwriter explains, "The reason we moved to Denver was to locate in a major city, make some headway publicity-wise and become known. If we can record and then sell five or ten thousand singles, that's going to make a record company sit up and take notice."

To make them sit up and take notice the band decided to finance its own simultaneous record and video project. After some urging by their manager, the record project, Kuni's "Young Boys," (b/w "Telling All the Girls") became the basis for their first video. Both song and video tell the story of a woman who prefers *younger* men. Kuni herself plays the part of the beautiful businesswoman by day and "cruiser" by night, roaming Denver's Colfax Avenue in her blue Mustang. Although one cable operator thought the subject matter was a bit too strong for his viewers' tastes, Kuni and the band aren't worried. "We took some

flack for it and some people thought we were getting ahead of ourselves. But it really worked out well for us." So well in fact that the video became one of six videos out of two hundred chosen to compete on MTV's Basement Tapes Competition which pits locally produced music videos against each other in a national television version of a battle of the bands.

Publicity is one of the things the band understands very well. When they decided to settle in Denver and concentrate on their careers they pushed one of the basic laws of publicity—be seen. "Some people choose to do all original material, do one-niters every couple weeks, and work [at other jobs] during the day," Kuni explains. "We choose to play other peoples' music as well as our own and *work* six nights a week." Even though they've relied on others' material for their club dates, the band strives to inject more and more original music into each date they play, such as when they opened for Foreigner in Colorado Springs and played a thirty-five minute set of their own songs.

To supply the band with new material Kuni needs to be prepared when the writing mood hits her. She keeps a pad and a pencil near and her portable keyboard within arm's reach. She also uses a rhyming dictionary and a thesaurus to help her develop ideas into full-blown songs. "I try to write songs that make sense and have good melodic structure," says Kuni, "because as a singer you're always singing someone else's vocal licks. I'm trying to write songs I *want* to sing."

ALIVE ENTERPRISES, Suite 700, 9000 Sunset Blvd., Los Angeles CA 90069. (213)275-5711. President: Shep Gordon. Management agency. Represents artists, groups and songwriters; currently represents 7 acts. Receives 20% minimum commission.
How to Contact: Prefers cassette with 2-4 songs and lead sheet. SASE. Reports in 3-5 weeks.
Music: Rock (all types), soul and top 40/pop. Works with "major record company signed artists." Current acts include Alice Cooper (rock); and Luther Vandross (R&B).

ALL STAR TALENT AGENCY, Box 82, Greenbrier TN 37073. (615)643-4208. Agent: Joyce Brown. Booking agency. Represents professional individuals, groups and songwriters; currently handles 5 acts. Receives 10-15% commission. Reviews material for acts.
How to Contact: Prefers reel-to-reel or cassette with 1-4 songs and lead sheet. SASE. Reports ASAP.
Music: Mostly country; also bluegrass, gospel, MOR, rock (country) and top 40/pop. Works primarily with dance, show and bar bands, vocalists, club acts and concerts. Current acts include Bill Carlisle and the Carlisles (country group); Ronnie Dove (MOR/country artist); Randy Parton (pop artist); Charlie McCoy (instrumentalist); Tommy Overstreet (country artist); and Del Wood (Grand Ole Opry star).

ALLIED BOOKING CO., Suite J, 2321 Morena Blvd., San Diego CA 92110. (619)275-5030. Contact: Jim Deacy. Booking agency. Deals with individuals in California and Arizona. Receives 10-20% commission.
How to Contact: Query. Prefers cassette with 5-10 songs. SASE. Reports in 2 weeks.
Music: Mostly dance-oriented; also bluegrass, blues, country, easy listening, folk, jazz, MOR, R&B, rock (50's or MOR) and top 40/pop. Works primarily with dance bands or groups with vocalists included. "We book all types of musical groups, and many different ones throughout the year."

*RAMON ALSINA, ARTIST REPRESENTATIVE, 228 E. 80th, New York NY 10021. (212)988-2542. President: Ramon Alsina. Management agency. Represents individual artists and groups. Deals with artists from anywhere. Currently handles 15 acts. Receives 10-30% commission. Reviews material for acts.
How to Contact: Write first and obtain permission to submit. Prefers cassette. Does not return unsolicited material.
Music: Mostly art songs and classical music. Works primarily with vocalists. Current acts include Priscilla Gordon, Alberto Figols and The Figols Family.

*AMERICAN ARTISTS, 312 Washington Ave. N, Minneapolis MN 55401. (612)339-4741. Contact: Owen Husney or Ron Soskin or Ken Greer. Management firm and recording studio. Represents artists, groups and songwriters. Receives variable commission. Reviews material for acts.
How to Contact: Submit demo tape only or demo tape and lead sheet. Prefers cassette with maximum 4 songs. SASE. Reports in 4-6 weeks.
Music: Dance-oriented, jazz, R&B, rock (all types), soul and top 40/pop.

AMIRON MUSIC, 20531 Plummer St., Chatsworth CA 91311. (818)998-0443. Manager: A. Sullivan. Management firm. Represents artists and groups in local area only; currently handles 6 acts. Receives 10-25% commission. Reviews material for acts.
How to Contact: Prefers cassette and lyric sheet. SASE. Reports in 1 month.
Music: Top 40/pop and rock. Works primarily with self contained groups. Current acts include Sunset (show group); Chozen Few (show group); and Paris (pop rock).

ANDERSON AGENCY, INC., 290 California Dr., Burlingame CA 94010. (415)342-8500. President: Don Anderson. Talent agency.
How to Contact: Prefers cassette with 3-5 songs and lead sheet.

MICHAEL ANTHONY AGENCY, 6007 W. 16th Ave., Lakewood CO 80214. Office Manager: Mary Collins. Management firm and booking agency. Represents artists and groups; currently handles 14 acts. Commission depends on services. Reviews material for acts.
How to Contact: Prefers cassette and lyric sheet. SASE. Reports in 1 month.
Music: "Hot 100 dance" and R&B. Works primarily with nightclub dance groups and concert-oriented show bands. Current acts include No Doubt About It, Midwest Coast, and The Blast (nightclub and concert acts).

ARCEE PRODUCTIONS, Suite 214, 1680 N. Vine St., Hollywood CA 90028. (213)871-8787. Talent Agents: Robb Cooper and John Hester. Represents artists, groups and songwriters; currently handles 66 acts. Receives 10% commission. Reviews material for acts.
How to Contact: "Submit photo, resume and demo tape." Prefers 7¹/₂ ips reel-to-reel or cassette with 3-5 songs. SASE. Reports in 60-90 days.

Music: Dance-oriented, easy listening, gospel, MOR, R&B, soul and top 40/pop. Works primarily with R&B chart artists, dance artists and top 40/pop bands. Current acts include Bonnie Pointer (R&B solo act); The Weather Girls (duo dance group); and Linda Clifford (R&B solo act).
Tips: "Be as courteous and polite to us as we will be to you. Keep in mind that there are many other songwriters and artists vying for the same opportunity to submit their work so be patient and professional."

PAT ARMSTRONG & ASSOCIATES, INC., Suite 202, 1500 Lee Rd., Lee Square Bldg., Orlando FL 32810. (305)299-0077. President: Pat Armstrong. Vice President: Jack Armstrong. Management firm, production company and music publisher. Represents artists, groups and songwriters; currently handles 8 acts. Receives 20% commission. Reviews material for acts.
How to Contact: Query by phone. Prefers cassette with 4-6 songs and lead sheet. SASE. Reports in 2 weeks.
Music: Progressive, rock (hard, country, heavy), top 40/pop and modern music. Works primarily with developing artists and bands. Current acts include Molly Hatchet (Southern rock group/Epic Records); Pat Travers (rock/PolyGram Records); Stranger (rock group/Epic Records); and Four In Legion (modern music/CBS Assoc. Label/CBS Records).

ARTISTS'/HELLER AGENCY, 7751-13 Alabama, Caioga Park CA 93304. (818)702-9276. President: Jerry Heller. Management firm. Represents artists, groups and songwriters; currently handles 15 acts. Reviews material for acts.
How to Contact: Query by mail. Prefers cassette with 4-7 songs. SASE. Reports in 1 month.
Music: R&B, jazz, rock, soul and progressive. Works primarily with songwriters, producers and concert groups. Current acts include Rose Royce (R&B); Rodney Franklin (jazz/R&B); and DFX2 (rock).

AYERS PRODUCTIONS INC., 70 Clay Hill Rd., Stamford CT 06905. (203)329-7335. President: Bud Ayers. Management firm. Represents artists and groups; currently handles 25 acts. Receives minimum 15% commission. Reviews material for acts.
How to Contact: "Contact me personally." Prefers VHS videocassette with 1-3 songs. SASE. Reports in 2 weeks.
Music: Mostly MOR and top 40; also country, easy listening, R&B and rock (all types). Works primarily with comedians, singers, groups (dance and show) and recording artists. Current acts include Debbie Reynolds, Rip Taylor, Onstage (show group) and Mike Douglas.
Tips: Artists should have "commitment to their art and be able to accept rejection and still persevere—be loyal when the breakthrough happens."

AZTEC PRODUCTIONS, 20531 Plummer St., Chatsworth CA 91311. (818)998-0443. General Manager: A. Sullivan. Management firm and booking agency. Represents individuals, groups and songwriters; currently handles 7 acts. Receives 10-25% commission.
How to Contact: Prefers 7¹/₂ ips reel-to-reel or cassette and lead sheet. SASE. Reports in 3 weeks.
Music: Disco, MOR, rock, soul and top 40/pop. Works primarily with club bands, show groups and concert groups. Current acts include El Chicano (Latin/rock); Abraxas (MOR); Storm (show group); Tribe (soul/R&B); New Street, Kelly Lynn, Ako, Zaral and Debbie Rockwell.

BANDSTAND (INTERNATIONAL) ENTERTAINMENT AGENCY, Box 844, Simcoe, Ontario N3Y 4T2 Canada. (519)426-3799. President: Wayne Elliot. Management and booking agency. Represents artists and groups; currently represents 12 acts. Receives 10-15% commission. Reviews material for acts.
How to Contact: Send promo kit. Prefers cassette, "but equipped for all types of demos including video." Does not return unsolicited material. Reports in 1 week.
Music: Mostly top 40 and comedy; also rock and pop. Works primarily with female vocalists, models, actresses and comedians. Current acts include Copter (rock); Rooster (top 40); and various local artists.

BARNARD MANAGEMENT SERVICES (BMS), 2219 Main St., Santa Monica CA 90405.(213)396-1440. Agent: Russell Barnard. Management firm. Represents artists, groups and songwriters; currently handles 2 acts. Receives 10-20% commission. Reviews material for acts.
How to Contact: Write first and obtain permission to submit cassette with 3-10 songs and lead sheet. SASE. Reports in 1 month.
Music: Bluegrass, blues, country, folk, R&B, rock, soul and top 40/pop. Works primarily with country crossover singers/songwriters. Current acts include Helen Hudson (singer/songwriter); and Mark Shipper (songwriter/author).

BAUER-HALL ENTERPRISES, 138 Frog Hollow Rd., Churchville PA 18966. (215)357-5189. Contact: William B. Hall III. Booking agency and production company. Represents individuals and groups; currently handles 21 acts. Receives 10-15% commission. Reviews material for acts, depending on engagement.

How to Contact: Query ("include photos, promo material, and record or tape") or submit demo tape and lyric sheet. Prefers cassette with 2-3 songs on demo. "Letter of inquiry preferred as initial contact." Does not return unsolicited material. Reports in 1 month.

Music: Marching band, circus and novelty ethnic. Works primarily with "unusual or novelty attractions in musical line, preferably those that appeal to family groups." Current acts include Kenneth McBride, (Irish singer-piano player); Wendy Hellyer (song stylist); and Russell Darr (bandmaster).

BELKIN PRODUCTIONS/BELKIN PERSONAL MANAGEMENT, Suite 205, 28001 Chagrin Blvd., Cleveland OH 44122. (216)464-5990. Management firm and production company. Represents artists, groups and songwriters; currently handles 6 acts. Reviews material for acts.

How to Contact: Query. Prefers cassette with 2-4 songs and lyric sheet. "Send a tape and follow up with a phone call." SASE. Please call back for report.

Music: Mostly top 40/pop, rock and dance-oriented; also R&B and church/religious. Works with commercial pop, R&B artists/songwriters, rock/adult contemporary artists and black acts. "Would like to pursue disco acts much more aggressively. We are involved in crossover acts." Current acts include The Michael Stanley Band (rock/pop/top 40); Donnie Iris (rock/pop); B.E. Taylor Group (rock/pop); Karen Jackson (AC/Christian contemporary); and Swankk (R&B).

HARVEY BELLOVIN, 410 E. 64th St., New York NY 10021. Contact: Harvey Bellovin. Personal manager. Represents artists, groups and lyricists/composers in New York area. Receives 10-20% commission. Reviews material for acts.

How to Contact: Write first or submit demo tape and lyric sheet. Prefers cassette. SASE. Reports in 3 weeks.

Music: MOR, rock, top 40/pop and musical scores. Works primarily with rock bands; composer/singer (MOR, rock, top 40/pop); lyricist and/or composer (musicals).

BGM RECORDS, #110, 4047 Naco Perrin, San Antonio TX 78217. (512)654-8773. President/General Manager: Bill Green. Booking agency, record company and publicity company. Represents artists, groups and songwriters; currently handles 7 acts. Receives 15% commisson. Reviews material for acts.

How to Contact: Prefers cassette with 1-4 songs and lyric sheet. SASE. Reports in 1 month.

Music: Mostly contemporary and traditional country. Works primarily with vocalists and vocal groups. Current acts include Bobby Jenkins; Dianna Hart; and Bo Garza (all country).

J. BIRD BOOKING AGENCY, 4905 S. Atlantic Ave., Daytona Beach FL 32029. (904)767-4707. Contact: John Bird. Booking agency. Represents artists and groups from anywhere; currently handles 104 acts. Receives 15-25% commission.

How to Contact: Prefers cassette with 3-4 songs and lead sheet. "Initial interview is usually by phone; after demo material is received we usually ask person to contact us again in 7-10 days." Does not return unsolicited material.

Music: Bluegrass, blues, church/religious, country, dance-oriented, easy listening, folk, jazz, R&B, soul, country rock and top 40/pop. Works primarily with "top 40 dance and show bands, rock bands (dance and concert), and concert groups (major label touring bands). Particularly active in national college concerts. Most of our demand is for dance bands since we generally work with high schools and universities." Current acts include Henny Youngman, Paul Paulson, and Bill Luby (comedians).

Tips: "We solicit established professional acts interested in touring full time. The groups should have or be willing to prepare a promotional package containing audio and/or videotape, photos, song, personnel, and equipment lists. Since we are the largest 'one nighter' agency in the Southeast, providing entertainment to colleges nationwide, artists submitting materials should be geared for that market."

BLADE AGENCY, Box 1556, Gainesville FL 32602. (904)372-8158 and 377-8158. General Manager: Charles V. Steadham Jr. Management firm and booking agency. Represents professional individuals and groups; currently handles 36 acts. Receives 15-20% commission. Reviews material for acts.

How to Contact: Query. Prefers cassette with 2-5 songs, publicity materials and itinerary. Does not return unsolicited material. Reports as soon as possible on solicited material.

Music: Bluegrass, blues, country, dance-oriented, easy listening, folk, MOR, rock (country), soul and top 40/pop. Current acts include Gamble Rogers (country/folk artist); Tom Parks (comedian); Mike Cross (country/folk artist); Mike Reid (MOR/pop); Truc of America (R&R/comedy); George Hamilton IV (country/gospel); Robert Nelson (comedy variety); Andy Andrews (comedy); Barbara Bailey Hutchison (folk/pop); and James Lee Stanley (MOR/pop).

WILLIS BLUME AGENCY, Box 509, Orangeburg SC 29116. (803)536-2951. President: Willis Blume. Management firm and booking agency. Represents artists and groups in the southeast; currently

handles 13 acts. Receives minimum 15% commission. Reviews material for acts.
How to Contact: Query by mail. Prefers cassette with 4 songs maximum. SASE.
Music: Mostly beach music and dance-oriented; also easy listening, MOR, R&B, soul and top 40/pop. Works primarily with show and dance bands. Current acts include Shagtime, The O'Kaysions, The Swingin' McDallons; (all beach/top 40 show acts); Maurice Williams & the Zodiacs; the Tams (beach/top 40/pop artists); Brass Town Ball (top 40/beach); and Second Nature (beach).

*BONNIE LOU ENTERPRISES, RD 3, Box 323, Seaford DE 19973. (302)629-6441. Manager: Bonnie L. Carver. Management agency. Represents artists. Currently handles 1 act. Receives 20% commission. Reviews material for acts.
How to Contact: Prefers cassette with 1-3 songs and lyric sheet. SASE. Reports in 4-6 weeks.
Music: Mostly country and top 40/pop. Works primarily with vocalists. Acts include Kim Marie.
Tips: "Make sure your songs have good hooks and are original and commercial."

BOUQUET-ORCHID ENTERPRISES, Box 18284, Shreveport LA 71138. (318)686-7362. President: Bill Bohannon. Management firm. Represents individuals and groups; currently handles 2 acts. Receives 15% minimum commission. Reviews material for acts.
How to Contact: Prefers cassette with 2-5 songs and lyric sheet. Include brief resume. SASE. Reports in 1 month.
Music: Country, rock (country), and top 40/pop. Works primarily with solo artists and small combos. Current acts include Adam Day and the Bandoleers (top 40/pop group).

BOYD RECORDS, 2609 NW 36th St., Oklahoma City OK 73112. (405)942-0462. President: Bobby Boyd. Management agency. Represents artists and songwriters. Receives minimum 25% commission.
How to Contact: Prefers 7½ ips reel-to-reel with 5-6 songs and lead sheet. "Send tapes that do not have to be returned." Does not return unsolicited material. Reports in 2 weeks.
Music: Country, rock, soul and top 40/pop. Current acts include Jim Whitaker (single); Dale Greear (single); and Belinda Eaves (single).

BROTHERS MANAGEMENT ASSOCIATES, 141 Dunbar Ave., Fords NJ 08863. (201)738-0880 or 738-0883. President: Al Faucera. Management firm and booking agency. Represents artists, groups and songwriters; currently handles 30-70 acts. Receives variable commission. Reviews material for acts.
How to Contact: Query by mail, arrange personal interview. Prefers cassette with 3-6 songs and lyric sheet. Include photographs. SASE. Reports as soon as possible.
Music: Mostly top 40/pop, dance and R&B; also blues, classical, country, show, easy listening, jazz, rock and soul. Works primarily with top 40 groups, preferably female; dance bands, show groups and 50s and 60s acts. Current acts include Waterfront (top 40/show); Chelsea (top 40/rock); and Benny Troy and Company (top 40/show).
Tips: "We need very commercial, chart oriented material."

AL BUNETTA MANAGEMENT, INC., Suite 215, 4121 Wilshire Blvd, Los Angeles CA 90010. (213)385-0882. President: Al Bunetta. Management firm. Represents artists and songwriters. Receives variable commission. Reviews material for acts.
How to Contact: Prefers cassette with 1-3 songs and lead sheet. SASE. Reports in 1 month.
Music: R&B, rock, new music, top 40/pop and adult contemporary. Works primarily with national recording artists. Current acts include John Prine (singer/songwriter/recording artist); and Matthew Wilder (pop).

C.A. MUSIC, Box 1990, Thousand Oaks CA 91360. Representative: Barb Voorhees. Publishing company. Represents gospel songwriters.
How to Contact: Prefers cassette with 1-3 songs and lead sheet. SASE. Reports in 3-5 weeks.
Music: Mostly gospel and contemporary Christian; also children's, choral and church/religious. Works primarily with contemporary and traditional gospel writers. Current writers include Cam Floria, Tim Hosman, David Graham, Si Simonson, Steve Taylor and Ronna Jordan.

C.P.W. SHOWTIME, INC., 5501 Lewis Ave., Toledo OH 43612. (419)478-2333. President: Pat Patton. Vice President: Chuck Levally. Management firm, booking agency and record company (Focus Records). Represents groups and songwriters; currently handles 36 acts. Receives variable commission. Reviews material for acts.
How to Contact: Submit demo tape and lead sheet; "follow up with phone call." Prefers cassette with 2-4 songs. SASE. Reports in 2 weeks.
Music: Progressive, rock and top 40/pop. Works primarily with nightclub and recording acts. Current acts include Shyster (pop/rock show act); Ebenezer (pop/rock show act); and Full Nelson (rock).
Tips: "Be professional and have good material."

CAN'T STOP PRODUCTIONS, INC., Suite 428, 420 Lexington Ave., New York NY 10170. (212)818-0640. International Manager: Hope Goering. General Manager: Russell Sidelsky. Management firm, production company and music publisher. Represents artists, groups and songwriters. Receives variable commission. Reviews material for acts.
How to Contact: Prefers cassette with 1-3 songs and lead sheet. SASE. Reports in 2 months.
Music: Dance-oriented, MOR, progressive, R&B, rock (no hard or country) and top 40/pop. Current acts include Ritchie Family; Village People; Break Machine (pop and R&B); Eartha Kitt (dance/pop).

CAPITOL BOOKING SERVICE, INC., 11844 Market St., North Lima OH 44452. (216)549-2155. President: David Musselman. Booking agency. Represents all types of entertainment; currently handles 7 acts. Reviews material for acts "on occasion.".
How to Contact: Query. Prefers cassette with minimum 3 songs. "We would like references. We also have video equipment, and if artist has videotape, we would like to see this." SASE. Reports ASAP.
Music: Mostly MOR; also country, dance-oriented, easy listening, folk, gospel, patriotic and top 40/pop. Works primarily with "self-contained musical groups that play all-around music for mixed audiences; young American or Las Vegas-type show reviews, some country and the New Seekers who are, of course, a name act from the '70s." Current acts include Life, Sunshine Express, Higher Power (show groups), Seekers (name act); Alann & Hays Show; Bobby Mercer Road Show (show and dance group); Eddie Jaye (ventriloquist and comedy M.C.); and JoAnn Castle (formerly of Lawrence Welk Show).
Tips: "Acts should have good literature, well choreographed and produced show."

*CELEBRITY ENTERPRISES, INC./MUSIC MARKETING INTERNATIONAL, INC., Box 390, Hollywood CA 90028. (213)366-1289. President: Buz Wilburn. Management firm, music publisher, record company and TV/movie production company. Represents artists, groups and songwriters; currently handles 6 acts. Receives minimum 20% commission. Reviews material for acts.
How to Contact: Prefers cassette with 3-6 songs and lead sheet. Include "brief information sheet about act or writer. All submissions should be brief and concise." SASE. Reports in 2 weeks.
Music: Country, easy listening, gospel, MOR, R&B, soul and top 40/pop. Works primarily with "individual artists who have a background of performing and can write. We are not interested in any act that doesn't have recording possibilities." Current acts include Sam Neely (performer/songwriter); Alex Harvey (performer/songwriter); Chris David (country/recording artist); and Calamity Jayne (songwriter/recording artist).
Tips: "We are only looking for dedicated and professional acts who are multi-talented. Send complete (but brief) information and we will give an immediate answer as to whether or not our company can work with the act."

CLOCKWORK ENTERTAINMENT MANAGEMENT AGENCY, Box 1600, Haverhill MA 01831. (617)373-6010. President: Bill Macek. Management firm and booking agency. Deals with artists throughout New England. Represents groups and songwriters; currently handles 6 acts. Receives 10-15% commission. Reviews material for acts.
How to Contact: Query or submit demo tape only. Include "interesting facts about yourself in a cover letter." Prefers cassette with 3-12 songs. "Also submit promotion and cover letter with tape." Does not return unsolicited material unless accompanied by SASE. Reports in 2 weeks.
Music: Rock (all types) and top 40/pop. Works primarily with bar bands and original acts. Current acts include Airway (4-piece FM rocker); The Atomix (5-piece FM rocker); and Quartet (4-piece high energy top 40/rock).

C-M-I RECORDS/TTA MANAGEMENT, 10125 227th Ave., Buckley WA 98321. (206)862-1877. Contact: Tom Thrasher. Management firm and record company. Represents artists, groups and songwriters in the Northwest; currently handles 4 acts. Receives 10-50% commission. Reviews material for acts.
How to Contact: Prefers cassette with 3-10 songs and lyric sheet. SASE. Reports in 1 month.
Music: Mostly gospel, contemporary Christian and country; also bluegrass, blues, easy listening, and folk. Works primarily with vocalists, show bands and concert groups. Current acts include Todd Smith (gospel rock); The Nashville Rebels (country rock); and Melissa Mason (contemporary Christian).

STEVE COHEN & ASSOCIATES, Suite 502, 9000 Sunset Blvd., Los Angeles CA 90069. (213)275-7329. Director, Artist Development: David Cook. Management firm. Represents artists, groups, songwriters and producers "mostly in our West Coast region, but could represent hit talent from anywhere;" currently handles 4 acts. Receives 10-20% commission. Reviews material for acts.

How to Contact: Query by mail. Send cassette with maximum 2-3 songs. "Well-produced, no piano/vocal demos. Send photo, resume or any other relevant materials." SASE required. Reports in 2 months or "2 days, depending on level of interest."
Music: Dance-oriented, R&B, rock and top 40. Works primarily with "recording artists, songwriters, soloists and bands." Current acts include Mary Wells (pop/R&B artist); Greg Watson (arranger, writer, producer, performer, overseas performance tours, publishing, Fantasy Records); Paulette McWilliams (solo and background singer and MCA Records recording artist) and Van Ross Redding (recently top 4 R&B artist).
Tips: "Submit hit songs only, i.e., A side, top 10 record. No ballads and no country, please."

COLLINS/BARRASSO INC., 280 Lincoln St., Allston MA 02134. (617)783-1100. Contact: Steve Barrasso or Tom Collins. Management firm. Represents artists, groups and songwriters. Receives 15-25% commission. Reviews material for acts.
How to Contact: Prefers cassette with 2-6 songs. SASE. Works with recording artists only. Reports in 1 month.
Music: Rock and top 40/pop. Current acts include Aerosmith (rock).

COMMUNICATION CONCEPT, Box 2095, Philadelphia PA 19103. (215)844-8736. President: S. Deane Henderson. Management firm and promotion and talent scout handling copyrights and trademarks. Represents artists, groups and songwriters; currently handles 13 acts. Receives 10-15% commission. Reviews material for acts.
How to Contact: Prefers cassette or VHS videocassette with 4-8 songs and lyric sheet. Does not return unsolicited material.
Music: Mostly rock, top 40 and gospel; also dance-oriented, easy listening, jazz, MOR, soul, top 40/pop and funk. Works primarily with dance bands and recording acts. Current acts include Verdell Colbert and Offspring (gospel); The Racers (rock); and Sparkles (top 40/R&B).
Tips: "Please submit your best tape or VHS video."

BURT COMPTON AGENCY, Box 160373, Miami FL 33116. (305)238-7312. Contact: Burt Compton. Booking agency. Represents groups; currently handles 36 acts. Receives 10-20% commission. Reviews material for acts.
How to Contact: Query by mail, then submit demo tape. Prefers cassette with 3-6 songs. "Include complete repertoire, 8x10 photo and resume." Does not return unsolicited material. Reports in 1 month.
Music: Mostly top 40/pop; also rock (hard/dance). Works primarily with dance and bar bands. Current acts include Heroes (dance band); Fantasy (recording/concert group); and Wildlife (recording/concert group).
Tips: "Have your promotional materials professionally packaged. We don't like having to decipher handwritten resumes with misspelled words and incomplete sentences."

CONTEMPORARY ARTIST MANAGEMENT, Box 250, Fern Park FL 32730. (305)834-6677. Artist Management: Monte Taylor, Terrie Miner and Fred Weiss. Management firm. Represents musical groups; currently handles 20 acts. Receives 10-15% commission. Reviews material for acts.
How to Contact: Write first. Prefers cassette with 4-6 songs and lyric sheet. SASE. Reports in 3 weeks.
Music: Mostly dance-oriented and top 40/pop; also MOR, R&B, rock and soul. Works primarily with high-energy show acts, including dance acts. Current acts include Coast to Coast, the Right Touch, and Franco and Mary Jane (show groups).

*CONTI PRODUCTION STUDIO, Box 970, Edgewater FL 32032. (904)427-2480. President: Dick Conti. Recording/video studio and management firm. Represents artists, groups and songwriters; currently handles 4 acts. Receives 10-33% of commission. Reviews material for acts, commercials, jingles, films and documentaries.
How to Contact: Prefers 7¹/₂ ips reel-to-reel or cassette and lead sheet. SASE. Reports in 1 month.
Music: Mostly country, new Christian and top 40/pop; also blues, children's, church/religious, easy listening, folk, gospel, R&B, MOR, rock and soul. Works primarily with large "Mike Curb Congregation" type groups, rock groups, show bands (new Christian), vocalists (R&B), church groups (children) and commercial/jingle writers and arrangers. Current acts include the Conti Family (family variety); and Gino Conti (Gino Vannelli type).

TIM COULTER & ASSOCIATES, Box 28097, Columbus OH 43228. (614)279-2300. President: Tim D. Coulter. Management firm, booking agency and public relations firm. Represents artists and groups; currently handles 3 acts. Receives 10-20% commission.
How to Contact: Submit background information and resume. Prefers cassette with 3 songs. SASE. Reports in 1 month.

Music: Mostly contemporary Christian; also church/religious, gospel and MOR. Works primarily with vocalists, bands and contemporary Christian music artists. Current acts include Ransom (art rock group); Terri Lynn (country/pop), and Dave Fullen (contemporary Christian artist).

COUNTRY STAR ATTRACTIONS, 439 Wiley Ave., Franklin PA 16323. (814)432-4633. Contact: Norman Kelly. Booking agency. Represents artists and musical groups; currently handles 10 acts. Receives 10-15% commission. Reviews material for acts.
How to Contact: Prefers 7¹/₂ ips reel-to-reel and cassette with 1-4 songs and lyric sheet; include photo. SASE. Reports in 2 weeks.
Music: Mostly country; also bluegrass, gospel, rock or top 40/pop. Works primarily with vocalists, self-contained country shows and bar bands. Current acts include Junie Lou (country); Lady Brown Sugar (rock singer with band); and Woodsmoke (country dance band).

CRASH PRODUCTIONS, Box 40, Bangor ME 04401-0040. (207)794-6686. Manager: Jim Moreau. Booking agency. Represents individuals and groups; currently handles 7 acts. Receives 10-25% commission.
How to Contact: Query. Prefers cassette with 4-8 songs. Include resume and photos. "We prefer to hear groups at an actual performance." SASE. Reports in 2 weeks.
Music: 50's-60's, country rock and country. Works primarily with groups who perform at night clubs and outdoor events (festivals and fairs). Current acts include Tim Ferrell & Cabin Country Band (bluegrass); Nitewind (country); and Mainly Country (country).

CROSBY MUSIC AGENCY, 7730 Herschel Ave., La Jolla CA 92037. (619)454-0383. Agent: Bonnie Woods. Booking agency. Deals primarily with regional artists. Represents artists and groups; currently handles 80+ acts. Receives 10-20% commission.
How to Contact: Submit demo tape, photo and song list. "Evaluation usually within 2 weeks. SASE for return of material."
Music: Jazz, rock (hard rock and country rock), top 40 and new wave. Works with wide variety of performers; show bands, dance bands, bar bands and duos. Current acts include Snails (new wave); and Bob Crosby Orchestra (jazz).
Tips: "Send a complete promotional package including a good photo, complete song list, and clear demo tape."

D. L. ENTERPRISES LTD., Suite F, 913 S. Hill St., Oceanside CA 92054. (619)722-1795. Vice President, Sales: Dennis Levinson. Booking agency. Represents artists, groups and theater shows; currently handles 12 acts. Receives 10-15% commission. Reviews material for acts.
How to Contact: Prefers cassette with 2-5 songs and lyric sheet. Include photo. SASE. Reports in 1 month.
Music: Mostly dance-oriented and top 40/pop; also classical, country, MOR, rock and soul. Works primarily with dance bands, show groups and concert groups. Current acts include War (concert act/funk/rock); Tierra (Latin/soul); and Iron Butterfly (concert act/rock).
Tips: "Have your materals as original as possible."

DAWN PRODUCTIONS/INTERNATIONAL TALENT, Box 300, Mt. Gretna PA 17064. President: Joey Welz. Management firm, booking agency and record company. Represents artists, groups and songwriters; currently handles 4 acts. Receives minimum 15% commission. Reviews material for acts.
How to Contact: Prefers cassette with 4-8 songs. Does not return unsolicited material. Reports in 1 month "if we can use material."
Music: Mostly rock, country and top 40/pop; also easy listening and R&B. Works primarily with dance and bar bands. Current acts include Joey Welz of Bill Haley's Comets, Santo of Santo & Johnny and Gerry Granahan.

MARV DENNIS & ASSOCIATES, INC., 1002 18th Ave. S, Nashville TN 37212. (615)320-7022. Management firm, booking agency, music publisher and record producer. Represents artists, groups and songwriters; currently handles 30 acts. Receives 10-15% commission. Reviews material for acts.
How to Contact: Write first and obtain permission to submit. Prefers cassette with 1-3 songs. Include b&w photo of artist. Does not return unsolicited material. Reports in 1 month "only if used.".
Music: Mostly country and top 40/pop; also country, dance-oriented and all types of rock. Current acts include Wright Bros. (country); Ronnie Reno (country); Johnsons (show); Jackson Hwy. (top 40) and Custers Last Band (country).

DOUBLE TEE PROMOTIONS, 1439 SW. Columbia, Portland OR 97201. (503)221-0288. Contact: Carole Pucik. Management firm. Represents artists, groups and songwriters; currently handles 3 acts.

Receives minimum 15% commission. Reviews material for acts.
How to Contact: Query by mail. Prefers cassette with minimum 2 songs. Does not return unsolicited material. Reports in 1 month.
Music: Mostly rock; also blues, dance-oriented, R&B and top 40/pop. Works primarily with show bands. Current acts include Shock (funk group); Sequel (top 40); and Marlon McClain (R&B artist).

TIM DRAKE PRESENTS, Box 8586, Woodcliff Lake NJ 07675. (201)391-0707. Management, concert promotion and talent buying agent for universities and clubs. Represents artists, groups and songwriters; currently handles 3 acts. Receives 10-20% commission. "With some artists, especially the undeveloped act, we work on retainer; management fees are based on the services we perform." Reviews material for acts.
How to Contact: "Please submit a well recorded demo. If unknown artist, submit tape, biography, press clippings, etc." Prefers cassette with 3-5 songs. SASE. Reports in 2 weeks.
Music: Rock (all types) and top 40/pop. Works with touring rock acts, jazz fusion artists and groups. "We deal primarily with concert acts, as our main business is concert promotion. However, on the management end of things we have helped develop some very talented and commercially potential artists. We don't look for new, undeveloped acts, but if we see or hear something sensational, we'll pursue it." Current acts include John Macey; (jazz fusion artist); Billy Falcon (rock act); and Tomboy (rock act).
Tips: "Take the time to carefully prepare your submitted tape. Try to make your presentation as professional as possible."

DYNAMIC TALENT ASSOCIATES, Box 13584, Atlanta GA 30324. (404)872-4000. Vice President, Promotions: Marie Sutton. President: Alex Janoulis. Booking agency. Represents individuals and groups; currently handles 6 acts. Receives 10-15% commission.
How to Contact: Prefers cassette with 2-3 songs. "Send photos and bio." Reports ASAP.
Music: Blues, jazz and rock (new music). Works with top 40 bands and rock and blues bands.. Current acts include Starfoxx (top 40/rock); The Night Shadows (new wave); Diamond Lil (female impersonator); Mike Angelo and the Idols; and The Pigs.

RICHARD LEE EMLER ENTERPRISES, Suite 1000, 8601 Wilshire Blvd., Beverly Hills CA 90211. (213)659-3932. Contact: Richard Lee Emler. Represents composers and songwriters; currently handles 20 acts. Receives 15-20% commission. Reviews material for film and TV use.
How to Contact: Query. Prefers cassette. SASE. Reports in 2-3 months.
Music: "Instrumental music and songwriting for films and television. This includes MOR, country, jazz, disco, rock, soul, top 40 and classical." Current clients include Johnny Harris, Michael J. Lewis, Peter Matz, Gil Melle, Nelson Riddle, George Tatro, William Kraft, Allyn Ferguson, Richard Addrisi, Jeff Filbar, Patty Dahlstrom, Richard Markowitz, Fred Karlin, and Jim Halsey Client Group.
Tips: "Get as much experience as possible, wherever possible."

GINO EMPRY PUBLIC RELATIONS & PERSONAL MANAGEMENT SERVICES, INC., Suite 104, 25 Wood St., The Maples, Toronto, Ontario M4Y 2P9 Canada. (416)977-1153. President: Gino Empry. Management firm, booking agency and public relations firm. Represents artists, groups and songwriters; currently handles 15 acts. Receives 10-20% commission. Reviews material for acts.
How to Contact: Write first. Prefers cassette or videocassette with 2-6 songs. SAE and IRC. Reports in 1 month.
Music: Mostly MOR, dance-oriented, and jazz. Works primarily with vocalists and dance bands. Current acts include Spitfire; Ann Marie Moss; and Peggy Lee (night club artist).
Tips: "Send full background and current photos with demo."

ENCORE PRODUCTIONS, 14049 Gratiot, Detroit MI 48205. (313)526-8760. President: Vic Pettenuzzi. Management firm and booking agency. Represents original rock bands. Receives 20-25% commission. Reviews material for acts.
How to Contact: Prefers cassette with 4-5 songs and lyric sheet. SASE. Reports in 2 weeks.
Music: Rock. Current artists include Duffy King (pop rock).

ENTERTAINMENT MANAGEMENT ENTERPRISES, 454 Alps Rd., Wayne NJ 07470. (201)694-3333. President: Richard Zielinski. Management firm. Represents artists and musical groups; currently handles 2 acts. Receives minimum of 20% commission. Reviews material for acts.
How to Contact: Prefers cassette or ½" VHS or ¾" U-matic videocassette (if possible) with 4-6 songs and lyric sheet. Include 8x10 glossy and bio. "Let us know, by mail or phone, about any New York area performances so we can attend." SASE. Reports in 2 weeks.
Music: Mostly rock. Works primarily with rock groups with vocals, synthesized rock and contemporary

singers. Current acts include This Part of the Body (original rock group); Scripture (progressive rock) and Voyager (progressive rock).
Tips: "A good press kit is important."

S. L. FELDMAN & ASSOCIATES, Suite 200, 1334 W. 6th Ave., Vancouver, British Columbia V6H 1A7 Canada. (604)734-5945. Management Assistant: Denise Donlon. Management firm, booking agency and music publisher. Represents artists, groups and songwriters; currently handles 150 acts. Reviews material for acts.
How to Contact: Prefers cassette with minimum 3 songs and lyric sheet. SASE. Reports in 1 month.
Music: Mostly rock and dance pop; also MOR, R&B and top 40/pop. Works primarily with recording artists, vocalists, top 40 commercial originals. Current acts include Trooper (pop), Images in Vogue (modern pop), and D.O.A. (hard rock).

THE FELTON AGENCY, Box 740, Paul ID 83347. (208)438-5439. Agent: Chuck Felton. Management firm and booking agency. Represents artists, groups and songwriters; currently handles 12 acts. Receives 10-15% commission. Reviews material for acts.
How to Contact: Query by mail. Prefers cassette with 3-5 songs and lyric sheet. SASE. Reports in 3 weeks.
Music: Mostly country, country rock and MOR; also dance-oriented, rock and top 40/pop. Works primarily with country, MOR, and country rock groups and lounge bands. Current acts include Mari Ellen (country singer); Mixed Company (country trio); and Roy Bell (country artist).
Tips: "Must be neat in appearance and have no excessive habits."

FRED T. FENCHEL ENTERTAINMENT AGENCY, 2104 S. Jefferson Ave., Mason City IA 50401. General Manager: Fred T. Fenchel. Booking agency. Represents professional individuals and groups; currently handles 15 acts. Receives 15-20% commission. Reviews material for acts.
How to Contact: Query. Prefers cassette. SASE. Reports in 3 weeks.
Music: Country, easy listening, gospel, rock and top 40/pop. Current acts include Deep River Band (country); Spectrum (4-piece rock); Windsong (variety/rock band); and Citrus (pop rock/country band).

FISHER & ASSOCIATES ENTERTAINMENT, INC., 2238 Park Rd., Charlotte NC 28203. (704)332-9090. Agent: Dave Fisher. Booking agency. Represents musical groups in the Southeastern states including North Carolina, South Carolina, Virginia, Georgia, Tennessee, Alabama, Mississippi and Florida; currently handles 60 groups. Receives 15-20% commission. Reviews material for acts.
How to Contact: Prefers cassette with 6-10 songs. "Include resume, bio, references and publicity photos." SASE. Reports in 1 month.
Music: Dance-oriented, funk, rock (commercial and danceable) and top 40/pop and variety groups. Works primarily with club and lounge groups (4 to 8 pieces), bar bands, and dance groups suitable for the young adult market (ages 16-40). Current acts include Sugarcreek (top 40/rock); Shuffle (top 40/variety); Contrazz (rock); The Mighty Majors (top 40/funk); Clockwork (top 40/rock); Threshold (top 40/funk); Thin Men (top 40); Sneaky (top 40/variety/show); and Teaser (top 40/funk).

FLASH ATTRACTIONS AGENCY, 38 Prospect St., Warrensburg NY 12885. (518)623-9313. Agent: Wally Chester. Management firm and booking agency. Represents artists and groups; currently handles 4 exclusive and 100 nonexclusive acts. Receives 15-20% commission. Reviews material for acts.
How to Contact: Query by mail. Prefers cassette with 1-6 songs and lyric sheet. SASE. Reports in 1 month.
Music: Mostly top 40, country, Hawaiian and MOR; also blues, dance-oriented, easy listening, gospel, jazz, Spanish and country rock. Works primarily with singles, duos and trios; floor show groups and lounge acts. Current acts include Bobby Cook Show (50s revival show); Prince Pablo's Calypso Revue (Trinidad steel band); Joe Eigo's Elvis Show (Elvis dedication act); Mirinida and the American Gentlemen (country show-revue); Kaena and Her Polynesian Paradise Revue; Claudia Villa (Italian-Mediterranean band and show); North Country Preservation Dixieland Jazz Band; Wally Chester and the Chordsmen Trio; and Paul Baron's Harmonica Rascals.

JOAN FRANK PRODUCTIONS, Suite 101, 9550 Forest Lane, Dallas TX 75243. (214)343-8737. Manager: R.D. Leonard. Booking agency. Represents individuals and groups; currently handles varying number of acts. Receives 10-15% commission. Reviews material for acts.
How to Contact: Query. Prefers cassette tapes. SASE. Reports in 2 weeks.
Music: Mostly dance-oriented; also country and easy listening. Works primarily with dance bands, show bands, combos and singles. Current acts include the Gary Lee Orchestra (big band); The Dave Harris Combo (dance); and Texas (country show and dance group).

RITA FRANKLIN, 2599 N. Park Blvd., Cleveland Heights OH 44106. (216)321-7297. Contact: Rita Franklin. Jazz, classical public relations firm. Represents artists, groups and songwriters. Receives 10% minimum commission. Reviews material for acts.
How to Contact: Query by mail. Prefers cassette or ½" VHS videocassette and lyric sheet. Does not return unsolicited material. Reports in 1 month.
Music: Jazz, blues and classical. Works primarily with jazz artists—solo instrumentalists, show bands, dance bands, bar bands and vocalists. Current acts include Carl Ace Carter/Keyboard (jazz solo or combo—opening act of Cleveland-Akron Kool Jazz Fest/84); Eddie Heywood (solo or combo pianist); Duke Jenkins (jazz trio); and Cleveland Octet (classical jazz and strings—spinoff of The Cleveland Orchestra).

THE FRANKLYN AGENCY, #312, 1010 Hammond St., Los Angeles CA 90069. (213)272-6080. President: Audrey P. Franklyn. Management agency, public relations firm, SRS/Hollywood judge and American Song Festival judge. Represents artists, musical groups and businesses; currently handles 7 acts. Receives 5-15% commission. Reviews material for acts.
How to Contact: Query by mail, arrange personal interview or submit demo tape and lead sheet. Prefers cassette/video cassette with 4 songs on demo. SASE. Reports in 1 month.
Music: Mosly rock, C&W and pop; also blues, easy listening, gospel, jazz, MOR, progressive, and R&B. Works primarily with rock bands and single soloist singers. Current acts include Marilyn Johnson (pop singer); Marco Valenti (pop and semi-classical); and Lennart Flindt (jazz pianist).
Tips: "No amateurs—be funded for promotional efforts."

FREDDIE CEE ATTRACTIONS, 193 Konhaus Rd., Mechanicsburg PA 17055. (717)766-7644.Contact: Fred Clousher. Booking agency. Represents groups and comedy and novelty acts in Pennsylvania, Maryland, Virginia, West Virginia, New York, New Jersey and Ohio; currently handles approximately 75 acts. Receives 10-20% commission.
How to Contact: Prefers cassette or VHS videocassette with 5-10 songs. Include "photos, list of credits, etc." Does not return unsolicited material. Reports in 3 weeks.
Music: Mostly country, ethnic/novelty and top 40; also bluegrass, gospel, easy listening, Hawaiian and German. Works primarily with "marketable groups in country, country rock, bluegrass, gospel, variety show groups, etc." Current acts include the Hawaiian Revue '86 (show and dance act); Showdown (country/rock); and Harmonica Rascals (vaudeville).
Tips: "We obtain employment for marketable groups and performers. Those desiring to use our services should submit complete promo material (demo tape, photos, credits, etc.)"

FROST & FROST ENTERTAINMENT, 3985 W. Taft Dr., Spokane WA 99208. (509)325-1777. Agent: Dick Frost. Booking agency. Represents individuals and groups; currently handles 15 acts. Receives 15% commission.
How to Contact: Query. Prefers cassette with 5 songs and lyric sheet. Include information on past appearances, as well as list of references. SASE. Reports in 2 weeks.
Music: Mostly country and MOR; also dance-oriented, easy listening, rock (country and 50s) and top 40/ pop. Works primarily with dance bands, show bands and individual artists. Currently acts include Tex Williams (western act); Kay Austin (C&W/MOR act); and Stagecoach West.
Tips: "Send promo package, glossy and performing locations."

FTM ENTERPRISES, INC., Box 691431, Los Angeles CA 90069. (213)550-0130. President: Toby Mamis. Management firm. Represents artists, groups, songwriters and producers; currently handles 3 acts. Receives 15-25% commission. Reviews material for acts.
How to Contact: Prefers cassette with 3-6 songs and lead sheet. "If writer is also an artist/performer, enclose photo, bio and press clippings." SASE. Reporting time varies.
Music: Mostly rock, pop and top 40; also country, dance-oriented, easy listening, and MOR. Works primarily with "self-contained" rock bands. Current acts include Little Girls (rock band); Shell (rock singer; and Caron Maso (songwriter).

GAIL AND RICE PRODUCTIONS, 11845 Mayfield, Livonia MI 48150. (313)427-9300. Vice President: Chris Nordman. Booking agency. Represents individuals and groups; currently handles 25 acts. Receives 10-20% commission.
How to Contact: Submit demo tape and lead sheet. Prefers cassette with 3-6 songs on demo. Does not return unsolicited material. Reports in 3 weeks.
Music: Bluegrass, children's, country, dance-oriented, jazz and top 40/pop. Works primarily with "self-contained groups (1-8 people), show and dance music, listening groups, and individual name or semi-name attractions." Current acts include Dream Dance (vocal/dance act); Glenn Haywood (comedian/ventriloquist); and Tim Rowlands (comedy/juggling).

BOB GALLION PRODUCTIONS, (formerly Showcase Attractions), Box 78, Fairview OH 43736. (614)758-5812. President: R.H. Gallion. Management firm and booking agency. Represents individuals, groups and songwriters; currently handles 44 acts.
How to Contact: Write first or submit demo tape. Prefers cassette. Does not return unsolicited material. Reports in 2 months.
Music: Mostly country; also bluegrass, folk, gospel, MOR and top 40/pop. Works primarily with country and gospel artists and groups. Current acts include Bob Gallion (country); Patti Powell (country); The Younger Brothers Band; and Susquehanna River Band.

MICK GAMBILL ENTERPRISES, INC., Suite 12, 1617 N. El Centro, Hollywood CA 90028. (213)466-9777. President: Mick Gambill. Management firm and booking agency. Represents West Coast groups; currently handles 15 acts. Receives 15-20% commission. Reviews material for acts.
How to Contact: Prefers cassette with 3-6 songs. Also submit bio and songlist. SASE. Reports in 2 weeks.
Music: Light pop, jazz and top 40/pop. Works primarily with dance bands. Current acts include Calmrads (top 40); Steppin' Lazer (original ska); and Gregg Nestor (classical guitar).

AL GENTILE'S ORCHESTRA, 105 S. Elm St., Wallingford CT 06492. (203)265-5170. Contact: Al Gentile. Management firm and booking agency. Represents artists, groups and songwriters; currently handles "several" acts. Payment made "upon conclusion" of work. Reviews material for acts.
How to Contact: Write first and obtain permission to submit. Prefers cassette with minimum 6 songs and lyric sheet. SASE. Reports in 2 weeks.
Music: Mostly dance; also bluegrass, classical, country, easy listening, folk, jazz, Spanish, R&B, rock, top 40/pop and oldies. Works primarily with dance bands at weddings and shows. Current acts include Commuters (top 40 and oldies band); Nancy Knorr (vocalist); and The Sentamentalists.
Tips: "Follow up on our suggestions."

GLO MANAGEMENT CORP., Suite B, 3505 E. Livingston, Columbus OH 43227. (614)237-0336. President: William Davis. Management firm. Represents artists, groups and songwriters; currently handles 3 acts. Negotiates fees and royalties. Reviews material for acts.
How to Contact: Write first and obtain permission to submit. Prefers cassette with minimum 3 songs and lead sheet. SASE. Reports in 2 weeks.
Music: Jazz, R&B and soul. Works primarily with dance bands. Current acts include The Deele, "Griffin", Victor Burks, and Duane Mitchell.

DAVID GOLIATH AGENCY, Box 11960, Chicago IL 60611. (312)561-0027. Booking Manager: Dave Wright. Management firm and booking agency. Represents artists, groups and songwriters; currently handles 25 acts. Receives 15-20% commission. Reviews material for acts.
How to Contact: Write first and obtain permission to submit. Prefers cassette with 5-10 songs. SASE. Reports in 1 month.
Music: Mostly R&B/funk, soul/top 40 and pop; also blues, church/religious, dance-oriented disco funk, gospel, jazz, MOR and soul. Works primarily with dance bands. Current acts include "Lovers" (R&B/soul); "First Command Band" (R&B/pop), and Stutz (progressive rock).

GARY GOOD MANAGEMENT, 2500 NW 39th St., Oklahoma OK 73112. (405)947-1503. Contact: Gary Good. Management firm. Represents artists, groups and songwriters mainly from Oklahoma; currently handles 10 acts. Receives 15% commission. Reviews material for acts.
How to Contact: Prefers cassette or videocassette with 1-5 songs and lyric sheet. SASE. Reports ASAP.
Music: Mostly pop country, country and MOR; also dance-oriented, easy listening and top 40/pop. Works primarily with solo vocalists and variety club bands. Current acts include The Tim Sullvian Band; Julie Grafa (vocalist); and Rusty Aldridge (vocalist/songwriter).

BILL GRAHAM MANAGEMENT, 201 11th St., San Francisco CA 94103. (415)864-0815. Creative Development: Mick Brigden. Management firm. Represents artists and groups; currently handles 6 acts. Reviews material for acts.
How to Contact: Prefers cassette and lead sheet. SASE. Reports as soon as possible.
Music: Mostly rock and pop ballads; also progressive, R&B, and top 40/pop. Works primarily with original songwriters and vocalists. Current acts include Santana; Marc Anthony Thompson; John Hiatt; Charlie Peacock; and Bob Dylan.
Tips: "Rather than emphasize commercial sound, emphasize originality."

GRAND TALENT INTERNATIONAL, Suite 605, 1750 Kalakaua Ave., Honolulu HI 96826. (808)955-5758. President: Mark Nishimoto. Booking agency. Represents artists and groups. Receives 15% commission. Reviews material for acts.

How to Contact: Write first and obtain permission to submit. Prefers cassette with minimum 4 songs. SASE. Reports in 2 weeks.
Music: Mostly rock; also top 40/pop. Works primarily with dance and bar bands. Current acts include Wiz Kids (top 40); and John Gloria Band (variety).

GREAT PLAINS ASSOCIATES, INC., Suite 208, 706 Massachusetts, Lawrence KS 66044. (913)841-4444. Contact: Mark Swanson or Stuart Doores. Booking agency. Represents groups in Midwest; currently handles 30 acts. Receives 10-20% commission. Reviews material for acts.
How to Contact: Prefers cassette with 3-5 songs. SASE.
Music: Country, R&B, rock and soul. Works primarily with dance bands "for college mini-concerts to bar band dances." Current acts include The Ryde (contemporary rock); Unidos (soul); and Blue Wave (beach band).
Tips: "We are constantly looking for and expect our artists to have a *definite* idea of what they want and where they are going."

GREIF-GARRIS MANAGEMENT, 8467 Beverly Blvd., Los Angeles CA 90048. (213)653-4780. Vice President: Sid Garris. Management firm. Represents artists, groups and songwriters; currently handles 3 acts. Receives minimum 15% commission. Reviews material for acts.
How to Contact: Write first and obtain permission to submit. Prefers cassette with 3-5 songs. SASE. Reports ASAP.
Music: All types of "good music." Current acts include The New Christy Minstrels (folk); Michael Smotherman (pop); and Womack & Womack (R&B/pop).
Tips: "Artists should be critical enough to ensure that what is being sent is the *best* of their possible ability."

THE GROUP, INC., 1957 Kilburn Dr., Atlanta GA 30324. (404)872-6000. General Manager: Hamilton Underwood. Vice President: Marie Sutton. Management agency. Represents individuals and groups. Currently handles 6 acts. Receives 10-25% commission.
How to Contact: Prefers cassette or videocassette with 2-3 songs. Include photo and bio. Does not return unsolicited material. Reports ASAP.
Music: Mostly rock; also blues, jazz, progressive and top 40/pop. Works with concert, show and bar bands. Current acts include Mike Angelo and the Idols (new music funk band); Jump Street (Southern rock and new wave band); and Mike Lorenz (country/gospel artist-songwriter).

BOB HALE TALENT/LJ PRODUCTIONS, 502 N. 20th, Billings MT 59101. (406)245-2174. President: Bob Hale. Management firm and booking agency. Represents artists, groups and songwriters; currently handles 15 acts. Receives 15% (booking) to 20% (management). Reviews material for acts.
How to Contact: Prefers 7½ ips reel-to-reel or cassette with maximum 5 songs. "Demo should emphasize vocal with minimum amount of production." SASE. Reports in 2 weeks.
Music: Bluegrass, country, dance-oriented, easy listening, rock (hard, country), MOR and top 40/pop. Works primarily with country, bluegrass and top 40/pop. Current acts include Prairie Fire (country show group); Lost Highway Band (rock/country rock group); Linda Jordan (country/country rock artist); Clint Jackson (country single); Back to Back (country group); The Brothers Plus (country show group); and Your Move (rock group).

GEOFFREY HANSEN ENTERPRISES, LTD., Box 63, Orinda CA 94563. (415)937-6469. Artist Relations: J. Malcom Baird. Management firm. Represents artists, groups and songwriters. Receives 15-25% commission. Also paid on a contract basis. Reviews material for acts.
How to Contact: Submit demo tape, lead sheet, photograph and cover letter. Prefers cassette. SASE.
Music: Top 40/country and MOR in English, Spanish, French and Japanese. Works with top 40 and country artists; recording acts and overseas international stars. Current acts include Bert Friel (MOR/ Hawaiian artist); Pilita Corrales (top 40 Spanish/English MOR); and Mort Schuman (French 50s rock).
Tips: "We are always looking for new talent. Anyone who has a demo and is interested in the international scope of the entertainment industry, contact us. We are ready to listen."

HARMONY ARTISTS, INC., Suite 200, 8831 Sunset Blvd., Los Angeles CA 90069. (213)659-9644. President: Michael Dixon. Vice President: J.D. Ross. Booking agency. Represents groups; currently handles 60 acts. Receives 10-15% commission. Reviews material for acts.
How To Contact: Prefers cassette with 3-5 songs and lyric sheet, photo and promotional material. Reports in 2 weeks.
Music: Easy listening, MOR, progressive, rock and top 40/pop. Current acts include Ice, Red; Bank, Taxi; and Mick Smiley.

GEORGE HARNESS ASSOCIATES, 27 N. Lake Rd., Springfield IL 62707. (217)529-8550. President: George Harness. Management firm and booking agency. Represents artists and groups. Receives 10-20% commission. Reviews material for acts.
How to Contact: Query by mail. Prefers cassette or videocassette with 6-8 songs and lyric sheet. SASE. Reports in 2 weeks.
Music: Mostly MOR and top 40/pop; also dance-oriented. Current acts include Alcazar; Earl Turner & The Vann Company; and Moses & Highbrows (all show & dance acts).

HAT BAND MUSIC, Sound 70 Suite N-101, 210 25th Ave. N., Nashville TN 37203. Project Manager: Douglas Casmus. Management firm and publishing company. Represents artists, groups and songwriters; currently handles 6 acts. Reviews material for acts.
How to Contact: Query by mail. Cassettes only with 1-2 songs and typed lyric sheet. "Submissions *must* include SASE if you expect a reply or tape returned."
Music: Country, progressive, rock and top 40/pop. Works primarily with major recording artists. Current acts include Charlie Daniels Band (country rock); Dobie Gray (country); David Murphy (country); Nicolette Larson (country/pop); Dickey Betts (country); and Johnny Cobb (rock).

GLENN HENRY ENTERTAINMENT AGENCY, 1304 Crestline, Santa Barbara CA 93105. (805)687-1131. Contact: Glenn Henry. Booking agency. Represents individuals and groups; currently handles 16 acts. Receives 10-15% commission. Reviews material for acts.
How to Contact: Query or arrange personal interview. Prefers 8-track cartridge with 3-6 songs. Artist may submit 8x10 promo pictures and/or credits. SASE. Reporting time varies.
Music: Country (modern), MOR, rock and top 40/pop. Works with lounge and hotel bands (all top 40/ MOR) with female vocalist if possible and/or modern country dance groups. At present, needs pop rock band with female vocalist. Current acts include Paradox (top 40/MOR); Hot Foot (top 40/MOR); and Steve Woods (country).

HITCH-A-RIDE MANAGEMENT, Box 201, Cincinnati OH 45201. (606)371-5469. Manager: J.H. Reno. Management firm, booking agency and publishing company. Represents professional individuals, groups and songwriters; currently handles 4 acts. Receives 15% commission. Reviews material for acts.
How to Contact: Write first and obtain permission to submit. Prefers cassette with 1-4 songs and lyric sheet. SASE. Reports in 1 month.
Music: Bluegrass, country and MOR. Works primarily with vocalists. Current acts include Sheila Reno; Pam Hanna and Jack Reno (country vocalists).

DAVID J. HULL MUSIC ENTERPRISES, 16325 Addison, Southfield MI 48075. (313)559-4871. President: David J. Hull. Management and accounting firm. Represents artists, groups and songwriters in the Michigan area; currently handles 23 acts. Reviews material for acts.
How to Contact: Write first and obtain permission to submit. Prefers cassette with 3-6 songs. Include pictures. SASE. Reports in 3 weeks.
Music: Mostly blues and jazz; also R&B. Works primarily with instrumental groups that do original material and copy. Current acts include Debit Productions (studio); Blues Buzz Band (blues); and Rockett 88's (R&B).

IBOA MUSIC, Box 313, Jacksonville FL 32201. Director: William Patterson. Management firm and music publisher. Represents artists, groups and songwriters; currently handles 2 acts. Receives 20-50% commission. Reviews material for acts.
How to Contact: Query by mail. Prefers cassette with 1-3 songs. Does not return unsolicited material.
Music: Blues, easy listening, R&B and soul.

IEA/INTERNATIONAL ENTERTAINMENT ASSOCIATES, Professional Arts Bldg., Suite 818, 1616 Pacific Ave., Atlantic City NJ 08401. (609)347-0484. President: Danny Luciano. Booking agency and record producer. Represents artists, groups and songwriters from anywhere. Receives 10-25% commission. Reviews material for acts.
How to Contact: Prefers 7½ ips reel-to-reel or cassette with 4-8 songs and lead sheet. "No 8-tracks. Include picture and promotion package if self-contained performing artist." SASE. Reports in 6 weeks.
Music: Country, MOR, R&B, soft country rock and top 40/pop. Works primarily with dance bands, show groups and recording artists. Current acts include Atlantic City III; Mixx; and Focus.

IF PRODUCTIONS, INC., % Omnipop Enterprises, Suite 225, 223 Jericho Turnpike, Mineola NY 11501. (516)248-4019. Branches: 22240 Schoenborn St., Canoga Park CA 91304. (818)883-4865. New York: Producer/Staff writer: Tom Ingegno. Los Angeles: Producer/Staff writer: Mike Frenchik. Management agency and production company. Represents individuals, groups and songwriters; current-

ly handles 4 acts. Receives 15-20% commission. Reviews material for acts.
How to Contact: Query. Prefers cassette with 3-5 songs and lyric sheet. SASE. Reports in 3 weeks.
Music: MOR, progressive, rock and top 40/pop. Works primarily with recording acts and solo performers. Current acts include Thrills (rock act); Tony Monaco (songwriter/recording artist); Dave Fullerton (songwriter/recording artist); and Pat O'Brien (songwriter/recording artist).

INTERMOUNTAIN TALENT, Box 942, Rapid City SD 57709. (605)348-7777. Contact: Ron Kohn. Management firm and concert production agency. Deals with artists from the upper-midwest region. Represents artists and groups; currently handles 14 acts. Receives 10-20% commission. Reviews material for acts.
How to Contact: Query. Prefers cassette with 3-5 songs and lyric sheet. SASE. Reports in 2 weeks.
Music: Mostly rock; also top 40/pop. Current acts include Hod Rod Dee Luxx; Doctor K and the Shantays (rock bands); and Midwest Express (country band).

*INTERNATIONAL ARTIST MANANGEMENT, 1931 S.E. Morrison, Portland OR 97214. (503)238-0236. Vice-President of Operations: Gary W. Perman. Management firm. Represents recording artists and groups; currently handles 4 acts. Receives 15-20% commission. Reviews material for acts.
How to Contact: Prefers cassette with 2-4 songs, photo and biography. SASE. Reports in 3-4 weeks.
Music: Rock (all types), R&B, top 40/pop and country-rock. Current acts include Thin Man (rock), Chrisopher De'Nine (rock); The Receivers (top 40); and The Esquires (R&B).

INTERNATIONAL ENTERTAINMENT, Box 50727, Washington DC 20004-0727. (703)590-5928. Director: Charles B. Roberts. Management firm/booking agency and consultant. Represents artists, groups and songwriters; currently handles 3 acts. Receives 10-25% commission. Reviews material for acts.
How to Contact: Submit demo tape with 1-4 songs; "include 8x10 photo, bio and credits." Does not return unsolicited material. Reports in 1 month.
Music: Mostly progressive, top 40/pop and techno-rock; also dance-oriented, R&B, and soft rock. Current acts include Anthem (progressive rock).

*J.D. PRODUCTIONS, LTD., Box 444, Taylor MI 48180. (313)374-0168. President: John D. Lollio. Management firm, booking agency, music publisher and record company. Represents artists, groups and songwriters; currently handles 6 acts. Receives 10-15% commission. Reviews material for acts.
How to Contact: Query by phone first. Prefers cassette with minimum 2 songs. SASE. Reports in 1 week.
Music: Country and gospel; also MOR and top 40/pop. Works primarily with country and country rock groups. Current acts include Johni Dee (country); W.P. Carnes (contemporary); and LeMoine (A/C).
Tips: "We are always interested in new material."

JEANNE JENNAY TALENT & ASSOCIATES, Suite 274, 9404 Genesee Ave., LaJolla CA 92037. (619)291-0333. Contact: Jeanne Jennay. Booking agency. Represents artists, groups and songwriters in local area only; currently handles 7 acts. Receives 15-20% commission. Reviews material for acts.
How to Contact: Prefers cassette with 5-12 songs and lyric sheet. Does not return unsolicited material. Reports in 1 month.
Music: Mostly top 40; also country and gospel. Works primarily with vocalists and dance bands. Current acts include Tom Jepperson, Sandee Hirsh and Steve Robow.
Tip: "Looking for original material for my acts to record."

NED KANTAR PRODUCTIONS, INC., 6000 Oliver Ave. S, Minneapolis MN 55419. (612)861-1212. President: Ned Kantar. Booking agency. Represents artists and groups; currently handles 10 acts. Receives 20% commission. Reviews material for acts.
How to Contact: Prefers cassette and lyric sheet. SASE. Reports in 1 month.
Music: Mostly MOR and pop; also children's, dance-oriented and jazz. Works primarily with vocalists and dance bands. Current acts include Jim Mitchell (vocalist).

KATONA PRODUCTIONS, INC., Box 100, Toccoa GA 30577. (404)779-2711. President: Tommy Scott. Management firm. Represents artists and songwriters; currently handles 10 acts. Receives variable commission. Reviews material for acts.
How to Contact: Query by mail. Prefers cassette demo. SASE. Reporting time varies.
Music: Country and "medicine show." Current acts include David Everett, Chuck Cross and Jaff Whitley.

BEN KAYE INTERNATIONAL, Suite 38, 4824 Cote des Neiges Rd., Montreal, Quebec H3V 1G4 Canada. (514)739-4774. President: Ben Kaye. Management firm, booking agency and record producer. Represents artists, groups and songwriters; currently handles 6 acts. Receives variable commission "depending on the name value of the talent." Reviews material for acts.
How to Contact: Prefers cassette with 1-3 songs, lyric sheet and resume. SAE and IRC. Reports in 1 month.
Music: Mostly top 40/pop, hard rock and dance-oriented; also easy listening, MOR ballads and country rock. Works primarily with pop artists ("both English and French, because of our location"), hard rock groups and dance-oriented groups; "most write their own material but we are constantly on the look-out for strong writers." Current acts include Handle With Care (dance-oriented group); Lady Luck (pop rock group); Overload (dance/rock group); and Ted Tevan (radio personality-narrator "The Ballad of America").

HOWARD KING AGENCY, INC., #104, 9060 Santa Monica Blvd., Los Angeles CA 90069. (213)858-8048. President: Howard King. Management firm and booking agency. Represents artists, groups and songwriters. Receives 10-15% commission. Reviews material for acts.
How to Contact: Prefers cassette with maximum 3 songs, photo, publicity material and lyric sheet. SASE. Reporting time varies.
Music: Mostly top 40; also country, dance-oriented, easy listening, jazz, MOR, rock and pop. Works primarily with top 40 artist singles, duos and groups.

BOB KNIGHT AGENCY, 185 Clinton Ave., Staten Island NY 10301. (718)448-8420. General Manager: Bob Knight. Management firm, booking agency, music publishing and royalty collection firm. Represents artists, groups and songwriters; currently handles 20 acts. Receives 10-20% commission. Reviews material for acts.
How to Contact: "Phone calls accepted 6-9 p.m. (Eastern time)." Prefers cassette or videocassette with 5-10 songs and lead sheet "with bio and references. Send photos of artists and groups." SASE. Reports in 1 month.
Music: Mostly top 40/pop; also easy listening, MOR, R&B, soul and rock. Works primarily with lounge groups, high energy dance, 50's acts and show groups. Current acts include The Elegants (oldie show); Ad-Libs (60s group); and Supergold (grease show).

*KOPPERFIELD ENTERPRISES, Box 241, Cameron MO 64429. (816)632-6039. Manager: E.K. Bruhn. Management and booking agency, record company (Crusader), music publisher (Time Minstrel Music) and video firm (Masterpeace Productions). Represents individual artists, groups and songwriters. Deals mainly with local artists. Currently handles 5 acts. Receives 10-20% commission. Reviews material for material for acts.
How to Contact: Write or call first and obtain permission to submit. Prefers cassette, 7¹/₂ ips reel-to-reel or ¹/₂" or ³/₄" videocassette with 3-5 songs and "optional" lyric sheet or lead sheet. "Include resume and write up of intentions." SASE. Reports in 10 weeks.
Music: Mostly country, gospel and pop/top 40. Works primarily with vocalists and groups for county fairs and family shows. Acts include Elaine Sanders, Mary Dale and Kopperfield.

BOB KUBAN, 5 Biritz Court, St. Louis MO 63137. (314)869-6056. Contact: Bob Kuban. Represents artists and groups; currently handles 10 acts. Receives minimum 15% commission.
How to Contact: Query by mail. Prefers cassette with maximum 5 songs and lyric sheet. SASE. Reports in 2 weeks.
Music: Mostly top 40; also soul and pop. Works primarily with top 40 and big band dance bands. Current acts include Bob Kuban Brass (top 40, soul and big band); Everyday People (top 40 and soul); and Collage (top 40, jazz, standards). "All are very dance-oriented."
Tips: "I need good top 40 dance material."

L.D.F. PRODUCTIONS, Box 406, Old Chelsea Station, New York NY 10011. (212)925-8925. President: Mr. Dowell. Management firm and booking agency. Represents artists and choirs in the New York area. Receives 15-25% commission.
How to Contact: Write first and obtain permission to submit. Prefers cassette with 2-8 songs and lyric sheet. SASE. Reports in 1 month.
Music: Mostly black gospel; also choral and church/religious. Works primarily with vocalists and choirs. Current acts include L.D. Frazier (gospel artist/lecturer); and Frazier's (gospel workshop choir).
Tips: "Those interested in working with us must be original, enthusiastic and persistent."

*L 2 MANAGEMENT, Box 372, Flint MI 48501-0372. (313)695-3790. President: Thomas W. Lotts. Management agency. Represents individual artists and groups. Deals with artists from anywhere. "We

actively seek artists for and from the foreign marketplace." Currently handles 5 acts. Receives 15-25% commission. Reviews material for material for acts.
How to Contact: Write and obtain permission to submit, or arrange personal interview. Prefers cassette or VHS, NTSC or PAL videocassette with maximum 3 songs and typed lyric sheet. SASE. Reports in 12 weeks.
Music: "Only highly commercial" pop/rock, country and raggae. Works primarily with solo artists, pop-rock acts and self-contained hard rock and heavy metal acts. Acts include Tera Daven, John Dee, and Renee Roya Jackson.

LANDSLIDE MANAGEMENT, 928 Broadway, New York NY 10010. (212)505-7300. Principals: Ted Lehrman and Libby Bush. Management firm. Represents singers and songwriters; currently handles 6 acts. Receives 15% commission. Reviews material for acts.
How to Contact: Submit demo tape or ¹/₂" videocassette and lead sheet "of potential hit singles only—not interested in album cuts." SASE. "Include picture and resume if you're submitting yourself as an act."
Music: Country-pop, dance-oriented, MOR, rock (soft, pop), soul and top 40/pop. Works primarily with vocalists and rock groups. Current acts include Susie Vaughn-Raney, Deborah Dotson, Sally Yorke, Kevin Cort, Peter Lieberman, and Touch of Class.

GARY LAZAR MANAGEMENT, 3222 Belinda Dr., Sterling Heights MI 48077. (313)977-0645. Contact: Gary Lazar. Management firm, booking agency and music publisher. Represents artists, groups and songwriters; currently handles 6 acts. Receives 10-20% commission. Reviews material for acts.
How to Contact: Prefers cassette or ³/₄" or VHS videocassette wth maximum 3 songs and lead sheet. Does not return unsolicited material. Reports in 1 month.
Music: Rock (hard), children's and top 40/pop. Works primarily with recording artists, club bands and songwriters/lyricists. Current acts include Mark Farmer (rock act/songwriter); Kenny Rankin (pop recording artist); and The Cadillac Kids (rock band).

BUDDY LEE ATTRACTIONS, INC., Suite 300, 38 Music Square E., Nashville TN 37203. (615)244-4336. Artists and Groups Contact: Tony Conway. Songwriters Contact: Nancy Dunn. Management firm and booking agency. Represents individuals and groups; currently handles 60 acts. "Principally, we deal with established name acts who have recording contracts with major labels." Receives 10-15% commission. Reviews material for acts.
How to Contact: Prefers cassette with minimum 4 songs and lead sheet. Does not return unsolicited material. Reports as soon as possible on solicited material.
Music: Bluegrass, country, MOR, rock, soul and top 40/pop. Works primarily with concert attractions. Current acts include Danny Davis and the Nashville Brass (country/MOR instrumental); Willie Nelson and Family; Waylon Jennings (country/pop); Johnny Rivers (pop/rock); Vern Gosdin, Neil Young, David Allan Coe, George Strait, Bill Monroe and Porter Wagoner (all country artists).

JOHN LEVY ENTERPRISES, INC., Suite 1606, 5455 Wilshire Blvd., Los Angeles CA 90036. (213)934-0255. President: John Levy. Management agency. Represents individuals and songwriters; currently handles 3 acts. Receives 10-20% commission.
How To Contact: Prefers 7¹/₂ ips reel-to-reel or cassette with 1-5 songs and lead sheet. SASE. Reports in 2 weeks.
Music: Jazz, soul and top 40/pop. Current acts include Nancy Wilson, Ramsey Lewis, Joe Williams and Eddie Harris (all vocalists).

LIGHTHOUSE ATTRACTIONS, Box 158793, Nashville TN 37215. President: Tim Tye. Management firm and booking agency. Represents artists, groups and songwriters; currently handles 5 acts. Receives 15-20% commission. Reviews material for acts.
How to Contact: Write first. Prefers cassette with 3-5 songs, bio and lyric sheet. SASE. Reports in 2 weeks.
Music: Mostly country and top 40/pop; also easy listening, MOR and country rock. Works primarily with self-contained acts (groups or solo artists) interested in working the NACA college circuit, equally talented in writing and performing. Current acts include OuterBrooks (pop/rock band); and Alan Baker (songwriter/performer).

LINGERING MUSIC, INC., 2 Bay St., Thomaston ME 04861. (207)354-8928. President: Chuck Kruger. Management firm and booking agency. Represents artists, groups and songwriters in the Northeast; currently handles 4 acts. Receives 10-15% commission. Reviews material for acts.
How to Contact: Write first and obtain permission to submit. Prefers 7¹/₂ ips reel-to-reel, cassette or videocassette with 2-5 songs. "Brief biography okay, but let material speak for itself." SASE. Reports in 1 month.

Music: Mostly MOR; also country, dance-oriented, easy listening, folk, gospel, jazz, progressive, R&B, rock, soul, top 40/pop, calypso and reggae. Works primarily with soloists, trios and dance bands. Current acts include Chuck Kruger (singer/songwriter); The Fabulous Prizes (club trio); and Cruzan Confuzion Band (dance and college concert band).

LOCONTO PRODUCTIONS, 7766 NW 44th St., Sunrise FL 33321. (305)741-7766 or (305)940-2626 (Miami). President: Frank X. Loconto. Management firm. Represents artists and groups. Receives 10-25% commission. Reviews material for acts.
How to Contact: Prefers cassette with maximum 3 songs. "We are looking primarily for country artists and songs with strong hooks and crossover potential." SASE. Reports in 1 month.
Music: Mostly country; also bluegrass, children's, church/religious, country, easy listening, folk, gospel, MOR, and top 40/pop. Works primarily with country vocalists, country bands, MOR vocalists and bluegrass artists. Current acts include Donna Perito, Jeanne Cia, and Dick Contino.

RON LUCIANO MUSIC CO., Box 263, Hasbrouck Heights NJ 07604. (201)288-8935. Branch: Ron Luciano Music Company (South), Box 263, Brigantine NJ 08203. (609)266-2623. President: Ron Luciano. Management firm and booking agency. Represents artists, group and recording/specialty acts; currently handles 7-8 acts. Receives 10-20% commission. Reviews material for artists.
How To Contact: Query or submit picture and biography. Prefers 7¹/₂ ips reel-to-reel or cassette with 4-8 songs. "Can also approach by sending a copy of their record release." SASE. Reports in 2-6 weeks.
Music: Disco, MOR, rock, soul and top 40/pop. Works with 4- or 5- piece, self-contained groups "that play in Holiday Inns, Sheratons, etc. We also book a lot of oldie groups like the Belmonts and Flamingos." Current acts include Voyage (top 40/disco); Legz (rock); Spit-N-Image (rock group); Lee Estrada (tribute to Elvis show); and Charles Lamont.

RICHARD LUTZ ENTERTAINMENT AGENCY, 5625 0 St., Lincoln NE 68510. (402)483-2241. General Manager: Cherie Worley. Management firm and booking agency. Represents individuals and groups; currently handles 200 acts. Receives 15-20% minimum commission. Reviews material for acts.
How to Contact: Query by phone. Prefers cassette or videocassette with 5-10 songs and lead sheet. SASE. Reports in 1 week.,
Music: Mostly top 40 and country; also dance-oriented and MOR. Works primarily with show and dance bands for lounge circuit. "Acts must be uniformed." Current acts include Debbie Fry Show (variety); Sweet N' Country (country group); and Top Secret (top 40 group)
Tips: "Send photo, resume, tape, partial song list and include references. Add comedy, conversation, etc., to your videocassette."

M & M TALENT AGENCY INC., 915 Sibley Tower Bldg., Rochester NY 14604. (716)325-2930. Contact: Carl Labate. Management firm and booking agency. Represents artists and groups; currently handles 15 acts. Receives 15-25% commission. Reviews material for acts.
How to Contact: Prefers cassette with minimum 3 songs and lyric sheet. SASE. Reports in 3 weeks.
Music: Mostly top 40; also dance, rock and R&B. Works primarily with vocalists, dance groups and recording artists. Current acts include Michael Pallini (top 40/dance); Margaret Wilson (R&B); and Beyond (dance/rock).

LEE MAGID, INC., Box 532, Malibu CA 90265. (213)858-7282. President: Lee Magid. Management firm and music publisher. Record labels include LMI (jazz) and Grassroots (blues and country). Represents artists, groups, songwriters and comics, etc.; currently handles 10 acts. Receives 20-25% commission. Reviews material for acts.
How to Contact: Prefers cassette or videocassette with 3-4 songs. SASE. Reports in 3 weeks—"sometimes longer."
Music: Blues, country, gospel, jazz, R&B, rock and soul. Works primarily with self-contained and solo singers and instrumental jazz groups. Current acts include Gloria Lynne (jazz vocalist); Ernie Andrews (pop/jazz vocalist); Rags Waldorf (rock/jazz vocalist and keyboard); Becky Bishop (country artist); the L.A. Jazz Choir; and Big Joe Turner (blues artist).

ED MALHOIT AGENCY, Box 2001, Claremont NH 03743. (603)542-8777. Agents: Ed Malhoit, Kathy Shull, Jeff Camp. Management firm and booking agency. Represents groups in eastern US; currently handles 60 acts. Receives 10-20% commission. Reviews material for acts.
How to Contact: Write first. Prefers cassette with minimum 5 songs. SASE. Reports in 1 month.
Music: Rock. Current acts include Stone Cross, Robert Allen Band, Downpour, Hazbin Bros., Double Cross, Fox, and 8084 (all rock concert/club acts.)

MANAGEMENT VII, 1811 NE. 53rd St., Ft. Lauderdale FL 33308. (305)776-1004. Contact: Vic and Romona Beri. Management firm. Represents artists, groups and songwriters; currently handles 11 acts.

Receives 10-20% commission. Reviews material for acts.
How to Contact: Prefers cassette with 3-10 songs and lyric sheet. SASE. Reports in 1 month.
Music: Country, MOR and top 40/pop. Current acts include Dan Riley (guitar vocals/comedy); Gene Merolo (guitar vocals/comedy); Ferguson & Taylor (group/vocals); Perelli (group/vocals); and Seinta's (group, solo, vocals).

MARS TALENT AGENCY, 168 Orchid Dr., Pearl River NY 10965. (914)735-4569. Contact: Arnie Kay. Management firm and booking agency. Represents artists and groups; currently handles 7 acts. Receives 10-20% commission. Reviews material for acts.
How to Contact: Write first and obtain permission to submit. Prefers cassette and lead sheet. SASE. Reports in 3 weeks.
Music: Easy listening, MOR and R&B. Works primarily with artists and groups from the 50s and 60s era. Current acts include Crystals, Duprees, Earls, Freddy Cannon, Regents, Cleftones, and Reparata and the Delrons.

RICK MARTIN PRODUCTIONS, 125 Fieldpoint Road, Greenwich CT 06830. (203)661-1615. President: Rick Martin. Personal manager and independent producer. Represents artists, groups, songwriters, actresses, vocalists, and comedians; currently handles 5 acts. Receives maximum 25% commission. "Occasionally, we are hired as consultants, production assistants or producers of recording projects." Reviews material for acts.
How to Contact: Write first and obtain permission to submit. Prefers reel-to-reel or cassette with 2-4 songs and lyric sheet. SASE. "We prefer serious individuals who represent themselves professionally." Reports in 2-4 weeks.
Music: Mostly top 40 and rock; also dance-oriented, easy listening and pop. Works with "2 rock groups, female vocalist, several songwriters and actress/vocalist (pop)." Current acts include Babe (all female revue—top 40); Eddie and Ruth Ayres (comedy/vocalists); and Marisa Mercedes (vocalist/pianist).
Tips: "Don't spend a lot of money on recordings, but be prepared to have some financial backing if attempting to be an artist. Depend on yourself for everything including, most importantly, creativity. Present material in the simplest way."

MASADA MUSIC, INC., 888 8th Ave., New York NY 10019. (212)757-1953. President: Gene Heimlich. Management consultant firm and production house. Deals with artists in East Coast region only. Represents artists, groups and songwriters; currently handles 3 acts. Receives 10-20% commission or salary against commission. Reviews material for acts.
How To Contact: Write first to obtain permission to submit or to arrange personal interview. Prefers 7½ ips reel-to-reel or ½" videocassette with 2-5 songs. SASE. Reports in 3 weeks.
Music: New age, dance, contemporary, progressive, pop and film scores. Works with singers/songwriters, vocalists and composers. Current acts include Raphael (new age); Gabriell Roth and the Mirrors (contemporary); and Pepe Castillo & Manuel (Latin).
Tips: "Present clean, simple demos and focus on your market."

MEADOWLARK VENTURES, Box 7218, Missoula MT 59807. (406)728-2180. Contact: Chris Roberts or David Englund. Management firm and booking agency. Represents groups in the western US; currently handles 70 acts. Receives 15-20% commission.
How to Contact: Write first for permission to submit or arrange personal interview. Songwriters and artists may submit video cassette. Prefers cassette with 3-7 songs. SASE. Reports in 2 weeks.
Music: Mostly rock; also MOR, R&B and top 40/pop. Works primarily with bands. Current acts include Prophecy (top 40 rock); Kinroq (rock); and Pressure (top 40 rock).
Tips: "Follow through. Be organized. Have promotional material."

JOHN MEDLAND PRODUCTIONS, (formerly Medland Management), 334 Dufferin St., Toronto, Ontario M6K 1Z6 Canada. (416)536-4882. President: John Medland. Represents local artists and musical groups; currently handles 2 acts. Receives 10-20% commission. Reviews material for acts.
How to Contact: Groups should include bios, photo, repertoire, personnel and equipment list. Prefers cassette with 1-5 songs. SAE and IRC. Reports in 1 month.
Music: Mostly top 40/pop; also rock, dance-oriented and 50s rock. Works primarily with full time traveling bands (bars, colleges, etc.). Current acts include S.X.S. (top 40/pop); and Idle Threat (tribute to Billy Idol).

MEIER TALENT AGENCY, 511 W. 3rd, Hazleton PA 18201. (717)454-8767. Contact: Harold Meier. Management firm and booking agency. Represents artists and groups; currently handles 13 acts. Receives 15-20% commission. Reviews material for acts.
How to Contact: "Call—we will send forms." Prefers cassette with 5-10 songs. SASE. Send photos, song list and references. Reports in 2 weeks.

Music: Mostly top 40/pop; also dance-oriented, easy listening, MOR , pop rock and soul. Works primarily with dance bands. Current acts include Greg Palmer/Spice of Life (show and dance); Kik/Sharon Norris (showy dance); and Geoff & Claudia (dance duo).

MENES LAW CORP., Suite 1240, 1901 Avenue of the Stars, Los Angeles CA 90067. (213)277-4895. Attorneys: Barry Menes and Paul I. Menes. Law firm handling business affairs and some limited management. Represents companies, artists, groups, songwriters and some publishing companies. "Mostly paid by the hour, but on occasion will accept contingency over guarantee."
How to Contact: Prefers cassette. Include bio. SASE. Reports in 1 month.
Music: All types. Works primarily with bands, solo artists and songwriters. Current clients include Lee Ritenour (jazz/pop band); and Four Tops (R&B/pop band).

GREG MENZA ARTIST MANAGEMENT, 2055 Mt. Paran Rd. NW, Atlanta GA 30327. (404)262-6444. Director: Greg Menza. Management firm, booking agency and concert producers. Represents artists, groups and songwriters; currently handles 9 acts. Receives 10-20% commission. Reviews material for acts.
How to Contact: Query by mail. Prefers cassette or ½" videocassette with 3-6 songs. Reports in at least 1 month. "Include SASE if you wish material returned. Send only high quality finished demos."
Music: Gospel, rock (contemporary Christian), church/religious and secular. Works primarily with contemporary Christian rock artists. Current acts include Servant; Rick Cua; and Tami Gunden (all Christian contemporary music).

MERCANTILE MUSIC, Box 2271, Palm Springs CA 92263. (619)320-4848. President: Kent Fox. Management firm and booking agency. Represents artists, groups and songwriters; currently handles 2 acts. Receives 10-25% commission. Reviews material for acts.
How to Contact: Prefers cassette with 3-12 songs. SASE. Reports in 1 month.
Music: Country, easy listening, MOR, rock and top 40/pop. Works primarily Fair dates.

MICHAEL PRODUCTIONS, Box 6129, Toledo OH 43614. (419)385-3306. Director: Mike Nitsch-ke. Management firm, booking agency, concert promoter and record producer. Represents artists, groups and songwriters; currently handles 12 acts. Receives 10-20% commission. Reviews material for acts.
How to Contact: Prefers cassette with 3-6 songs and lyric sheet. SASE. Reports in 2 weeks.
Music: Mostly jazz, MOR and dance-oriented; also blues, classical, easy listening, progressive, R&B, soul and top 40/pop. Works primarily with jazz artists, vocalists, big bands, composers and arrangers.

MIDDLETON'S PUBLIC RELATIONS & MANAGEMENT, 322 Smith Rd., Polk City FL 33868. (813)984-1286. President: Ben Middleton. Management and booking agency. Represents artists, groups and songwriters; currently handles 20 acts. Receives 10-20% commission. Reviews material for acts.
How to Contact: Prefers cassette with 3-5 songs. SASE. Reports in 1 month.
Music: Country, dance-oriented, easy listening, gospel, R&B, soul and top 40/pop. Works primarily with dance bands and vocal groups. Current acts include Genobia Jeter (contemporary gospel artist, Arista Records); Glenn Jones (R&B/top 40 artist, RCA Records); Isaac Douglas (gospel artist, Savoy-Arista Records), Sam Jones, (actor and recording artist); Kevin Mayes; and Albertina Walker.

*THE GILBERT MILLER AGENCY, Suite 243, 21243 Ventura Blvd., Woodland Hills CA 91364. (818)888-6363. Agent: Jeff Miller. Booking agency. Represents musical and variety/novelty groups; currently handles 12 acts. Receives 15% commission. Reviews material for acts.
How to Contact: Write to obtain permission to submit. Prefers cassette with 3-6 songs, 8x10 photo and lyric sheet. SASE. Reports in 2 weeks.
Music: Mostly rock. Works primarily with heavy metal/commercial hard rock groups. Current acts include Terriff with Frank Dimino of Angel (heavy metal); Scarlet with Andy Parker of U.F.O (hard rock); and Perfect Stranger (new wave).

MPL ASSOCIATES, LTD., Box 2108, Phoenix AZ 85001. President: Louis P. Goldstein. Management firm. Represents artists and songwriters; currently handles 2 acts. Receives 10-20% commission. Reviews material for acts.
How to Contact: Prefers cassette with 1-5 songs and lead sheet. "Be sure that any tapes submitted have clear vocals and be sure to include a lead sheet for each song . . . and a current picture if possible." SASE. Reports within 2 weeks to 1 month.
Music: Country, easy listening, MOR and top 40/pop. Works primarily with songwriters and songwriting performers. Current acts include Jack Wright and Keira Hayes (vocalists/songwriters).

*ALEXANDER MURPHY, JR., ESQ., Box 427, 145 N. Narberth Ave., Narberth PA 19072. (215)668-9302 or 431-1833. Contact: Alexander Murphy. Attorney. Represents artists, groups and songwriters. Receives 5-10% commission or hourly rate. Reviews material for acts.
How to Contact: Write first and obtain permission to submit. Prefers cassette with 3-4 songs. Include bio. SASE. Reports in 1 month.
Music: Mostly rock and top 40/pop; also jazz and MOR. Works primarily with bands, solo performers and songwriters.

MUSIC CITY PROMOTIONS, 3410 Dieppe St., Saskatoon, Saskatchewan S7M 3S9 Canada. (306)382-0330. Manager: Dave Calyniuk. Booking agency. Represents groups in Sasketchewan; currently handles 50 acts. Recieves 8-20% commission.
How to Contact: Write first and obtain permission to submit. Prefers cassette with 2-4 songs and lyric sheet. SASE. Reports in 1 month.
Music: Mostly top 40, country rock and commercial rock; also country and dance-oriented. Works primarily with dance bands. Current acts include Nightcrossing (top 40); The Infants (top 40); and Peter Kingsmill (country).

MUSIC UNLIMITED LTD, 2310 College Ave., Regina, Saskatchewan S4P 1C7 Canada. (306)586-1333. President: Chris M. Siller. Management firm and booking agency. Represents artists and groups; currently handles 75 acts. Receives 15-20% commission. Reviews material for acts.
How to Contact: Write first and obtain permission to submit. Prefers cassette or VHS videocassette with 6-12 songs and lyric sheet. Include complete bio and song list. SAE and IRC. Reports in 2 weeks.
Music: Mostly top 40/pop, country rock and MOR; also dance and country. Works primarily with dance bands. Current acts include Crystal River (country rock); and Mike McDonald & Calico (country rock).

MUSKRAT PRODUCTIONS, INC., 44 N. Central Ave., Elmsford NY 10523. (914)592-3144. Contact: Bruce McNichols. Represents individuals and groups; currently represents 11 acts. Deals with artists in the New York City area. Reviews material for acts.
How to Contact: Write first. Prefers cassette with 3 songs minimum. SASE. Reports "only if interested."
Music: "We specialize in old-time jazz, dixieland and banjo music and shows;" also country and jazz. Works primarily with dixieland, banjo/sing-along groups to play parties, Mexican mariachi bands and specialty acts for theme parties, dances, shows and conventions. Current acts include Smith Street Society Jazz Band (dixieland jazz); Your Father's Mustache (banjo sing-along); and Harry Hepcat and the Boogie Woogie Band (50s rock revival).

FRANK NANOIA MANAGEMENT, 1999 N. Sycamore Ave., Los Angeles CA 90068. (213)874-8725. President: Frank Nanoia. Management firm. Represents artists, groups and songwriters; currently handles 11 acts. Receives 15-20% commission. Reviews material for acts.
How to Contact: Prefers 7^{1}/$_{2}$ or 15 ips reel-to-reel or cassette with 3-5 songs and lead sheet. Does not return unsolicited material. Reports "only if material is above average."
Music: Mostly R&B, top 40/pop and jazz fusion; also country, dance-oriented, easy listening, MOR, gospel and soul. Works primarily with vocalists and show groups. Current acts include Marc Allen Trujillo (vocalist); Paramour (show group), and The Tim & Dan Show (show band).

NEVADA TALENT AND BOOKING, c/o Ward Johns, Suite 101, 550 E. Plumb Lane, Reno NV 89502. (702)827-3648. Management firm and booking agency. Represents artists, groups and songwriters; currently handles 15-25 acts. Receives 7^{1}/$_{2}$-15% commission. Reviews material for acts.
How to Contact: Write first to obtain permission to submit or to arrange personal interview or submit demo tape. Prefers cassette or VHS or Beta video cassette with 4-10 songs and lyric sheet.
Music: Mostly pop/rock and new wave; also country and all other types. Works primarily with rock groups, original jazz artists and original rock/pop/soul/R&B artists. Current acts include Michael De Jong (blues); Lavry Nozew (jazz); and Phil Delta and the Delta band (country).
Tips: "It's important to have VHS or Beta tape and a professional 16-24 track demo. Also send pictures and printed resume."

*NEW ARTIST'S PRODUCTIONS, 131 Connecticut Ave., N. Bay Shore NY 11706. (516)666-1876. Professional Department: Jeannie G. Walker. Management agency, record company and music publisher. Estab. 1984. Represents individual artists, groups and songwriters. Deals with local artists, regional artists and artists from anywhere. Currently handles 12 acts. Receives 20% commission. Reviews material for acts.
How to Contact: Prefers cassette and lyric sheet. SASE. Reports in 6 weeks.

Music: Mostly pop, country and easy listening; also rock, gospel and blues. Works primarily with vocalists and dance bands. Current acts include Rory Bennett, Cherokee, and Platinum.

NOTE-ABLE ENTERTAINMENT, Suite 1703, 4900 Francis Rd., Richmond, British Columbia V7C 4R5 Canada. (604)984-9674. President: Jai Allan. Management firm and booking agency. Represents artists and groups; currently handles 11 acts. Receives 10-15% commission. Reviews material for acts.
How to Contact: Write first. Prefers cassette with 2-4 songs and lyric sheet. SAE and IRC. Reports in 1 month.
Music: Mostly MOR, rock and country. Works primarily with dance and show bands. Current acts include Roy Warren and Stateline (dance and show band); The Note-Ables (show group); and Echo (rock group).

N2D/BREEZEWAY PUBLISHING COMPANIES, Box 23684, Nashville TN 37202. Contact: Douglas Casmus. Management firm and publisher. Represents artists, groups, songwriters and comedians; currently handles 1 act. Reviews material for acts.
How to Contact: Prefers cassette or videocassette with 1-2 songs and lyric sheet. SASE. Reports in 1 month.
Music: Country, new music, dance and comedy. Current acts include David Murphy (country).
Tips: "Looking for great songs—any format! Also open to crazy and novelty material."

OHIO RECORDS, Box 655, Hudson OH 44236. (216)650-1330. A&R Director: Russ Delaney. Management firm. Represents artists and groups; currently handles 6 acts. "We are an independent label (BMI affiliated) and if we record material we handle the publishing gratis." Reviews material for acts.
How to Contact: Prefers cassette with 6-10 songs and lead sheet. SASE. "Do not expect your material back immediately. If we are looking for material for our artists we would be happy to review new material. Sometimes we review only at time of recording sessions. Don't call us, we'll call you."
Music: Country. Works primarily with theater/stage artists and groups. Current acts include Buckeye Strings (vocalists and instrumentalists); Russ Thomas (vocalist/drummer); and Bob Beers (vocalist/lead guitar/bass).

OPERATION MUSIC ENTERPRISES, 233 W. Woodland Ave., Ottumwa IA 52501. (515)682-8283. President: Nada C. Jones. Management firm and booking agency. Represents artists, groups and songwriters; currently handles 8 acts. Receives 15% commission. Reviews material for acts.
How to Contact: Prefers cassette and lyric sheet. Artists should include references. SASE. Reports in 6-8 weeks.
Music: Mostly country; also blues. Works primarily with vocalists, songwriters and show-lounge groups. Current acts include Reesa Kay Jones (country vocalist and recording artist); Prairie Fire (country show group); and Hugo J. Huck (songwriter).

ORANGE BLOSSOM PRODUCTIONS, #1B, 417 East 89th St., New York NY 10028. (212)289-8110. President: Douglas Tuchman. Booking agency and production company. Represents groups; currently handles 3 acts. Receives minimum 15-20% commission. Reviews material for acts.
How to Contact: Prefers 7¹/₂ ips reel-to-reel or cassette with 4-8 songs recorded "live. Make package as complete as possible." SASE. Reports in 2 weeks.
Music: Mostly bluegrass; also traditional country. Works primarily with touring show bands (concerts, festivals, etc). Current acts include Bill Harrell and The Virginians (bluegrass band); John Herald Band (bluegrass, country); and Hammy and Artie Traum (folk).
Tips: "We will not accept for consideration any songs sent us that writer has not copyrighted for his/her protection. Only video tapes and/or in-concert cassette (or reel-to-reel) tapes accepted for consideration. Return postage must accompany material sent us."

ORPHEUS ENTERTAINMENT, Box 647, Orange NJ 07051. (201)375-5671. Contact: A&R Department. Management firm and production company. Represents music and variety artists, producers and songwriters; currently handles 12-15 acts. Receives 10-33¹/₃% commission. Reviews material for acts.
How to Contact: Query by mail. Prefers cassette with 2-6 songs and lead sheet. Does not return unsolicited material. Reports in 1 month.
Music: Mostly pop, comedy and jazz; also MOR, progressive, R&B, rock, soul, top 40 and fusion. Works primarily with original recording and concert artists. Current acts include Jimmy Ponder (guitar jazz); Where We Live (fusion/progressive rock); Michal Urbaniak; (fusion/jazz); Mack Goldbury and the Jazz Explosion (jazz); Dave Valenti (Latin/jazz); Willie Asbury (comedy); Albert Owens (comedy); Whyte Lyte (progressive rock); Grover Kemble and Blow Daddyo (vocal blues/jazz); Noel Pointer (pop); Instant Instant (pop); and Project 19 (progressive rock).

*P. D. Q. DIRECTIONS, INC., 1474 N. Kings Rd., Los Angeles CA 90048. (213)394-8442. President: Leo Leichter. Management agency and production company. Represents artists and musical groups from anywhere; currently handles 5 acts. Receives 15-25% commission. Reviews material for acts (cassettes and videos only).
How to Contact: Prefers cassette with 4-6 songs and lead sheet. Does not return unsolicited material. Reports in 1 month.
Music: Country, rock (country), top 40/pop and MOR. Current acts include Peter McCann (award winning songwriter); Johnny Guitar Watson (R&B); Herman Brood (rock); Society of Seven (MOR); Glen Yarbrough (contemporary); The Limeliters (contemporary); and The Diamonds (50s rock).
Tips: "Artists should be earning at least $100,000/year and have strong work experience and professional stage presence."

PARADISE PRODUCTIONS, Box 8721, Honolulu HI 96815. (808)942-8564. General Manager: Kathy Koran. Management firm and booking agency. Represents artists, groups and songwriters. Receives minimum 15% commission. Reviews material for acts.
How to Contact: Prefers cassette with minimum 4 songs and lyric sheet. SASE. Reports in 1 week.
Music: Mostly rock, top 40/pop, soul, easy listening and Las Vegas style show groups; also dance-oriented, jazz, MOR, progressive, R&B and light rock. Works primarily with Las Vegas show groups, dance bands and vocalists and high energy rock concert groups. Current acts include Rod Young (Las Vegas show band); Triple X (concert rock group); and Bobby Hutton (soul/pop show group).
Tips: "Polished songs and show are most desirable."

PEEVER TALENT & MANAGEMENT, 2464 Brasilia Circle, Mississauga, Ontario L5N 2G1 Canada. (416)826-1701. Contact: David M. Peever. Management firm and booking agency. Represents artists, groups and songwriters; currently handles 5 acts. Reviews material for acts.
How to Contact: Write first. Prefers cassette with 3-5 songs. SAE and IRC. Reports in 1 week.
Music: Country. Current acts include Harold MacIntyre (country singer); and Larry Coad (country producer/writer).

PELICAN PRODUCTIONS, 300 Monroe Ave., Rochester NY 14618. President: Peter Morticelli. Management firm and publishing company; currently handles 3 acts. Receives 15-25% commission. Reviews material for acts.
How to Contact: Prefers cassette with 2 songs. Does not return unsolicited material.
Music: Mostly rock (all kinds); also top 40/pop. Works with "any type of act as long as the songwriting ability is very strong." Currently represents Duke Jupiter (mainstream rock artist); Icon (melodic heavy rock); and Wrathchild (English glam rock).

PEOPLE SONG, INTERNATIONAL, Rt. 3, Sweeney Hollow, Franklin TN 37064. (615)794-5712. General Manager: Jeff Engle. Artist Relations: Perry N. Wilson. Management agency, booking agency and music publisher. Represents artists, musical groups and songwriters from anywhere; currently handles 10 acts. "The agency end charges 10% flat; the management end charges 15% flat." Reviews material for acts.
How to Contact: Prefers cassette with 1-4 songs and lead sheet. SASE. Reports in 1 month.
Music: MOR, progressive rock, rock, and top 40/pop. Current acts include Gene Cotton (pop/rock singer-songwriter); Oliver (pop/rock singer-songwriter); Dianne Darling (pop/rock singer-songwriter); Marc Speer and Hot Rocks (rock act); American Ace (rock band); and Ashley Cleveland (singer/songwriter).
Tips: "We are not currently looking to sign new artists, but we are looking for good songs."

*PERFECTION LIGHT PRODUCTIONS, Box 690, San Francisco CA 94101. (415)626-0655. Vice President: Gregory DiGiovine. Management agency and production company. Represents artists, groups and producers in Northern California; currently handles 2 acts. Receives negotiable commission. Reviews material for acts.
How to Contact: Prefers cassette with 1-4 songs and lyric sheet. Does not return unsolicited material.
Music: Dance-oriented, R&B, rock, soul and top 40/pop. Works primarily with R&B/pop solo artists and groups. Current acts include Narada Michael Walden (R&B/pop artist).

PERFORMING ARTISTS CONSULTANTS, A16, 6120 2nd St. SE, Calgary, Alberta T2H 2L8 Canada. (403)253-0494. Vice President and Agent: Frank Scott. Booking agency. Represents artists and groups; currently handles 20 acts. Receives 15-25% commission.
How to Contact: Write or call first and obtain permission to submit or to arrange personal interview. Prefers cassette/videocassette or record with 2-6 songs and lyric sheet. SAE and IRC. Reports in 1 month.
Music: Mostly rock; also bluegrass, blues, country, dance-oriented, R&B, soul and top 40/pop. Works

primarily with bar bands and recording acts. Current acts include Mat Minglewood (southern rock); Powder Blues (blues); and The Charlton Showband (Irish/country).

PAUL PETERSON CREATIVE MANAGEMENT, (formerly Good Karma Productions), 6335 W. 50th St., Mission KS 66202. (913)362-5804. Contact: Paul Peterson. Management agency. Deals with Midwest artists only. Represents artists and groups; currently handles 2 acts. Receives 20% commission. Reviews material for acts.
How to Contact: Prefers cassette or ³/₄'' videocassette with 2-4 songs and lyric sheet. SASE. Reports in 2-3 weeks.
Music: Rock (hard and country), jazz and top 40/pop. Works with rock, pop and country rock bands, concert and recording artists only and songwriters. Current acts include Dogs (pop rock band); and Guido Toledo, songwriter.

PHIL'S ENTERTAINMENT AGENCY LIMITED, 889 Smyth Rd., Ottawa Ontario K1G 1P4 Canada. (613)731-8983. Booking agency. Represents artists and groups; currently handles 25 acts. Receives 10-15% commission. Reviews material for acts "occasionally."
How to Contact: Query by mail. Prefers cassette with 4-7 songs. SAE and IRC. Reports in 1 month.
Music: Mostly country, MOR and "old rock 'n' roll. Works primarily with recording artists, groups and singles. Current acts include Gerry Allard (recording artist); Todd Nolan & Band (recording artist); and Lyoness & Judy Woodstock (recording artist).
Tips: "Keep agency supplied with up-to-date promo material and develop entertainment ability."

PHOENIX ARTISTS MANAGEMENT LIMITED, 425¹/₂ Church St., Toronto, Ontario M4Y 2C3 Canada. (416)964-6464. President: Kathy Kernony. Management firm and booking agency. Represents artists "across Canada or others working in Canada;" currently handles 100 actors/singers. Receives 10-15% commission.
How to Contact: Query by mail. Prefers cassette as demo. SAE and IRC. Reports in 1 month.
Music: Music for theatrical or television use. Works primarily with performers (actors/singers). Current acts include Barbara Hamilton (actress); Douglas Campbell (actor); and David Dunbar (actor/singer).

PLAIN COUNTRY RECORDS, Box 5412, Buena Park CA 90620. (213)630-0251. Contact: Leo J. Eiffert, Jr. Management firm and production company. Represents artists; currently handles 11 acts. Receives 20% commission. Reviews material for acts.
How to Contact: Query by mail or arrange personal interview. "Songs must be copyrighted with publishing open." Prefers cassette with 4-8 songs and lead sheet. SASE. Reports in 3 weeks.
Music: Mostly country. Works primarily with bar bands and vocalists. Current acts include Leo J. Eiffert, Jr. (country artist); Bill Rybold (songwriter); and Crawfish Band (country group).

BRIAN POMBIERE PRODUCTIONS, INC., Suite 4, 205 Mount Royal West, Montreal, Quebec H2T 2T2 Canada. (514)849-5252. Booking agency. Represents groups; currently handles 20 acts. Receives 10-15% commission. Reviews material for acts.
How to Contact: Prefers cassette with minimum 4 songs and lyric sheet. SAE and IRC. Reports in 3 weeks.
Music: Mostly top 40 and funk; also hard rock and rock. Works primarily with dance bands and show bands. Current acts include XMEN (top 40); Kinky Foxx (funk); Quickstep (top 40); and The Web (top 40).

PREFERRED ARTIST MANAGEMENT, INC., 9701 Taylorsville Rd., Louisville KY 40299. (502)267-5466. President: Dan Green. Secretary: David H. Snowden. Management agency. Deals with artists in eastern United States and Midwest states. Represents artists and groups; currently handles 7 acts. Receives 10-20% commission. Reviews material for acts.
How to Contact: Query. Prefers cassette with 3-5 songs and lead sheet. SASE. Reports in 2 weeks.
Music: Dance, rock (funk, medium) and top 40/pop. Works with bar artists ranging from bar bands to both single and group concert acts. Current acts include Flip City (top 40/original artists); Eddie Miles (a salute to Elvis) and Blitz Kids (top 40/original artists).

PRESTIGE ENTERTAINMENT AGENCIES, LTD., 304-4680 Elk Lake Drive, Victoria, British Columbia V8Z 5M1 Canada. (604)658-5202. President: Paul Mascioli. Management firm and booking agency. Represents artists and groups. Receives 10-20% commission. Reviews material for acts.
How to Contact: Prefers cassette and lyric sheet. Does not return unsolicited material. Reports if interested.
Music: Mostly pop, MOR and country; also blues, children's, dance-oriented, easy listening, folk, gospel, jazz, R&B, rock, soul and pop. Works primarily with vocalists. Current acts Glory-Anne

Carriere (club/concert/record artist); Ann Mortifee (concert/recording artist); and Valdy (concert/recording artist).

PRISM PRODUCTIONS, INC., Box 8125, Ann Arbor MI 48107. (313)665-4755. Contact: Tom Stachler, Lee Berry. Management firm, booking agency and concert promoter. Represents artists, groups and songwriters; currently handles 5 acts. Receives 10-20% commission.
How to Contact: Prefers cassette and lyric sheet. Does not return unsolicited material. Reports in 2 weeks.
Music: Mostly rock; also blues, reggae, dance-oriented, progressive and top 40/pop. Works primarily with progressive dance groups. Current acts include SLK (rock/ska group); Buzztones (pop-dance group); and Dick Siegel (blues/folk songwriter).

PROCESS TALENT MANAGEMENT, 439 Wiley Ave., Franklin PA 16323. (814)432-4633. Contact: Norman Kelly. Management agency. Represents artists and groups; currently handles 15 acts. Receives 10-15% commission. Reviews material for acts.
How to Contact: Write or call first and obtain permission to submit. Prefers 7^1/$_2$ ips reel-to-reel, cassette or 8-track cartridge with 2-6 songs. SASE. Reports in 2 weeks.
Music: Mostly country; also bluegrass, country, gospel, jazz and rock. Works primarily with vocalists, self-contained country shows and bar bands. Current acts include Junie Lou (country); Lady Brown Sugar (rock); and Woodsmoke (bar band).

PROGRESS ENTERTAINMENT, 5500 S. Marginal Rd., Cleveland OH 44103. (216)881-7888. President: Joe Simone. Agent Contact: Jack Springer. Management firm and label placement. Represents artists, groups and songwriters; currently handles 6 acts. Receives 20% commission. Reviews material for acts.
How to Contact: Prefers cassette with 4 songs and lead sheet. SASE; "will return material upon request." Reports in 2 weeks.
Music: Mostly rock, black, international and top 40/pop. Current acts include Dazz Band (R&B, Motown Records); Sekou (R&B); Tony Evan (top 40/pop); Jonah Koslin (pop/rock—"The Latest" R&B); Candela (R&B/Latin, Arista Records); and Sekou Bunch (R&B).
Tips: "Exceptional talent can only succeed with exceptional management."

PROGRESSIVE TALENT MANAGEMENT, INC., 2014 W. 8th St, Erie PA 16505. (814)455-3042. President: Daniel F. Lewis. Management firm and booking agency. Represents artists, groups and songwriters; currently handles 10 acts. Receives 10-20% commission. Reviews material for acts.
How to Contact: "Phone me to discuss what you have in mind," query by mail, or submit demo tape and lead sheet. "One-half inch VHS videotape is desirable if the artist is a writer/performer." SASE. Reports in 1 week "unless we are very busy."
Music: R&B, rock (top 40), soul and top 40/pop. Works primarily with "groups that are very top 40 oriented and career minded." Current acts include Arkay IV (R&B); Thrust (jazz); and Diablo (country).
Tips: "We take pride in representing truly professional artists and we are very selective. We look for people who are intelligent, cooperative, and willing to be dedicated to the pursuit of their goals."

QUADRANGLE MANAGEMENT, INC., Suite 365, 845 Via de la Paz, Pacific Palisades CA 90272. (213)459-2559. President: Bill Traut. Management and production company. Represents artists, groups and songwriters; currently handles 6 acts. Receives 15-20% commission.
How to Contact: Write first. Prefers cassette with 1-4 songs. SASE "with enough postage." Reports in 4 weeks.
Music: Hard rock, pop rock and R&B. Works primarily with concert attraction bands and R&B bands. Artists include Larry Weiss (songwriter); Y&T (heavy metal rock); Osamu Kitajima (guitar, koto & biwa); Judy Roberts (jazz/pop singer); and The Impressions.
Tips: "Send your credits along with your demos."

THE RAINBOW COLLECTION, LTD., Box 300, Solebury PA 18963. (215)297-8437. A&R Director: Herb Gart. Management, production and publishing firm. Represents artists, groups and songwriters; currently handles 6 acts. Receives 20% commission. Reviews material for acts.
How to Contact: Prefers cassette or VHS or Beta videocassette with 3 songs. Does not return unsolicited material. Reports in 4-6 weeks.
Music: Rock, pop, heavy metal, country and dance-oriented. Works "almost exclusively with strong songwriters whether they are solo artists or bands." Current acts include Jack Bruce, Da Pliars and Between the Sheets.
Tips: "Don't necessarily worry about current trends in music. Just do what you do to the best of your ability. With our company the song is the thing even if production-wise it's in its infant stages. If you feel you have a great and unique talent, contact us."

THE RECORD COMPANY OF THE SOUTH (RCS), 5220 Essen Lane, Baton Rouge LA 70898. (504)766-3233. President: Cyril E. Vetter. Vice President: Andrew Vetter. Management agency, music publisher and record company. Represents artists, groups and songwriters; currently handles 5 acts. Receives 20-25% commission. Reviews material for acts.
How to Contact: Prefers cassette with 2-6 songs and lyric sheet. SASE. Reports in 6 weeks.
Music: Country, R&B, rock, soul and top 40/pop. Works primarily with artists, bands and songwriters. Current acts include Irma Thomas (top 40/pop and R&B); Luther Kent (top 40/pop and R&B); and Butch Hornsby (country).

RECORD MUSIC, INC., Box 182, Middle Village, New York NY 11379. (212)898-3027. President: Peter Paul. Management firm, record promoter, music publisher and record producer. Represents artists, groups and songwriters worldwide. Reviews material for acts.
How to Contact: Prefers cassette. SASE. Reporting time "varies."
Music: Bluegrass, blues, country, dance-oriented, easy listening, jazz, MOR, progressive, R&B, soul, top 40/pop and novelty.

A.F. RISAVY, INC., 1312 Vandalia, Collinsville IL 62234. (618)345-6700. Divisions include Artco Enterprises, Golden Eagle Records, Swing City Music and Swing City Sound. Contact: Art Risavy, Bill Montgomery. Management firm and booking agency. Represents artists, groups and songwriters; currently handles 50 acts. Receives 10-15% commission. Reviews material for acts.
How to Contact: Write first and obtain permission to submit or to arrange personal interview. Prefers 7¹/₂ ips reel-to-reel or cassette with 2-6 songs and lyric sheet. SASE. Reports in 2 weeks.
Music: Mostly rock, country, MOR and top 40; also all other types. Current acts include Sneakers, Street Corner Symphony, and Philthy McNasty.
Tips: Artists should be "well-dressed, polished and ambitious. VHS videotapes are very helpful."

RISING STAR PRODUCTIONS, INC., Drawer 723608, Atlanta GA 30339. (404)429-0010. Agent: Lynda Sommers. Management firm and booking agency. Represents artists and groups; currently handles 60-80 acts. Receives 20% commission. Reviews material for acts.
How to Contact: Write first and obtain permission to submit. Prefers cassette with 3-5 songs. Does not return unsolicited material. Reports in 2 weeks.
Music: Bluegrass, country, dance-oriented, easy listening, folk, jazz, MOR, rock and top 40/pop. Works primarily with dance bands.

ROADWORK, INC., 1475 Harvard St. NW, Washington DC 20009. (202)234-9308. Director: Amy Horowitz. Booking agency "promoting women's culture in the arts, multi-racial and cross-cultural programming." Represents artists, groups, songwriters, and performing artists (dance, mime, poetry)—"women only;" currently represents 2-5 acts. Receives 10-20% commission.
How to Contact: Query by mail. Prefers cassette with 2-5 songs and lead sheet. Does not return unsolicited material.
Music: Blues, dance-oriented, gospel, jazz, Spanish, R&B, rock and soul. Current acts include Sweet Honey in the Rock (black acappella singers); Ferron (folk); Robin Flower (bluegrass); Toshi Reagon (rock band); Teresa Trull; and Barbara Higbie.

ROCK-A-BILLY ARTIST AGENCY, Box 4740, Nashville TN 37216. (615)865-4740. A&R Director: S.D. Neal. Management firm, booking agency and record company. Represents artists and groups; currently handles 6 acts. Receives 15% commission. Reviews material for acts.
How to Contact: Prefers cassette with 2-6 songs and lyric sheet. SASE. Reports in 3 weeks.
Music: Mostly rock and country; also all other types including rockabilly. Works primarily with vocalists. Current acts include Dixie Dee, Rhythm Rockers, and Rufus Thomas.

RODANCA MUSIC, 3627 Park Ave., Memphis TN 38111. (901)454-0300. Music publisher. Represents songwriters from anywhere; currently handles 15 acts. Receives standard commission. Reviews material for acts.
How to Contact: Prefers 7¹/₂ ips reel-to-reel or cassette with 4 songs and lead sheet. Does not return unsolicited material. Reports in 2 weeks.
Music: Mostly gospel; also R&B and pop-country. Works primarily with groups and solo vocalists. Current acts include Donald Watkins (gospel vocalist); St. Teresa Choir; and St. Louis Consolators.

JEFFREY ROSS MUSIC, Box D, Seattle WA 98109. (206)285-6838. Contact: Jeffrey Ross or Jan Charkow. Management agency. Represents artists, groups and songwriters; currently handles 3 acts. Receives 15% minimum commission. Reviews material for acts.
How to Contact: Prefers cassette with 4-6 songs. SASE. Reports in 3 weeks.

Music: Jazz, progressive, R&B, soul and top 40/pop. Works primarily with touring bands with members that write their own music. Current acts include Kenny G (writer/multi-reedist); Doc Severinsen and Xebron.
Tips: "It is important to set your goals based on what you do best. If you write well in a certain idiom, concentrate and develop what you do best before trying other directions. A strong intention to be successful in this business is fueled by acquired knowledge of how the music business operates."

RUSCH PRODUCTIONS INC., ENTERTAINMENT AGENCY, 3588 N. Thomas Rd., Freeland MI 48623. (517)781-1553. President: Dean A. Rusch. Booking agency. Represents groups in Michigan; currently handles over 300 acts. Receives variable commission. Reviews material for acts.
How to Contact: Write first and obtain permission to submit. Prefers cassette or VHS videocassette with 3-10 songs and lyric sheet. SASE. Reports in 2 weeks.
Music: Mostly top 40/pop; also C&W, dance-oriented, easy listening and rock. Works primarily with dance bands. Current acts include Ceyx; Dedication; Harmony; Steel Rose; and Infinity (all dance bands).

RUSTRON MUSIC PRODUCTIONS, Send all of Artist Song Submittals to: Suite 2, 150 SW 8th St., Pompano Beach FL 33060. (305)943-2753. Main Office: 33 Whittier, Hartsdale, NY 10530. (914)761-3025. ("Main office does not review new material—only South Florida Branch office does."). Artists' Consultant: Rusty Gordon. Composition Management: Ron Caruso. Management firm, booking agency, music publisher and record producer. Represents individuals, groups and songwriters; currently handles 6 acts. Receives 10-25% commission for management and/or booking only. Reviews material for acts.
How to Contact: Query, arrange personal interview, or submit in person. Prefers cassette with 3-6 songs and lead sheet. SASE. Reports in 1 month.
Music: Blues (country & rock), country (rock, blues, progressive), easy listening (ballads), R&B, folk/rock (contemporary/topical), MOR (pop style), rock (folk/pop), top 40/pop and salsa/disco. Current acts include Vincent & Sgarlata (reggae/blues/rock); Gordon and Caruso (songwriter/producers); Lois Britten (disco/rock/pop/singer/songwriter); Christian Camilo and the Tingalayo Rhythm Band (salsa-disco/pop); Dianne Mower and Jasmine (modern jazz instrumental and vocal); Casse Culver and the Belle Starr Band (progressive country); Lynda Martin-Davis and Eric Shaffer (pop-country/blues, performer-songwriters); and Maxine Lamarr (jazz/blues).

SAGITTARIAN ARTISTS INTERNATIONAL, 970 Aztec Dr., Muskegon MI 49444. (616)733-9251. Coordinator/Director: G. Loren Ruhl. Management firm. Represents individuals and songwriters; currently handles 6 acts. Receives 15-25% commission. Reviews material for acts.
How to Contact: Query. Prefers cassette or record with 2-4 songs and lead sheet. SASE. Reports in 1 month.
Music: Top 40/pop, blues, easy listening and jazz. Works primarily with show vocalists. Current acts include Ricky Briton (pop vocalist); Les Basilio (vocalist); and Tobie Columbus (pop vocalist).
Tips: "Material must be nightclub oriented."

SAGUARO BOOKING AGENCY, 2609 NW. 36th St., Oklahoma City OK 73112. (405)942-0462. General Manager: Bobby Boyd. Management firm and booking agency. Represents artists, groups and songwriters. Receives 25% commission. Reviews material for acts.
How to Contact: Write first and obtain permission to submit. Prefers 7½ ips reel-to-reel tape with 3-5 songs and lyric sheet. Does not return unsolicited material. Reports in 1 month.
Music: Mostly country; also R&B, rock and soul. Current acts include Dale Greear, Bobby Barnett, and Rebel Lee.

SCARLET AGENCY, 1548 N. 34th St., Milwaukee WI 53208. (414)993-9979. Manager: Deborah Williams. Booking agency. Represents artists, groups, dancers and singers; currently deals with local artists; would like to deal with artists from anywhere. Currently handles 4 acts. Receives 10-15% commission. Reviews material for acts.
How to Contact: Arrange personal interview. Prefers cassette with 2-3 songs and lyric sheet. SASE. Reports in 1 month.
Music: Mostly jazz, R&B and pop; also soul. Works primarily with show bands and dance bands (vocalists are included in the bands). "Most of my shows consist of all-around entertainment." Current acts include Coldblooded (jazz/R&B); and Ritz (model/dance).
Tips: "Be serious, professional, creative and willing to listen to new ideas."

SCOTT-DEAN AGENCY, 428 Hill St., Reno NV 89501. (702)322-9426. Contact: Steve Cox. Booking agency. Represents artists, groups and songwriters; currently handles 150 acts. Receives 10-15% commision. Reviews material for acts.

How to Contact: Write first and obtain permission to submit or arrange personal interview. Prefers cassette and lyric sheet. SASE. Reports in 2 weeks.
Music: Mostly top 40, country/rock and R&B; also country, dance-oriented, MOR, rock, soul and pop. Works primarily with dance and show bands. Current acts include Tommy Bell (country/rock/blues); Sidros Armada (show/lounge act); and Bubba Lou and the Humidors (show/blues group).

SEEDS, INC., Box 220601, Charlotte NC 28222. (704)376-4388. President: Bob Ferster. Management firm. Represents artists, groups and speakers from the southeast; currently handles 2 acts. Receives 15-25% commission. Reviews material for acts.
How to Contact: Query by mail. Prefers 15 ips reel-to-reel tape or cassette with 3-6 songs and lyric sheet. SASE. Reports in 1 month.
Music: Mostly contemporary Christian; also bluegrass, easy listening, gospel, MOR, rock (hard and pop) and top 40/pop. Works primarily with 4-7 member Christian rock bands. Current acts include Don Hall (MOR); Deliverance (gospel); and Heir Express (rock).

*MICKEY SHERMAN ARTIST MANAGEMENT & DEVELOPMENT, Box 20814, Oklahoma City OK 73120. (405)751-8954. President: Mickey Sherman. Management firm. Represents artists, groups and songwriters; currently handles 5 acts. Receives 15% commission. Reviews material for acts.
How to Contact: Prefers cassette with 1-3 songs and lead sheet. Does not return unsolicited material. Reports in 1 month.
Music: Mostly blues, easy listening, and country. Works primarily with vocalists, and dance/show bands. Current acts include Janjo (blues); Benny Kubiak (fiddler/western swing band); and Charley Shaw (country singer).

SIDARTHA ENTERPRISES, LTD., Box 1414, East Lansing, MI 48823. (517)351-6780. President: Thomas R. Brunner. Management firm and booking agency. Represents artists and groups; currently represents 30 acts. Receives 15-20% commission. Reviews material for acts.
How to Contact: "Always make phone contact first." Prefers cassette with at least 4 songs and lyric sheet. SASE. Reports in 1 month.
Music: Rock and top 40/pop. Works primarily with bar bands and recording acts. Current acts include Donna Rawlins Band (top 40); Savage Grace (rock); and Chasel (top 40).

SIMMONS MANAGEMENT CO., Suite 106, 5214 Western Blvd., Box 18711, Raleigh NC 27619-8711. (919)851-6196. President: Harry Simmons. Management firm. Represents producers, artists, groups and songwriters; currently handles 6 acts. Receives 15-20% commission. Reviews material for acts.
How to Contact: Prefers cassette with 3-6 songs and lyric sheet; also submit promotional material, photos and clippings. SASE. Reports in 3 weeks.
Music: Mostly modern pop, modern rock and new wave; also dance-oriented, MOR, R&B and top 40/pop. Works primarily with "original music recording acts or those that aspire to be." Current acts include Don Dixon (songwriter and producer); The Accelerators (Southern pop recording act); and The Right Profile (modern pop).
Tips: "We are not interested in strong songs; style is not so important."

T. SKORMAN PRODUCTIONS, INC., 2362 Barbados Dr., Winter Park FL 32792. (305)677-9399. Management firm. Represents groups; currently handles 25 acts. Receives 10-25% commission. Reviews material for acts.
How to Contact: "Phone for permission to send tape." Prefers cassette with 3 songs. Does not return unsolicited material. Reports in 1 month.
Music: Mostly top 40 and rock; also dance-oriented, MOR and pop. Works primarily with show and rock bands. Current acts include Smiles (show group); Sheer Energy (show group); and Make Believe (dance group).
Tips: "We need commercial hit material with a visual aspect."

DAN SMITH AGENCY, Box 3634, Shawnee Mission KS 66203. (913)648-3906. Contact: Dan Smith. Management firm and booking agency. Represents artists, groups and songwriters in the Midwest. Receives 10-20% commission. Reviews material for acts.
How to Contact: Prefers cassette with 3-5 songs and lyric sheet. SASE. Reports in 1 month.
Music: Mostly country rock, top 40, progressive and R&B; also bluegrass, blues, country, dance-oriented, folk, jazz, MOR and soul. Works primarily with dance and concert bands. Current acts include Riverrock (country rock); Glow (progressive rock); and Bob Smith (folk single).
Tips: "Have complete promo—bio, photo (glossy), song list, credits, etc."

SOPRO, INC., (Formerly South Productions, Ltd.), Box 227, Chicago Ridge IL 60415 (312)425-0174. Contact: Bud Monaco or Red Rose. Management firm and artist development firm. Represents artists and groups in the local region; currently handles 4 acts. Receives maximum 20% commission. Reviews material for acts.
How to Contact: Write first and obtain permission to submit. Prefers cassette with 3-6 songs and lead sheet. Does not return unsolicited material. Reports in 2 weeks.
Music: Mostly rock, dance-oriented and top 40; also R&B, MOR and progressive rock. Works primarily with concert rock and dance-oriented bands. Current acts include John Hunter (rock/dance); Don Griffin and The Griff Band (rock/R&B); Tony Wilson (top 40/rock); and The Midwest Expedition (rock).

SOUTHERN GRASS BOOKING, Box 262, RD 2, Landenberg PA 19350. (215)268-8166. Manager: Bob Paisley. Booking agency. Represents artists and groups in the northeast US only; currently handles 7 acts. Receives 10-20% commission. Reviews material for acts.
How to Contact: Write and obtain permission to submit. Prefers cassette with 1-3 songs and lead sheet. SASE. Reports in 3 weeks.
Music: Bluegrass and gospel. Works primarily with groups at festivals, shows and bars. Current acts include Southern Grass, Dixie Rebels and Clay Creek Ramblers.

SOUTHERN TALENT INTERNATIONAL, 2925 Fallowridge, Snellville GA 30278. (404)979-0847. President: John M. Titak. Management and booking agency. Represents groups and songwriters; currently handles 76 acts. Receives 10-15% commission. Reviews material for acts.
How to Contact: Prefers cassette with 3 songs and lead sheet. SASE. Reports in 1 month.
Music: Mostly rock; also bluegrass, dance-oriented, easy listening, R&B, rock, soul and top 40/pop. Works primarily with bar bands and recording artists. Current acts include Stalker, Bad Influence, and Ruby Starr.

SPIDER ENTERTAINMENT CO., 5 Portsmouth Towne, Southfield MI 48075. President: Arnie Tencer. Vice President: Joel Zuckerman. Management firm. Represents artists, groups and songwriters; currently handles 1 act. Receives minimum 20% commission. Reviews material for acts.
How to Contact: Prefers cassette with 3-6 songs. Does not return unsolicited material. Reports in 3 weeks.
Music: Mostly contemporary pop; also rock (hard) and top 40/pop. Works primarily with "R&R bands with good songs and great live shows." Current acts include The Romantics (R&R band).
Tips: Artists "must have commercially viable material."

STAR ARTIST MANAGEMENT INC., Box 114, Fraser MI 48026. (313)979-5115. President: Ron Geddish. Executive Vice President: Bruce Lorfel. Director of Canadian Operations: Brian Courtis. House Producers: Gary Spaniola. Directors of Public Relations: Susan Murphy, Chris Best, Nick Desantis. General Counselor: Tom Werner. West Coast Counselor: S.D. Ashley. House Label: Track Records. Management firm. Represents individuals, groups and songwriters; currently handles 10 acts. Receives 10-20% commission. Reviews material for acts.
How to Contact: Prefers cassette with 3-5 songs. SASE. Reports in 2 weeks.
Music: Modern music, progressive, rock and top 40/pop. Works primarily with new music and rock groups. Current acts include Toby Redd (Nemperor/CBS) (modern music); Bitter Sweet Alley (Orient/RCA) (rock); The Act (modern music); Red Alert (rock); The Look (A&M Records) (rock); The Singrays (modern music); Affections (rock); and D'Arts (modern music).

STARTIME MUSIC, Box 643, LaQuinta CA 92253. (714)564-4873. President: Fred Rice. Management firm. Music publisher, record company. Currently handles 3 acts. Receives 15-25% commission.
How to Contact: Prefers cassette or VHS videocassette with 1-2 songs and lead sheet. SASE. Reports in 6 weeks.
Music: Mostly novelty; also country, rock and top 40/pop. Current acts include Rob Carter (singer/composer); Neo (avant garde actor/composer); R.C. Cole (country singer); and Rockenstein (rock singer).

BILL STEIN ASSOCIATES INC., Box 1516, Champaign IL 61820. Artists Manager: Bill Stein. Management firm. Represents artists and groups; currently handles 40 acts. Receives 10-15% commission. Reviews material for acts.
How to Contact: Prefers cassette or videocassette with 3-6 songs and promotional material. SASE. Reports in 1 month.
Music: Mostly rock, country and R&B; also dance-oriented, progressive, and soul. Works primarily with bar and dance bands and concert groups. Current acts include Vicious Circle (top 40 dance); Antics (top 40 dance); and Incognatos (top 40, 50's, 60's).
Tips: "Send complete promo package including picture, tapes, song and equipment lists."

STINNETTE ENTERTAINMENT AGENCY, Box 06404, Portland OR 97206. (503)235-5988. President: Tom Stinnette. Booking agency. Represents artists and groups in Northwest, Alaska and Canada; currently handles 75 acts. Receives 10-20% commission.
How to Contact: Write first and obtain permission to submit. Prefers cassette with 5-10 songs. Does not return unsolicited material. Give references from appearances. Reports in 2 weeks.
Music: Mostly top 40/rock; also country, dance-oriented, MOR, 50s and country rock and pop. Works primarily with singles, duos, "on up to 6-piece groups." Current acts include Front Page (top 40/rock group); Room Service (top 40 rock group); and Sh-Boom (50s rock show).
Tips: "Be well rehearsed, and have good press kit, including 8x10 pictures."

STRAUMAN/GROSS MUSIC ASSOCIATES, 1635 Ritner St., Philadelphia PA 19145. (215)546-1507; 755-1898. Co-Directors: Lloyd Gross, Ed Strauman. Management firm, booking agency and record producer. Represents artists and groups in Pennsylvania, New Jersey and Delaware; currently handles 2 songwriters. Receives 10-20% commission. Reviews material for acts.
How to Contact: Write first and obtain permission to submit. Prefers cassette with 1-3 songs. SASE. Reports in 1 month.
Music: Mostly easy listening and MOR; also children's, choral, church/religious, jazz and top 40/pop. Works primarily with songwriters and vocalists.

*SUMMIT MANAGEMENT CORPORATION, Box 48833, Chicago IL 60648. (312)677-9178. Contact: Robert C. Acri or Al Curtis. Entertainment consultant "composed of Chicago area professionals, including musicians, attorneys, managers, and promoters. Dedicated to providing a myriad of musical consulting services." Receives maximum 20% commission and/or fee. Reviews material for acts.
How to Contact: Send pictures, bios and promotional material. Prefers cassette and lyric sheet or lead sheet.
Music: Mostly pop and country.

TALENT ASSOCIATE/T.E. YENOWINE, 10630 St. Rene Rd., Jeffersontown KY 40299. (502)267-5600. Agent: T.E. Yenowine. Management firm, booking agency and record producer. Represents artists and groups in the Ohio valley area; currently handles 75 acts. Receives 10-15% commission. Reviews material for acts.
How to Contact: Query by mail or arrange personal interview. Prefers cassette with 6-10 songs and lyric sheet. SASE. Include references, photo and song list. Reports in 1 week.
Music: Easy listening, MOR and top 40/pop. Works primarily with singles (musicians/vocalists), duos and trios. Current acts include Jerry Utley (vocalist); and Warner Anderson (one-man band).

TALENT ATTRACTIONS, Box 8542, Asheville NC 28814. (704)253-4161. President: Larry Phillips. Management firm and booking agency. Represents artists, groups and songwriters; currently handles 4 acts. Receives 10-20% commission. Reviews material for acts.
How to Contact: Prefers cassette or videocassette with 3-5 songs and lead sheet. SASE. Reports in 3 weeks.
Music: Country, rock and top 40/pop. Works primarily with 4-6 piece groups and single vocal artists. Current acts include Natalie Nugent (vocalist and actress); Joe Berry (country, top 40/pop vocalist); Johnny Weathers (MOR and classic country); and Justice (top 40/pop, country band).
Tips: "At present I am only interested in original copyrighted songs. An inexpensive cassette is sufficient. If I like the songs, I will ask for a studio demo."

TALENT MASTER, Box 158558, Nashville TN 37215. (615)320-0881. President: Steve Bess. Vice President: Charli McMillan. Booking agency. Represents artists and musical groups from Tennessee and surrounding states; currently handles 18 acts. Receives 15-20% commission.
How to Contact: Prefers personal interview (artist/group only) or submit demo tape/videocassette with good promo kit. Prefers live cassette with 1-3 songs. Does not return unsolicited material. Reports in 2-3 weeks.
Music: Country, dance-oriented, easy listening, MOR and rock (top 40, country). Works primarily with recording artists and dance and show bands. Current acts include Larry Hudson (recording artist); and Mary Burns (recording artist).

TALENT NETWORK INTERNATIONAL/JACKSON ENTERPRISES, (formerly AMJ International/Jackson Enterprises), Suite 807, 9000 Sunset Blvd., West Hollywood CA 90069. (213)550-0397. General Manager: Alice M. Jackson. Booking agency and music publisher. Represents artists, groups and songwriters; currently handles 35 acts. Receives 10% commission. Reviews material for acts.

Close-up

David Tasse
Booking Agent/Performer
Beloit, Wisconsin

If all good things come to those who wait, then Dave Tasse has it made. Tasse, who started in the booking business with $18 in his pocket, finds that the key to survival in a small market is to develop a reliable base of smaller successes and build and diversify from there. "Being patient and not trying to push success before it's due has been one of my greatest assets," says Tasse, "you've really got to learn patience in this business."

Although most of his bookings have been in nightclubs, Tasse sees the nature of his booking business, Magnet Attractions, beginning to change. "I used to be predominately a club agent but lately I've started getting into private sector bookings such as country clubs, conventions and private parties, mainly because the money factor is greater and the clients are very easy to work with. A big problem though is that many musicians have a 'nightclub mentality' and just don't have the professionalism required to handle these types of jobs."

To help him secure bookings, Tasse uses videos of his acts to "sell" prospective clients. "Video is a great sales tool. I often take a portable TV and VCR out to clubs, let the manager watch videos of several acts and let him decide which act he wants to hire. It's the greatest selling tool a performing musician could have."

In addition to his involvement in booking and video production Tasse also is a recording jazz musician (his current album is *Love Force*), has his own record and publishing companies, promotes concerts and hosts a popular traveling DJ show. Although he admits that occasionally these DJ shows may take work away from live musicians, he feels that the current trend towards the use of recorded music is making many complacent bands "sharpen up" and improve their musicianship.

Rather than have these two areas in direct competition Tasse has developed a new "angle," the singing DJ. In these shows the DJ sings and plays his instrument to recorded background music, thereby providing both the spontaneity of live music and the consistency of recorded music.

Although Tasse is developing key contacts in major music centers like Los Angeles and Nashville, he maintains that his home base will remain in the Midwest. While admitting that living in close proximity to one of the major music centers can have a positive effect on a musician's career he believes that a lot of good music produced in the Midwest goes unnoticed by the rest of the music industry.

"It's always a constant struggle for recognition in this industry. In my case, I'm attempting to overcome the problems of trying to be a metropolitan artist in a small Midwest town and I think the only way of doing that successfully is to associate with as many other local professionals as you can and work to improve the quality of music in your area. I guess my main goal is to be recognized for my creativity with music and not for the flash."

How to Contact: Prefers cassette ("copy only—do not send original") with 2-4 songs and lead sheet. SASE. Reports in 6-8 weeks.
Music: Blues, country, dance-oriented, MOR, R&B, modern country rock, soul, jazz and top 40/pop. Works primarily with "dance bands, combos, lounge groups, concert and jazz artists and singles." Current acts include Jerri C. Carroll (MOR artist); Eddie Simpson (R&B singer); Better Business Band (rock); Propege (rock) and Wind Jammer (rock).
Tips: "Be different. Present something unique in sound. Have good lyrics that tell a story."

TAS MUSIC CO./MAGNET ATTRACTIONS, 731 8th St., Beloit WI 53511. (608)362-4340. Contact: David Tasse. Booking agency, record company and music publisher. Represents 75 artists, groups and songwriters. Receives 10-20% commission. Reviews material for acts.
How to Contact: Write first and obtain permission to submit. Prefers cassette with 2-4 songs and lyric sheet. SASE. Reports in 3 weeks.
Music: Mostly MOR; also dance-oriented, jazz, rock, soul and top 40/pop. Works primarily with dance bands. Current acts include David Hulburt.

THRUST (INTERNATIONAL), Box 850, Pt. Dover, Ontario N0A 1N0 Canada. (519)426-3799. President: Wayne Elliot. Management agency and promotion and marketing firm. Represents artists, groups, comedians, models and actors. Receives 5-15% commission, "depending on services requested." Reviews material for acts.
How to Contact: Submit demo tape, promotion kit and lyric sheet. Prefers cassette, but "equipped for all types of demos, including video." Does not return unsolicited material. Reports in 1 week.
Music: Mostly top 40/pop and comedy; also rock. Works primarily with top 40 female vocalists, models, comedians and novelty-type acts.
Tips: "You have to look like a winner to be a winner. Gimmicks help a good manager—and talent."

TRIANGLE TALENT, INC., 9701 Taylorsville Rd., Louisville KY 40299. (502)267-5466. President: David H. Snowden. Booking agency. Represents artists and groups; currently handles 80 acts. Receives 10-20% commission. Reviews material for acts.
How to Contact: Query. Prefers cassette or VHS videocassette with 2-4 songs and lyric sheet. SASE. Reports in 2 weeks.
Music: Mostly rock/top 40 country and funk; also bluegrass and pop. Current acts include Pure Pleasure (disco/top 40); The Score (top 40); Hermalee (country) and Paradise (contemporary country).

UMBRELLA ARTISTS MANAGEMENT, INC., 2181 Victory Pkwy., Box 6507, Cincinnati OH 45206. (513)861-1500. President: Stan Hertzman. Management agency. Represents artists, groups and songwriters; currently handles 4 acts.
How to Contact: Prefers cassette with 3 songs and lyric sheet. SASE. Reports in 1 month.
Music: Progressive, rock and top 40/pop. Works with contemporary/progressive pop/rock artists and writers. Current acts include The Young Invaders, (AOR rock group); The Bears (modern band); Charlie Fletcher (pop rock, artist-songwriter); and Adrian Belew (artist/guitarist/songwriter). Credits include: Frank Zappa, David Bowie, Talking Heads, Garland Jeffreys, Tom Tom Club, Herbie Hancock, and Gary Platt (engineer/producer/songwriter/arranger).

VALEX TALENT AGENCY, Box 241, Ithaca NY 14851. (607)273-3931. Publishing President: John Perialas. Booking Vice President: Tom McNerney. Management firm, booking agency and publishing house. Deals with artists in northeast US only. Represents artists, groups and songwriters; currently handles 20-30 acts. Receives 15-25% commission. Reviews material for acts.
How to Contact: Prefers 7¹/₂ ips reel-to-reel or cassette with 3-6 songs and lead sheet. SASE. Reports in 1 month. "Songwriters please send material in care of John Perialas, Copper John Music; also send cassettes or 7¹/₂ ips tapes to same."
Music: Mostly top 40, rock and new wave; also country pop, dance-oriented, easy listening, MOR, R&B, rock, and pop. Works with vocalists, show, dance and bar bands. Current acts include the Works (rock); Cries (rock/new wave); and Screentest (top 40/pop/rock).
Tips: "After sending material allow appropriate time for material to be reviewed (2 weeks); then follow with call."

VELVETT RECORDING COMPANY, 517 W. 57th St., Los Angeles CA 90037. (213)753-7893. Manager: Aaron Johnson. Management firm and record company. Represents artists, groups and songwriters; currently handles 7 acts. Receives minimum 10-20% commission. Reviews material for acts.
How to Contact: Prefers cassette with 2-3 songs and lead sheet. SASE.
Music: Blues, gospel, church/religious, R&B, rock, soul and top 40/pop. Works primarily with show

and dance bands and vocalists. Current acts include Arlene Bell (soul/top 40/pop artist); Chuck Willis (blues artist); and Gifled Group (top 40/pop artists).

VOKES BOOKING AGENCY, Box 12, New Kensington PA 15068. (412)335-2775. President: Howard Vokes. Booking agency. Represents individuals, groups and songwriters; currently handles 25 acts. Receives 10-20% commission.
How to Contact: Query. Cassette only with 3-6 songs and lead sheet. SASE. Reports in 2 weeks.
Music: Bluegrass, country and gospel. "We work with bluegrass and hard country bands who generally play bars, hotels and clubs. However, we also book in ole-time artists as singles. We want nothing to do with hard rock or country rock." Current acts include Country Boys (country); 100% Proof Country (country); and Mel Anderson (country).

***VON KLEIST TALENT MANAGEMENT**, Box 310, Carmichael CA 95609. (916)485-9092. Contact: Rachel Minke. Management agency. Represents individual artists. Deals with local artists. Currently handles 1 act. Receives 10-15% commission. Reviews material for acts.
How To Contact: Prefers cassette or VHS 1/2" videocassette (if available) and lyric sheet and lead sheet. SASE. Reports in 3 weeks.
Music: Mostly contemporary, country and gospel; also blues and jazz. Works primarily with vocalists and back-up bands. Current acts include Rachel Minke.
Tips: "We are looking for original music for recording projects."

WILLIAM F. WAGNER AGENCY, Suite 218, 14343 Addison St., Sherman Oaks CA 91423. (818)501-4161. Owner: Bill Wagner. Management agency and record producer. Represents artists and groups; currently handles 4 acts. Receives 15% commission. "For recording production of artists other than my own clients I receive $100/hour, live studio time; $50/hour overdub, editing and mix-down time." Reviews material for acts.
How to Contact: Prefers 7 1/2 or 3 3/4 ips reel-to-reel (2- or 4-track) or cassette with 15 minutes maximum on tape and lead sheet. SASE. Reports in 2 weeks.
Music: Mostly top 40, standards an jazz; also blues, choral, country, dance-oriented, easy listening, MOR, progressive, Spanish, R&B, rock (all kinds), soul. Works primarily with vocalists, small groups (3-8 people) and big bands (18-20 people). Current acts include Marchand Melcher (country-pop vocalists); Candace Bennett (cabaret vocalist); and Dick Berk's Jazz Adoption Agency (10 piece jazz rock group).

WALTNER ENTERPRISES, 14702 Canterbury Ave., Tustin CA 92680. (714)731-2981. President: Steve Waltner. Management firm, music publisher and record company. Represents artists, groups and songwriters; currently handles 3 acts. Pays by "standard artist recording contract and standard songwriters contract." Reviews material for acts.
How to Contact: Prefers cassette with 2-4 songs and lead sheet. SASE. Reports in 1 month.
Music: Mostly country; also MOR and top 40/pop. Current acts include Jason Chase, Jay Daniel and Steve Shelby (all country, pop artists).

SHANE WILDER ARTISTS' MANAGEMENT, Box 3503, Hollywood CA 90078. (818)891-1185. President: Shane Wilder. Management firm. Represents artists and groups; currently handles 10 acts. Receives 15-25% commission. Reviews material for acts.
How to Contact: Prefers cassette with 4-10 songs and lyric sheet. SASE. Reports in 1 month.
Music: Mostly rock and country; also top 40/pop. Works primarily with single artists and groups. Current acts include Mike Franklin (country recording artist); Laurie Loman (singer); and Honey Wilder (actress).
Tips: "Make sure your work is highly commercial. We are looking for strong female country songs for major artists. Material should be available for publishing with Shane Wilder Music, BMI."

WINTERSWAN, Division of Great Plains Associates, Box 634, Lawrence KS 66044. (913)841-4444. Presidents: Mark Swanson, Scott Winters. Management firm. Represents groups; currently handles 1 act. Receives 10-20% commission. Reviews material for acts.
How to Contact: Prefers cassette with 3-7 songs and lyric sheet. SASE. Reports in 1 week.
Music: Country, R&B, rock (straight) and soul. Works primarily with dance/concert bands, for small college circuit and dance halls. Current acts include Blue Wave (beach music).

BILLY WOLFE & ASSOCIATES, Box 262, Abe Lincoln Station, Carteret NJ 07008-0262. (201)541-9422. President: Billy Wolfe. Vice President: Gary Hills. Management firm, booking agency and record producer. Represents individuals, groups, songwriters and show and oldie acts from the US, Canada, Japan, England, France, Sweden, Belgium and Holland; currently handles 65 acts. "We try to locate

outlets for all material we receive in our agency." Receives 10-20% commission; "the artist picks up his money directly—we receive deposits only with signed contracts." Reviews material for acts.
How to Contact: Prefers 7¹/₂ ips reel-to-reel or cassette with 6-12 songs and lyric sheet. "Send material with demo, photographs and short bio on yourself to get a better idea of the sender." SASE. Reports in 1 month.
Music: Mostly oldies, MOR and contemporary; also soul and R&B; also country, dance-oriented, easy listening, folk, progressive, rock (country), Polish, French and top 40/pop. Works primarily with dance and show bands and groups with "just plain good clean sounds." Current acts include The Crests (oldies/MOR); The Brooklyn Bridge (oldies/MOR); and Billy J. Kramer and the Dakotas (oldies/MOR).
Tips: "We welcome new songwriters as well as new groups; we want to develop tomorrow's hit artist as well as our agency's future."

RICHARD WOOD ARTIST MANAGEMENT, 42 Clinton Ave., Staten Island NY 10301. (212)981-0641. Contact: Richard Wood. Management firm. Represents musical groups. Currently handles 1 act. Receives 10-15% commission. Reviews material for acts.
How to Contact: Prefers cassette and lead sheet. SASE.
Music: Mostly R&B and top 40/pop; also MOR. Works primarily with "high energy" show bands. Current acts include Hot Pepper (show band).
Tips: "Please be versatile and able to make changes in material to suit the type of acts I book."

WORLD WIDE MANAGEMENT, 1767 Front St., Yorktown Heights NY 10598. (914)962-2727. A&R Director: Mr. Stevens. Management firm and booking agency. Represents artists, groups, songwriters and actors. Receives 15-40% commission. Reviews material for acts.
How to Contact: Write first and obtain permission to submit or to arrange personal interview. Prefers cassette with 3-5 songs. SASE. Reports in 1 month.
Music: Mostly rock, jazz and folk; also bluegrass, blues, country and R&B. Works primarily with vocalists and rock bands. Current acts include Geri Gunn (writer/performer); The Norm (progressive rock); and Gollum (rock).

DOUGLAS A. YEAGER PRODUCTIONS, 300 W. 55th St., New York NY 10019. (212)245-0240. Manager: Jerry Burnham. Management firm. Represents artists; currently handles 6 acts. Receives 15-25% commission. Reviews material for acts.
How to Contact: Prefers cassette with 2-4 songs and lyric sheet. SASE. Reports in 1 month.
Music: Mostly R&B and dance; also soul and pop country. Works primarily with female R&B singers. Current acts include Livinston Taylor, Richie Havens, and Levon Helm.

ZANE MANAGEMENT, INC., 700 Three Penn Center, Philadelphia PA 19102. (215)563-1100. President: Lloyd Zane Remick. Management agency. Represents artists, songwriters and athletes; currently handles 5 acts. Receives variable commission.
How to Contact: Prefers cassette and lyric sheet. SASE. Reports in 3-4 weeks.
Music: Children's, dance, easy listening, folk, gospel, jazz (fusion), MOR, rock (hard and country), soul and top 40/pop. Current acts include Phil Hurtt; Bunny Sigler (disco/funk); Pieces of a Dream (consultant); and Grover Washington, Jr. (management).

Play Producers & Publishers

Today's wise playwright keeps it simple: Shows with uncomplicated sets and small casts are a must for little theaters with limited facilities and funds. Even on Broadway, rising costs force producers and directors to seek material that can be produced inexpensively.

However, Broadway need not be—and should not be—your only goal. Many local groups—dinner theaters, children's theaters, high school and college groups, and community theaters—provide outlets for musicals.

You should work closely with at least one theater group to get a look at theater operation. Working with a local group—in any capacity—will give you a pragmatic grounding in what you can and can't do on stage. If it's impossible for you to work on plays, watch them. Attend as many musicals (non-musicals too) as possible. Regional theaters and dinner theaters give plenty of opportunities to witness high-quality productions.

These same groups are open to original work from local playwrights, and are excellent testing grounds for your musical. Once your play has proven itself locally, you can send reviews of the performances along with a letter asking permission to submit your musical to producers in New York and elsewhere.

For more information write play publishers, request copies of their catalogs and order a few playscripts to study. This will give you an idea of how song lyrics relate to the entire show, how and when songs are woven into the plot, and the number of songs used.

Writers of musicals receive royalties in the form of a percentage of box office receipts or a flat fee per performance. Payment policies of individual producers and publishers are given in their listings. Other monies may come as royalties for sales of scripts and cast albums.

*ALLENBERRY PLAYHOUSE, Boiling Springs PA 17007. (717)258-6120. Managing Director: Nelson Sheeley. Play producer. Produces 9 plays (2 musicals)/year. Pays 3-5% royalty. Query with synopsis. SASE. Reports as soon as possible.
Musicals: "Other than established material, we are looking for small cast, 4-10 characters, simply produced musicals—they should run between 2-2½ hrs in length. Take into account that we are in a conservative, religiously oriented part of the country. Four letter words are fairly taboo, but then again, it depends on the four letter word! Stay away from what middle America finds objectionable: excessive dwelling on any violation of the Ten Commandments, slurs on the country (not necessarily the government), nudity, or esoteric subject matter."
Recent Productions: *Annie*; *Pirates of Penzance*; and *The Music Man*.

AMAS REPERTORY THEATRE INC., 1 E. 104th St., New York NY 10029. (212)369-8000. Artistic Director: Rosetta Le Noire. Administrator: Jerry Lapidus. Development Director: Richard Hunter. Play Producer. Produces 6 musicals/year. Also presents 2 children's theater productions and one summer tour. "AMAS is dedicated to bringing all people—regardless of race, creed, color or religion—together through the creative arts. In writing for AMAS, an author should keep this overall goal in mind." Does not pay for manuscripts but "provides a top quality New York showcase with a good record of commercial pick-ups." Query with synopsis or submit complete script with cassette of score (or partial score).
Musicals: Musicals only. "All works to be performed by multi-racial casts. Musical biographies especially welcome. Cast size should be under 15 if possible, including doubling. Because of physical space, set requirements should be relatively simple. Does not want to see material with explicit sex or violence or very strong language. Prefer themes of love, joy and togetherness."
Recent Productions: *Blackberries*, by Joseph George Caruso (minstrel shows/vaudeville); *Northern Boulevard*, by Carleton Carpenter and Kevin Brofsky (living in NY in transition); and *Manhattan Serenade*, by L. Alter/A. Heller/K. Cottrell (musical revue).

AMERICAN THEATRE ARTS, Play Development Program, 6240 Hollywood Blvd., Hollywood CA 90028. (213)466-2462. Play Development Director: Pamela Bohnert. Mounts 5 productions per year. "Ideally, one is original play. ATA houses 2 Equity-waiver theaters, plus a conservatory. Shows run 6-8

weeks; Thursday, Friday, and Saturday nights and Sunday matinee. Royalty varies, especially if work goes on to Equity houses. "No unsolicited scripts. Submit synopsis, letter of inquiry and SASE for response. Please include complete cast description and set requirements. Response time 6-8 weeks. If script is requested, reports in 3-4 months."
Musicals: "Musicals with 8-12 characters maximum. One-set shows.
Recent Productions: *Richards' Cork Leg*, by Brendan Beehan (Irish satire); *River Wind*, by John Jennings (young love; mid-life crisis); and *The All Star Radio Broadcast of 1939*, by John Terry Bell and Rolly Fanton (old-time radio).

ARENA PLAYERS REPERTORY THEATRE, 296 Route 109, East Farmingdale NY 11735. (516)293-0674. Producer: Frederic De Feis. Play producer. Produces 30 plays/year. Plays performed in a "professional, arena-style repertory theater playing to a broad cross-section of teenagers to senior citizens, drawn from all over Long Island as well as Manhattan." Pays royalty averaging $600-1,200. Query with synopsis. SASE. Reports in 1 month.
Musicals: "We are particularly interested in full-length intimate musicals which can be mounted with minimal orchestration and are well-suited to production in a small, arena-style theater."
Recent Productions: *Umbrellas of Cherbourg*, by Demy; and *I Love My Wife*, by Michael Stewart and Cy Coleman.

ARKANSAS STATE UNIVERSITY-BEEBE CAMPUS, Box H, Beebe AR 72012. (501)882-6452. Director of Theater: L.R. Chudomelka. Play producer. Produces 6 plays (3-4 musicals)/year. Plays are performed in a "600 seat theater (proscenium) in a city of 4,000, 30 miles from metropolitan area of more than 200,000." Pays royalty. Submit complete manuscript and score. SASE. Reports in 2 weeks.
Musicals: "Material should be within the ability of traditional community college with traditional and non-traditional students: simple dancing, innovative and traditional, not over-sophisticated (somewhat family oriented). Variety of music styles and balanced major role shows—no 'star' shows. Flexible cast size, props, staging, etc. We do not want extremes, unnecessary profanity or 'operatic' material."
Recent Productions: *Anything Goes*, by Cole Porter ("Love Boat of the 30s"); *The Drunkard*, by Barry Manilow (classical melodrama); and *Oklahoma*, by Rogers and Hammerstein.
Tips: "Music should be singable and vary in style. Songs should be an intricate part of the show and not just put in for spectacle. Major roles should be balanced between 4 or 5 characters, rather than one-character shows with chorus."

ASOLO STATE THEATER, Drawer E, Sarasota FL 33578. (813)355-7115. Literary Manager. Play producer. Produces 8 plays (1 musical)/year. Plays are performed at the Asolo Theater (325-seat proscenium house) or by the Asolo Touring Theater (6-member company touring the Southeast). Pays 5% minimum royalty. Query. SASE.
Musicals: "We want small non-chorus musicals only. They should be full-length, any subject, with not over 6 in the cast. There are no restrictions on production demands; however, musicals with excessive scenic requirements may be difficult to consider. We no longer accept unsolicited manuscripts or tapes. Inquiries should be made in the form of a letter, a one-page synopsis, and a self-addressed, stamped postcard."
Recent Productions: *Dames at Sea*, by Haimsohn/Miller/Wise; *The Drunkard*, by Herrod/Manilow; and *Man with a Load of Mischief*, by Clifton/Tarver.
Tips: "Musicals are produced infrequently here due to the 'classical' basis of Asolo's repertory and inability to 'job-in' musical-theater talent."

*BOARSHEAD: MICHIGAN PUBLIC THEATER, 425 S. Grand Ave., Lansing MI 48933. (517)484-7800. Artistic Director: Nancy-Elizabeth Kammer. Play producer. Produces 9 plays/year. Audiences are "mainly white upper-middle-class, college-educated, middle-aged." Theatre capacity is 249 with ¾ thrust stage. Pays 6-9% royalty or $65/peformance. Query with synopsis, character breakdown and set description. SASE.
Musicals: Seeking musicals with "small cast, 2 acts or cabaret length, and limited orchestration. Can be political or social commentary. New experimental forms are fine. Intelligent, witty, sensitive, good plays are what we look for. Four to eight characters in cast is common—ideal cast size 4-5. Works with extremely tight budget." No "large casts, extensive set changes or orchestration."
Recent Production: *None of the Above*, by Peter D. Sieruta (comedy dealing with teenage love and family values); *Foxfire*, by Hume Cronyn and Susan Cooper (Appalachian family) and *Gift of the Magi*, by O. Henry, adapted by Peter Ekstrom.

CALIFORNIA STATE COLLEGE, BAKERSFIELD, DEPARTMENT OF FINE ARTS, 9001 Stockdale Hwy., Bakersfield CA 93309. (805)833-3093. Assistant Professor of Theater: Jeffrey Mason.

Associate Professor of Theater: Anita Mucha-DuBratt. Chairman, Fine Arts: Jerome Kleinsasser. Play producer. Produces 4 plays/year (1 musical every other year). Plays performed in the 500-seat Dore Theatre to the college community and the community at large. Pays minimum $25/performance. Query. Does not return unsolicited material. Reports in 1 month.
Musicals: Looking for "exciting plays with unit set and small casts."
Recent Productions: *Trial By Jury*, by Gilbert and Sullivan (punk/new wave treatment of operetta); *Camelot*, by Lerner and Lowe; and *The Threepenny Opera*, by Brecht and Weill.

WILLIAM CAREY COLLEGE DINNER THEATRE, William Carey College, Hattiesburg MS 39401. (601)582-5051, ext. 228. Managing Director: O.L. Quave. Play producer. Produces 2 plays (2 musicals)/year. "Our dinner theater operates only in summer and plays to family audiences." Payment negotiable. Submit complete manuscript and score. SASE. Reports as soon as possible.
Musicals: "Plays should be simply-staged, have small casts (8-10), and be suitable for family viewing; two hours maximum length. Score should require piano only, or piano, electric piano, and drums."
Recent Productions: *Ernest in Love*; and *Rodgers and Hart: A Musical Celebration*; and *Side by Side*, by Sondheim.

*CARROLL COLLEGE, Little Theatre, Helena MT 59625. (406)442-3450, ext. 276. Director of Theater: Jim Bartruff. Play producer. Produces 4-5 plays (1 musical)/year. "Our plays are produced in our Little Theatre for campus and community. The Little Theatre is a small proscenium house with flexible seating (90-120)." Pays $25-100/performance. Query or submit complete manuscript score and tape of songs. SASE. Reports in 6 weeks.
Musicals: "We consider all types of plays geared for small cast (8-12 people) and minimal settings (unit preferred). Scoring should be for piano and percussion. Also considers arrangement for guitar—keyboards—piano. Original material is preferred, but not readily available."
Recent Productions: *Good News*, by Schwab/De Sylva/Brown/Henderson (1920s campus life); *Joseph and the Amazing Technicolor Dreamcoat*, by Weber/Rice (Old Testament); and *A God in the Bush Is Worth Two in the Hand*, by Harper/Holmes (an original musical based on the life of Moses).
Tips: "Find a place, any place, to do it and get it done. Stay involved with the production. Don't be afraid to make changes if you need to. The best way to discover 'what works' is to get it done. There are literally thousands of little markets yearning for new and good material."

CENTENARY COLLEGE, THEATRE DEPARTMENT, Shreveport LA 71134-0188. (318)869-5242. Chairman: Robert R. Buseick. Play producer. Produces 6 plays (2 musicals)/year. Plays are presented in a 350-seat playhouse to college and community audiences. Submit ms and score. SASE. Reports in 1 month.
Recent Productions: *Annie*; *Moliere*; *Trixie True, Teen Detective*; and *The Unsinkable Molly Brown*.

CIRCLE IN THE SQUARE THEATRE, 1633 Broadway, New York NY 10019. (212)307-2700. Literary Advisor: Robert Pesola. Play producer. Produces 3 plays/year; occasionally produces a musical. Query with a letter and 1-page synopsis. Reports in 3-4 months.
Musicals: "We are actively looking for original material."
Recent Production: *Pal Joey*.

DAVID J. COGAN, 330 West 42 St., New York NY 10036. Contact: David Cogan. Play producer. Produces 1 play/year. Produces musical comedy, straight comedy, and drama in New York. Pays on a royalty basis, or buys script outright for $5,000 maximum. Query. SASE. Reports in 1 month.
Musicals: Interested only in completed projects.
Recent Productions: *A Raisin in the Sun*, by Hannesbury (drama); and *The Odd Couple*, by Neil Simon (comedy).

THE CRICKET THEATRE, Hennepin Center for the Arts, 528 Hennepin Ave., Minneapolis MN 55403. (612)333-5241. Associate Artistic Director: Sean Michael Dowse. Play producer. Produces 6-8 main stage shows, also Works-in-Progress shows. Pays negotiable royalty; or per diem, honorarium or commission. Submit complete ms and cassette tape of songs. SASE. Reports in 6 months.
Musicals: "We seek chamber musicals with small cost and small orchestra—mainstream yet adventurous. New American playwrights and songwriters can use our Works-In-Progress program to develop new work."
Recent Productions: *Billy Bishop Goes to War*, by John Gray with Eric Peterson (WWI Ace); *Tintypes* (immigrants in early 20th century US); and *Side by Side*, by Sondheim.
Tips: "Try to get a workshop of play done at the theatre you wish to work with."

CYPRESS COLLEGE THEATER ARTS DEPARTMENT, 9200 Valley View St., Cypress CA 90630. (714)821-6320. Theater Arts Department Chairman: Kaleta Brown. Play producer. Produces 6-7 plays (2 musicals)/year. "Our audience at Cypress College is basically a middle-class, suburban audience. We have a continuing audience that we have built up over the years. Our plays now are produced in our Campus Theater (seating capacity 623) or workshop theater (maximum seating capacity 250)." Payment varies with each production. Submit complete ms, score and 7¹/₂ ips reel-to-reel tape of songs. SASE. Reports in 1 month.

Musicals: "We must do large-cast shows, generally, because the shows are done as a class. Because we are on a slightly limited budget, we must look carefully at scenery requirements, costume requirements and props.

Recent Productions: *Damn Yankees*; *A Funny Thing Happened on the Way to the Forum*; *The Cherry Orchard*; *Taming of the Shrew*; *Man for All Seasons*; and *Our Town*.

Tips: "Open show with a large group, energetic number. Intersperse dance (especially tap) throughout shows and end with a 'ripping' choral number."

*DORSET THEATRE FESTIVAL, Box 519, Dorset VT 05251. (802)867-2223. Artistic Director: Jill Charles. Play producer. Produces 5-6 plays (1-2 musicals)/year. Dorset Theatre Festival is a non-profit, Equity (LOA) company producing summer seasons at the Dorset Playhouse in southern Vermont, four hours from New York City. Pays negotiated royalty. Query with synopsis, character breakdown and set description. SASE. Reports in 12-16 weeks.

Musicals: Seeks "only full-length works with broad audience appeal. Style may be realistic or theatrical; topics can be historical or contemporary but should have broad appeal and be simply orchestrated. We never use more than 5 pieces in orchestra and prefer musicals that can be done with three musicians. We also consider plays with music which may not be completely dependent on musical numbers—if so, we prefer those that can be done with piano only. Cast should be limited, preferably 10 for a musical (small chorus is feasible), but total should not exceed 6-8 principals and 4-8 in chorus. There's no point in sending us material that demands huge sets, large cast or an orchestra."

Recent Productions: *You Never Know*, by Cole Porter (special revival farce with music, 1938); *Nobody and Me*, by C.A. Philips (play with songs—psychic phenomenon); and *A Penny Earned*, by Annie Lebaus/Stephen Kelsey (musical adaption of *Miser*).

Tips: "Original presentation should contain intelligent, businesslike query letter, cast and set requirements, synopsis, list of songs, description of instrumentation, and sample pages of dialogue and lyrics." If script is requested, it should be accompanied by an audio cassette of songs.

EAST WEST PLAYERS, 4424 Santa Monica Blvd., Los Angeles CA 90029. (213)660-0366. Artistic Director: Mako. Administrator: Janet Mitsui. Play producer. Produces 6 plays/year. "We have produced original musical revues and some children's musicals in our theater which is a 99-seat Equity waiver house. Our actors are professional actors. We are an Asian-American theater and consequently the audience is primarily ethnic in makeup." Pays 5% minimum royalty. Query with synopsis. SASE. Reports in 2 months.

Musicals: "We look for material dealing with Asian-American culture and produce adult and children's musicals in book and/or revue form. We set no limitations on the writing approach. We look for theme and above all originality. We primarily produce shows with casts under 15. The stage is not huge and has certain limitations; however, we do have a turntable at our disposal."

Recent Productions: Previously produced *The Threepenny Opera*, by Brecht/Weill (English low life); *Pacific Overtures*, by Sondheim/Weidman (opening of Japan); and *Happy End*, by Brecht/Weill (Salvation Army vs. hoods); (original) *Pinoys in Space* (sci-fi spoof) and *Christmas in Camp* (Japanese internment camps) both by Dom Magwili.

*EMPIRE STATE INSTITUTE FOR THE PERFORMING ARTS (ESIPA), Empire State Plaza Albany NY 12223. (518)474-1199. Literary Manager: Barbara R. Maggio. Play producer. Produces 8 plays (3 musicals)/year. Plays performed for student audiences grades K-12, family audiences and adult audiences. Two theatres: main theatre seats 950 with full stage, studio theatre seats 450 with smaller stage. Pay negotiable. Submit complete manuscript, score and tape of songs. SASE. Reports in 16 weeks.

How to Contact: Submit complete manuscript, score and tape of songs. SASE. Reports in 16 weeks.

Musicals: Looking for intelligent and well-written book with substances, a score that enhances and supplements the book and is musically well-crafted and theatrical. Length: up to 2 hours. Could be play with music, musical comedy, musical drama, or opera. Excellence and substance in material is essential. Cast could be up to 25; orchestra size up to 15. No "incomplete scripts and scores."

Recent Productions: *Raggedy Ann*, by William Gibson/Joe Raposo (musical play); *Wind in the Willows*, by Jakes/Stravelo (musical comedy); and *Prince & the Pauper*, by Vrecke/Leslie/Alexander (play with music).

Tips: "There is a great need for musicals that are well-written with intelligence and substance and suitable for young audiences."

Close-up

Loretta Libbé Lotman
Musical Playwright
Los Angeles, California

"Craft will sustain you when inspiration's not there," says Loretta Liebbe Lotman, musical playwright and veteran of over 32 productions in L.A. and elsewhere. Lotman has spent the better part of her theatre career developing her craft outside the mecca of Broadway—and helping others do the same.

Lotman's initial contact with musical theatre came from her high school choral director who instilled in her the need for a firm grounding in the basics of the craft and an appreciation for the realities of the business. "When you write musicals, all aspects of artistry and commercialism have to be taken into consideration," she explains. "You've got to know who your audience is and how you're going to bring enough people into a 'house' to financially sustain your artistic work. It's not compromising; it's a collaboration of elements. In musical theatre you are dealing with every one of the major art forms—comedy or drama, music and lyrics, dance, and costume and set design—and all these art forms must work in harmony with each other."

Although she feels that musicals can provide talented songwriters with "an excellent chance to show a body of work," the aspiring musical playwrights must ground themselves in the basics. Her approach: "Familiarize yourself with the great musicals. Find out which shows made it and why. Pay attention to structure. Realize that theatre is *not* television. Unlike television, in live theatre there is a nonspeaking additional character in every play called the audience, and no two audiences are ever the same. You never know what the response is going to be. Try to scale down the number of people involved. If you can write a 2-, 3-, or 4-character musical, you have a very good chance of getting it produced somewhere if the quality is good enough.

"Don't forget the importance of the book (or libretto) when writing your musical," she continues. "Remember that the book should move along at a brisk pace, tell a story, introduce characters, set up the songs and most importantly, provide genuine emotional (or comedic) conflict to make the songs moments that people wish to dwell upon. A song in a musical is meant for those moments when words alone are not enough."

Lotman, together with composer Kevin Kaufman, cofounded and coproduced *Broadway on Sunset*, an innovative, weekly 2-hour showcase that ran for 18 months. It featured a fully staged excerpt from a musical currently looking for production; a one hour in-depth interview with someone intimately involved in the theatre business (guests included Billy Goldenberg, Sammy Cahn, Danny Simon, and Al Kasha and Joel Hirschorn); a 15 minute staged excerpt from a play currently in production. "We developed *Broadway on Sunset* to help provide that first step. It presented excerpts from 48 shows of which 12 went into full production here in Los Angeles and beyond," recalls Lotman.

From her first musical *Kazoo*, to her current project entitled *Silverstar* and a planned future attempt to write both music and book for *Jerusalem*, Loretta Lotman continues polishing her craft, patiently waiting for her first break on Broadway. "If there's one thing I've learned," says Lotman, "it's that a musical is not written, it's rewritten."

FORT SALEM THEATRE, Box 10, Salem NY 12865. (518)854-9200. Producer: Quentin C. Beaver. Produces 6 plays (3 musicals)/year. Plays presented at Fort Salem Theatre, Salem NY—summer stock in Washington County area. Pays $100-250/performance. Query with synopsis. SASE. Reports in 1 month.
Musicals: Musicals should be "full-length, contemporary, entertaining (not heavy) and include comedy (most important) and good chorus numbers. Sets must be simple and cast should include no more than 4 principals, 10 secondary leads and 8 dancers." Does not want "historic, period, overly dramatic or absurd material. Should be family-oriented."
Recent Productions: *Exit Who*, by Fred Carmichael; and *My Husband, The Wife*, by Jack Sharkey.

SAMUEL FRENCH, INC., 45 W. 25th St., New York NY 10010. (212)206-8990. Editor: Lawrence R. Harbison. Play publisher. Publishes about 80 scripts (8 musicals)/year. Plays used by community, stock and dinner theaters, regional repertories, and college and high school markets. Pays 10% royalty on play scripts sold, generally an advance against future royalties, and a per-performance royalty depending on various factors. "We take 10-20% agency fee. Submit only the libretto (book). If we like it, we may ask to hear music." SASE. Reports in 8 weeks minimum. If the work has been recommended for further consideration, the process may take considerably longer.
Musicals: "We publish primarily New York-produced musicals, though we do occasionally bring out a show which has not had a New York City production. These are intended primarily, but not necessarily, for children's and community or dinner theaters. No religious material. We are particularly looking for small-cast, easy-to-produce musicals with good female roles. We are not interested in publishing big, splashy 'Broadway' musicals—unless they have been done on Broadway. Send us only the book of your musical. Musicals succeed or fail on the basis of their book, not their music. If we like the book, we may ask to hear a tape of the score."
Recent Publications: *The Rink*, book by Terrence McNally, lyrics by Fred Ebb, music by John Kander; *Dracula, The Musical?*, by Rick Abbot; and *The Human Comedy*, libretto by William Dumaresq; music by Galt MacDermott.
Tips: "Start small. Do a small-cast, easy-to-produce, inexpensive show. Then, once you have achieved a 'track record,' only then, try your Broadway musical. Never, ever, imitate what you think is 'commercial'—it never *will* be. Remember that musicals today are practically operas. In other words, they are mostly sung. Work with a director to develop concept.

*****GEORGE STREET PLAYHOUSE**, 9 Livingston Ave., New Brunswick NJ 08901. (201)846-2895. Literary Manager: Alexis Green. Associate Artistic Director: Maureen Heffernan. Produces 6-7 plays (1-2 musicals)/year. "We are a 360 seat thrust theater working under a LORT C-contract with a 4,000 subscriber base." Pays by royalty or outright purchase. "Each situation is handled individually." Query with synopsis, character breakdown and set description. SASE. Reports in 12 weeks.
Musicals: "We are interested in a variety of theme and formats. We aren't seeking to limit the things we read."
Recent Productions: *The Importance of Being Earnest*, by Oscar Wilde (comedy); *Night Mother*, by Marsha Norman (drama); and *A Little Night Music*, by Stephen Sondheim (musical).

GEORGIA COLLEGE THEATRE, Box 654, Milledgeville GA 31061. (914)453-5139. Director: John P. Blair Jr. Play producer. Produces 3-4 plays (1-2 musicals)/year. "Plays are presented in 1,100 capacity proscenium to small-town, provincial audience whom we are trying to educate." Pays 50% royalty. Submit complete manuscript and score. SASE. Reports in 1 month.
Musicals: "We like popular, crowd pleasing musicals. We have a fairly provincial audience that wants to be enterained. We cannot handle casts of more than 35 comfortably. Our space is limited with no fly or wing space to speak of."
Recently Produced: *My Fair Lady*; *HMS Pinafore*; and *Fantasticks*.

THE GOODMAN THEATRE, 200 S. Columbus Dr., Chicago IL 60603. Artistic Director: Gregory Mosher. Occasionally produces musicals. Submit synopsis (summary, production demands, cast size, style, etc.) with SASE for consideration. Send to the Office of the Literary Manager.

GREEN MOUNTAIN GUILD, White River Junction VT 05001. (802)295-7016. Managing Director: Marjorie O'Neill-Butler. Play producer. Produces 18 plays (8-10 musicals)/year. Produces plays for a summer theater audience in 2 locations in Vermont: White River Junction and Killington. Pays $75 minimum/performance. Query with synopsis. Send script and cassette with music. SASE. Reports in 1 month.
Musicals: "We are looking for musicals with a small cast, a good story line, well-developed characters, songs and music that come naturally out of the story and music that works with piano and drums only." No frivolous material. Prefers one-set shows.

Recent Productions: *Jenny Lind*, by David Harlay (an original play); *Sweeney Todd*, by Stephen Sondheim; *Student Prince*, by Sigmund Romberg; *Naughty Marietta*, by Victor Hubert; and *Hello Dolly*, by Jerry Harman.

*HONOLULU THEATRE FOR YOUTH, Box 3257, Honolulu HI 96801. (808)521-3487. Artistic Director: John Kauffman. Play producer. Produces 8 plays (1 musical)/year. "Our audences are young people from kindergarten through high school." Pays by royalty. Query with synopsis, character breakdown and set description, or submit complete manuscript and score. SASE. Reports in 12 weeks. **Musicals:** "We seek material that speaks to young people—fairy tales, history, literature, other cultures, science fiction. Maximum time is 90 minutes. Musical requirements must be simple. Cast size is generally 6-10."
Recent Productions: *The Code Breaker*, by Pauline C. Conley (science fiction); *Raven the.Hungry*, by Nick DiMartino (Pacific Northwest Coast Indian mythology); and *The Best Christmas Pagent Ever*, by Barbara Rubinson (Christmas comedy).

HOWARD UNIVERSITY, DEPARTMENT OF DRAMA, Washington DC 20059. (202)636-7050. Chairperson: Dr. Geoffrey Newman. Play producer. Produces 1 play/year. Pays $75-100/performance. Submit complete ms and cassette of songs. SASE. Reports in 4 months.
Recent Productions: *Black Images/Black Reflections*, by Kelsey Collie; *The Whiz* by Charlie Smalls, choreographed by Lewis Johnson; *Strike Heaven on the Face*, by Richard Wesley; and *Black Orpheus*, by Laverne Reed.

HUDSON GUILD THEATRE, 441 W. 26 St., New York NY 10001. (212)760-9810. Producing Director: David Kerry Heefner. Play producer. Produces 5 plays (1 musical)/year. "Plays are done at the Hudson Guild Theatre to very diverse audiences, ages 25-65." Pays $750 for a limited run. Submit complete manuscript and tape. SASE. Reports in about 2 months.
Musicals: "The only limitation is that material should *not* have been performed in New York before." Maximum cast size should be 20 people.
Recent Productions: *Hooters*, by Ted Tally; *Breakfast with Les and Bess* by Lee Kalcheim; *Blood Relations* by Sharon Pollock; *Vamps and Rideouts*, by Julie Styne and Phyllis Newman; *Wednesday*, by Julia Kearsley; *Getting Along Famously*, by Michael Jacobs; and *Brownstone*, by Josh Rubin Peterlarson and Andrew Cadiff.
Tips: "Don't imitate. Stretch the bounds of musical theatre."

*ILLINOIS THEATRE CENTER, 400A Lakewood, Park Forest IL 60466. (312)481-3510. Artistic Director: Steve S. Billig. Play producer and resident theatre. Produces 8 plays (3 musicals)/year. "We are a subscription theatre—equity during season, non-equity during summer." Pays by royalty or per performance. "These are negotiable and vary with publisher." Query with synopsis, character breakdown and set description; or submit complete manuscript, score and tape of songs. SASE. Reports in 2 weeks.
Musicals: Looking for "themes of family interest—humor preferable to drama—with small cast. No topical satire."
Recent Productions: *Charlotte Sweet*, by Michael Colby (Victorian melodrama (all music); *Joseph and the Amazing Technicolor Dreamcoat*, by Weber & Rice (rock musical); and *Most Happy Fella*, by Frank Loesser (dramatic musical).

INDIANA REPERTORY THEATRE, 140 W. Washington, Indianapolis IN 46204. (317)635-5277. Literary Manager: Janet Allen. Produces 10 full-length plays (2 full-length musicals, 10 cabarets)/year. Audiences are: "Mainstage—produce 1 musical/year; conservative, middle-class audience, accustomed to classics; Upperstage—produce 1 musical/year; more liberal, younger audience, will accept a certain amount of experimentation and new forms; Cabaret—a regular audience which expects a 90-minute, musical format, comic piece. A certain amount of irreverence is expected, satire is welcome." Pays 5-6% royalty. Query with synopsis. SASE. Reports in 2-3 months.
Musicals: "Our main forum for new musicals is our Cabaret Theatre. We rarely consider new musicals for either of our other 2 theatres. Our Cabaret Theatre runs all year, is a nightclub setting, and is set up for 90-minute performances, due to production schedule. Musicals can take the form of revue or plotted material, are often composer retrospective shows or modern comedy situations. All shows accompanied by piano only. Cast size cannot exceed 5 (4 is usual); *very* minimal staging (the stage is 8'x15'); simple props but no scenery except backdrop; costumes are emblematic—evening wear with added pieces is standard."
Recent Productions: (previously produced) Upperstage—*Pump Boys and Dinettes*, by Tommy Thompson et al; Mainstage—*South Pacific*, by Rodgers and Hammerstein; and *Tintypes*, by Mel Marvin (turn of the century nostalgia); (original) *Murder in the Capitol*, by Tom Haas (40's myster spoof); *Ho, Ho, Ho,*

The Christmas Show (plotless seasonal collection) and *Annette Saves The World* (60s beach spoof), both by Paul Moser.

INTAR, INTERNATIONAL ARTS RELATIONS, INC., Box 788, New York NY 10108. (212)695-6134. Artistic Director: Max Ferra. Play producer. Produces 3 plays (1 musical)/year. Plays are performed in New York City. Pays $1,000-1,500 outright purchase. Query, submit complete ms and score, and/or send resume. SASE. Reports in 1 month.
Musicals: "We are seeking material by Hispanics about Hispanics with a maximum cast of 10 and minimum 5 musicians." Length: 1-1½ hours.
Recent Productions: *Exiles* by Ana Maria Simo (woman exiled from Cuba); and *Sarita*, by Maria Irene Fornes; and *Savings*, by Dolores Prida (a New York city multi-ethnic neighborhood in the throes of gentrification).

LOS ANGELES (INNER CITY) CULTURAL CENTER, 1308 S. New Hampshire Ave., Los Angeles CA 90006. (213)387-1161. Executive Director: C. Bernard Jackson. Produces 6-8 plays (3 musicals)/year. A "multi-ethnic, multi-cultural arts organization." Pays 6% royalty. Query with synopsis. Does not return unsolicited material. Reports in 3 months.
Musicals: "Those with a point of view that lend themselves to utilizing people of all ethnic backgrounds."
Recent Productions: *Nifty Fifties*, book, music and lyrics by Dootsie Williams (unscrupulous record producers exploit novice songwriters); *Fight the Good Fight*, by "Chip" Fields (good and evil vie for the souls of the Los Angeles teenagers); and *Piano Bar*, by C. Bernard Jackson (Amazon legend in contemporary setting).

MANHATTAN THEATRE CLUB, 321 E. 73 St., New York NY 10021. (212)288-2500. Literary Manager: Jonathan Alper. Play producer. Produces 10 plays (1-2 musicals)/year. Plays are performed at the Manhattan Theatre Club before varied audiences. Pays negotiated fee. Send synopsis first *or* a letter of recommendation with the manuscript or "send a cassette of several of your songs." SASE. Reports in 6 months.
Musicals: Small cast, original work. "Small scale musicals—revue types are best because of theatre's limited space. *No* historical drama, verse drama or children's plays."
Recent Productions: *Real Life Funnies*, by Alan Menken and Howard Ashman (topical New York City); *Livin' Dolls*, by Scott Wittman and Marc Shaiman; *Ain't Misbehavin'*, by Fats Waller and Richard Maltby; *On the Swing Shift*, by Michael Dansicker and Sarah Schlesinger; and *New Tunes*, by Jonathon Sheffer and Alan Paul (revue).

MID-PLAINS COMMUNITY COLLEGE, State Farm Rd., North Platte NE 69101. (308)532-8980. Chairman, Humanities Division and Theater Director: Colin Taylor. Play producer. Produces 3 plays (1 musical)/year. Plays performed "at the college auditorium (small house) and on tour to area schools." Query with synopsis or submit complete manuscript and score. SASE. Reports in 1 month.
Musicals: Needs musicals, prefers to work with a small cast, "flexible staging a necessity. Beginning singers need consideration. We cannot fly scenery, but use free-standing sets and projections in a 'theatre of light.' We work with a limited budget and unlimited imagination."
Recent Productions: *Fiddler on the Roof*, (musical); *Paint Your Wagon*, (musical); *The Children's Hour*, (drama); and *Guys & Dolls* (musical).

*MUSICAL HORIZONS, (formerly Yellow Brick Promises), Suite 27, 17800 E. Colima Rd., Rowland Heights CA 91748. (818)912-0741. Creative Coordinators: Michael Ricciardi and David Holmes. Play producer and publisher. "We are also a writers' organization in the process of developing a creative repertory company." Publishes/produces 4 musicals/year. "We are a young organization of writers looking to expand. We have been producing our own work in equity-waiver type theatres and local high schools. Now we are looking for new writers (composers and librettists) to work with us. By offering our work as well as that of others, we can begin to be the creative 'umbrella' organization we desire to become. We are also looking for good tech people to create the costume, choreography, and lighting and sound guides we want to bring out with each show. We have a standard royalty schedule and at present work on 50/50 split. Arrangers are welcome and are paid outright if no profit participation expected. " Query with synopsis. Include tape of show's opening number, best ballad, and "11 o'clock song (a song like 'Everything's Coming Up Roses' from *Gypsy*)." SASE, but use a pre-printed reply form or postcard. Reports ASAP, synopsis with 3-song tape, usually within 1 month; complete manuscript with score, usually within 3 months. "We will be offering a catalog to schools and little theatres in October 85."
Musicals: "Any audience-pleasing, well-plotted show with a good story line—anything creative without being vulgar. We prefer musicals in two acts, but would like to see musical one-acts, thematically

related. Show ideas should be *universally* appealing; we don't want to see any unbelievable characters, stereotyped story lines or reworks of tired formulas. Be original. Work with a classic story in the public domain first to get your feet wet. Go from there to conceive new ideas. There *is* room in theater for original story lines. Also, keep it simple. Excessive sets, costumes, and scenery description don't make the show. Casts should be 5-21 people with good roles for both men and women. We look for musical biographies, fantasies and comedies and musical adventures like *Man of La Mancha*. We are all members of the Dramatists Guild of America and welcome other members. If you submit a complete ms it should be in standard script format with all lyrics printed or within the scripts. When we ask for a script from a synopsis and tape, be sure to include a character description, a list of scenes, a complete tape of all musical numbers you have available. Simple piano OK. A set sketch would be most helpful."
Recent Productions: *The Wizard of Oz* (original adaptation of classic story with new original score); *Skylark*, (a teenager growing up in Shakespeare's time); and *A Moment With Mister "C"*, (Christmas musical fantasy), all by Ricciardi, Ames and Clement.
Tips: "Don't ever give up. Develop your craft every single day. Keep writer's notebooks. We want to work with new writers and possibly bring them directly into our organization working with us in a collaborative association. Those who live in the California area might do well by writing us a letter about themselves, their skills, and their asprirations to write musicals."

NASHVILLE ACADEMY THEATRE, 724 2nd Ave. S., Nashville TN 37210. (615)254-9103. Director: Guy Keeton. Play producer. Produces 4 plays (1 musical)/year. Plays are performed in a 696-seat theater for audiences ranging in age from kindergarten through high school. Pays $20-40/performance. Submit complete ms and score. SASE. Reports "after play-reading committee is through."
Musicals: "We want wholesome entertainment for various age groups, e.g. *Cinderella* for the very young, *Tom Sawyer* for teens and pre-teens and *Man of La Mancha* for high schoolers. Average cast size is 15. We do not want to see any poorly written, sensational or pornographic materials."
Recent Productions: *Rumpelstilskin*, by Keeton, Giles and Wheaton (fairy tale); *The Mikado*, by Gilbert and Sullivan (comic opera); and *Rapunzel*, by Keeton and Wheaton (fairy tale).
Tips: "For children's theatre, the music must be lively, short and help develop the plot."

NEGRO ENSEMBLE COMPANY, Suite 800, 165 W. 46th St., New York NY 10036. (212)575-5860. Artistic Director: Douglas Turner Ward. Play producer. Produces 4 plays/year. Pays by percentage of box office take. Submit complete manuscript and score. SASE. Returns material "only if writer insists, otherwise, play is kept on file."
Musicals: "Submit only plays that deal with black life and the black experience."
Recent Production: *A Soldier's Play*, by Charles Fuller.

*NEW YORK SHAKESPEARE FESTIVAL, 425 Lafayette St., New York NY 10003. (212)598-7100. Contact: Play/Musical Department. Play producer. Produces 12 plays (approximately 2 musicals)/year. Plays performed in New York City in any of six theaters, including the Delcorte Theatre in Central Park. Query with synopsis, character breakdown and set description. SASE. Reports in 12 weeks.
Musicals: "High quality musicals are important. We would like to see more current contemporary isues addressed and would like to hear more contemporary sounding music used. If interested, we will require a 'demo' quality cassette of score." No staging limitations "but financing a production is a consideration."
Recent Productions: *La Boheme*, by Puccini (with Linda Ronstadt); *The Human Comedy*, by Galt MacDermot (William Saroyan novel); and *A Chorus Line*, by Michael Bennett, et al. (dancers).
Tips: "We are not looking for 'songs'—we want musicals with strong books. New forms for opera and musicals are welcome."

THE NICOLET PLAYERS, Nicolet College, Box 518. Rhinelander WI 54501. (715)369-4476. Play producer. Produces 6 plays (2 musicals)/year. "Nicolet College is a small community college of about 1,000 students, in a town of about 10,000 people." Pays $25-125/performance. Query with synopsis and tape, if possible. SASE. Reports in 1 week.
Musicals: "We consider musicals that are interesting and theatrical. We have a small stage, a ³/₄ thrust, which is approximately 25-feet in diameter and limited backstage area. No fly space, just a ceiling 12 feet above the stage. Keep it small and simple."
Recent Productions: *I Do! I Do!*, by Schmidt and Jones; *Pirates of Penzance*, by Gilbert and Sullivan; *Company*, by Stephen Sondheim and *The Mikado*, by Gilbert & Sullivan.

NORTH CAROLINA CENTRAL UNIVERSITY, DEPARTMENT OF DRAMATIC ART, Box 19593, Durham NC 27707. (919)683-6242. Chairperson: Linda Kerr Norflett, Ph.D. Play producer. Produces 4 plays (1-2 musicals)/year. "North Carolina Central University is a traditionally black university but the theater program is racially mixed. We put great emphasis on producing new works by black playwrights as well as other minorities. Pays by royalty. Query with synopsis or submit tape of songs with or without manuscript and score. SASE. Reports in 2 weeks.

Musicals: "We are looking for plays that are preferably non-racial or racial with clean humanistic themes, music and dance compilations (revue styles), musical dramas, and experimental performance pieces. Be as creative and experimental as your talent will allow and don't underestimate the power of metaphor. Keep staging simple, props at a minimum and cast size below 20." Does not want culturally limiting material.

Recent Productions: *Don't Bother Me, I Can't Cope*, by Micki Grant (race relations); *Guys and Dolls*; *Purlie* (race relations); *Deadwood Dick, The Legend of the West*; *Black Nativity*; *Death and the King's Horseman* (Nigerian); *Resurrection of Lady Lester*, by Oyamo; and *Vanities*.

*NORTHLIGHT THEATRE, 2300 Green Bay Rd., Evanston IL 60201. (312)869-7732. Assistant Artistic Director: Jimmy Bickerstaff. Play producer. Produces 5 plays (2 musicals)/year. Audience is age 35-45 average; upper mid-class, ²/₃ suburban; most college or post-grad educated. Pay negotiable, "depending on circumstances." Query with synopsis, character breakdown and set description. SASE. Reports in 4 weeks.

Musicals: "Musicals/adaptations are generally developed in-house through collaboration of artists. Musicals here are small cast (fewer than 10) with minimum scenic and orchestral requirements. We do not want material lacking thematic substance. It must have depth and sophisticated level of artistic craftsmanship."

Recent Productions: *Teibele & Her Demon*, by Isaac B. Singer & Eve Friedman (adaptation of Singer short story); *Quartermaine's Terms*, by Simon Gray (midwest premier of off-Broadway hit about British school for foreigners); and *City on the Make*, by Jeff Berkson, Denise De Clue, John Karrakin (original musical based on works of Nelson Algren—developed in-house).

OFF CENTER THEATRE, 436 W. 18th, New York NY 10011. (212)929-8299. Producer: Abigail Rosen. Play producer. Produces 6 plays (2 musicals)/year. The plays are performed "off-Broadway." Pays percentage of box office receipts after initial expenses have been recouped. Submit complete ms, score and type of songs. SASE. Reports in 1 month.

Musicals: Issue oriented, small cast.

Recent Productions: *Just for Fun—The Music of Jerome Kern* (revue); *Biting the Apple*, by Tony McGrath and Stanley Sirdman (revue); and *Hello, This Is Barbara, I'm Not in Right Now . . .*, by Barbara Schottenfeld (singles in New York City).

*OLD GLOBE THEATRE, Box 2171, San Diego CA 92112. (619)231-1941. Associate Director: Robert Berlinger. Play producer. Produces 12 plays/year of which a varying number are musicals. "This is a regional theatre with three spaces: 500 seat proscenium, 225 seat arena, and large outdoor festival stage. We serve an audience base of over 225,000." Query with synopsis, character breakdown and set description. Does not return unsolicited material. Reports in 12-16 weeks.

Musicals: "We look for skill first, subject matter second. No prescribed limitations though the playwright should be aware of the fiscal realities of producing musicals and should not be unrealistic. No unsolicited work."

Recent Productions: *Of Mice and Men*, by John Steinbeck; *Kiss Me Kate*; and *Othello*.

Tips: "Craft comes first."

*ONE ACT THEATRE COMPANY OF SAN FRANCISCO, 430 Mason St., San Francisco CA 94102. (415)421-5355. Artistic Director: Simon L. Levy. Play producer. Produces 16 plays (1 musical)/year. "Venue is a 99-seat, Equity-waiver theatre in downtown San Francisco. 60% of audience are subscribers—wide demographics." Pays negotiable royalty or per performance. Query with synopsis, character breakdown and set description. SASE. Reports in 16 weeks.

Musicals: No "revues or children's musicals."

Recent Productions: *Statements After*, by Athol Fugard (apartheid); *Taco Jesus*, by Michael Lynch ("4 square gospel"); and *Nice People Dancing*, by Lee Blessing ("Texas" comedy).

*PAPER MILL PLAYHOUSE, Brookside Dr., Milburn NJ 07044. (201)379-3636. Dramaturg: Jeffrey Solis. Play producer. Produces 6 plays (4 musicals)/year. "Audience based on 32,000 subscribers; plays performed in 1192-seat proscenium theatre." Pays by royalty or will option play under Dramatist Guild. Query with synopsis, character breakdown, set description and tape of songs; or submit complete manuscript and tape of songs through agent only. SASE. Reports in 8 weeks.

Musicals: Seeking "traditional Broadway sized musicals—either original or adaptations. One act plays are not considered. Developing works can be submitted to our musical workshop series." A synopsis of book plus tape of songs should be submitted first. Scores not necessary. Letter of introduction should accompany each submitted synopsis. No cast size limitations—minimum of 5 characters usually to maximum size of 40-45." No nudity, profanity, etc.

Recent Productions: *Guys & Dolls*, by Loesser/Burrows; *Side by Side by Sondheim*, by Stephen Sondheim; and *Desert Song*, by Romberg/Hartack/Hammerstein.

Tips: "Works not yet ready for full production on main stage may be considered for playreading and musical workshop series."

JOSEPH PAPP, New York Shakespeare Festival/Public Theater, 425 Lafayette St., New York NY 10003. (212)598-7130. Plays and Musicals Dept. Director: Gail Merrifield Papp. Producing theater organization. Produces approximately 15 plays (2 musicals)/year. "Productions are at the Public Theater; a three-story complex of six theaters, ranging in size from 100 to 300 seats: Anspacher (where *Hair* premiered), Newman (where *A Chorus Line* premiered), Shiva Theater, Martinson Hall (where *Runaways* premiered), and LuEsther Hall. There is also The Delacorte, a 2,300 seat amphitheater in Central Park where both *Pirates of Penzance* and *Two Gentlemen of Verona* began before moving to Broadway. NYSF produces in both nonprofit and commercial sectors. Royalty payments are related to existing agreements in the theatrical field." Submit complete ms including lyrics and cassette of music. SASE. Reports in 2 months.

Musicals: "Interested in good stories expertly written and in the sound of good, contemporary popular music. No restriction as to subject matter, how a story is told or styles of music. Dance music integrated into the work is encouraged. We require a completed text, lyrics and music. The music does not have to be scored, but must be submitted on cassette. Size of cast and band should be within reasonable limits. Not interested in standard Broadway music."

Recent Productions: Puccini's *La Boheme* new English version by David Spencer, new orchestrations by Michael Starobin (with Linda Rondstadt); *The Mystery of Edwin Drood* book, lyrics and music by Rupert Holmes; based on the unfinished novel by Charles Dickens; and *I'm Getting My Act Together and Taking It on the Road*," with book and lyrics by Gretchen Cryer and music by Nancy Ford.

PENNSYLVANIA STAGE COMPANY, 837 Linden St., Allentown PA 18101. (215)434-6110. Associate Director/Literary Manager: Pam Pepper. Play producer. Produces 7 plays (1 musical)/year. "We are a LORT C theatre with a subscriber base of approximately 6,000 people. Plays are performed at the Pennsylvania Stage Company in the J.I. Rodale Theatre." Pays "fee for right to produce and 1% of future earnings." Query with synopsis, character breakdown and set description. SASE, as well as a tape of the music. Reports in 6-8 weeks.

Musicals: "We are interested in full-length musicals which reflect the social, historical and political fabric of America. We have no special requirements for format, structure or musical involvement. We ask that once submission of a musical has been requested, that it be bound, legibly typed and include SASE. Cast limit of 18, but we prefer cast limit of 12. One set or unit set. Ours is a 274 seat house, there is no fly area and a 23-foot prescenium opening. Please do not send script first."

Recent Productions: *Just So*, by Mark St. Germain (based on Rudyard Kipling's *Justso Stories*); *Shim Sham*, by Johnny Brandon and Eric Blau (Buddy Bradley, an American tap and jazz choreographer); *Feathertop*, by Bruce Peyton and Skip Kennon (Nathaniel Hawthorne short story); *Song of Myself*, by Gayle Stahlhuth, Gregory Hurst and Arthur Harris.

Tips: "Consider the importance of what the musical is to say. Book and lyrics should have equal weight—lyrics should further the plot rather than arrest it."

PERFORMANCE PUBLISHING CO., Baker's Plays, 100 Chauncy St., Boston MA 02111. (617)432-1280. Editor: John B. Welch. Play publisher. Publishes 18-28 plays (6-10 musicals)/year. Plays are used by children's theaters, junior and senior high schools, colleges and community theaters. Pays standard nonprofessional royalty/performance. Submit complete ms, score and cassette tape of songs. SASE. Reports in 3 months.

Musicals: "We prefer large cast, contemporary musicals which are easy to stage and produce. We like children's musicals if the accompaniment is fairly simple. Plot your shows strongly, keep your scenery and staging simple, your musical numbers and choreography easily explained and blocked out. Originality and style are up to the author. We want innovative and tuneful shows but no X-rated material. We are very interested in the new writer and believe that, with revision and editorial help, he can achieve success in writing original musicals for the non-professional market."

Recent Publications: *Great All American Backstage Musical*, by Tim Kelly and Jack Sharkey (spoof of Hollywood); *Cat in the Castle*, by Bill Solly (children's fantasy); and *O Happy Day*, by Jane Staab and Susan Kusoff (Christmas musical).

Tips: "Think about audience support and craft your work for that audience interest."

PLAYWRIGHTS' PLATFORM, INC., 43 Charles St., Boston MA 02114. (617)720-3770. President: Patrick Flynn. Literary Manager: Robert Kinderic. Developmental theater for new plays by New

England playwrights only. "New project for musicals in planning. Sophisticated general audience from Greater Boston area. Some presentations (staged readings) at the Charles Playhouse and at the Lyric Stage." Pays average $20/reading; "nothing for workshops." Submit complete ms, score and cassette tape of songs. SASE. Reports in 60-90 days.

Musicals: "No artistic mandate. Experimental forms and unique perspective encouraged. No current programs specifically for musical development. What is in planning will not emphasize choreographic values, but, instead, collaboration between playwright, and lyricist. Applicants must reside in New England."

ROUND HOUSE THEATRE, 12210 Bushey Dr., Silver Spring MD 20902. (301)468-4233. Production Office Manager: Betty Clark. Produces 6 plays (1 musical)/year. "Audience subscriber base is between 35-60 years." Payment by "individual contract with each playwright." Submit complete ms, score and cassette tape of songs. "Include SAS postcard for acknowledgement and SASE for script return." Reports in approximately 1 year.

Musicals: Plays should be "well-written, single unit set, maximum of 20 cast members. Almost any topic, if well-written. Send bound copy of script, typed with score included within binding if possible. Must include cassette of all original music, in order as included in script. Uses minimum size orchestra (no more than 6, $^3/_4$ thrust stage with no fly space and minimum wing space). We produce traditional as well as original, from standards like *Man of La Mancha* to off-beat contemporary like *In Circles*.

Recent Productions: *In Circles* , by Gertrude Stein/Al Carmines; and *The Threepenny Opera*, by Brecht/Weil.

*THE SECOND STAGE, Box 1807, Ansonia Station, New York NY 10023. (212)787-8302. Dramaturg: Mr. Kim Powers. Play producer. Produces 4-5 plays/year (0-1 musicals)/year. Produces plays for sophisticated, intelligent, young (30's-40's) audience in open proscenium space—138 seats. Pays fee. Submit complete manuscript, score and tape of songs. SASE. Reports in 4-5 months.

Musicals: Seeking musicals of "any kind—contemporary, adventuresome" for cast of 12 ("roughly the limit"). Limited backstage/fly space.

Recent Productions: *Short Eyes*, by Miquel Pinero (prison drama); *Serenading Louie*, by Lanford Wilson (serious domestic play); and *Painting Churches*, by Tina Howe (family comedy-drama).

SHOWBOAT MAJESTIC, Foot of Broadway, Cincinnati OH 45202. (513)241-6550. Producing Director: Suellen Childs. Play producer. Produces 5 plays (3 musicals)/year. Plays are produced on the Showboat Majestic, the last of the original floating theaters located on the Ohio River. Pays $150/performance. "Most musicals are rented through New York. We follow regular royalty rental plan from them." Query. SASE. Reports in 1 month.

Musicals: "We are seeking original songs, musical comedies no longer than two hours with an intermission, revues and small cast shows." No avant-garde or experimental scripts. Cast should be less than 10.

Recent Productions: *The Fantasticks*, by Schmidt and Jones; *Gold Dust*, by Wann; *I Do! I Do!*, by Schmidt and Jones; *Show Me Where the Good Times Are*; and *Da* (Broadway); and *A Funny Thing Happened on the Way to the Forum*.

Tips: "Begin with an acknowledged good story line. Find a play in the public domain that could be turned into a musical."

*SOCIETY HILL PLAYHOUSE, 507 S. 8th St., Philadelphia PA 19147. (215)923-0210. Director of Script Development: Walt Vail. Play producer. Produces 5 plays (1 musical)/year. Plays are performed in a 250-seat auditorium. Pay negotiable "depends on piece." Query with synopsis, character breakdown and set description. SASE. Reporting time varies.

Musicals: Desires contemporary, off-beat musicals. Small cast (6-12) preferred. No historical material.

Recent Productions: *The Good Woman of Setzuan*, by Bertolt Brecht; *The Blacks*, by Jean Genet; and *Ulysses in Nighttown*, by James Joyce.

*SOHO REPERTORY THEATRE, 80 Varick St., New York City NY 10013. (212)925-2588. Artistic Director: Jerry Engelbach. Play producer. Produces 6 plays (1 musical)/year. Plays performed in off-off-broadway, AEA Tier 4 code, 100-seat thrust-stage theatre with high ceilings. Pays negotiable fee for initial run, or royalty for extended run. Query "with description (no synopsis) of the play and how it will work as a theatre piece." Does not return unsolicited material. Reports in 2 weeks on queries; 90 days on submitted material.

Musicals: "The music must be *excellent*, the script literate, the piece as a whole conductive to inventive, 3-dimensional staging. Looking for "adult mentality, sophisticated wit, situations of interest to grown-up people, i.e., emphatically non-broadway oriented with maximum cast size of 12. Orchestration is limited by budget to 2-5 pieces, e.g., our successful musical *Mandrake* used piano and harp."

Recent Productions: *The Crimes of Vautrin*, by Nicholas Wright, After Balzac (the irony of society); *Mandrake*, music by Anthony Bowles, book by Michael Alfreds (satire on political and sexual mores); and *Energumen*, by Mac Wellman (spy spoof/dark comedy).

SOUTHERN CONNECTICUT STATE UNIVERSITY, DEPARTMENT OF THEATRE, New Haven CT 06515. (203)397-4431. Chairman: Sigurd A. Jensen. Play producer. Produces 4-6 plays (1-2 musicals)/year. Plays performed to general audiences and college students. Pays $25/performance or standard royalty. Submit cassette and/or manuscript. SASE. Reports ASAP—"depends on time of year."
Musicals: "We are interested in any musicals as long as they are not religious or polemical in a narrow sense." Should require small cast, props, staging, etc. Does not want "big, old-fashioned musicals."
Recently Produced: *Guys & Dolls*, by Dr. Cashman; and *Anything Goes*.

*STAGE ONE, 721 W. Main St., Louisville KY 40202. (502)589-5946. Associate Artistic Director: Curt L. Tofteland. Play producer. Produces 6 plays (1-3 musicals)/year. Plays are performed for school and family audience in 626-seat thrust style theatre. Pays 5% royalty; $25-75/performance, or by commission. Submit complete manuscript score and the tape of songs. SASE. Reports in 12 weeks.
Musicals: "We want classic children's tales in honest adaptations, or stories of interest to kids,. Length: 60-120 minutes, one or two act. Preferred cast size—12 or under." No "camp or fractured fairy-tales."
Recent Productions: *Glass Christmas Tree*, by Wheeler/Cornett (child labor in 1908); *Tom Sawyer*, by Markham, Leiton, Stockton (Twain novel); and *Pinocchio*, by Mason (collected tales).

SUSQUEHANNA UNIVERSITY THEATRE, Susquehanna University, Selinsgrove PA 17870. (717)374-9700. Producer: Larry D. Augustine. Play producer. Produces 12-15 plays (1 musical)/year. Plays are produced in 1,500-seat auditorium and in a 160-seat theater to a general audience of high school students through senior citizens. Pays royalty. Query with synopsis. SASE. Reports in 3 weeks.
Recent Productions: *Mame*, by Jerry Herman; *Company*, by Sondheim and Forth; and *Fiddler On the Roof*, by Stein/Bock/Harnick.

THEATER FOR THE NEW CITY, 162 2nd Ave., New York NY 10003. (212)254-1109. Director: George Bartenieff. Play producer. Produces 40-50 plays (6 musicals)/year. Plays are performed for a mixed audience. "Some writers are commissioned; others share the box office take with actors." Submit complete manuscript with lyrics. SASE. Reports in 12-18 months.
Musicals: No limitations on cast size, props, staging, etc. "No children's plays with bunny rabbit feel."
Recent Productions: *The Conduct of Life*, by Maria Irene Fornes; *Hamletmachine*, by Heiner Mueller; and *The Age of Invention*, by Theodora Skipitares.

THEATRE FOR YOUNG AMERICA, 7204 W. 80th St., Overland Park KS 66204. (913)648-6400. Artistic Director: Gene Mackey. Play producer. Produces 8 plays (2-3 musicals)/year. For children, preschool to high school. Pays $10-25/performance. Query with synopsis. SASE. Reports in 1 month.
Musicals: 1-1¹/₂ hour productions with small cast oriented to children and high-school youths. "A clear, strong, compelling story is important; a well known title is very important."
Recent Productions: *Androcles and the Lion*, by Aurand Harris and Glen Mack (music); *The Tale of Peter Rabbit*, by Rita Lovett and Gene Mackey (adapted from Beatrix Potter's *Peter Rabbit*); *The Hare and the Tortoise*, by Cheryl O'Brien and Gene Mackey (adapted from Aesop's fable); *Tom Sawyer*, by Michael Dansicker and Sarah Marie Schlesinger (adapted from Mark Twain's novel); *Little Red Riding Hood*; and *Chicken Little*, by Gene Mackey.

*THEATREWORKS/USA, 131 W. 86 St., New York NY 10024. (212)595-7500. Assistant to the Artistic Director: Laurie M. Levy. Play producer. Produces 2-4 musicals/year (all musicals). "We play for young and family audiences in schools, community centers and theatres. Also, the Promenade Theatre in New York City." Pays 6% royalty "for writers, to be divided if more than one. Submit manuscript or outline and tape of songs." SASE. Reports in 8-16 weeks.
Musicals: Seeking all types of musicals for young and family audiences including fairytales, historical, fantasy, adaptations of classics and contemporary works—issue-oriented. Our shows are one hour in length. Cast size limited to 6 or less. Shows tour; therefore all scenery, props, and costumes must be portable by van." No opera.
Recent Productions: *Rapunzel*, by David Crane, Marta Kauffman, and Michael Skloff (musical version of fairytale); *When the Cookie Crumbles*, (musical revue on subject of divorce); and *Play to Win*, by James De Jongh, Carles Cleveland and Jimi Foster (musical biography of Jackie Robinson).

UNIVERSITY OF MAINE AT FORT KENT, Pleasant St., Fort Kent ME 04743. (207)834-3162. Director of Performing Art: Charles Closser. Play producer. Produces 5 plays (1 musical)/year. Plays are produced in a university theater to university and community audience. Pays $300 maximum for royalty or $100 maximum/performance. Query with synopsis. SASE. Reports in 1 month.

Musicals: "We are looking for musicals of 2 hours for general audience family theater. No strong language, nudity or shows with more than six sets."

Recent Productions: *Anything Goes*, by Cole Porter (musical comedy); *Applause*; *I Do! I Do!*; and *Little Mary Sunshine*, by Rich Besoyan.

CEDRIC VENDYBACK, Brandon University, Brandon, Manitoba R7A 6A9 Canada. (204)727-9662. Professor: C. Vendyback. Play producer. Produces 2-6 plays/year. Rarely produces musicals. Audience is urban and rural, middle-class, faculty and students. Pays $25-75/performance. Query with synopsis. SAE and IRC. Reports in 1 month.

Musicals: Prefers "one- to three-act; social comment, smallish cast. We also like simple props and staging. Nothing lavish, possibly revue style."

Recent Productions: *The Crucible*, by Miller (social conscience); *The Love of Four Colonels*, by Ustinov (good vs. evil); and *The Pirates of Penzance*, by Gilbert & Sullivan.

Tips: "Study Rodgers and Hart for good melody and witty lyrics. Also study *The Music Man*, *Pal Joey*, *Guys and Dolls*, etc. Eschew *bleak* melodies and lyrics of recent times. Audiences are pining for and in need of warmth and quality."

WABASH COLLEGE THEATER, Wabash College, Crawfordsville IN 47933. (317)362-0677. Chairman/Theater Department: James Fisher. Play producer. Produces 4 plays (1 musical)/year. "Musicals are produced occasionally as schedule and personnel permit. Audience is small college town and the male student body of the college. We have two theaters: a 370-seat intimate proscenium with lift for stage; and a black box, seating up to 150. Looking for plays with moderate size cast with more male than female roles." Pays standard royalty. Query with synopsis or submit complete ms and score. SASE. Reports as soon as possible.

Musicals: Any type. Plays require mostly male characters with small- to medium-size orchestra and up to 25-30 in cast.

Recent Productions: *Guys and Dolls*; *Cabaret*; *Fantasticks*; *Canterbury Tales*; *The Crimson Bird*, by Strawn and Enenbach (medieval French nightingale legend); and *S.H. Ades*, by Seward (ghosts and aspiring showbiz hopeful).

WALDO ASTORIA PLAYHOUSE, 7428 Washington, Kansas City MO 64134. Producer: Richard Carothers. Play producer. Produces 12 plays (1 musical)/year. For general audience. Pays negotiable royalty. Submit complete ms. SASE. Reports in 1 month.

Musicals: Wants musical comedy. "No special format, just appeal to public taste. Three acts, 40-40-40 maximum, rated G. Do not exceed 15 in cast with minimal orchestra; we have a relatively small stage. Not interested in burlesque."

Recent Productions: *The Owl and the Pussycat*; *Hello Dolly*; *Charlie's Aunt*; and *The Unsinkable Molly Brown*.

Tips: "Don't over write. Don't become too attached to any particular song. Be open minded in working with the director and producers."

*****WALNUT STREET THEATRE COMPANY**, 9th & Walnut Sts., Philadelphia PA 19107. (215)574-3550. Contact: Literary Manager. Play producer. Produces 5 plays (1 musical)/year. Plays produced on a mainstage with seating for 1,052 to a family audience. Pays 8-9% royalty. Query with synopsis, character breakdown and set description. SASE. Reports in 20 weeks.

Musicals: "We are looking for musicals that can be performed to a family audience at Christmas time. We would like to remain open on structure and subject matter and would expect a tape with the script. Cast size: around 30 equity members; prefers one set with variations. No gratuitous violence, nudity or obscene language."

Recent Productions: *Music Man*, by Meredith Willson; and *Oliver*, by Lionel Bart.

Tips: Send a well produced demo tape."

WATERLOO COMMUNITY PLAYHOUSE, Box 433, Waterloo IA 50704. (319)235-0367. Managing Director: Charles Stilwill. Play producer. Produces 12 plays (1-5 musicals)/year. "Our audience prefers solid, wholesome entertainment, nothing risque or with strong language. We perform in Hope Martin Theatre, a 368-seat house." Pays $25-150/performance. Submit complete ms, score and tape of songs on cassette. SASE.

Musicals: "Casts may vary from as few as 6 people to 54. We are producing children's theater as well. We're especially interested in new adaptations of classic children stories."

Recent Productions: *The Hobbit*, *Godspell*, *Christmas on Angel Street*, *Annie*, *The Sound of Music*, and *Magic Theatre*.

*WHOLE THEATRE, INC., 544 Bloomfield Ave., Montclair NJ 07042. (201)744-2996. Associate Artistic Director: Apollo Dukakis. Play producer. Produces 5 plays/year. Payment varies. Query first. SASE. Reports in 10 weeks.

Musicals: Looking for "musicals in which you care about the characters—otherwise no restrictions as to theme or style. Send just a brief plot and theme description plus number in cast, sets, etc., and any other technical considerations. Must be small cast (3-6) with one set or unit set."

Recent Productions: *Of Mice & Men*, by John Steinbeck; *Absurd Person Singular*, by Alan Azckbaum (comedy of class); and *Sorrows of Frederick*, by Romulus Lenneg (Frederick the Great).

*WILMA THEATER, 2030 Sansom St., Philadelphia PA 19103. (215)963-0249. Artistic Director: Jiri Zizka. Play producer. Produces 4-5 plays (1-2 musicals)/year. Audience is sophisticated, adventurous, off-beat and demanding. Space is 100-seat theater. Pays $30/performance or will negotiate. Submit complete manuscript and score or submit complete manuscript, score and tape of songs. SASE. Reports in 6-10 weeks.

Musicals: Seeks "innovative, staging, universal issues, political implications and inventive, witty approach to subject." Emphasizes ensemble style—group choreography, actors and musicians overlapping, with new approach to staging and style. Do not exceed 4 musicians, cast: under 12, (ideally under 8), stage space: 30x20." No "kitchen musicals."

Recent Productions: *Happy End*, by Brecht & Weill (social change); *Hairy Ape*, by O'Neil (self-identity); and *The Insect Comedy*, (human weakensses).

Services & Opportunities

Contests and Awards

Songwriter or musician competitions can be pleasant and sometimes lucrative endeavors. What's more, participation in contests is a good way to expose your work and your talents. Some contests—the American Song Festival and Music City Song Festival, for instance—are judged by music publishers and other industry officials, guaranteeing a professional hearing for your material. Contacts, and sometimes contracts, result from a good showing in a major competition.

Contests may not seem to be a good "market" in the usual sense, yet you are selling yourself and your work. Thus, marketing techniques shouldn't be forgotten. Each contest you enter, for example, should be studied so that you can slant your material to the award you seek.

Contests listed here encompass all types of music and all levels of composition expertise. Most of these contests are annual. Read each listing carefully and write a letter to any that interest you, asking that you be put on the list to receive information about upcoming competitions.

AMERICAN SONG FESTIVAL, (formerly Songsearch Contest), Box 57, Hollywood CA 90028. (213)463-7178. ASF Director: Steven Fisher. Presented by The National Academy of Songwriters. Formerly conducted by Sterling Recreation Organization. Deadline: Feb. 1, 1986. Open to everyone. Nominal entry fee. For more information, send a self-addressed stamped envelope marked "American Song Festival Info Request."

Purpose: To draw national attention to the emergence of new music in our culture, and to give new songwriters the opportunity to have their work evaluated by professionals and presented to the industry and the general public as the best of America's new songs.

Requirements: "A song is defined as being words and music. Any new song is eligible if a recorded version has not been released for sale to the public before the winners are notified."

Categories: "There is both a song and a lyric competition. Song competition categories include: rock/new wave (rock-and-roll, country rock to heavy metal to the most urban new wave songs); gospel/inspirational (songs of a religious or spiritual nature); pop/adult contemporary (pop songs with a softer sound that might appeal to an older audience; includes crossover type songs that might be performed by Anne Murray, Kenny Rogers, Lionel Richie, Dan Fogelberg and Little River Band); country/folk (songs in the style of Johnny Cash, Tammy Wynette, Waylon Jennings, Dolly Parton, Oak Ridge Boys and the like, as well as folk songs, bluegrass songs and songs on traditional instruments such as autoharps, zithers and dulcimers); black-oriented (songs with funky rhythms and/or black dialect in the styles of Kool & The Gang, Shalamar and some Doobie Brothers; also includes blues and reggae, as well as songs in a jazz vocal style). Please refer to these descriptions, as any song may be entered in more than one category."

Awards: To be established.

Close-Up

Steven Fisher
ASF Contest Director
Los Angeles, California

One of the best ways inexperienced, unpublished songwriters can gauge the quality of their work is to enter a songwriting contest. Very often the opportunity to have work critiqued by music business professionals can provide the inspiration or direction needed to turn "just another song" into a hit record.

The largest and most well known of these contests is The American Song Festival. The ASF was started in 1973 under the sponsorship of the Sterling Recreation Organization and run by that organization until they turned it over to The National Academy of Songwriters (NAS) in 1984. Steven Fisher, NAS Research Director, is the 1986 contest director.

Although there are no major rule changes from previous years, Fisher says the 1986 contest will differ in one important way—professionals and amateurs will compete together. "I think that if you want to compete in the music business you need to begin as soon as possible. Making amateurs compete separately from professionals isn't really doing them any justice. There are amateurs that are every bit as good as professionals."

The ASF competition is a "great vehicle for getting your material heard, especially by the very top people in the industry," says Fisher. "ASF has always been strongly supported by the music business. The opportunity just to be heard and possibly win a contest like this can do amazing things for a writer's career."

The contest will feature both a song and a lyric competition. Song competition categories include Rock/Pop, Country/Folk, R&B/Soul, Gospel/Inspirational and Adult Contemporary/Easy Listening. More than one song can be entered but each must be on a separate tape. The lyric competition has similar categories.

In addition to the valuable exposure you and your song will receive, entrants will also be vying for a number of valuable prizes, including cash, musical instruments and possibly even a publishing contract.

As for any tips he might have for entrants, Fisher cautions writers to "follow instructions in the contest pamphlet *to the letter*, making sure all materials are labeled with name, address, phone number and title of the work. Send the best recording you can. Your tape does not have to be studio produced but music and lyrics should be clear and free of extraneous noise."

Even though national contests like ASF muster vigorous competition, ASF expects between 25,000 and 40,000 entrants this year, sometimes even the losers can come out winners—being picked up by a publisher, producer or A&R person involved in the judging as judges can request name and address of an entrant for later contact if desired. "That's one of the advantages of entering your songs or lyrics in a contest like ASF," says Fisher.

See the ASF listing in this section for deadline dates and more information. For an entry form and additional information send a self-addressed, stamped-envelope to ASF Information Request, Box 57, Hollywood, California 90028.

ASCAP FOUNDATION GRANTS TO YOUNG COMPOSERS, ASCAP Bldg., 1 Lincoln Plaza, New York NY 10023. (212)595-3050. Director of Grants: Margaret Jory. For composers. Purpose: to provide grants to young composers to help them pursue their studies in music composition and develop their skills or talents.

Requirements: "Applicants must be citizens or permanent residents of the US who have not reached their 30th birthday by January 15. Applicants must submit professional recommendations; complete an application listing prior education, experience and background in the field of music; and submit 1 example of their composition. Music of any style or category will be considered. Submissions must be original works and not previously published or winners of previous competitions or grants." Deadline: variable. Send for application; samples required. "Submit copies only. Score reproductions and/or manuscripts may be submitted on regular music paper or reproduced by an accepted reproduction process. Cassette tapes will be accepted also."

Awards: ASCAP Foundation awards grants of $500-2,500. Length: 1 year. Applications judged by screening-panel of musical authorities.

BMI AWARDS TO STUDENT COMPOSERS, 320 W. 57th St., New York NY 10019. (212)586-2000. Director: James G. Roy Jr. For composers of "serious concert music." Annual. Purpose: "to pick outstanding young (25 or under) composers and make cash awards for furthering their musical education."

Requirements: Applicants must not have reached their 26th birthday by Dec. 31 of the year preceding the Feb. 15th contest deadline. "Serious concert music is preferred to popular songs, but all music is considered. All geographic locations of the world, but applicant must be a citizen or permanent resident of the western hemisphere enrolled in an accredited public, private or parochial secondary school, in an accredited college or conservatory of music, or engaged in private study with recognized music teachers." Deadline: Feb. 15. One entry per student. Send for free application and rules. Rights retained. Entries returned, include SASE.

Awards: BMI Awards to Student Composers: "prizes totaling $15,000 ranging from $500 to $2,500 may be given to winning students, by check, with certificate of honor." Contest judged by "outstanding composers, music publishers and musicologists."

COMPOSERS GUILD, 2333 Olympus Dr., Salt Lake City UT 84124. (801)278-1745. President: Sharon Nielson. For songwriters and composers. "We are a nonprofit organization working to help the composer/songwriter. Each year we sponsor classes, workshops, seminars, a composition contest, and a performance at the Symphony Hall."

Requirements: "Annual dues of $25 entitles members to reduced entry fee for contest plus invaluable information kit. Cassette demo and lead sheet required for a *popular and jazz* entries only. No other restrictions." Deadline: August 31. Send for application.

Awards: $3,000 distributed among 8 categories: keyboard, popular, choral, vocal solo, arrangements, instrumental, jazz and children's music. The best-of-the-show (can be from any music category) is awarded $1,000. "Detailed critique is given to every contest entry. Applicants judged by professional, usually head of university music department or firmly established producer of performed music."

Tips: "Be as professional as possible—clear, neat manuscript. Have music taped on cassette. Sloppy manuscripts will not be accepted by Composers Guild."

MUSIC CITY SONG FESTIVAL, 490 A Allied Dr., Box 17999, Nashville TN 37217. (800)251-1791, (615)834-0025. Festival Director: Roy Sinkovich. "The 1986 Music City Song Festival will be the 7th annual song, vocal and lyric competition. The MCSF is the world's largest international competition for professionals and amateurs. The contest should begin in early 1986, with the entry deadline to be determined at a later date. We plan to announce our 1985 winners and kick off the 1986 MCSF with the distribution of our free, informative newspaper, the *MCSF Songwriters' Enquirer*. Readers can get on the newspaper mailing list by contacting MCSF at Box 17999, Nashville TN 37217 or (615)834-0025." Competition open to amateur and professional songwriters, vocalists and lyricists with categories of pop/top 40, MOR/easy listening, country, gospel and rock/R&B. Call or write for complete information.

Awards: Separate awards in all categories will be given for amateur and professional songwriting, lyric writing and amateur vocal performance. Prizes for a single award range from $50-5,000, with over $40,000 in cash, prizes, certificates and recording contracts to be awarded. Contest judged by active music industry professionals (publishers, association and record company executives, disc jockeys and promoters).

RICHARD RODGERS PRODUCTION AWARD, American Academy and Institute of Arts and Letters, 633 W. 155th St., New York NY 10032. (212)368-5900. Assistant to the Executive Director: Lydia Kaim. (Guidelines for this award are being revised. Address inquiries to foregoing address.)

THE UNIVERSITY OF MICHIGAN PROFESSIONAL THEATRE PROGRAM, The David B. Marshall Award, The Michigan League, Ann Arbor MI 48109. (313)763-5213. Contact: Associate Director. Musical theater contest. Gives 1 or more major award each year.

WORLD POPULAR SONG FESTIVAL, Yamaha Music Foundation, 3-24-22, Shimo Meguro, Meguro-ku, Tokyo, 153, Japan. Contact: Festival Committee.
Requirements: Entry must be an original song, which has never been published or performed in public. Application deadline is at end of June; Festival scheduled for end of October. For more information, please contact the Festival Committee by early 1986.
Awards: Awards include Grand Prize, Most Outstanding Performance Awards and Outstanding Song Awards. Cash award, certificate of honor and medallion are given to the winners.
Tips: "No matter which category has been entered, the deciding factors in selecting a winner are song quality and vocal interpretation."

Organizations

Songwriting is an individual's expression of emotion or sentiment, but that doesn't mean it has to be a lonesome, solitary task. Across the nation, many songwriter associations and support groups foster songwriting as a hobby or a full-time profession. Most large metropolitan areas have at least one established group serving local songwriters through workshops, seminars, critiques and other helpful programs.

Songwriters living virtually anywhere may affiliate with one of several national and international organizations, such as the Songwriters Guild (formerly AGAC), the Nashville Songwriters Association International (NSAI), or the National Academy of Songwriters (formerly Songwriters Resources and Services), in addition to a performing rights organization (for published or recorded songwriters only) such AS-CAP, BMI or SESAC.

The Songwriters Guild, for instance, offers regular ASK-A-PRO sessions, workshops, legal counseling and catalogue administration, and focuses on ongoing Congressional lobbying efforts on behalf of songwriters' rights.

NSAI offers showcases, seminar tapes, radio station bios of songwriters connected with recordings, and has recently teamed-up with the Songwriters Guild to co-produce an 11-point booklet on single-song contracts.

The National Academy of Songwriters (NAS), is a clearinghouse for information on songwriting, and provides members with a bimonthly newsletter including a tipsheet and collaborators' network. It also offers Songtalk seminar tapes, books on the entire spectrum of the music business, lead sheets, demo service and mail-in song critiques.

One great example of a regional organization which stays in constant touch with the recording and publishing industry is the well-known BMI sponsored Los Angeles Songwriters' Showcase (LASS) founded in 1971 by John Braheny and Len Chandler. Beginning on a shoestring budget, LASS has grown to capture the respect and support of the entire music industry through its now-legendary Wednesday Night Showcase, featuring publishers, A&R reps, artists and songwriters. Its well-run format includes performances, interviews and two complete song-pitching exercises each week, as well as many other valuable services.

Many smaller, but no less effective or helpful organizations, exist in mid-size population centers such as San Francisco, Minneapolis, Phoenix, Toronto and other cities.

Songwriters who live away from such population centers are very strongly encouraged to start their own support groups, whether they number three members or thirty. The strength of numbers, however small, may provide you with enough funds and resources to conduct your own critiques with a nearby publisher or organization. You can compare notes as a group and network your contacts in the industry for everyone's benefit. It also just helps to have someone with whom to share your thoughts and ideas, and you might find the ideal collaborator to complement your writing style.

Wherever you live, remember the old saying "Two heads are better than one" ... In a group setting, there's no limit to what you can learn and accomplish as a songwriter.—*Kevin Odegard*, Executive Director, National Academy of Songwriters

THE ACADEMY OF COUNTRY MUSIC, #915, 6255 Sunset Blvd., Box 508, Hollywood CA 90028. (213)462-2351. Executive Secretary: Fran Boyd. For "professional persons connected with the country music industry. For professional membership the person must be affiliated with the country music industry in some manner." Offers newsletter and showcases. "Purpose is to promote country music."

*AMERICAN COUNCIL FOR THE ARTS, 570 7th Ave., New York NY 10018. (212)354-6655. Contact: Membership Dept. "We are the leading private national nonprofit organization that serves all the arts." Members are state, regional and community arts agencies, arts centers, performing arts organizations, museums, libraries, parks and recreation departments, professional arts managers and artists and individuals interested in supporting the arts. Services include advocacy for the arts at the federal level; arts management training conferences and seminars; *Horizon* magazine with six *Vantage Point* supplements featuring articles about major issues facing the arts today; *ACA Update*, a monthly up-to-the-minute news bulletin; ACA Books (publisher and distributor of books on the arts); a research library of 15,000 books and documents; and reference and information services.

AMERICAN FEDERATION OF MUSICIANS (AFM), 1500 Broadway, New York NY 10036. (212)869-1330. Membership available to all qualified musicians and vocalists in the United States and Canada. "The American Federation of Musicians of the United States and Canada is the largest entertainment union in the world and exists solely for the advancement of live music and the benefit of its 250,000 members. In addition to enhancing employment opportunities for members the AFM aids members in negotiating contracts; enforces employers' observance of working conditions and wage scales; arbitrates members' claims at no cost to members; protects musicians from unfavorable legislation at the federal, state and local levels; negotiates pension, welfare and retirement benefits; offers instrument insurance to members; offers free job referral service to members who are seeking employment with traveling groups; and keeps membership informed of happenings in the business through its publication *International Musician*. Members also receive numerous benefits provided by each local." Initiation fees and local dues vary; a small percentage of work dues are contributed by members. Write for further information or contact AFM local nearest you."

AMERICAN GUILD OF MUSIC, Box 3, Downers Grove IL 60515. (312)968-0173. Registered Agent: Elmer Herrick. For musicians and students. Members are music studio operators, teachers, and students interested in teaching and performing. Offers competitions, instruction, lectures, newsletter, performance opportunities and workshops. "Purpose is to improve teaching methods, promote interest in string instruments, accordion, etc."

AMERICAN MECHANICAL RIGHTS AGENCY (AMRA), 2112 Broadway, New York NY 10023. (212)877-4077. Executive Director: Mrs. R.W. Miller. Members include songwriters and music publishers from the US, Canada and 18 European countries. Applicants must have a record released in the US. Purpose is to collect mechanical, synchronization and background royalties.

AMERICAN MUSIC CENTER, INC., Room 300, 250 W. 54th St., New York NY 10019. (212)247-3121. Executive Director: Nancy Clarke. For composers and performers. Members are American composers, performers, critics, publishers, and others interested in contemporary American music. Offers newsletter, circulating library of contemporary music scores, advice on opportunities for composers and new music performers, disseminates information on American music. Purpose is to encourage the creation, performance, publication, recognition of contemporary American music. Members receive the quarterly *AMC Newsletter*, professional "Opportunity Updates," eligibility for group health insurance, and the right to vote in AMC elections.

AMERICAN MUSIC CONFERENCE, 150 E. Huron, Chicago IL 60611. (312)266-8670. President: William McCormick, Jr. National nonprofit association for expanding the future of music. Membership includes companies and associations from musical instrument manufacturers and music publishers to educators and professional musician organizations. Offers competitions, publications and music promotional materials. "Purpose is to educate the public in the benefits of lifetime participation in music; to foster interest in the extension of music education in the schools; to increase appreciation of the value of music in the home, the church and the community; and to give recognition to the development of musical activities."

AMERICAN SOCIETY OF COMPOSERS, AUTHORS AND PUBLISHERS (ASCAP), 1 Lincoln Plaza, New York NY 10023. (212)595-3050. Director of Membership: Paul S. Adler. Membership Department Staff: Phyllis Fischler, Ellen Meltzer, Rick Morrison, Lisa Schmidt, Bill Velez. Members are songwriters, composers, lyricists and music publishers. Applicants must "have at least one song copyrighted for associate membership; have at least one song commercially available as sheet music, available on rental, commercially recorded, or performed in media licensed by the Society (i.e. performed in a nightclub or radio station) for full membership." Purpose: "ASCAP is a membership-owned, performing rights licensing organization that licenses its members' nondramatic musical compositions for public performance and distributes the fees collected from such licensing to its members based on a scientific random sample survey of performances." Primary value is "as a clearinghouse, giving users a practical and economical bulk licensing system and its members a vehicle through which the many thousands of users can be licensed and the members paid royalties for the use of their material. All monies collected are distrbuted after deducting only the societys cost of doing business."
Tips: "The Society sponsors a series of writers' workshops in Los Angeles, Nashville and New York;

open to members and nonmembers. Grants to composers available to members and nonmembers. Contact the public relations or membership departments in New York or the following branch offices: 6430 Sunset Blvd., Los Angeles CA 90028; 2 Music Square W., Nashville TN 37203; 52 Haymarket, London SW1Y4RP, England."

AMERICAN SOCIETY OF MUSIC ARRANGERS, Box 11, Hollywood CA 90078. President: Van Alexander. Secretary/Treasurer: Buddy Svarda. "In conjunction with American Federation of Musicians we are responsible for determining and protecting the rights and income of orchestrators." Full members are qualified arrangers, orchestrators and composers. Associate members are anyone in the music profession (playing musicians, students, songwriters, etc.). Offers newsletter. "Considered to be bellweather organization in field of arranging and orchestrating. Conducts workshops for composition and performance of works of members as well as instrumental clinics."

BLACK MUSIC ASSOCIATION (BMA), Suite 1905, 1500 Locust St., Philadelphia PA 19102. (215)545-8600. President: Ewart Abner. Executive Director: George Ware. For songwriters, musicians and anyone interested in music, entertainment, and arts industries. Members are individuals, companies and organizations involved in the music industry. Offers lectures, newsletter, workshops, industry contact resource center, seminars, annual tribute to renowned music contributor and an annual conference. "Purpose is the dedication to the advancement, enrichment, encouragement and recognition of black music."

BROADCAST MUSIC, INC. (BMI), 320 W. 57th St., New York NY 10019. (212)586-2000; 6255 Sunset Blvd, Suite 1527, Hollywood CA 90028; and 10 Music Square E., Nashville TN 37203. President: Edward M. Cramer. Senior Vice President: Theodora Zavin. Vice President, California: Ron Anton. Senior Vice President, Performing Rights: Frances Preston. Performing rights organization. "Applicants must have written a musical composition, alone or in collaboration with other writers, which is commercially published, recorded or otherwise likely to be performed. Purpose: BMI licenses the nondramatic performing rights of musical compositions to users of music which include radio and TV stations, hotels, night clubs, universities, colleges and the many other places in the US where music is publicly performed."

CANADIAN ACADEMY OF RECORDING ARTS & SCIENCES (CARAS), 89 Bloor St. E., Toronto, Ontario M4W 1A9 Canada. (416)922-5029. Executive Director: Daisy C. Falle. Serves songwriters and musicians. Membership is open to all employees (including support staff) in: broadcasting, record companies and producers, personal managers, recording artists, recording engineers, arrangers, composers, music publishers, album designers, promoters, talent and booking agents, record retailers, rack jobbers, distributors, recording studios and other music industry related professions (on approval). Applicants must be affliliated with the recording industry. Applications accepted year-round. Offers newsletter, performance opportunities, social outings, workshops and annual Juno Awards show. "CARAS strives to foster the development of the Canadian music and recording industries and to contribute toward higher artistic standards." Fees: $30/year.

CANADIAN RECORDING INDUSTRY ASSOCIATION (CRIA), 89 Bloor St. E., Toronto, Ontario M4W 1A9 Canada. (416)967-7272. President: Brian Robertson. Membership open to major record companies, independent record labels and recording studios. Applications accepted year-round. "CRIA is the 'voice' of the recording industry in Canada. Its 40 members represent over 98% of the sound recordings manufactured and sold in this country. The association represents the industry on many levels including communication with government, international liaison with music and recording industry organizations around the world, the control of record and tape piracy and other legal matters, and the direction of industry marketing programs such as the certification of gold and platinum records."

COMPOSERS GUILD, 2333 Olympus Dr., Salt Lake City UT 84124. (801)278-1745. President: Sharon Nielson. For songwriters and composers. "We are a nonprofit organization working to help the composer/songwriter. Each year we sponsor classes, workshops, seminars, a composition contest, and a performance at the Symphony Hall."

CONNECTICUT SONGWRITERS ASSOCIATION, Box 699, Orange CT 06477. (203)795-1032. Executive director: Don Donegan. "We are an educational, nonprofit organization dedicated to improving the art and craft of original music. We offer a monthly newsletter (subscription rate is $15 per year/12 issues), monthly seminars and song critique sessions, performing opportunities at songwriter showcases, song screening service, song tape library, discounts, awards and social outings. No eligibility requirements. Applications accepted year round. Ages range from 12 to 70. Annual membership

categories are: Individual $30, Student and Senior Citizen $20, Organizations $60, Sustaining $100, Benefactor $250, Lifetime $500. ("All memberships include newsletter subscription and are tax deductible to the extent allowed by law.")
Tips: "Members can learn about the music business, improve their songcrafting skills, gain performing opportunities and make collaboration contacts."

COUNTRY MUSIC ASSOCATION, INC. (CMA), Box 22299, Nashville TN 37202. (615)244-2840. Membership falls within following categories: advertising agency; artist manager/agent; artist/musician; composer; broadcast personality; international; publication; publisher; audio/video communications; record company; record merchandiser; talent buyer/promoter; and affiliated. Members must be directly and substantially involved in the country music industry. Offers monthly magazine, lists of industry contacts, special discounted insurance policies and rental car discount cards. Purpose is to promote country music. A new European office is in operation in London to work on expanding country music popularity throughout Europe.

COUNTRY MUSIC FOUNDATION OF COLORADO, Box 19435, Denver CO 80219. (303)936-7762. President: Gladys Hart. Serves songwriters and musicians, promoters, publishers and record companies to assist them in learning the proper method of presenting new material to the publisher. "The membership roster comes from the country music industry in general with special interest in the annual Colorado Country Music Festival." Offers lectures, newsletter, performance opportunities and an annual convention. Purpose is "to promote country music in all facets of the industry. The association provides new artists with information on the basic fundamentals essential for career advancement. Songwriters Day will be scheduled to include songwriter/publisher meeting. The evening show will be dedicated to the presentation of new material by bands and artists."
Tips: "The Songwriter Award has been added to the presentations at the Annual Colorado Country Music & Trade Convention and is voted on performance and recorded material."

THE DRAMATISTS GUILD, INC., 234 W. 44th St., New York NY 10036. (212)398-9366. Membership includes over 7,000 playwrights, composers, lyricists and librettists nationwide. "As the professional association of playwrights, composers, and lyricists, the Guild protects the rights of all theater writers, and improves the conditions under which they work. Additionally, the Guild encourages and nurtures the work of dramatics in the U.S. through its program of seminars and workshops. To be a member of The Dramatics Guild, you must have completed a dramatic work (a one-act or full-length play or component part- book, music or lyrics- of a musical) whether produced or not." The Guild offers legal advice and counseling on business problems related to playwright's work and a library, lectures, newsletter, and a quarterly magazine.

GOSPEL MUSIC ASSOCIATION (GMA), 38 Music Square W., Nashville TN 37203. (615)242-0303. Executive Director: Don Butler. For songwriters, broadcasters, musicians, merchandisers, promoters, performance licensing agencies, church staff musicians, talent agencies, record companies and publishers. Offers lectures, newsletter, workshops and awards programs.

INDIANAPOLIS SONGWRITERS, c/o Robert Najera, Box 176, McCordsville IN 46055. (317)335-2310. Founder: Robert Najera. Purpose is "to create an affiliation of serious minded songwriters, promote the artistic value of the musical composition, the business of music, and recognition for the songwriter and his craft. Sponsors quarterly newsletter, monthly mettings and monthly showcases."

INTERNATIONAL FAN CLUB ORGANIZATION, Box 177, Wild Horse CO 80862. (303)962-3543. Co-Presidents: Loudilla Johnson, Loretta Johnson and Kay Johnson. For songwriters, musicians and performers and their fan club presidents. Members are fan club presidents and/or artists/songwriters etc. Applicants must be involved in the field of country music. An artist must have a fan club—"we assist them in setting up the fan club although we do not personally manage each individual operation for them." Offers competitions, instruction, newsletter, performance opportunities, social outings, workshops, business meetings, overseas tours and showcases. Purpose is to promote/publicize country music in an effort to spread good will, understanding and enjoyment of it around the world. "We hold an annual overseas showcase (London), plus dinner/show/business meetings/showcases in Nashville, annually in conjunction with Fan Fair. We believe fan clubs are a vital part of any entertainer's life."

*****KERRVILLE MUSIC FOUNDATION INC.**, Box 1466, Kerrville TX 78029-1466. (512)257-3600. Executive Director: Rod Kennedy. The Kerrville Music Foundation was "founded in 1975 for the promotion and preservation of both traditional and new American music and has awarded more than $20,000 to musicians over the last ten years through open competitions designed to encourage excellence in songwriting, banjo, harmonica, mandolin and bluegrass bands."

THE LOS ANGELES SONGWRITERS SHOWCASE (LASS), 6772 Hollywood Blvd., Hollywood CA 90028. (213)462-1382. Co-Directors: Len H. Chandler Jr. and John Braheny. General Manager: Joy Wildin. "The Los Angeles Songwriters Showcase (LASS), a nonprofit service organization for songwriters, auditions more than 150 songwriters/month, both live and by tape. Less than 6% of the songs auditioned are presented in a showcase, making it a focus for record industry people looking for new songs and writer/artists. Writers must participate in the performances of their own material. LASS is sponsored by Broadcast Music, Inc. (BMI). LASS also provides counseling, conducts lectures, and interviews top music industry professionals at the Showcase. Two new features have been added to the Wednesday night Showcase: Cassette Roulette in which a different publisher every week critiques songs submitted on cassette that night; and Pitch-A-Thon in which a different producer every week screens songs for his/her current recording projects. The Showcase takes place every Wednesday night in front of an audience of songwriters and music industry; there is no prescreening necessary. LASS also produces an annual Songwriters Expo in November." General membership: $50/year. Professional membership: $65/year. Included in both "general" and "professional" membership benefits are: priorities to have tapes listened to first at Pitch-A-Thon sessions; discounts on numerous items such as blank tapes, books, demo production services, tapes of Songwriters Expo sessions and other seminars; and discounts on admission to the weekly showcase. Professional membership is by invitation or audition only and features special private pitch-a-thon sessions and referrals.

MISSOURI SONGWRITERS ASSOCIATION, INC., 3711 Andora Pl., St. Louis MO 63125. (314)894-3354. President: John G. Nolan, Jr. Serves songwriters and musicians. No eligibility requirements. Applications accepted year-round. "The Missouri Songwriters Association (a non-profit organization) was founded in 1979 with the purpose of offering education and career guidance in songwriting to its members. As a means toward that goal the organization offers: (1) an informative quarterly newsletter; (2) seminars on such diverse topics as creativity, copyright law, brainstorming, publishing, recording the demo, craft and technique, songwriting business, collaborating, etc.; (3) workshops including song evaluation, establishing a relationship with publishers, Broadway and off-Broadway, hit song evaluations, the writer vs. the writer/artist, Create-a-Song nights, the marriage of collaborators, the business side of songwriting, lyric craft, etc; (4) services such as collaborators referral, publisher contacts, consultation, recording discounts, musicians referral, library, etc."

MUSIC INDUSTRY EDUCATORS ASSOCIATION (MIEA), Suite 301, 1435 Bleury St., Montreal, Quebec H3A 2H7 Canada. Purpose: to establish and maintain standards of music industry education throughout the world; to encourage and facilitate interaction between the educational community and the music industry; to foster interaction among individuals involved with music industry education; to assist institutions involved in the development of programs in music industry education; and to promote music industry related research, scholarship and outstanding achievement. Offers quarterly newsletter, seminars and workshops, annual conventions in major recording center, e.g., Nashville. Membership: individual, $25/year; student, $5/year; pre-college or 2-year colleges, $50/year; 4-year and graduate colleges, $100/year; national or international commercial music industry, $250/year; regional commercial music industry, $150/year; and local commercial music industry, $75/year. Write for application and more information.

MUSICIANS CONTACT SERVICE, 6605 Sunset Blvd., Hollywood CA 90028. (213)467-2191. For musicians and bands seeking each other in the greater Southern California area. "Also for songwriters (composers and lyricists) seeking each other for collaboration only. An updated nationwide list of hundreds of songwriters seeking each other is provided for $20 for a one year listing."

NASHVILLE SONGWRITERS ASSOCIATION, INTERNATIONAL (NSAI), 803 18th Ave. S, Nashville TN 37203. (615)321-5004. Executive Director: Maggie Cavender. For songwriters. Applicants may apply for 2 memberships; "active membership is having had at least one song published with an affiliate of BMI, ASCAP or SESAC. An associate membership is for the yet-to-be-published writer and others interested in the songwriter." Offers newsletter, counseling, seminars, symposium, workshop, showcases and awards. "Purpose is to gain recognition for the songwriter, to serve any purpose toward this recognition and to pursue this on a worldwide basis."

NATIONAL ACADEMY OF POPULAR MUSIC/SONGWRITERS HALL OF FAME, 1 Times Square, New York NY 10036. (212)221-1252. General Manager: W. Randall Poe. President: Sammy Cahn. Curator: Oscar Brand. Manager/Archives: Frankie MacCormick. Serves songwriters, musicians, school groups and other visitors to the Songwriters' Hall of Fame Museum. Members are songwriters and those interested in songwriting. Offers library, research on songs and songwriters, special exhibits honoring songwriters and newsletter. Purpose: To honor and recognize the creators of American popular songs, to call attention to the important role of popular music in American life and history and to maintain a library and archive of music and music-related material. Membership year: July 1-June 30.

NATIONAL ACADEMY OF SONGWRITERS (NAS), 6772 Hollywood Blvd., Hollywood CA 90028. (213)463-7178. Executive Director: Kevin Odegard. A nonprofit organization dedicated to the education and protection of songwriters. Membership is general—$45/year; professional—$60/year. Offers SONGBANK song registration service, group legal, financial and audit services, hotline, counseling, song critique, seminars, publishers' workshops, songwriters network and tipsheet in newsletter, courses on songwriting, songwriting business and theory, library, lead sheet service and more. "We offer services to all songwriter members, from street-level to superstar." NAS also operates songwriting competitions, such as SONGSEARCH/AMERICAN SONG FESTIVAL.

NATIONAL MUSIC PUBLISHERS' ASSOCIATION, INC., 18th fl., 205 E. 42nd St., New York NY 10017. (212)370-5330. Chairman: Salvatore T. Chiantia. Executive Vice President: Edward P. Murphy. Trade association for popular music publishers. Eligible members include "any person, firm, corporation or partnership actively engaged in the business of publishing music in the U.S.A. for a period of at least one year, whose musical publications have been used or distributed on a commercial scale or who assumes the financial risk involved in the normal publication of musical works." Offers newsletter, workshops, special reports and information.

NEW ORLEANS JAZZ CLUB OF CALIFORNIA, Box 1225, Kerrville TX 78029. (512)896-2285. President: Bill Bacin. For songwriters, musicians and jazz fans. Members support the preservation and development of jazz music and musicians, primarily the traditional and mainstream styles. Offers instruction, library, newsletter, performance opportunities and referral services.

NORTHERN CALIFORNIA SONGWRITERS ASSOCIATION, #8, 407 California Ave., Palo Alto CA 94306. (415)327-8296. Director: Tobey Hall. Serves songwriters and musicians. "Our 600 members are lyricists and composers from ages 16-80, from beginners to several professional songwriters." No eligibility requirements. Applications accepted year-round. Offers annual Northern California Songwriting Conference, monthly visits from major publishers, instruction, lectures, library, newsletter, performance opportunities and workshops. Dues: $35/year. "Our purpose is to provide the education and opportunities that will support our writers in producing and marketing outstanding songs."
Tips: "NCSA's functions draw local talent and nationally recognized names together. This is a trememdous value to writers outside a major music center."

PACIFIC NORTHWEST SONGWRITERS ASSOCIATION, Box 98324, Seattle WA 98188. (206)824-1568. "We are a nonprofit association, dedicated to serving the songwriters of the Pacific Northwest. Our focus is on professional songwriting for today's commercial markets. We offer monthly workshops, newsletters and a music directory. "We welcome new members. Anyone interested in the PNWSA may send a cassette and lyric sheets of two songs. A simple home recording of one voice backed by a piano or guitar is sufficient. If you write music only, just send a cassette. If you write lyrics only, just send lyric sheets. Be sure to put your name, address and phone number on each piece of your material. Enclose a SASE of appropriate size with full postage, and we'll return your material along with our current workshop schedule. If you have any questions, just give us a call." Membership: $25/year.

PERFORMING RIGHTS ORGANIZATION OF CANADA LIMITED (PRO), 41 Valleybrook Dr., Don Mills, Ontario M3B 2S6, Canada. (416)445-8700. Writer/Publisher: Mark Caporal. Publicity Manager: Nancy Gyokeres. For Canadian songwriters and publishers. Offers competitions, magazine, workshops, advice and direction. Purpose is to collect performance royalties and distribute them to songwriters and publishers.

RADIO & TV REGISTRY, 314 W. 53rd St., New York NY 10019. (212)582-8800. Manager: Roland Young. Serves songwriters, musicians and announcers. Members are professional freelance musicians and songwriters. "Most jingles and record dates produced in New York City are booked through our office." Applicants must be union members and be recommended by two registry members and an opening must be available. Applications accepted year-round. "We provide a telephone answering service geared to the needs of the music industry. We take 'work calls' for our members and relay messages to them."
Tips: "Most music contractors in New York City find it convenient to call us to leave a work call for musicians or songwriters." Musicians Roster and complete information available by calling the business office (212)246-7676.

SANTA BARBARA SONGWRITERS' GUILD, Box 2238, Santa Barbara CA 93120. (805)569-2533. President: Don Ollis. "The Guild is a non-profit organization for aspiring songwriters, performers, those interested in the music industry, and anyone interested in original music. The Guild sponsors monthly cassette tape presentations to L.A. publishers, with the top five member songs awarded studio time and gift certificates. Also sponsored are workshops, plus classes and lectures on studio recording, synthesis, music business contracts and copyright law, record production, song marketing, music composition, lyric writing, vocal techniques, and a directory of local music services and organizations." Membership is $25/year.

SESAC, INC., 10 Columbus Circle, New York NY 10019. (212)586-3450. Branches: 11 Music Circle S., Nashville TN 37203; 9000 Sunset Blvd., Los Angeles CA 90069. Executive Vice President of Affiliation: Vincent Candilora, New York. Membership Director, Los Angeles: Kathy Cooney. Vice President/Director of Country Music: Dianne Petty, Nashville. Vice President/Director of Gospel Music: Jim Black, Nashville. For writers and publishers who have their works performed by radio, television, nightclubs, cable TV, etc. in all types of music. "Prospective affiliates are requested to present a demo tape of their works which is reviewed by our Screening Committee." Purpose of organization is to collect and distribute performance royalties to all active affiliates. Send membership applications to New York or Los Angeles for all types of music; contact Nashville office for country or gospel music.

SONGWRITERS ASSOCIATION OF WASHINGTON, Suite 632, 1377 K St. NW, Washington DC 20005. (202)682-7361. "The Songwriters Association of Washington was established in 1979 as a nonprofit organization. Today we are a thriving group of over 400 amateur and professional songwriters, lyricists, musicians, recording technicians and music industry professionals. Each month we publish a newsletter and sponsor a showcase along with workshops and seminars that not only spotlight our members' talents but increase their knowledge of the music business as well." Applications accepted year-round."

THE SONGWRITERS GUILD, (formerly AGAC: The American Guild of Authors and Composers), 6430 Sunset Blvd., Hollywood CA 90028. (213)462-1108. Regional Director: Jane David. Serves songwriters. Members are pre-professional and professional songwriters, composers, lyricists, melodists, film and TV scorers. No eligibility requirements other than the "desire to be a songwriter." Applications accepted year-round. Offers instruction, lectures, newsletter, monthly ask-a-pro sessions and workshops. "The Songwriters Guild is a protective and advisory agency for songwriters."

THE SONGWRITERS GUILD, (formerly AGAC: The American Guild of Authors and Composers), Suite 306, 276 Fifth Ave., New York NY 10001. (212)686-6820. West Coast: 6430 Sunset Blvd., Hollywood CA 90028. (213)462-1108. Nashville: United Artists Tower, 50 Music Square West, Nashville TN 37203. (615)329-1782. Founded as the Songwriters' Protective Association in 1931, name changed to American Guild of Authors and Composers in 1958, and expanded to AGAC/The Songwriters Guild in 1982. Effective 1984, the organizational name is The Songwriters Guild. President: George David Weiss. Executive Director: Lewis M. Bachman. National Projects Director: Bob Leone. West Coast Regional Director: Jane David. Nashville Regional Director: Kathy Hyland. "A full member must be a published songwriter. An associate member is any unpublished songwriter with a desire to learn more about the business and craft of songwriting. The third class of membership comprises estates of deceased writers. The Guild contract is conceded to be the best available in the industry, having the greatest number of built-in protections for the songwriter. The Guild's Royalty Collection Plan makes certain that prompt and accurate payments are made to writers. The ongoing Audit Program makes periodic checks of publishers' books. For the self-publisher, the Catalogue Administration Program (CAP) relieves a writer of the paperwork of publishing for a fee lower than the prevailing industry rates. The Copyright Renewal Service informs members a year in advance of a song's renewal date. Other services include workshops in New York and Los Angeles, free Ask-A-Pro rap sessions with industry pros (see Workshops), critique sessions, collaborator service and newsletters. In addition, the Guild reviews your songwriter contract on request (Guild or otherwise); fights to strenghten songwriters' rights and to increase writers' royalties by supporting legislation which directly affects copyright; offers a group medical and life insurance plan; issues news bulletins with essential information for songwriters; provides a songwriter collaboration service for younger writers; financially evaluates catalogues of copyrights in connection with possible sale and estate planning; operates an estates administration service; and maintains a non-profit educational foundation (The Songwriters Guild Foundation).

*SOUTH FLORIDA MUSIC ASSOCIATION (SFMA), 8404 W. McNab Rd., Tamarac FL 33321. (305)722-6010 (M-F; 10 a.m. to 4 p.m.). Executive Director: Ray C. Rohlfing. A nonprofit club of songwriters and music business professionals "dedicated to the development and advancement of the independent songwriter across the United States which provides information, education and critique in local area workshops and via the mail, for 'isolated' writers."

Requirements: No membership fee. Conducts local (Ft. Lauderdale/Miami) workshops, showcases and seminars featuring guest speakers. Offers 8-week courses covering contemporary songwriting methods and the music business. Also offers song critique service and individual in-depth critique sessions. "There are reaonsable fees for courses and critiques." Also offers songwriters' collaboration exchange at no charge. Write for specific information.

SOUTHWEST VIRGINIA SONGWRITERS ASSOCIATION, Box 689, Salem VA 24153. President: Sidney V. Crosswhite. (703)380-2921. Vice President: Adrian Willis. (703)563-9238. Non-profit tax exempt organization which sponsors monthly newsletter, mail-in critique service, and monthly meetings featuring song critiques, guest speakers and workshops. One-time initiation fee is $15. Dues are $12/year.

THEATRE COMMUNICATIONS GROUP, INC., 355 Lexington Ave., New York NY 10017. (212)697-5230. Serves composers, lyricists, librettists for the theater. "TCG has a constituency of nonprofit professional theaters for which it is the national organization. It provides services in casting, personnel and management, as well as numerous publications and literary services, to organizations and individuals. TCG publishes a monthly magazine, *American Theatre*; *New Plays USA* (anthology series); *Artsearch* (biweekly newsletter), and provides employment information for theater artists, managers and technicians. The Literary Services Department annually publishes *Dramatists Sourcebook* and also operates *Plays in Process* (a script circulation service). Writers of musicals may benefit from this program if their works receive full production at a TCG constituent theater and have not been otherwise published. The Publications Department is responsible for *Theatre Profiles*, the biennial illustrated reference guide to America's nonprofit professional theatre, and *Theatre Directory*, the annual pocket-sized contact resource of theatres and related organizations. Criteria for membership in TCG include longevity of operation, professional orientation and standards, and size of operating budgets. Membership benefits include discounts on TCG publications and services; free subscriptions to *American Theatre*; invitations to TCG workshops and conferences; access to TCG personnel files and information services. While individuals cannot become members, TCG's many publications are available to all."

VOLUNTEER LAWYERS FOR THE ARTS, Suite 711, 1560 Broadway, New York NY 10036. (212)575-1150. Administrator: Eleanor Rachel Luger. For songwriters, musicians and all performing, visual, literary and fine arts artists. Offers legal assistance and representation to eligible individual artists and arts organizations who cannot afford private counsel. Also sells manuals and guides on arts-related issues. In addition, there are affiliates nationwide who assist local arts organizations and artists. Offers conferences lectures, seminars and workshops.

 The asterisk before a listing indicates that the listing is new in this edition. New markets are often the most receptive to freelance contributions.

Publications of Interest

This section is divided into two groups. The first lists magazines that inform songwriters about songwriting and the music industry in general. These periodicals contain articles on songwriters, publishers, record company executives, how-to pieces and trends in the industry.

Before investing in a subscription, read what each editor says about his magazine. Some are of great interest to musicians as well as songwriters while others are aimed at only songwriters or a particular type of music (e.g., country, rock).

Most of these magazines can be purchased at newsstands. This gives you a chance to look first, then decide which benefit you as a songwriter or songwriter/musician. If you can't find a certain publication on the newsstand, write the publisher for more information.

Books are the second part of the section and answer many questions about the actual process of writing songs, along with detailed information on different aspects of the industry (contracts, copyright, etc.). Most will be available at your local library or bookstores. If not, write the publisher whose name is listed with each book.

BILLBOARD, (The International Newsweekly of Music and Home Entertainment), Billboard Publications, Inc., 1515 Broadway, New York NY 10036. (212)764-7300. Subscription address: Box 1413, Riverton NJ 08077. Senior Vice President of Circulation: Ann Haire. Promotion Director: Greta Gentile. Weekly magazine; 100 pages. "*Billboard* documents the most recent developments in the music business, every week." Includes record charts, industry information, and "the thousands of weekly events" that tell what is happening in the music business.

*COUNTRY SONG ROUNDUP, Charlton Publications, Inc., Charlton Bldg., Derby CT 06418. Contains lyrics to currently popular country songs and interviews with country artists, songwriters and disc jockeys. Monthly magazine.

HIT PARADER, Charlton Publications, Inc., Charlton Bldg., Derby CT 06418. Bimonthly magazine. Contains lyrics to top 40, rock, country and soul songs. Articles on rock music personalities, information about trends in the music industry and rock music in particular.

MUSIC CITY NEWS, Suite 601, 50 Music Square W., Box 22975, Nashville TN 37202. Monthly country music publication focusing on the Nashville music scene; 40 pages. Circulation: 100,000. Host of the Music City News Cover Awards and the Top Country Hits of the Year Awards for songwriters, both nationwide television programs. Also publishes articles on Nashville songwriters. One songwriters special issue each year.

MUSIC CONNECTION, Suite 201, 6640 Sunset Blvd., Hollywood CA 90028. (213)462-5772. Contact: Subscription Dept. Biweekly magazine; 48 pages. "*The Music Connection* is a local musicians'/songwriters' trade magazine. Departments include a gig guide connecting musicians and songwriters with agents, producers, publishers and club owners; a free classified section; music personal ads; interviews with music industry executives and major artists; and articles on songwriting, publishing and the music business."

MUSICIAN MAGAZINE, Billboard Publications, Inc., Box 701, Gloucester MA 01930. (617)281-3110. President: Gordon P. Baird. Executive Editor: Jonathan Baird. Magazine published 12 times/year; 116 pages. "*Musician* is a magazine for musicians and music afficionados in the rock, soul, and jazz fields. We provide an insightful look into the creative process through the artist's own words."

SIGMA ALPHA IOTA QUARTERLY: PAN PIPES, Sigma Alpha Iota, National Music Fraternity, 2820 Webber St., Sarasota FL 33579. National Executive Offices: 4119 Rollins Ave., Des Moines, IA 50312. Editor: Margaret Maxwell. For musicians at undergraduate, graduate and professional levels. Magazine published 4 times/year (Fall, Winter, Spring and Summer); 24 pages except 48 pages/Winter issue. "We cover articles with the emphasis on the American composer. The Winter issue is devoted to American Music and the American composers, with a section devoted to the latest publications of their music."

TRUSTY TIPS FROM THE COLONEL, Trusty International, Rt. 1, Box 100, Nebo KY 42441. (502)249-3194. President: Elsie Childers. Monthly 1-page newsletter. "Producers and artists who need material contact us and we fill an 8¹/₂x11 sheet full of names and addresses of people needing songs for recording sessions or shows and types of song material needed. Subscribers to our sheet have been placing their songs regularly through tips from our tip sheet. Sample copy for SASE and 25¢."

WASHINGTON INTERNATIONAL ARTS LETTER, Allied Business Consultants, Inc., 325 Pennsylvania Ave. SE, Washington DC 20003. (202)328-1900. Business Manager: Thomas Snyder. Publisher: Daniel Millsaps. Magazine published 10 times/year; 8 pages. "WAIL concentrates on discovering new sources of funding for the arts and keeping up with policy changes in funding by governments, private foundations, and businesses which give out grants to individual creative and performing artists. We publish in addition, the Arts Patronage Series, which are directories where all this information is under one cover and updated periodically. We are the major source of information about funding for the arts in the US. Songwriters and composers can get grants for their work through our information and keep informed about Congressional actions which affect their lives. Areas covered include vexatious problems of taxation, etc. as well as how to get money for projects."

*YOUNG MUSICIANS, The Sunday School Board of the Southern Baptist Convention, 127 9th Ave. N., Nashville TN 37234. (615)251-2100. Contact: Church Music Dept. Music Editor: Sheryl Davis Tallant. Quarterly magazine; 52 pages. Publishes music for use by 4th, 5th and 6th graders in church choirs. Includes spiritual and musical concept songs and activities, plus music insert containing four or five anthems. "This is an excellent publication to which songwriters whose interests and skills lie in the area of composing for children may submit their original manuscripts."

Books

THE BILLBOARD BOOK OF THE TOP 40 HITS (1955 To The Present), by Joel Whitburn. Published: 1983. 512 pages. Price; $14.95. "A definitive listing of all records making the Top 40 on *Billboard*'s charts from 1955 to the present." Published by Watson-Guptill Publications, 1515 Broadway, New York NY 10036.

BREAKIN IN TO THE MUSIC BUSINESS, by Alan H. Siegel, entertainment attorney for over 25 years. Published: 1983. 274 pages. Price: $8.95. Talks about how to prepare and present professional quality demo tapes, choosing a competent lawyer and manager, the copyright laws and how they affect the songwriter, royalties, advances and contracts (the economics of the music business), and more. Includes interviews with some of the most influential people in the music business. Published by Cherry Lane Books, Port Chester NY 10573.

THE CRAFT OF LYRIC WRITING, by Sheila Davis. Published: 1985. 350 pages. Price: $16.95. Based on her popular classes at The Songwriters Guild and The New School, this book is the first complete guide to the lyric writing process. Lyric writers will learn and practice how to: apply basic principles of good writing to lyrics, analyze song structure and select the most effective form for their lyrics, make rhyme, meter and beat work for them, choose the tone and point of view that best conveys their message, check their first draft for common pitfalls and edit and rewrite for polished, professional results. Davis also gives advice on collaboration and songwriter's organizations. Each chapter includes assignments and suggestions for practice and self critique. Published by Writer's Digest Books, 9933 Alliance Rd., Cincinnati, OH 45242.

THE ENCYCLOPEDIA OF THE MUSIC BUSINESS, by Harvey Rachlin. Published: 1981. 524 pages. Price: $18.95. A comprehensive and lucid reference work with more than 450 entries that cover in meticulous detail all facets of the music business: The Copyright Law, contracts, recording and production, the recording industry, unions and trade association, technology, and much more. Includes photos, charts, tables, diagrams, and other illustrative material. Published by Harper & Row, 10 E. 53rd St., New York NY 10022.

HOW TO BE A SUCCESSFUL SONGWRITER, by Kent McNeel and Mark Luther. Published: 1978. 224 pages. Price: $7.95. Mac Davis, Paul Williams, Henry Mancini and twenty other successful songwriters tell you how they do it. Published by St. Martin's Press, 175 5th Ave., New York NY 10010.

HOW TO BECOME A SUCCESSFUL NASHVILLE SONGWRITER, by Michael J. Kosser. Published: 1981. 100 pages. Price: $4.95. The inside information on how to make your living as a songwriter in Nashville. Available through the Nashville Songwriter's Association, 25 Music Square W., Nashville TN 37203.

IF THEY ASK YOU, YOU CAN WRITE A SONG, by Al Kasha & Joel Hirschhorn. Published: 1979. 352 pages. Price: $12.95. The A-Zs of how to write songs from two Academy Award-winning songwriters. Published by Simon and Schuster, Inc., 1230 Avenue of the Americas, New York NY 10020.

MAKING IT WITH MUSIC, by Kenny Rogers and Len Epand. Published: 1978. Price: $6.95. Practical information on forming a group and making it succeed: equipment, recording, touring, songwriting and taking care of your money. Published by Harper & Row, 10 E. 53rd St., New York NY 10022.

MAKING MONEY MAKING MUSIC (No Matter Where You Live), by James Dearing. Published 1982. 320 pages. Price: $12.95. The author shows you how to build a successful music career in your own community—playing clubs in solo or group acts, performing in radio and TV jingles, operating a recording studio, teaching and selling lyrics through the mail. Published by Writer's Digest Books, 9933 Alliance Rd., Cincinnati OH 45242.

MORE ABOUT THIS BUSINESS OF MUSIC, by Sidney Shemel and M. William Krasilovsky. Published: 1982. 204 pages. Price: $12.95. A practical guide to five additional areas of the music industry not treated in *This Business of Music*: serious music, background music and transcriptions, tape and tape cartridges, production and sale of printed music, and live performances. Published by Billboard Publications, Inc., 1515 Broadway, New York NY 10036.

THE MUSIC BUSINESS: CAREER OPPORTUNITIES AND SELF-DEFENSE, by Dick Weissman. Published: 1979. Price: $6.95. Covers all facets of the music industry: how record companies operate, the functions of agents and personal managers, the field of commercials, the roles of the performing and the studio musician, music publishing, contracts, record production, unions, radio, using your college education, and careers in music. Published by Crown Publishers, Inc., 1 Park Ave., New York NY 10016.

THE PERFORMING ARTISTS HANDBOOK, by Janice Papolos. Published 1984. 224 pages. Price: $15.95. This book gives you the business basics necessary to advance your professional music career including: self-promotion, resumes, letters, debut recitals, press releases, videotapes, union affiliations, taxes, demos and much more. Published by Writer's Digest Books, 9933 Alliance Rd., Cincinnati OH 45242.

THE PLATINUM RAINBOW (How to Succeed in the Music Business Without Selling Your Soul). "*The Platinum Rainbow* (updated 1982, 239 pages. Price: $9.95) by Grammy Award-winning record producer Bob Monaco and nationally syndicated music columnist James Riordan, gives you an inside look at the recording industry and tells you how to think realistically in a business based on fantasy; how to promote yourself, how to get a manager, producer or agent; how to get free recording time, how to make a deal, how to recognize and record a hit song, how to be a session musician, how to kick your brother out of the band, how to put together the six key elements a record company looks for. There are quotes from some of the biggest names in pop music and a complete analysis of: *The Song*; *The Studio*; *The Stage*; *Demo Or Master*; *Cutting A Record*; *Hooks And Arrangements*; *The Producer*; *The Engineer*; *The Budget*; *The Basic Track*; *Vocals*; *Overdubs*; *The Mix*; *The 24 Track Monster*; *Things You Can Hear But Can't See*; *The Deal*; *The Creative Businessman*; *The Music Attorney*; *The Manager, Agent,*

Promoter; *The Artist As Vendor*; *Leverage, Clout And The Ladder*; *Getting A Job With A Record Company*; *Gigs*; *The Golden Reel To Reel And The Platinum Turntable*; *Staying Happy*; *Waiting To Be Discovered And Nine Other Popular Myths About The Music Business.* Also included is a complete and updated directory of record companies, producers, managers, publishers, agents, studios, engineering schools, concert promoters, all the names, addresses and phone numbers of who to contact." Published by Swordsman Press, 15445 Ventura Blvd., Suite 10, Box 5973, Sherman Oaks CA 91413.

THE SONGWRITER'S DEMO MANUAL AND SUCCESS GUIDE, by George Williams. Published 1984. 193 pages. Price: $12.95. "Shows the songwriter and group how to make a professional demo tape at home or in the recording studio. Explains how the music business operates, who the important people are, how to make contact with them and how to 'sell' your songs in person and by mail. The author, a published songwriter and studio owner, covers the complete demo process: choosing the songs, rehearsing, arranging, finding an inexpensive recording studio, how to get free recording time and other money saving tips." Available from Music Business Books, Box 413, Riverside CA 92502. (714)682-8942.

THE SONGWRITER'S GUIDE TO CHORDS AND PROGRESSIONS, by Joseph R. Lilore. Published: 1982. 48 pages method/instruction book and 90 minute cassette. Price - $14.95. 58 chord outlines, each showing a different principle frequently used in popular music. Includes easy-to-understand charts and covers all major and minor scales and keys. Gives songwriters ideas for new and commercially proven chords and progressions. Available through Lionhead Publishing, Box 1272, Clifton NJ 07012 or at your local music store.

THE SONGWRITER'S HANDBOOK, by Harvey Rachlin. Published: 1977. Starts with the basic components of a song and covers the entire spectrum of the profession—from the conception of an idea for a song to getting it recorded. Published by Funk & Wagnalls, 10 E. 53rd St., New York NY 10022.

THE SONGWRITER'S RHYMING DICTIONARY, by Sammy Cahn. Published: 1983. 224 pages. Price: $17.95. Cahn gives his ingenious system for organizing end rhymes, and also insights from his own experience as a multi-award-winning legend among songwriters. Published by Facts on File Publications, 460 Park Ave. S., New York NY 10016.

THE SONGWRITERS' SUCCESS MANUAL, by Lee Pincus. Published: 1976. Price: $6.95. Answers to many questions including do-it-yourself publishing, how much a songwriter can earn, and four ways songwriters lose money. Published by Music Press, Box 1229, Grand Central Station, New York NY 10017.

THIS BUSINESS OF MUSIC, by Sidney Shemel and M. William Krasilovsky. (Updated 1979). 575 pages. Price: $18.50. Edited by Paul Ackerman. A practical guide to the music industry for publishers, songwriters, record companies, producers, artists and agents. Published by Billboard Publications, Inc., 1515 Broadway, New York NY 10036.

Workshops

Songwriting, like any other craft is something that must be continually worked on and improved in order to assure a consistently good product. Workshops are an excellent way of providing the outside expertise, feedback and motivation necessary for you to improve your craft.

Although most workshops are located in or near the major music centers of Los Angeles, Nashville and New York, there are some organizations—such as The Songwriters Guild, The Nashville Songwriters Association and The National Academy of Songwriters—which offer traveling workshops.

If you can't make it to one of the major music centers to attend a workshop, why not start your own? Many local songwriting organizations already sponsor or will consider co-sponsoring workshops for their members on a regular or semi-regular basis.

The following is a list of some of the more well known national and regional workshops. Each listing includes type and length of workshop(s) offered, as well as costs and admission requirements.

ASCAP "WELCOMES SONGWRITERS" SERIES, % ASCAP, 2nd Floor, 6430 Sunset Blvd., Hollywood CA 90028. (213)466-7681. ASCAP Western Executive Director: Todd Brabec. Workshop Director: Julie Horton. Offers programs for songwriters: "ASCAP offers a tuition-free, 8-week workshop series during which songs are performed and evaluated by a well-known songwriter or publisher guest moderator. Song casting and placement are discussed. The various song markets are analyzed. Additional workshops include The Business and Creative Sides of Writing for Film and Television; Black Contemporary Music; and Symphonic Music. Class size: 25-40 students in each workshop. Length: approximately 2 hours. Workshop classes take place at ASCAP as well as at outside forums. A piano and stereo and cassette tape playback system are among the facilities. Applicants are selected based on material submitted on cassette by prospective members. Write or phone ASCAP for information.

DICK GROVE SCHOOL OF MUSIC, 12754 Ventura Blvd., Studio City CA 91604. (818)985-0905. Contact: Jay Huckabay. Offers programs for songwriters in lyric writing, composition, harmony, theory, and rhythmic dictation. Instructors include Doug Thiele, John D'Andrea, Mark Jordan and Jack Smalley. Workshops are offered for guitarists, bassists, drummers, keyboardists, vocalists and brass, reed and string players. Other classes include arranging, conducting, ear-training, improvisation, film scoring, music preparation and sight-singing." Four 10-week terms/calendar year. Enrollment is 800/term; average class size is 15. Classes range from $75-150 covering five-ten 2-hour sessions. Some classes require texts or materials that are not included in the tuition fee. Complete classroom facilities. "We offer year long, full-time programs for arrangers/composers, vocalists and players. We also offer The Composition and Musicianship Program (COMP) for students wishing a primary career as songwriter and the related experience in record producing, the record industry and publishing. Students will obtain in-depth experience in all styles of song composition and concept from both the lyrical and compositional aspects." Applicants must be "interviewed prior to enrolling for placement. Certain classes require auditions." Request current catalog by mail or telephone.

NATIONAL ACADEMY OF SONGWRITERS (NAS) WORKSHOPS, 6772 Hollywood Blvd., Hollywood CA 90028. (213)463-7178. Staff Members: Kevin Odegard, K.A. Parker, Kriss Wagner, Pete Luboff, William Gladstone and Jai Josefs. "Offers programs for songwriters including Publishers' Evaluation Workshops, SONGTALK seminar series featuring top names in songwriting, lyric writing, demo production and more." Attendance: up to 30/workshop. Length: 2-4 hours/workshop. Membership is $45/year, professionals $60/year. Send for application. NAS is a nonprofit membership organization dedicated to the protection and education of songwriters. NAS also provides a bimonthly newsletter containing tipsheet "Open Ears" and collaborators' network.

FRANKS SILVERA WRITERS' WORKSHOP, 3rd Floor, 317 W. 125 St., New York NY 10027. (212)662-8463. Contact: Garland Lee Thompson. "Our workshop is open to *all* writers who are prepared to have their work read by members of the actors' pool. Each year 70-80 plays are read. Third World and women writers are especially encouraged."

SONGWRITER SEMINARS AND WORKSHOPS, 928 Broadway, New York NY 10010. (212)505-7332. President: Ted Lehrman. Vice President: Libby Bush. Offers programs for songwriters: intermediate pop songwriting; advanced workshop; and at-home songwriter workshop. Cycles begin in September, February and June. Approximately 10 in each songwriter workshop. Each cycle lasts eight weeks. "Our programs stress the craft and business realities of *today's* pop music industry. We guide our members in the writing of the hit single song (both lyrics and music) for those recording artists who are open to outside material. We also share with them our considerable experience and expertise in the marketing of commercial pop music product. Our instructors, Ted Lehrman and Libby Bush, both members of ASCAP, have had between them more than 80 songs recorded and commercially released here and abroad. They continue to be highly active in writing and placing pop songs for publication. Industry guests (record producers, record company, A&R people, publishers etc.) frequently attend workshop sessions." Workshops: Pop Songwriting—Preparing for the Marketplace; Advanced Songwriter Seminar and Workshop—Ready for the Marketplace. Cost of 8 week workshops: $135-140. Cost of at-home songwriter workshop: $15/lyric; $20/song. Private song and career consultation sessions: $40/hour. Top 40 single stressed. Collaboration opportunities available. No housing provided. Interviews/auditions held for songwriters and singer/songwriters to determine which workshop would be most helpful. Call for free brochure and/or set up interview.

THE SONGWRITERS ADVOCATE (TSA), 47 Maplehurst Rd., Rochester NY 14617. (716)266-0679. Director: Jerry Englerth. "TSA is a non-profit educational organization that is striving to fulfill the needs of the songwriter. We offer two opportunities for songwriters including: 1) a evening school course pertaining to the Craft and Business, which covers copyright law, methods and procedures of songwriting, home and professional demo recording, publishing and co-publishing, song sharks, functions of ASCAP, BMI, SESAC, Songwriter's Guild etc.; 2) song evaluation workshops that afford songwriters the opportunity to bounce their songs off other songwriters and receive an objective critique and improve their craft. TSA evaluates tapes and lyric sheets via the mail. In addition, for those of you who wish to have a demo made, TSA will also be able to accommodate you." Price list is available upon request. Cost: TSA membership $10/year. Must be member to receive discounts or services.
Tips: "We do not measure success on a monetary scale, ever. It is the craft of songwriting that is the primary objective. If a songwriter can arm himself with knowledge about the craft and the business, it will increase his confidence and effectiveness in all his dealings. However, we feel the songwriter should be willing to pay for professional help that will ultimately improve his craft and attitude. And by all means, join and strongly support a songwriting organization."

THE SONGWRITERS GUILD, (formerly AGAC: The American Guild of Authors and Composers Workshops), 6430 Sunset Blvd., Hollywood CA 90028. (213)462-1108. Regional Director: Jane David.
Ask-A-Pro: "2-hour music business rap session to which all writers are welcome, held on the first Thursday of each month at 7:00 pm. Features industry professionals fielding questions from new songwriters." Offered year-round. 100-150/meeting. Each session lasts 2 hours. Free to all Guild members, $2 for non-members. Reservations necessary. Phone for more information.
Jack Segal's Songwriting Workshop: "designed to give the songwriter additional techniques to write for today's song market. Both lyrics and music will be treated in terms of contemporary content and form. Song evaluation at every meeting. Workshop activities will include: the basics—form; content; design; tools; collaboration; the demo; the lyric and lead sheet; and the music business. Offered year-round. 12-15/class. Each session lasts 2 hours. Cost: $130 to Guild members, $175 to nonmembers for a 10-week course. All applicants must submit a tape and Jack Segal will make final selections."

THE SONGWRITERS GUILD, (formerly AGAC: The American Guild of Authors and Composers Workshops), 276 Fifth Ave., New York NY 10001. (212)686-6820. National Projects Director: Bob Leone.
Ask-A Pro: "2-hour weekly music business rap session to which all writers are welcome. It features industry professionals—publishers, producers, record company executives, artists—fielding questions from new songwriters." Offered year-round. 25-30/meeting. Charge: free to members, $2 to nonmembers. Phone reservation necessary. Moderator is Linda Mahoney.
Song Critique: Published and ready-to-be-published Guild songwriters can play one song at the Guild's New York headquarters, 276 Fifth Ave., New York NY. These weekly 2 hour sessions start at 5 pm every Thursday night. Nonmembers are invited to attend and help provide feedback. Call (212)686-6820 to make a reservation. The moderator of Song Critique is Guild Projects Director Bob Leone. Critique sessions are also held in Los Angeles (213)462-1108 and Nashville (615)329-1782.
Hit Songwriting Workshop: "This workshop is designed to introduce the songwriter to the basics of writing commercial songs, with focus on both lyrics and music. Pop, soul, rock, dance and country songwriting will be discussed. Areas to be covered include formats, titles, themes, hooks, concept

records, melody writing and the making of demos." Offered year-round with 10 to 12 in each workshop. Instructor is Lou Stallman whose songs have been recorded by Aretha Franklin, Deniece Williams, Laura Nyro, The Supremes, Robert John and many more. Cost: $130 to Guild members, $175 for nonmembers to cover ten 2-hour sessions.

The Craft of Lyric Writing: Conducted by NYU Adjunct Professor Sheila Davis. In the college-accredited Basics Course—designed for the new professional as well as the pre-professional—students learn the 3 classic song forms, the 5 components of a well-written lyric and the top-10 writing principles. Weekly assignments require writing to a form, a title, a theme and a melody, and techniques are stressed that lead to craftsmanship. Beyond The Basics is a continuing seminar/workshop for "graduates" of the Basics Course who have made a career committment to lyric writing. Challenging assignments are criticized in depth and rewriting is required to achieve recordable results. Students receive special exercises to overcome individual writing problems, expand productivity, and develop the third eye of self-criticism. Unique music industry tie-ins afford class members opportunities to write special assignments. Applications to the year-round, 10-week courses must be accompanied by two typed lyrics. Classes are limited to 10-12 students. Cost: $130 to Guild members; $175 for nonmembers.

Appendix

The Business of Songwriting_____

Being creative is not enough to assure success as a songwriter. A little business savvy is a great advantage when you approach music executives who may themselves be more business-oriented than creative.

The articles in this section give you insights into the structure and operation of the music business as well as detailed information on contracts, copyright, submitting your songs, and more.

The Structure of the Music Business

Los Angeles, New York City and Nashville claim the largest concentrations of companies involved in the music business. There are, of course, companies in cities across the country which continue to make important contributions to today's music scene. But it's the decisions made in the three music centers that determine the direction the industry takes: which songs are published, which artists are signed to recording contracts and which records are released.

No matter which city you're dealing in, the chart showing the structure of the music business (Chart 1, on the front leaves of this book) shows the possible routes a song can take to becoming published, recorded and released. Those routes include taking your songs to the A) artist; B) artist's manager; C) music publisher; D) independent record producer; or E) the record company.

Choosing where to submit your songs depends on many things. If you know a recording artist (A) personally and have a song you think would suit him, approach the artist first. If he likes the song he will take it to his producer and, if the producer agrees, it will be scheduled for the artist's recording session.

If you don't know an artist personally, you might try to contact the artist's personal manager (B). You can also submit your songs to the independent record producer (D), or the A&R director of a record company (E). They are always looking for songs for the artists they produce. If they and their artists think your song is a hit, it will be recorded and released.

If the artist being produced by the independent producer is already signed to a recording contract, the song will be released on that record company's label. Many times, however, the independent producer will pay for and produce a session by an artist who is not yet under contract to a recording company. The producer then tries to sell the master tape of that session to the A&R directors of various recording companies. If he sells the master and negotiates a contract for the artist, the record is released on that label.

Each of the above approaches to the music industry requires that, somewhere along the line, someone either publishes your song or recommends a publisher. The advantage to those approaches is that many artists, producers, and record companies *do* have their own publishing companies. Since publishing means money if the song is successful and more money if it is recorded by other artists, a good song can have even greater appeal to artists, producers and record companies if the publishing is "open" (if the song has not yet been published).

There is much to be said, however, for taking your songs to a publisher (C) *first*. The publisher pitches (an industry term meaning to play your songs for artists and producers who might record them) your songs to artists, producers and A&R directors. Major publishers in music centers are regularly sent notification of who will be recording and when.

The greatest advantage, then, to approaching a music publisher first is his know-how and clout with the industry as a whole. You can concentrate on your business—writing songs—while the publisher works on getting cuts (recordings) on the songs you write. Some publishers do encourage their writers to do some pitching. That is not necessarily bad since it keeps the writer even closer to what's happening in the industry.

Any one (or a combination) of these ways of getting your song heard, published, recorded and released is the best way if it works for you. In this book are listed music publishers, record companies, record producers and managers with specifications on how to submit your material to each. The choice is yours.

Submitting Your Songs

Here are guidelines to help when submitting material to companies listed in this book:

- Read the listing and submit exactly what a company asks for and exactly how it asks that it be submitted.
- Listen to each demo before submitting to make sure the quality is satisfactory.
- Enclose a brief, neat cover letter of introduction. Indicate the types of songs you're submitting and, if you wish, recording artists you think they might suit.
- Include typed or legibly printed lyric sheets. If requested, include a lead sheet. Place your name, address and phone number on each lead or lyric sheet.
- Label neatly each tape and tape box with your name, address, phone number and the names of songs on the tape in the sequence in which they appear.
- Keep a record of the date, the names of the songs and the company to which you are submitting.
- Include a SASE for the return of your material. Your return envelope to companies based in countries other than your own should contain a SAE and International Reply Coupons (IRC).
- Wrap and tie the package neatly and write or type the address and your return address so they are clearly visible. Your package is the first impression a company has of you and your songs, so neatness is very important.
- Mail First Class. Stamp or write "First Class Mail" on the package and on the SASE you enclose. Don't send by registered mail. The recipient must interrupt his day to sign for it and many companies refuse all registered mail.

The query letter should be neat (preferably typewritten), brief and pleasant. Explain the type of material you have and ask about their needs and current submission policy.

To expedite a reply, you can enclose a self-addressed stamped postcard asking the information you need to know. Your typed questions (see Sample Reply Form) should be direct and easy for the receiver to answer. Don't forget to include a line for the respondent's name and title. Also remember to place the company's name and address in the upper left-hand space on the front of the postcard so you'll know what company it was you queried. Queries, like tape submissions, should be recorded for future reference.

Sample Reply Form

I would like to hear:

( ) "Name of Song"   ( ) "Name of Song"   ( ) "Name of Song"

I prefer:

( ) reel-to-reel   ( ) cassette   ( ) video cassette

( ) Beta ( ) VHS

With:

( ) lyric sheet   ( ) lead sheet   ( ) either   ( ) both

( ) I am not looking for material at this time, try me later.

( ) I am not interested.

Name _____   Title _____

Submitting in Person

A trip to Los Angeles, New York or Nashville can give you an inside glimpse of the music business at work. If you've planned ahead, outlined your schedule, made appointments, and carefully prepared demos, you have only to reap the rewards of first-hand reaction to your material. Use the geographic index at the end of both the Music Publishers and Record Companies sections to contact, before you leave home, companies you'd like to visit.

Take several reel-to-reel and cassette copies and lyric sheets of each of your songs. More than one of the companies you visit may ask that you leave a copy with them. If the person who's reviewing material likes a song, he may want to play it for someone else. There's also a good chance the person you have the appointment with will have to cancel (expect that occasionally), but wants you to leave a copy of your songs and he will contact you later.

Listen attentively to what the reviewers say. When you return home, summarize their reactions to your material and look for similarities in their critiques. That information will be invaluable as you continue to submit material to the people who now know you personally.

The Money

The songwriter's payment comes in the form of royalty checks. Unless your contract stipulates you will receive a salary or advance on future royalties, you shouldn't expect your first money before three to six months after the song is released.

A look at the royalties chart (Chart 2, on the back leaves of this book) shows that the songwriter receives:

● Mechanical royalties from the sale of records and tapes.

- Performance royalties for airplay on radio and TV, plays on jukeboxes and live performances.
- Foreign royalties from foreign sub-publishers.
- Money for sheet music, choral arrangements and folio sales.

Mechanical royalties are due the songwriter and the publisher every time a recorded copy of your song is sold and not returned. You and the publisher split a portion of that revenue (50-50 is standard). The Copyright Royalty Tribunal has set maximum royalty at 4¢/song.

The money for mechanical royalties flows from retail record shops to the record company. The record company then pays the music publisher 4¢ per record *sold*. You and the publisher split the 4¢ less reasonable publisher's expenses. Reasonable publisher's expenses means only the cost incurred for that particular song: phone calls, postage, etc.

The songwriter also shares 50-50 in any royalties the publisher receives from the sub-publisher who collected the publishing monies generated by your songs in the foreign music market.

The publisher pays you a share of the profit from the sale of sheet music, orchestrations, choral arrangements and folio sales. You earn 3-8% for each sheet of piano music sold and about 10% of the wholesale price of orchestrations, choral arrangments and folios.

Periodically (usually every six months) the publisher sends the songwriter a check that reflects his share of the mechanical royalties, foreign sub-publishing royalties, and sheet music, orchestrations, choral arrangements and folio sales.

Performance royalties are collected from radio and television stations, night clubs and jukeboxes by the performance rights organizations (ASCAP, BMI and SESAC). A published songwriter *must* belong to the same organization to which the publisher belongs. You'll notice that many publishers listed in this book have affiliate companies belonging to a different performance rights organization. That allows the publisher to deal with writers of more than one affiliation.

Each performance rights organization has its own unique method of determining how many times your song is performed during a given period. Their primary difference is *how* they make that determination. ASCAP monitors individual radio and television stations as well as concerts and clubs where music is performed. BMI uses logs sent them from radio and TV stations. SESAC uses the charts of the trade magazines (*Billboard* and *Cash Box*) to determine the popularity of individual songs. ASCAP charges a membership fee. BMI and SESAC do not.

The songwriter receives a statement of performances and a royalty check from his chosen performance rights organization quarterly. The amount earned depends on how many times the organization determined the song was performed.

ASCAP, BMI and SESAC are highly professional and reputable friends of the songwriter. To look into the specific policies, procedures, benefits and requirements of each before joining, use the addresses given in our Organizations & Clubs section to write them. Also, consult the chapter on these organizations in *This Business of Music* by Sidney Shemel and M. William Krasilovsky (Billboard Publications).

Copyright

One of the questions songwriters frequently ask is, "How do I protect my songs?" The answer is that since the new copyright law went into effect January 1, 1978, your songs are automatically copyrighted for life plus fifty years the moment you put them to paper or tape. To ascertain and protect your ownership of that copyright, however, you must register your songs. To register your song(s) send the following to the Register of Copyrights, Library of Congress, Washington DC 20559:

- a tape or lead sheet of your song(s).
- a government form PA, available on request from the Copyright Office or your local Federal Information Center.
- $10 registration fee which will cover the cost of registering as many songs (by

the same writers) as you wish to submit for registration at one time.

It may take as long as four months before you receive your certificate of registration from the Copyright Office. However, since your songs are copyrighted from the moment of creation, you may use the copyright symbol immediately, affixing it to all written and taped copies of your songs. That is a "c" with a circle around it, followed by the date the song was written and your name (© 1985 John Doe).

Write the Copyright Office for more information and/or a copy of the Copyright Law. All information is free.

Record Keeping

Your record keeping should include a list of income from royalty checks as well as expenses incurred as a result of your songwriting business: cost of tapes, demo sessions, office supplies, postage, traveling expenses, dues to songwriting organizations, class and workshop fees, and publications of interest. It's also advisable to open a checking account exclusively for your songwriting activities, not only to make record keeping easier, but to establish your identity as a business for tax purposes.

The Rip Offs

There are those who use the music business as a means to unfairly exploit others. Here are some guidelines to help you recognize when you've come upon such a person or company:

- *Never pay* to have your songs published. A reputable company interested in your songs assumes the responsibility and cost of promoting your material. That company invests in your material because it expects a profit once the song is recorded and released.
- Never pay to have your music "reviewed." Reviewing material—free of charge—is the practice of a reputable company.
- Never pay to have your lyrics or poems set to music. "Music mills"—for a price—may use the same melody for hundreds of lyrics and poems. Publishers can recognize one of these melodies as soon as they hear one.
- Read *all* contracts carefully before signing and don't sign any contract you're unsure about or that you don't understand.
- Don't pay a company to pair you up with a collaborator. Better ways include contacting organizations which offer collaboration services to their members (see the Organizations and Clubs section in this book).
- Don't "sell your songs outright." It's unethical for anyone to offer you such a proposition.
- If you are being offered a "recording contract" you should not be expected to pay upfront for the session, musicians, promotion, etc. Major record companies recoup such expenses from record sales. If you *are* asked to pay expenses upfront, beware. No matter how much is promised to you verbally or in your contract, you will probably never see a return on your money. With such companies, it's a good idea to ask to speak with other artists who have signed such contracts with them before signing one yourself. And if, after weighing expenses, you think you can afford the longshot, then it's your decision. Read the stipulations of the contract carefully, however, and go over them with an attorney.
- Verify any situation about a company or individual if you have doubts: 1) contact the performance rights organization with which they are affiliated; 2) check with the Better Business Bureau in the town where they're located; 3) contact professional organizations listed in our Organization and Clubs section.

Co-Writing

A quick check of the charts in *Billboard* or *Cash Box* will show that collaboration is not just an alternative way of writing—it's the most popular way. Among its advantages is the instant feedback and criticism of the songs you're writing. Another plus for collaboration is the talent that each songwriter brings to the task.

Where do you find collaborators? Check the bulletin board at your local musician's union hall. Professional organizations like The National Academy of Songwriters in Los Angeles; The Songwriters Guild in New York City and Los Angeles, and The Nashville Songwriters Association International (NSAI) in Nashville offer collaboration services. Check the Organizations and Clubs section for addresses.

Alternatives

Alternatives a songwriter might consider other than the popular music market are advertising agencies, audiovisual firms, the theater and writing songs for local and regional performers. Each is a specialized market requiring not only talent, but technical knowledge of that particular field.

The "total package" resulting from work in any of these alternative categories will most always result from the "team" efforts of several or many people other than yourself. Working with advertising agencies and audiovisual firms means not only getting involved with the company's production staff, but many times even with their clients. Likewise, the playwright may find himself working with the musical director, production staff and technical crew as his work is being staged. The personal manager and the artist (or group) will be part of that "team" when you're writing for local or regional performers.

Read the appropriate section introductions in this book for further information on these markets.

Answers to Your Contract Questions

By Bob Leone

What should I look for in a publishing contract?

The following points should appear in every writer's contract:
- (a). The publisher will, within a reasonable period of time (one year, 18 months, two years), cause the release of a commercial sound recording, failing which the writer can cancel the contract and recapture all rights to the song.
- (b). Royalties payable by the publisher should not be less than what is specified in The Songwriters Guild Contract.
- (c). The publisher cannot alter either the lyrics, the music or the title of the song without the permission of the writer.
- (d). All demo costs should be paid by the publisher.
- (e). Be certain to set up a royalty payment schedule.
- (f). Specify the writer's right to audit the publisher's records.
- (g). Specify that all contract disputes be submitted to arbitration.

When should I expect to be asked to sign a contract?

A contract should be entered into immediately after a publisher has agreed to accept the song. The writer should not wait until a recording artist or producer has accepted or cut the song because, if there are points to be negotiated, the writer might find him/herself in an inferior position.

Do I even need a contract?

Yes. The contract spells out the exact terms, conditions and rights of each party, thereby avoiding future disputes.

Bob Leone is National Projects Director for The Songwriters Guild. He is also a composer/keyboardist who has worked with such artists as Stevie Nicks, Patti Smith, Joey Heatherton and Pam Johnson, and was principal writer and player for the former RCA recording group Flame. He was assisted on this feature by **Lewis M. Bachman**, *Guild Executive Director and* **Alvin Deutsch, Esq.**, *Guild Counsel.*

What problems might I encounter if I do not sign a contract?

If a song is recorded and the writer does not have a contract, then there would not be a document to govern the relationship between the publisher and the writer. Among the things that can be disputed are the rate of royalties, the term of the agreement, due dates of royalties, and the publisher's ability to change the music or lyrics.

Is there a standard songwriters contract? If so, what are some of the usual clauses I could expect to encounter?

Many publishers offer contracts that are similar to each other. In a publisher's form contract one may expect to find the following:
- (a). Copyright is assigned by the writer for the full period under the law (life plus fifty years).
- (b). Royalties may not be paid on all types of usages.
- (c). Demo charges as an advance against royalties.
- (d). Publisher retains rights for full copyright period even if the song is never published.
- (e). Publisher can change the lyrics, music and/or title without approval of the writer.
- (f). The right to audit is limited or non-existent.

What is an exclusive songwriter contract? Are there advantages to considering one?

An exclusive songwriter's contract would govern a writer's services to a publisher for a specified time period (six months, one year) with options to extend usually on the publisher's side. The advantages to a writer are:
- (a). Most of these types of contracts provide for weekly advances.
- (b). Publisher would "work" the songs so that advances could be recouped.
- (c). Not having to "shop" for a publisher.
- (d). Possibility of working with other writers who are also under contract.

The possible disadvantages are:
- (a). A certain number of acceptable songs may have to be written each year or contract is automatically extended.
- (b). Option to extend is solely the publisher's.
- (c). May have to accept less favorable contract terms.
- (d). You cannot deal with any other publishers during the term of the contract.

Should an attorney review the contracts?

In all cases, except when the Songwriters Guild form is being used, an attorney should review the contract. The Guild's contract was drawn up by its attorneys and is considered to be the best minimum songwriters contract available (as long as there are no changes made).

What are some of the other related contractual agreements I might be asked to enter into?

Other types of contractual agreements a writer may be asked to enter into include:

(a). Option—Some publishers do not want to sign a writer if they can not obtain a commercial recording. In this case, they use the option form which gives them an exclusive period of time (six months to one year) to obtain a cut. Once they do, they will issue the contract.

(b). Employment For Hire—Some publishers will ask the writer to sign this form of agreement which will extend to the publisher all rights for the full term of copyright (life plus 50 years). The writer would then be unable to exercise the right of recapture for the United States, which is granted under the 1976 Copyright Law. In effect, the publisher, not the writer, is the composer/lyricist.

Overview of the Popular Songwriters Contract

Paragraph 1

Writer assigns his song to the Publisher throughout the world for a designated number of years, not to exceed forty (40) (or thirty-five (35) years from the date of first release of a commercial sound recording). (The term reflects the provisions of the 1976 Copyright Revision Law.) The shorter the term, the better for the Writer, because if the song is successful, he/she can re-negotiate more favorable financial terms at an earlier time. The length of the term would depend on the bargaining strength and reputation of the Writer.

Paragraph 2

This recognizes that the Writer is a member of a particular performing rights society (either ASCAP, BMI, or SESAC) and that this Contract will not interfere with the Writer's collection of performing rights proceeds directly from his/her performing rights society. It is crucial that the Writer and Publisher are members of the same performing rights society.

Paragraph 3

Writer warrants that the song was written by him/her, is original, and that Writer has the right to enter into the agreement.

Paragraph 4

Sets forth royalties to be paid for various types of uses of the song. Note that the Contract sets forth *minimum* amounts that Writer must receive. Of course, Writer is free to attempt to negotiate for higher royalty rates. If no amounts are filled in, the minimum amounts apply (see Paragraph 20 of the initial contract). Paragraph 4(k) provides that the initial publisher, may not, without the Writer's written consent, grant certain licenses not specifically permitted by the contract (e.g.) use of the title of the song; to give a dramatic representation of the song; synchronization, licenses, etc.).

Paragraph 5

This applies if there is more than one Writer. If so, each Writer will share royalties equally, unless specified otherwise in Paragraph 23.

Paragraph 6

This requires the Publisher to have a commercial sound recording of the song made and released within twelve (12) months from the date of the Contract or to pay Writer a sum of not less than Two Hundred and Fifty ($250.00) Dollars for the right to extend this period for not more than six (6) months. If Publisher does not comply, the Contract terminates and all rights return to Writer.

When the sound recording is cut, Publisher is required to give Writer six (6) copies of the sound recording.

Under Paragraph 6(c), Publisher must either (i) publish and offer for sale regular piano copies of the song within thirty (30) days of release of the sound recording; or (ii) make a piano arrangement or lead sheet of the song within thirty (30) days of execution of the Contract (with six (6) copies to be given to the Writer). The parties must select which of the above alternatives will apply.

Paragraph 7

Deals with the Publisher's sub-licensing of the song in foreign countries. It guarantees that the Writer will receive no less than 50% of the revenue by the Publisher from rights licensed outside the U.S.

Paragraph 8

Explains what happens when the Contract terminates (i.e. all rights revert to Writer, subject to any outstanding licenses issued by the Publisher and the latter's duty to account for monies received after termination).

Paragraph 9

Deals with exploitation of the song in a manner not yet contemplated and thus not specifically covered in the Contract. Any such exploitation must be mutually agreed upon by the Writer and the Publisher.

Paragraphs 10, 11 and 12

Deal with the method of payment of royalties to the Writer and the Writer's right to inspect Publisher's books.

Paragraph 13

Various uses of the song, such as sound recordings and arrangements, are considered "derivative works" under the Copyright Law. Often, such derivative works can have more financial value than the original sheet music. This provision provides that when the Contract terminates, the Publisher loses all rights in such derivative works, as well as in the original version of the song.

Paragraphs 15 and 16

Deal with bringing lawsuits against infringers and defending lawsuits in the event someone claims that the Writer's song infringed a copyright.

Paragraph 17

In the event there is a dispute between the Writer and the Publisher and they cannot resolve it, such dispute is to be settled by arbitration (generally considered a more expeditious and inexpensive means of settling claims).

Paragraph 18

This places restrictions on Publisher's rights to sell the Writer's song to another publisher other than as part of the Publisher's entire catalog.

the songwriters guild

NOTE TO SONGWRITERS: (A) DO NOT SIGN THIS CONTRACT IF IT HAS ANY CHANGES UNLESS YOU HAVE FIRST DISCUSSED SUCH CHANGES WITH *THE SONGWRITERS GUILD*; (B) FOR YOUR PROTECTION PLEASE SEND A FULLY EXECUTED COPY OF THIS CONTRACT TO *THE SONGWRITERS GUILD*.

POPULAR SONGWRITERS CONTRACT

© Copyright 1978 AGAC/the songwriters guild

AGREEMENT made this .... day of .... , 19 ...... , between

....

(hereinafter called "Publisher") and ....

....

(Jointly and/or severally hereinafter collectively called "Writer");

WITNESSETH:

Composition
**(Insert title
of composition→
here)**

(Insert number→
of years here)

1. The Writer hereby assigns, transfers and delivers to the Publisher a certain heretofore unpublished original musical composition, written and/or composed by the above-named Writer now entitled ....

.... (hereinafter referred to as "the composition"), including the title, words and music thereof, and the right to secure copyright therein throughout the entire world, and to have and to hold the said copyright and all rights of whatsoever nature thereunder existing, for

.... *not more than 40* years from the date of this contract or 35 years from the date of the first release of a commercial sound recording of the composition, whichever term ends earlier, unless this contract is sooner terminated in accordance with the provisions hereof.

Performing
Rights Affiliation
(Delete Two)

2. In all respects this contract shall be subject to any existing agreements between the parties hereto and the following small performing rights licensing organization with which Writer and Publisher are affiliated:

→ (ASCAP, BMI, SESAC). Nothing contained herein shall, or shall be deemed to, alter, vary or modify the rights of Writer and Publisher to share in, receive and retain the proceeds distributed to them by such small performing rights licensing organization pursuant to their respective agreement with it.

Warranty

3. The Writer hereby warrants that the composition is his sole, exclusive and original work, that he has full right and power to make this contract, and that there exists no adverse claim to or in the composition, except as aforesaid in Paragraph 2 hereof and except such rights as are specifically set forth in Paragraph 23 hereof.

Royalties

4. In consideration of this contract, the Publisher agrees to pay the Writer as follows:

(Insert amount of advance here) → (a) $................as an advance against royalties, receipt of which is hereby acknowledged, which sum shall remain the property of the Writer and shall be deductible only from payments hereafter becoming due the Writer under this contract.

Piano Copies (b) In respect of regular piano copies sold and paid for in the United States and Canada, the following royalties per copy:

Sliding Scale

(Insert percentage here) → ....% (in no case, however, less than 10%) of the wholesale selling price of the first 200,000 copies or less; plus

..........% (in no case, however, less than 12%) of the wholesale selling price of copies in excess of 200,000 and not exceeding 500,000; plus

..........% (in no case, however, less than 15%) of the wholesale selling price of copies in excess of 500,000.

Foreign Royalties

(Insert percentage here) → (c) ....% (in no case, however, less than 50%) of all net sums received by the Publisher in respect of regular piano copies, orchestrations, band arrangements, octavos, quartets, arrangements for combinations of voices and/or instruments, and/or other copies of the composition sold in any country other than the United States and Canada, provided, however, that if the Publisher should sell such copies through, or cause them to be sold by, a subsidiary or affiliate which is actually doing business in a foreign country, then in respect of such sales, the Publisher shall pay to the Writer not less than 5% of the marked retail selling price in respect of each such copy sold and paid for.

Orchestrations and Other Arrangements, etc.

(d) In respect of each copy sold and paid for in the United States and Canada, or for export from the United States, of orchestrations, band arrangements, octavos, quartets, arrangements for combinations of voices and/or instruments, and/or other copies of the composition (other than regular piano copies) the following royalties on the wholesale selling price (after trade discounts, if any):

(Insert percentage here) → ....% (in no case, however, less than 10%) on the first 200,000 copies or less; plus

..........% (in no case, however, less than 12%) on all copies in excess of 200,000 and not exceeding 500,000; plus

..........% (in no case, however, less than 15%) on all copies in excess of 500,000.

Publisher's Song Book, Folio, etc.

(e) (i) If the composition, or any part thereof, is included in any song book, folio or similar publication issued by the Publisher containing at least four, but not more than twenty-five musical compositions, the royalty to be paid by the Publisher to the Writer shall be an amount determined by dividing 10% of the wholesale selling price (after trade discounts, if any) of the copies sold, among the total number of the Publisher's copyrighted musical compositions included in such publication. If such publication contains more than twenty-five musical compositions, the said 10% shall be increased by an additional ½% for each additional musical composition.

Licensee's Song Book, Folio, etc.

(ii) If, pursuant to a license granted by the Publisher to a licensee not controlled by or affiliated with it, the composition, or any part thereof, is included in any song book, folio or similar publication, containing at least four musical compositions, the royalty to be paid by the Publisher to the Writer shall be that proportion of 50% of the gross amount received by it from the licensee, as the number of uses of the composition under the license and during the license period, bears to the total number of uses of the Publisher's copyrighted musical compositions under the license and during the license period.

(iii) In computing the number of the Publisher's copyrighted musical compositions under subdivisions (i) and (ii) hereof, there shall be excluded musical compositions in the public domain and arrangements thereof and those with respect to which the Publisher does not currently publish and offer for sale regular piano copies.

Professional Material and Free Copies

(iv) Royalties on publications containing less than four musical compositions shall be payable at regular piano copy rates.

(f) As to "professional material" not sold or resold, no royalty shall be payable. Free copies of the lyrics of the composition shall not be distributed except under the following conditions: (i) with the Writer's written consent; or (ii) when printed without music in limited numbers for charitable, religious or governmental purposes, or for similar public purposes, if no profit is derived, directly or indirectly; or (iii) when authorized for printing in a book, magazine or periodical, where such use is incidental to a novel or story (as distinguished from use in a book of lyrics or a lyric magazine or folio), provided that any such use shall bear the Writer's name and the proper copyright notice; or (iv) when distributed solely for the purpose of exploiting the composition, provided, that such exploitation is restricted to the distribution of limited numbers of such copies for the purpose of influencing the sale of the composition, that the distribution is independent of the sale of any other musical compositions, services, goods, wares or merchandise, and that no profit is made, directly or indirectly, in connection therewith.

Mechanicals, Electrical Transcription, Synchronization, All Other Rights

(g) **(Insert percentage here)** .... % (in no case, however, less than 50%) of:

All gross receipts of the Publisher in respect of any licenses (including statutory royalties) authorizing the manufacture of parts of instruments serving to mechanically reproduce the composition, or to use the composition in synchronization with sound motion pictures, or to reproduce it upon electrical transcription for broadcasting purposes; and of any and all gross receipts of the Publisher from any other source or right now known or which may hereafter come into existence, except as provided in paragraph 2.

Licensing Agent's Charges

(h) If the Publisher administers licenses authorizing the manufacture of parts of instruments serving to mechanically reproduce said composition, or the use of said composition in synchronization or in timed relation with sound motion pictures or its reproduction upon electrical transcriptions, or any of them, through an agent, trustee or other administrator acting for a substantial part of the industry and not under the exclusive control of the Publisher (hereinafter sometimes referred to as licensing agent), the Publisher, in determining his receipts, shall be entitled to deduct from gross license fees paid by the Licensees, a sum equal to the charges paid by the Publisher to said licensing agent, provided, however, that in respect to synchronization or timed relation with sound motion pictures, said deduction shall in no event exceed $150.00 or 10% of said gross license fee, whichever is less; in connection with the manufacture of parts of instruments serving to mechanically reproduce said composition, said deductions shall not exceed 5% of said gross license fee; and in connection with electrical transcriptions, said deduction shall not exceed 10% of said gross license fee.

Block Licenses

(i) The Publisher agrees that the use of the composition will not be included in any bulk or block license heretofore or hereafter granted, and that it will not grant any bulk or block license to include the same, without the written consent of the Writer in each instance, except (i) that the Publisher may grant such licenses with respect to electrical transcription for broadcasting purposes, but in such event, the Publisher shall pay to the Writer that proportion of 50% of the gross amount received by it under each such license as the number of uses of the composition under each such license during each such license period bears to the total number of uses of the Publisher's copyrighted musical compositions under each such license during each such license period; in computing the number of the Publisher's copyrighted musical compositions for this purpose, there shall be excluded musical compositions in the public domain and arrangements thereof and those with respect to which the Publisher does not currently publish and offer for sale regular piano copies;

(ii) that the Publisher may appoint agents or representatives in countries outside of the United States and Canada to use and to grant licenses for the use of the composition on the customary royalty fee basis under which the Publisher shall receive not less than 10% of the marked retail selling price in respect of regular piano copies, and 50% of all other revenue; if, in connection with any such bulk or block license, the Publisher shall have received any advance, the Writer shall not be entitled to share therein, but in part of said advance shall be deducted in computing the composition's earnings under said bulk or block license. A bulk or block license shall be deemed to mean any license or agreement, domestic or foreign, whereby rights are granted in respect of two or more musical compositions.

Television and New Uses

(j) Except to the extent that the Publisher and Writer have heretofore or may hereafter assign to or vest in the small performing rights licensing organization with which Writer and Publisher are affiliated, the said rights or the right to grant licenses therefor, it is agreed that no licenses shall be granted without the written consent, in each instance, of the Writer for the use of the composition by means of television, or by any means, or for any purposes not commercially established, or for which licenses were not granted by the Publisher on musical compositions prior to June 1, 1937.

Writer's Consent to Licenses

(k) The Publisher shall not, without the written consent of the Writer in each case, give or grant any right or license (i) to use the title of the composition, or (ii) for the exclusive use of the composition in any form or for any purpose, or for any period of time, or for any territory, other than its customary arrangements with foreign publishers, or (iii) to give a dramatic representation of the composition or to dramatize the plot or story thereof, or (iv) for a vocal rendition of the composition in synchronization with sound motion pictures, or (v) for any synchronization use thereof, or (vi) for the use of the composition or a quotation or excerpt therefrom in any article, book, periodical, advertisement or other similar publication. If, however, the Publisher shall give to the Writer written notice by certified mail, return receipt requested, or telegram, specifying the right or license to be given or granted, the name of the licensee and the terms and conditions thereof, including the price or other compensation to be received therefor, then, unless the Writer (or any one or more of them) shall, within five business days after the delivery of such notice to the address of the Writer hereinafter designated, object thereto, the Publisher may grant such right or license in accordance with the said notice without first obtaining the consent of the Writer. Such notice shall be deemed sufficient if sent to the Writer at the address or addresses hereinafter designated or at the address or addresses last furnished to the Publisher in writing by the Writer.

Trust for Writer

(l) Any portion of the receipts which may become due to the Writer from license fees (in excess of offsets), whether received directly from the licensee or from any licensing agent of the Publisher, shall, if not paid immediately on the receipt thereof by the Publisher, belong to the Writer and shall be held in trust for the Writer until payment is made; the ownership of said trust fund by the Writer shall not be questioned whether the monies are physically segregated or not.

Writer Participation

(m) The Publisher agrees that it will not issue any license as a result of which it will receive any financial benefit in which the Writer does not participate.

Writer Credit

(n) On all regular piano copies, orchestrations, band or other arrangements, octavos, quartets, commercial sound recordings and other reproductions of the composition or parts thereof, in whatever form and however produced, Publisher shall include or cause to be included, in addition to the copyright notice, the name of the Writer, and Publisher shall include a similar requirement in every license or authorization issued by it with respect to the composition.

Writers'

5. Whenever the term "Writer" is used herein, it shall be deemed to mean all of the persons herein defined as "Writer" and any

Respective Shares

and all royalties herein provided to be paid to the Writer shall be paid equally to such persons if there be more than one, unless otherwise provided in Paragraph 23.

Release of Commercial Sound Recording
(Insert period not exceeding 12 months)

6. (a) (i) The Publisher shall, within..................months from the date of this contract (the "initial period"), cause a commercial sound recording of the composition to be made and released in the customary form and through the customary commercial channels. If at the end of such initial period a sound recording has not been made and released, as above provided, then, subject to the provisions of the next succeeding subdivision, this contract shall terminate.

(Insert amount to be not less than $250)
(Insert period not exceeding six months)

(ii) If, prior to the expiration of the initial period, Publisher pays the Writer the sum of $........(which shall not be charged against or recoupable out of any advances, royalties or other monies theretofor paid, then due, or which thereafter may become due the Writer from the Publisher pursuant to this contract or otherwise), Publisher shall have an additional............months (the "additional period") commencing with the end of the initial period, within which to cause such commercial sound recording to be made and released as provided in subdivision (i) above. If at the end of the additional period a commercial sound recording has not been made and released, as above provided, then this contract shall terminate.

(iii) Upon termination pursuant to this Paragraph 6(a), all rights of any and every nature in and to the composition and in and to any and all copyrights secured thereon in the United States and throughout the world shall automatically re-vest in and become the property of the Writer and shall be reassigned to him by the Publisher. The Writer shall not be obligated to return or pay to the Publisher any advance or indebtedness as a condition of such re-assignment; the said re-assignment shall be in accordance with and subject to the provisions of Paragraph 8 hereof, and, in addition, the Publisher shall pay to the Writer all gross sums which it has theretofore or may thereafter receive in respect of the composition.

Writer's Copies

(b) The Publisher shall furnish, or cause to be furnished, to the Writer six copies of the commercial sound recording referred to in Paragraph 6(a).

Piano Copies, Piano Arrangement or Lead Sheet
(Select (i) or (ii))

(c) The Publisher shall

(i) within 30 days after the initial release of a commercial sound recording of the composition, make, publish and offer for sale regular piano copies of the composition in the form and through the channels customarily employed by it for that purpose;

(ii) within 30 days after execution of this contract make a piano arrangement or lead sheet of the composition and furnish six copies thereof to the Writer.

In the event neither subdivision (i) nor (ii) of this subparagraph (c) is selected, the provisions of subdivision (ii) shall be automatically deemed to have been selected by the parties.

Foreign Copyright

7. (a) Each copyright on the composition in countries other than the United States shall be secured only in the name of the Publisher, and the Publisher shall not at any time divest itself of said foreign copyright directly or indirectly.

Foreign Publication

(b) No rights shall be granted by the Publisher in the composition to any foreign publisher or licensee inconsistent with the terms hereof, nor shall any foreign publication rights in the composition be given to a foreign publisher or licensee unless and until the Publisher shall have complied with the provisions of Paragraph 6 hereof.

Foreign Advance

(c) If foreign rights in the composition are separately conveyed, otherwise than as a part of the Publisher's current and/or future catalog, not less than 50% of any advance received in respect thereof shall be credited to the account of and paid to the Writer.

Foreign Percentage

(d) The percentage of the Writer on monies received from foreign sources shall be computed on the Publisher's net receipts, provided, however, that no deductions shall be made for offsets of monies due from the Publisher to said foreign sources; or for advances made by such foreign sources to the Publisher, unless the Writer shall have received at least 50% of said advances.

No Foreign Allocations

(e) In computing the receipts of the Publisher from licenses granted in respect of synchronization with sound motion pictures, or in respect of any world-wide licenses, or in respect of licenses granted by the Publisher for use of the composition in countries other than the United States, no amount shall be deducted for payments or allocations to publishers or licensees in such countries.

Termination or Expiration of Contract

8. Upon the termination or expiration of this contract, all rights of any and every nature in and to the composition and in and to any and all copyrights secured thereon in the United States and throughout the world, shall re-vest in and become the property of the Writer, and shall be re-assigned to the Writer by the Publisher free of any and all encumbrances of any nature whatsoever, provided that:

(a) If the Publisher, prior to such termination or expiration, shall have granted a domestic license for the use of the composition, not inconsistent with the terms and provisions of this contract, the re-assignment may be subject to the terms of such license.

(b) Publisher shall assign to the Writer all rights which it may have under any such agreement or license referred to in subdivision (a) in respect of the composition, including, but not limited to, the right to receive all royalties or other monies earned by the composition thereunder after the date of termination or expiration of this contract. Should the Publisher thereafter receive or be credited with any royalties or other monies so earned, it shall pay the same to the Writer.

(c) The Writer shall not be obligated to return or pay to the Publisher any advance or indebtedness as a condition of the re-assignment provided for in this Paragraph 8, and shall be entitled to receive the plates and copies of the composition in the possession of the Publisher.

(d) Publisher shall pay any and all royalties which may have accrued to the Writer prior to such termination or expiration.

(e) The Publisher shall execute any and all documents and do any and all acts or things necessary to effect any and all re-assignments to the Writer herein provided for.

Negotiations for New or Unspecified Uses

9. If the Publisher desires to exercise a right in and to the composition now known or which may hereafter become known, but for which no specific provision has been made herein, the Publisher shall give written notice to the Writer thereof. Negotiations respecting all the terms and conditions of any such disposition shall thereupon be entered into between the Publisher and the Writer and no such right shall be exercised until specific agreement has been made.

Royalty

10. The Publisher shall render to the Writer, hereafter, royalty statements accompanied by remittance of the amount due at the

Statements and Payments

times such statements and remittances are customarily rendered by the Publisher, provided, however, that such statements and remittances shall be rendered either semi-annually or quarterly and not more than forty-five days after the end of each such semi-annual or quarterly period, as the case may be. The Writer may at any time, or from time to time, make written request for a detailed royalty statement, and the Publisher shall, within sixty days, comply therewith. Such royalty statements shall set forth in detail the various items, foreign and domestic, for which royalties are payable thereunder and the amounts thereof, including, but not limited to, the number of copies sold and the number of uses made in each royalty category. If a use is made in a publication of the character provided in Paragraph 4, subdivision (e) hereof, there shall be included in said royalty statement the title of said publication, the publisher or issuer thereof, the date of and number of uses, the gross license fee received in connection with each publication, the share thereto of all the writers under contract with the Publisher, and the Writer's share thereof. There shall likewise be included in said statement a description of every other use of the composition, and if by a licensee or licensees their name or names, and if said use is upon a part of an instrument serving to reproduce the composition mechanically, the type of mechanical reproduction, the title of the label thereon, the name or names of the artists performing the same, together with the gross license fees received, and the Writer's share thereof.

Examination of Books

11. (a) The Publisher shall from time to time, upon written demand of the Writer or his representative, permit the Writer or his representative to inspect at the place of business of the Publisher, all books, records and documents relating to the composition and all licenses granted, uses had and payments made therefor, such right of inspection to include, but not by way of limitation, the right to examine all original accountings and records relating to uses and payments by manufacturers of commercial sound recordings and music rolls; and the Writer or his representative may appoint an accountant who shall at any time during usual business hours have access to all records of the Publisher relating to the composition for the purpose of verifying royalty statements rendered or which are delinquent under the terms hereof.

(b) The Publisher shall, upon written demand of the Writer or his representative, cause any licensing agent in the United States and Canada to furnish to the Writer or his representative, statements showing in detail all licenses granted, uses had and payments made in connection with the composition, which licenses or permits were granted, or payments were received, by or through said licensing agent, and to permit the Writer or his representative to inspect at the place of business of such licensing agent, all books, records and documents of such licensing agent, relating thereto. Any and all agreements made by the Publisher with any such licensing agent shall provide that any such licensing agent will comply with the terms and provisions hereof. In the event that the Publisher shall instruct such licensing agent to furnish to the Writer or his representative statements as provided for herein, and to permit the inspection of the books, records and documents as herein provided, then if such licensing agent should refuse to comply with the said instructions, or any of them, the Publisher agrees to institute and prosecute diligently and in good faith such action or proceedings as may be necessary to compel compliance with the said instructions.

(c) With respect to foreign licensing agents, the Publisher shall make available the books or records of said licensing agents in countries outside of the United States and Canada to the extent such books or records are available to the Publisher, except that the Publisher may in lieu thereof make available any accountants' reports and audits which the Publisher is able to obtain.

(d) If as a result of any examination of books, records or documents pursuant to Paragraphs 11(a), 11(b) or 11(c) hereof, it is determined that, with respect to any royalty statement rendered by or on behalf of the Publisher to the Writer, the Writer is owed a sum equal to or greater than five percent of the sum shown on that royalty statement as being due to the Writer, then the Publisher shall pay to the Writer the entire cost of such examination, not to exceed 50% of the amount shown to be due the Writer.

(e) (i) In the event the Publisher administers its own licenses for the manufacture of parts of instruments serving to mechanically reproduce the composition rather than employing a licensing agent for that purpose, the Publisher shall include in each license agreement a provision permitting the Publisher, the Writer or their respective representatives to inspect, at the place of business of such licensee, all books, records and documents of such licensee relating to such license. Within 30 days after written demand by the Writer, the Publisher shall commence to inspect such licensee's books, records and documents and shall furnish a written report of such inspection to the Writer within 90 days following such demand. If the Publisher fails, after written demand by the Writer, to so inspect the licensee's books, records and documents, or fails to furnish such report, the Writer or his representative may inspect such licensee's books, records and documents at his own expense.

(ii) In the further event that the Publisher and the licensee referred to in subdivision (i) above are subsidiaries or affiliates of the same entity or one is a subsidiary or affiliate of the other, then, unless the Publisher employs a licensing agent to administer the licenses referred to in subdivision (i) above, the Writer shall have the right to make the inspection referred to in subdivision (i) above without the necessity of making written demand on the Publisher as provided in subdivision (i) above.

(iii) If as a result of any inspection by the Writer pursuant to subdivisions (i) and (ii) of this subparagraph (e) the Writer recovers additional monies from the licensee, the Publisher and the Writer shall share equally in the cost of such inspection.

12. If the Publisher shall fail or refuse, within sixty days after written demand, to furnish or cause to be furnished, such statements, books, records or documents, or to permit inspection thereof, as provided for in Paragraphs 10 and 11 hereof, or within thirty days after written demand, to make the payment of any royalties due under this contract, then the Writer shall be entitled, upon ten days' written notice, to terminate this contract. However if the Publisher shall:

(a) Within the said ten-day period serve upon the Writer a written notice demanding arbitration; and

(b) Submit to arbitration its claim that it has complied with its obligation to furnish statements, books, records or documents, or permitted inspection thereof or to pay royalties, as the case may be, or both, and thereafter comply with any award of the arbitrator within ten days after such award or within such time as the artibrator may specify;

then this contract shall continue in full force and effect as if the Writer had not sent such notice of termination. If the Publisher shall fail to comply with the foregoing provisions, then this contract shall be deemed to have been terminated as of the date of the Writer's written notice of termination.

Default in Payment or Prevention of Examination

Derivative Works 13. No derivative work prepared under authority of Publisher during the term of this contract may be utilized by Publisher or any other party after termination or expiration of this contract.

Notices 14. All written demands and notices provided for herein shall be sent by certified mail, return receipt requested.

Suits for Infringement 15. Any legal action brought by the Publisher against any alleged infringer of the composition shall be initiated and prosecuted at its sole cost and expense, but if the Publisher should fail, within thirty days after written demand, to institute such action, the Writer shall be entitled to institute such suit at his cost and expense. All sums recovered as a result of any such action shall, after the deduction of the reasonable expense thereof, be divided equally between the Publisher and the Writer. No settlement of any such action may be made by either party without first notifying the other; in the event that either party should object to such settlement, then such settlement shall not be made if the party objecting assumes the prosecution of the action and all expenses thereof, except that any sums thereafter recovered shall be divided equally between the Publisher and the Writer after the deduction of the reasonable expenses thereof.

Infringement Claims

16. (a) If a claim is presented against the Publisher alleging that the composition is an infringement upon some other work or a violation of any other right of another, and because therof the Publisher is jeopardized, it shall forthwith serve a written notice upon the Writer setting forth the full details of such claim. The pendency of said claim shall not relieve the Publisher of the obligation to make payment of the royalties to the Writer hereunder, unless the Publisher shall deposit said royalties as and when they would otherwise be payable, in an account in the joint names of the Publisher and the Writer in a bank or trust company in New York, New York, if the Writer on the date of execution of this contract resides East of the Mississippi River, or in Los Angeles, California, if the Writer on the date of execution of this contract resides West of the Mississippi River. If no suit be filed within nine months after said written notice from the Publisher to the Writer, all monies deposited in said joint account shall be paid over to the Writer plus any interest which may have been earned thereon.

(b) Should an action be instituted against the Publisher claiming that the composition is an infringement upon some other work or a violation of any other right of another, the Publisher shall forthwith serve written notice upon the Writer containing the full details of such claim. Notwithstanding the commencement of such action, the Publisher shall continue to pay the royalties hereunder to the Writer unless it shall, from and after the date of the service of the summons, deposit said royalties as and when they would otherwise be payable, in an account in the joint names of the Publisher and the Writer in a bank or trust company in New York, New York, if the Writer on the date of execution of this contract resides East of the Mississippi River, or in Los Angeles, California, if the Writer on the date of execution of this contract resides West of the Mississippi River. If the said suit shall be finally adjudicated in favor of the Publisher or shall be settled, there shall be released and paid to the Writer all of such sums held in escrow less any amount paid out of the Writer's share with the Writer's written consent in settlement of said action. Should the said suit finally result adversely to the Publisher, the said amount on deposit shall be released to the Publisher to the extent of any expense or damage it incurs and the balance shall be paid over to the Writer.

(c) In any of the foregoing events, however, the Writer shall be entitled to payment of said royalties or the money so deposited at and after such time as he files with the Publisher a surety company bond, or a bond in other form acceptable to the Publisher, in the sum of such payments to secure the return thereof to the extent that the Publisher may be entitled to such return. The foregoing payments or deposits or the filing of a bond shall be without prejudice to the rights of the Publisher or Writer in the premises.

Arbitration

17. Any and all differences, disputes or controversies arising out of or in connection with this contract shall be submitted to arbitration before a sole arbitrator under the then prevailing rules of the American Arbitration Association. The location of the arbitration shall be New York, New York, if the Writer on the date of execution of this contract resides East of the Mississippi River, or Los Angeles, California, if the Writer on the date of execution of this contract resides West of the Mississippi River. The parties hereby individually and jointly agree to abide by and perform any award rendered in such arbitration. Judgment upon any such award rendered may be entered in any court having jurisdiction thereof.

Assignment

18. Except to the extent herein otherwise expressly provided, the Publisher shall not sell, transfer, assign, convey, encumber or otherwise dispose of the composition or the copyright or copyrights secured thereon without the prior written consent of the Writer. The Writer has been induced to enter into this contract in reliance upon the value to him of the personal service and ability of the Publisher

in the exploitation of the composition, and by reason thereof it is the intention of the parties and the essence of the relationship between them that the rights herein granted to the Publisher shall remain with the Publisher and that the same shall not pass to any other person, including, without limitations, successors to or receivers or trustees of the property of the Publisher, either by act or deed of the Publisher or by operation of law, and in the event of the voluntary or involuntary bankruptcy of the Publisher, this contract shall terminate, provided, however, that the composition may be included by the Publisher in a bona fide voluntary sale of its music business or its entire catalog of musical compositions, or in a merger or consolidation of the Publisher with another corporation, in which event the Publisher shall immediately give written notice thereof to the Writer; and provided further that the composition and the copyright therein may be assigned by the Publisher to a subsidiary or affiliated company generally engaged in the music publishing business. If the Publisher is an individual, the composition may pass to a legatee or distributee as part of the inheritance of the Publisher's music business and entire catalog of musical compositions. Any such transfer or assignment shall, however, be conditioned upon the execution and delivery by the transferee or assignee to the Writer of an agreement to be bound by and to perform all of the terms and conditions of this contract to be performed on the part of the Publisher.

Subsidiary Defined

19. A subsidiary, affiliate, or any person, firm or corporation controlled by the Publisher or by such subsidiary or affiliate, as used in this contract, shall be deemed to include any person, firm or corporation, under common control with, or the majority of whose stock or capital contribution is owned or controlled by the Publisher or by any of its officers, directors, partners or associates, or whose policies and actions are subject to domination or control by the Publisher or any of its officers, directors, partners or associates.

Amounts

20. The amounts and percentages specified in this contract shall be deemed to be the amounts and percentages agreed upon by the parties hereto, unless other amounts or percentages are inserted in the blank spaces provided therefor.

Modifications

21. This contract is binding upon and shall enure to the benefit of the parties hereto and their respective successors in interest (as hereinbefore limited). If the Writer (or one or more of them) shall not be living, any notices may be given to, or consents given by, his or their successors in interest. No change or modification of this contract shall be effective unless reduced to writing and signed by the parties hereto.

The words in this contract shall be so construed that the singular shall include the plural and the plural shall include the singular where the context so requires and the masculine shall include the feminine and the feminine shall include the masculine where the context so requires.

Paragraph Headings

22. The paragraph headings are inserted only as a matter of convenience and for reference, and in no way define, limit or describe the scope or intent of this contract nor in any way affect this contract.

Special Provisions

23.

Witness: ....

Publisher ....

By ....

Witness: ....

Address ....

Writer ....(L.S.)

Witness: ....

Address ....

Soc. Sec. # ....

Writer ....(L.S.)

Witness: ....

Address ....

Soc. Sec. # ....

Writer ....(L.S.)

Address ....

Soc. Sec. # ....

FOR YOUR PROTECTION,
SEND A COPY OF THE FULLY SIGNED CONTRACT TO *THE SONGWRITERS GUILD.*

* * * * *

Special Exceptions to apply only if filled in and initialed by the parties.

☐ The composition is part of an original score (not an interpolation) of

  ☐ Living Stage Production   ☐ Motion Picture   ☐ Night Club Revue

  ☐ Televised Musical Production

which is the subject of an agreement between the parties dated ...., a copy of which is hereto annexed. Unless said agreement requires compliance with Paragraph 6 in respect of a greater number of musical compositions, the Publisher shall be deemed to have complied with said Paragraph 6 with respect to the composition if it fully performs the terms of said Paragraph 6 in respect of any one musical composition included in said score.

The Sub-Publishing Agreement

This is a sub-publishing agreement/contract which Brian Ross has written and used over the years. Use it as a guideline to any international agreement offered to you in the future. Study carefully the elements of the agreement and be familiar with its contents so that you can readily identify the pluses and minuses of other international contracts.

YOUR COMPANY NAME (Publisher)
(or Songwriter's Name)

AGREEMENT made this _____ day of _____ 1986
by and between (Your name or name of your publishing firm)
Your Address _____
(hereinafter referred to as the "Owner") and
Your sub-publisher's name_____
(hereinafter referred to as the "Publisher")

Agreement

The Owner hereby represents and warrants that it is the owner of the rights conveyed in this agreement in and to the musical composition entitled: (The name of your song) by (Your Name). (Musical composition is hereinafter referred to as the "said composition.")

The Owner grants to the Publisher the following rights for (How Long? Negotiable, i.e. one year, or more) subject to the terms and restrictions contained in this agreement:

a) The sole and exclusive right to print, reprint, publish and sell the said composition in   (Name of Country)   (hereinafter referred to as the "licensed territory"), but not elsewhere.
b) The exclusive right to license public performances (including broadcasting) for profit or otherwise, of the said composition in the licensed territory.
c) The exclusive right to grant non-exclusive rights for the manufacture and sale in the licensed territory only of all mechanical, electrical, electronic, and magnetic devices including Compact Disc (CD) and other devices now known or known in the future for the reproduction of said composition and to collect the customary royalty rate prevailing in the licensed territory.
d) The non-exclusive right to grant non-exclusive synchronisation licenses for the use of the said composition in motion pictures and television films produced within the licensed territory, and of making copies of said motion pictures and exporting such copies into all countries of the world, provided however, that the Publisher shall in each instance obtain the Owner's written or cabled approval.
e) The right in the licensed territory only to adapt, arrange or translate the said composition, to change the title thereof, to substitute the lyrics therefore, or to make any other changes in the said composition, to make it suitable for publication in the licensed territory. All such resulting versions of the said composition shall be the property of the Owner.

The right of the publisher to license public performances is made subject to the rights of (ASCAP or BMI) in said composition and upon the condition that the Publisher shall register said composition promptly with the national performance rights society operating in the licensed territory, affiliated with (ASCAP or BMI) and to notify it to pay _____ of the full Publisher's share of performance fees on said composition (and all resulting versions) to (BMI or ASCAP) for the account of the Owner. No advance payments made hereunder shall be charged to the Owner's share of performance fees. In the event there is no affiliation between (BMI or AS-CAP) and any one or more performing rights societies administering performing rights in the said composition in one or more countries of the licensed territories, the full publisher's share of all performance fees on said composition from any such country shall be paid to the Publisher, who shall pay (Negotiable)   to the Owner.

The Owner warrants and represents and agrees that it has not granted and shall not grant to any other person, firm or corporation any right, license or privilege which shall in any way diminish or impair any of the rights, licenses or privileges herein granted to the Publisher for the licensed territory, and the Owner shall execute and deliver any and all instruments, papers and documents that may be required by the Publisher for the purpose of exercising, protecting and perfecting any of the rights herein granted.

The Publisher agrees to pay to the Owner the following royalties:

a) (Negotiable) % of the marked retail selling price of sheet music, dance orchestration or any other arrangement of this said composition sold, paid for and not returned in the licensed territory. The Publisher and Owner agree that no royalties be paid on professional copies, copies sold but not paid for, copies issued for advertising and exploitation purposes.

b) (Negotiable) % of royalties for each and every use of said composition in the licensed territory in any book, album, folio, or other composite publication.

c) (Negotiable) % of all sums actually paid by users for the reproduction rights granted to the Publisher in this agreement.

d) (Negotiable) % of all sums received by the Publisher from the licensing of synchronisation rights of the said composition with motion picture films produced within the licensed territory.

e) (50% or negotiable) % of any and all other sums received by the Publisher from *any* source whatsoever with respect to the said composition.

f) The percentages agreed upon in this contract shall be based on the full 100% (one hundred percent) collected at source, and no deductions shall be allowed for any percentage payable or retained by any sub-licensee or agent of the Publisher.

In further consideration of the rights granted by the Owner to the Publisher under this agreement, the Publisher agrees to pay or has paid to the Owner at the signature of this agreement, the minimum guaranteed compensation (ADVANCE) of U.S. (Negotiable $) which is non-recoupable under any circumstances. This agreement shall not become effective until such minimum guaranteed compensation has been received by the Owner. (Note: The Publisher may ask you to agree that he is not obligated to pay any other monies under this agreement until such minimum guaranteed advance shall have been fully earned and recouped by the Publisher from all royalties and other sums, exclusive of performance fees, due to the owner pursuant to this agreement) THIS POINT IS NEGOTIABLE!

The Publisher agrees to pay all royalties required to be paid to one or more author(s), composer(s), or editor(s) of such adaptations, translations, lyrics and other versions of the said composition and Publisher further agrees to hold the Owner free and harmless of any claims and liabilities therefor.

The Publisher agrees that all editions of said composition published in the licensed territory shall bear proper copyright notice, and the following notice shall be printed at the bottom of the title page:

© 1986 by (The Name of Your Company)

There shall likewise be printed at the bottom of the title page a statement to the effect that the said edition is authorized for sale in the licensed territory only. The name of the original composer(s) and/or author(s) shall appear on the title page of all editions of said composition published in the licensed territory.

a) The Owner shall mail to the Publisher, at no charge, six (6) copies of any available sheet music or orchestration published by the Owner of said composition.

b) The Publisher shall mail to the Owner, at no charge, six (6) copies of any and all editions (sheet music) as published in the licensed territory of said composition, promptly upon publication thereof.

Each quarter, (every 90 days), or if agreed upon by Publisher and Owner, semi-annually, (every six months), without fail, each and every year of this agreement the Publisher shall render to the Owner statements of royalties payable in accordance with the provisions of this agreement. Such statements shall show the number of copies sold and royalties accruing to the Owner under this agreement from all sources during the agreed upon payment period (which is negotiable), and each such statement shall be of any and all sums shown to be due and payable in U.S. DOLLARS. Note that Brian Ross has specified U.S. Dollars. Because of the difference in exchange rates from country to country in U.S. dollars, you could earn less than what you deserve by accepting foreign currency and then having your bank exchange the currency to U.S. Dollars)

*Special Note here about your right to audit that statement—The Publisher shall permit the Owner or his representative to inspect at the place of business of the Publisher during usual business hours and upon serving reasonable notice to the Publisher all books, records and other documents relating to the said composition for the purpose of verifying royalty statements rendered by the Publisher, or which sums might be considered as delinquent under the terms hereof.

Any rights of any kind not specifically granted to the Publisher under this agreement are retained by the Owner.

*Note: This next clause is your guarantee that this Publisher is going to get you a cover record in a reasonable amount of time or you are going to get your song back (reversion clause) and you keep the ADVANCE you received.

a) The Publisher shall secure the release of one (1) or more phonograph records of said composition on a major phonograph label in the licensed territory no later than (one year) after the date of the agreement; the Publisher shall advise the Owner promptly of the artist name, label, name and catalog number of said phonograph record and any further phonograph records of the said composition released in the licensed territory. The Publisher undertakes to use all reasonable means and efforts to exploit the said composition in the licensed territory.

b) In the event that the Publisher shall fail to comply with the provisions of Paragraph 13 (a) by the required date, all rights herein conveyed to the Publisher shall automatically revert to Owner.

c) Six (6) months after the publication of the said composition in the licensed territory the Publisher shall have the right to include the said composition in a folio, album or similar publication, published by it, but said composition may not be published in magazines, books, etc. without the prior written approval of the Owner.

In the event that the Publisher does not fulfill all obligations assumed by it hereunder or does not observe all the conditions specified herein, the Owner has the right to require the Publisher to do so by notifying the Publisher to that effect by registered letter, and unless the Publisher shall comply therewith within sixty (60) days following the mailing of the registered letter, the Owner has the right to *terminate* this agreement. In the event that the Publisher is adjudicated bankrupt or insolvent, this agreement shall in no way relieve the Publisher from the performance of its obligations under this agreement, and the recapture by the Owner of the rights granted herein shall be in addition to and not in limitation of any other rights the Owner may have by reason of the Publisher's *breach* of the terms of this agreement. No rights, titles or interests granted to the Publisher under this agreement may be transferred or licensed to any other parties without the prior written approval of the Owner.

The Owner appoints the Publisher to bring suits or proceedings to protect the copyright and all the copyright rights in and to the said composition and all resulting versions in the licensed territory, but all at the expense of the Publisher, and the Publisher accepts such appointment. The Publisher shall not bring any suit in the name of the Owner or join the Owner as a party plaintiff in any suit or proceeding without the prior written approval of the Owner. All sums recovered as a result of such suits or proceedings shall, after the deduction of reasonable attorney fees and expenses thereof, as *mutually* agreed upon by Publisher and Owner, be divided equally between the Owner and the Publisher.

This agreement shall not be considered one of partnership or joint venture.

This writing contains the entire agreement (Paragraph 1-17) between the parties hereto with respect to the subject matter hereof and shall be construed to have been written under the laws of (your home state). The parties hereto agree to execute and deliver all papers and documents required to effectuate the terms hereof. This agreement cannot be changed, waived or altered unless same shall be in writing and signed by all parties. Any such change shall be considered an addendum or attachment and be affixed to this writing and labeled as Attachment A, B, C, etc. and signed and agreed upon by both parties. This agreement shall inure (pass into use) to the benefit of and shall be binding upon the parties hereto and their respective successors and assigns.

IN WITNESS WHEREOF, the parties hereto have caused this agreement to be duly executed as of the day and year first written above.

_____
Your name or publishing firm

_____
Your foreign publishers name
(Sub-Publisher)

Great Demos: The Secret to Songwriting Success

BY GEORGE WILLIAMS

What Is a Demo?

A professional demo tape is a high quality recording which demonstrates to music business professionals the quality of songs you write and is the songwriter's best sales tool. The right demo can mean the difference between a record and a rejection. If the first 20 seconds of your demo fail to catch a song screener's attention, you've failed. In that short period of time a skilled screener can tell whether or not you've got talent. That's how crucial a demo can be.

Music business professionals often judge the quality of your songs by the quality of your recording. Your songs could be the greatest since Lennon and McCartney but if you've recorded them on a cheap cassette recorder they'll sound cheap. One of the major complaints of music business professionals is that they receive too many poorly recorded demos.

Types of Demos

There are three types of demos:
- The simple piano/vocal or guitar/vocal demo
- The basic track demo, usually with vocal, bass, drums, guitar or piano
- The master demo, a fully produced recording suitable for pressing records.

Publishers, producers, record companies and artists will each want the type of demo which best meets his individual needs. Not all publishers want simple piano/vocal demos nor do all record companies require master quality demos. Learning each prospect's requirements and preferences will save you a lot of time, trouble and wasted money.

What Type of Demo Do You Need?

If you are a songwriter attempting to interest a publisher or producer in your songs, you will need a simple piano/vocal or guitar/vocal or basic track demo. Publishers and producers listed in *Songwriter's Market* usually specify what type of demo they prefer. To always be prepared, I suggest you have both a simple demo and a basic track demo.

If you are a singer/songwriter or are in a group attempting to land a recording contract, you will need at least a basic track demo. However, I recommend that anyone attempting to land a recording contract present a master quality demo. Major record companies are deluged with dozens of tapes each day and only the very best sound will stand out.

Where to Record—at Home or in the Studio

Where you decide to record your demo depends on how much money you have to spend and where you feel most comfortable. There are many "demo" recording studios which specialize in this type of work. Their prices are usually quite reason-

George Williams *is the author of* The Songwriter's Demo Manual and Success Guide *and has over 20 years' experience in the music business as a performer, studio musician, songwriter, producer and jingle writer. He owns his own recording studio and jingle business in southern California.*

able because competition is fierce and many are struggling to stay in business. Recording in a studio in the short run will be far less expensive than setting up your own home recording studio. However, if you plan to pursue a career as a songwriter or recording artist, setting up your own home recording studio will save you a lot of money in the long run and help you to develop as a songwriter and as a artist.

Studio Recording

Some advantages of studio recording are:
- It will be cheaper in the short run.
- Studios are equipped with the finest recording and signal processing equipment which can help your demo to sound professional.
- You'll have a recording engineer to operate the equipment who may also be able to make suggestions which will improve your demo.

Finding a Demo Studio

First, look in your local Yellow Pages under recording studios. If you live in a small town, you may have to check the Yellow Pages of the nearest large city. If you still can't find one, try writing to *Mix Magazine*, 2608 9th Street, Berkeley CA 94710. *Mix* is the recording industry trade magazine and puts out a recording studio directory for each part of the country. To locate a studio in Canada look into *Music Directory Canada* put out by *Canadian Musician Magazine* (832 Mount Pleasant Road, Toronto, Ontario M4P 2L3).

Once you've located several studios in your area, call for rates. Ask if the studio has a piano, organ or other musical instruments available and if there will be a charge to use them during sessions. Most studios do not charge for the use of studio instruments.

How Many Tracks Do I Need?

You don't need 16 or 24 tracks though many studios may try to convince you otherwise. They're only trying to make more money. You can make a good basic track demo on an 8 track or even a 4 track, if you will tell the engineer exactly what instruments you intend to record. This will also save a great deal of money on the recording tape used on the 4 or 8 track versus the 16 or 24 track.

Cutting Studio Costs

A decent 8 track recording studio should cost no more than $25 an hour. Attempt to bargain with the studio by offering them say, $75 for four hours. If the studio won't bargain on price, try another studio.

To save money on recording tape, lease an 8 track master tape for the duration of your recording. After the 8 track master is mixed down to stereo 2 track, the 8 track master will be erased. You can save money this way, however, once the master 8 track tape has been erased, you can't go back to remix or re-record certain parts you may later decide need to be done over.

Above all, the best way to save money in the studio is to rehearse thoroughly. By being prepared you will eliminate costly mistakes and reruns. If you are going to use a small group, try to work with musicians who have played in a studio before. They will generally be more relaxed and will make fewer mistakes which again means you'll minimize recording time.

Mixing

Assuming you've already made a 4 or 8 track recording, you will have to have it mixed down to a stereo half-track copy on quarter inch tape. From this quarter inch, half-track copy you will make the cassette copies to send out. Make certain you stay with the engineer while he mixes your tape. Be sure to tell him how you want each song to sound. If you want more reverb on the vocal, tell him, otherwise he won't know. Don't forget, you're the boss because you're paying the bill. Don't be intimidated by all those red and green lights. You have ears, use them. Tell the engineer *exactly* what you want to hear.

Home Recording

With the recent introduction of affordable recording equipment, it is possible for you to own a home recording studio. There are two types of recording systems you can easily set up at home:
- The 4 track cassette recorder with built-in mixer
- The 4 or 8 track reel to reel recorder with mixer and stereo amplifier.

Four track cassette recorders with built-in mixers such as the Teac 144, 244 or Fostex 250, are the cheapest and most portable. However, the sound quality of these 4 track cassette systems is only 55% of the 4 track and 8 track reel to reel recorders. Still, tapes recorded on these systems sound quite professional. Most come with DBX noise reduction which means you can do numerous over-dubs without creating a lot of tape noise. And, if you're constantly moving around, consider that these systems weigh approximately 25 pounds, making them easy to move and set up.

Four and 8 track reel to reel systems cost more and are bulkier, but yield higher quality demos. I'd suggest buying an older model, used recorder such as the Teac A-3340S 4 track or the Tascam 80-8 8 track recorder.

In addition, you'll need a mixer designed for recording with your multi-track recorder. Generally, PA mixers will not do the job. They are often stereo boards and are electronically noisy. Smaller mixers like the Teac Model 2 and Model 3, which are no longer manufactured, make great little boards. If you have a 4 track, you'll need a mixer with 4 inputs and 4 outputs. If you have an 8 track, you'll need 8 inputs and 8 outputs on the mixer. Also, it is imperative that each input channel have assignment buttons which will enable you to assign an incoming signal to a particular track just by pushing a button.

Ten Tips for Better Demos

1. **A demo tape should contain three or four of your best songs.** Place your strongest songs up front. These songs should be the most commercial songs you've written. They should be the kinds of songs people listen to on the radio and will want to buy. They should be simple, direct and have a very catchy chorus or "hook." The hook is that instantly recognizable piece of music that captures (hooks) the listener and makes the song memorable. Without a great hook you can't have a truly commercial song.

2. **Each song should be no more than three minutes.** Keep intros to 15 seconds or less. Don't waste the song screener's time with instrumental breaks. You're trying to sell your songs not your instrumental skill.

3. **Keep the vocal out front.** The vocal should be very clear so the listener can understand the words being sung. Remember: The lyrics are half your song. If the listener can't understand the words, you're dead.

4. **A pleasant voice will help sell your songs.** If you can't sing well, have someone else sing your songs. A pleasant voice will attract the song screener to your demo and will make it easier for him to listen to the entire tape.

5. **Spend as little money on demos as possible.** You don't have to record in a 16 or 24 track recording studio. It's possible to make a simple demo at home with a good reel to reel tape recorder, some good recording tape and two good microphones. If you don't have this recording equipment, there are lots of demo recording studios that will do the job for you. A decent demo studio should cost no more than $25 an hour for two track recording. In many places you can get 8 track recording for that price.

6. **Thoroughly rehearse your songs before attempting to demo them.** You should be able to demo three or four songs in an hour in the studio if you're well rehearsed. Being prepared means you'll save time in the studio and that means you'll save money.

7. **Edit your tape so there is 4 or 5 seconds between songs.** After your reel to reel tape is recorded make cassette copies to send to publishers, producers, recording artists and record companies. NEVER SEND THE ONLY COPY OF YOUR DEMO TO ANYONE FOR ANY REASON. If your "master" demo is lost in the mail—and many are—all your time, hard work and money will have been wasted. Mail out copies only!

8. **Make certain you indicate the title and order of appearance of each of the songs on the cassette label along with your name, address and phone number.** You'd be surprised how many people don't do this. Country star Terri Gibbs forgot to do this and it took producer Ed Penney five years to locate her before she recorded "Somebody's Knockin'." So make certain your name, address and phone number are on ALL your tapes.

9. **It should go without saying that there shouldn't be any extra noises on your tape,** like car horns honking, babies crying or dogs barking. All that should be heard is a *good clean recording* showing the quality of songs you write.

10. **Be sure to** *include typed lyrics* of each song with your name, address and phone number on each sheet.

By making the best demo possible you'll be far ahead in the race toward songwriting success. Remember: The demo tape is your best sales tool.

How to Be a Music Market Detective————————

BY BARBARA NORTON KUROFF

Today's top acts don't advertise for songs, and stars aren't listed in telephone books and rarely in any other directory, including *Songwriter's Market*. So if you've written what you think could be a hit for a specific recording artist, how do you get your song to him?

Fortunately, the producers, publishers and managers around star performers *are* accessible. They are the people who play a big part in decisions concerning the stars' careers, including the choice of material for recording sessions. Get your song to one of these people and you get your song to the artist, assuming, of course, that the people around the artist think your song is good. This is not to say these people are easy to reach—they are not—but a music market detective can ferret them out.

Your Music Market Notebook

Begin your search by assigning one page of a notebook for each artist you think you might have songs for; these pages are your artist information sheets. Use each sheet to record the names, addresses and phone numbers of the artist's record companies, producers, publishers and managers. To get this information begin by looking around your home. Do you own albums by any of the artists you've listed in your notebook? If so, their covers and labels are loaded with clues.

Album covers give the name (and possibly address) of an artist's record company and also the name of the producer. If song titles and their writers and publishers are not listed on the album covers, they can be found on the record label. Album liner notes might also reveal valuable information about an artist or group: how a particular song came to their attention or why they recorded it; or a new musical or career direction the act might be undertaking.

Check album dates, however. Since we're talking about popular artists, you can assume if albums are more than a year old, there may be a more recent one available in your local record shop with new information.

Once you've found the names of record companies and publishers of the artists you wish to submit songs to, be sure to check the index of *Songwriter's Market*.

The Corner Newsstand

Your next stop should be your local magazine stand, if they carry the weekly music industry trade magazines, *Billboard* or *Cash Box*.

The charts in *Billboard* and *Cash Box* list today's most popular songs in a variety of musical categories—Adult Contemporary, Hot 100, Country, Black, Jazz, Classical, etc. At the top of each chart is a guide to reading the information given in the entries: producer, writer, label, publisher, etc. *Cash Box* does not list producers, but otherwise the charts in both publications give information in a somewhat similar format.

Barbara Norton Kuroff *is a songwriter and former editor of* Songwriter's Market.

The trades also offer the songwriter information about what's happening in the music business in Los Angeles, Nashville, New York City, and across the US and around the world: industry events, new companies, executive changes, artist news, new releases. This is all information you can use in your songwriting career. Read the ads, too, especially those announcing an artist's newest release. Often the name and perhaps the address and phone number of the artist's manager can be found there.

Although the charts change weekly, songs by top artists climb and then fall slowly back down the charts for weeks. Therefore, for your purpose of finding the names of labels, producers and publishers of particular artists, it is sufficient to purchase a trade magazine once every few weeks. (Don't forget to keep the receipts to claim as a business expense when song royalties start coming in.)

Annual subscriptions to the trades are expensive but keep in mind the value of other publications that may be included in the subscription rate. *Cash Box* automatically sends subscribers their *Annual Directory*, selling separately for $17.50 if purchased by mail. Included in this directory are the names, addresses and phone numbers of hundreds of music publishers and record companies, but no submission information.

The Local Library

Both publications can be found in the music sections of many libraries. They're usually available for reference only and can't be checked out. Libraries subscribing to either trade magazine should also have that publication's annual directory of publishers and record companies.

Even if your library does not subscribe to *Billboard* or *Cash Box*, they probably do have phone directories for cities across the country—including Los Angeles, New York (Manhattan), and Nashville. Unlike the famous artists they represent, music publishers and record companies *are* listed in phone books, not only with their phone numbers but also their addresses.

Phone books don't include zip codes with the addresses, but you can refer to the *Zip Code and Post Office Directory*, published annually by the US Postal Service. There should be one in the library; if not, you will find one in your local post office. If you call and ask, most libraries will even look up a company's address and phone number for you, or you can use the phone company's directory service, usually limited to answering a certain number of requests per call.

Getting Closer

Your music market notebook by now should pin-point your artists and the names, addresses and phone numbers of their record companies and publishers; the names of their producers; and possibly the names of their managers. What you don't know is which of those names would be the best to first submit material to.

My advice would be to work toward getting your material to the person with the most to say in the artist's choice of material—the producer. Unfortunately, so far you only have the names of the artists' producers—no addresses or phone numbers. You will have obtained some information from *Songwriter's Market* and might have been observant enough to notice some producers listed in *Billboard International Buyer's Guide* as the A&R director of record companies. You might also have been lucky enough to find some in the L.A., Nashville or Manhattan phone books. But the producer who does not always work out of an office but spends most of his time in various recording studios is not an easy person to track down. You must now find another route to them.

The addresses and phone numbers of all the artists' record companies and many of their publishers that you *do* have in your music market notebook will become your key to getting your songs to the producers who can get them to the artists.

Zeroing In

For several reasons the record company is the best place to start tracking a producer. Record companies are big-business operations with regular hours; receptionists and secretaries are paid to answer phones and handle mail. It's been my experience that these front desk people are amiable, capable and helpful, as long as you don't abuse their good qualities by being overly demanding, calling every other day, or keeping them on the phone too long.

When you get someone on the phone, be upfront and to the point. Know what you intend to say: "I'm (*your name*) and I'm trying to contact (*the producer's name*), or the person who reviews material for (*the artist's name*). If the producer has an office in the studio—many times he will—you may be switched there immediately. If he doesn't have an office in the studio, the receptionist may give you an address and phone number where the producer can be contacted. If she doesn't volunteer this valuable information, be sure to ask for it.

On the other hand, you could get no farther than: "I'm sorry, we aren't allowed to give out that information," or "We don't accept any outside material." Don't get discouraged. Remember you also have names and addresses of several publishers of the artist's recently recorded songs. The producer may have worked closely with these publishers. It could even be that the artist or the producer owns one of the publishing houses. So try the same routine with the music publishers written in your notebook.

Whomever you talk with at recording companies or publishing houses, make notes in your notebook on when you called, whom you talked with, and what was said. Jot down things like "He's in Europe at Midem" or "He'll be tied up for the next few weeks producing a session on Linda Ronstadt." This could be valuable information later, even as conversation, when you finally do talk with the big, busy producer.

If the person on the other end of the line gives you permission to submit material, establish some way your package can be easily identified when it arrives at the office. Often a receptionist—let's call her Susan—will tell you to write her name on your package. When your tape arrives at the office, Susan sees her name, knows she must have talked with you, and so lays it on the producer's desk (or at least sees it's somewhere near the top of the unsolicited tapes). I'm not saying this procedure works every time. What I am saying is that it has worked many times for unknown songwriters. Even well-known songwriters use it as a way of seeing that their material is heard.

When calling long distance, remember time differences. When it's 9 a.m. in New York City and people are already at their desks with their fourth coffee, it's 8 a.m. in Nashville, where many music industry people don't arrive in their offices until 10, and only 6 a.m. in Los Angeles where a producer may just be finishing up an all-night recording session.

In Conclusion

If you've been a diligent music market detective, you may find yourself invited to submit songs to people who spend thousands of dollars just on the production of one song. Your submissions cannot be mediocre songs only your family and friends like. Your songs must be worked and honed until they are better than the best. If they are not, all your detective work will have been in vain.

I think that by keeping a music market notebook you will no longer feel helpless in an industry that can often intimidate beginners (and even those who are successful). Recognize your own ability to dig for information and use resources that help get your songs to anyone in any music center without leaving your own home town.

Glossary

A&R Director. Record company executive who deals with new artists, songs and masters coordinating the best material with a particular artist.

A/C. Adult contemporary.

Advance. Money paid to the songwriter or recording artist before regular royalty payments begin. Sometimes called "upfront" money, advances are deducted from royalties.

AFM. American Federation of Musicians. A union for musicians and arrangers.

AFTRA. American Federation of Television and Radio Artists.

AGAC. American Guild of Authors and Composers, now called The Songwriter's Guild.

AIMP. Association of Independent Music Publishers.

AOR. Album-oriented rock.

Arrangement. Adapting a composition for performance by other instruments, voices or performers.

ASCAP. American Society of Composers, Authors and Publishers.

A-side. Side one of a single promoted by the record company to become a hit.

Assignment. Transfer of rights to a song from writer to publisher.

Audiovisual. Presentations using audio backup for visual material.

Bed. Prerecorded music used as background material in commercials.

Beta. ½" videocassette format.

BMA. Black Music Association.

BMI. Broadcast Music, Inc.

Booking agent. Solicits work and schedules performances for entertainers.

b/w. Backed with.

C&W. Country and western.

CAPAC. Composers, Authors & Publishers of Canada Ltd.

CARAS. Canadian Academy of Recording Arts and Sciences.

Catalog. The collected songs of one writer, or all songs handled by one publisher.

CCC. California Copyright Conference.

Chart. The written arrangement of a song.

Charts. The weekly trade magazines' lists of the bestselling records.

CHR. Contemporary Hit Radio.

CIRPA. Canadian Independent Record Producers Association.

CMRRA. Canadian Musical Reproduction Rights Association.

Collaborator. Person who works with another in a creative situation.

CMA. Country Music Association.

CMPA. Church Music Publishers Association.

Copyright. Legal protection given authors and composers for an original work.

Cover record. A new version of a previously recorded song.

CPM. Conference of Personal Managers.

CRIA. Canadian Recording Industry Association.

Crossover. A song that becomes popular in two or more music fields.

Cut. Any finished recording; a selection from an LP; or to record.

Demo. A rough recording, usually a tape, of a song.

Disc. A record.

Distributor. Sole marketing agent of a record in a particular area.

Donut. Jingle with singing at the beginning and end and only instrumental background in the middle.

Engineer. A specially trained individual who operates all studio recording equipment.

Evergreen. Any song that remains popular year after year.

EP. Extended play record (usually 12") containing more selections than a standard single, but fewer than a standard LP.

FICAP. Federation of International Country Air Personalities.

Folio. A softcover collection of printed music prepared for sale.

GMA. Gospel Music Association.

Harry Fox Agency. Organization that collects mechanical royalties.

Hook. A memorable "catch" phrase or melody line which is repeated in a song.

ILA. Independent Record Labels Association.

IMU. International Musicians Union.

ips. Inches per second; a speed designation for tape recording.

IRMA. International Record Manufacturers Association.

Jingle. Usually a short verse set to music designed as a commercial message.

LP. Designation for long-playing record played at 33⅓ rpm.

Lead sheet. Written version (melody, chord symbols and lyric) of a song.

Leader. Plastic (non-recordable) tape at the beginning and between songs for ease in selection.

Lyric sheet. A typed copy of a song's lyrics.

Market. A demographic division of the record-buying public.

Master. Edited and mixed tape used in the production of records.

MCA. Music Critics Association.

Mechanical right. The right to profit from the physical reproduction of a song.

Mechanical royalty. Money earned from record and tape sales.

MIEA. Music Industry Educators' Association.

Mix. To blend a multi-track recording into the desired balance of sound.

MOR. Middle of the road.

Ms. Manuscript.

Music publisher. A company that evaluates songs for commercial potential, finds artists to record them, finds other uses such as TV or film for the songs, collects income generated by the songs and protects copyrights from infringement.

NAIRD. National Association of Independent Record Distributors.

NARAS. National Academy of Recording Arts and Sciences.

NARM. National Association of Record Merchandisers.

NAS. National Academy of Songwriters, formerly Songwriters Resources and Services (SRS).

Needle-drop. Use of a prerecorded cut from a stock music house in an audiovisual soundtrack.

NMA. Nashville Music Assocation.

NMPA. National Music Publishers Association

NSAI. Nashville Songwriters Association International.

NSG. National Songwriters' Guild.

Performing rights. A specific right granted by US copyright law that protects a composition from being publicly performed without the owner's permission.

Performing rights organization. An organization that collects income from the public performance of songs written by its members and then proportionally distributes this income to the individual copyright holder based on the number of performances of each song.

Personal Manager. Guides and advises artist in his career.

Pitch. To attempt to sell a song by audition; the sales talk.

Playlist. List of songs that a radio station will play.

Plug. A favorable mention, broadcast or performance of a song. Also means to pitch a song.

Points. Percentage paid to producers and artists for records sold.

Press. To manufacture a record.

PROCAN. Performing Rights Organization of Canada Ltd.

Producer. Person who supervises every aspect of recording a song.

Production company. Company that specializes in producing jingle packages for advertising agencies. May also refer to companies that specialize in audiovisual programs.

Professional manager. Member of a music publisher's staff who screens submitted material and tries to get the company's catalog of songs recorded.

Program director. Radio station employee who screens records and develops a playlist of songs that station will broadcast.

Public domain. Any composition with an expired, lapsed or invalid copyright.

Purchase license. Fee paid for music used from a stock music library.

Query. A letter of inquiry to a potential song buyer soliciting his interest.

R&B. Rhythm and blues.

Rate. The percentage of royalty as specified by contract.

Release. Any record issued by a record company.

Residuals. In advertising, payments to singers and musicians for subsequent use of a commercial.

Rhythm Machine. An electronic device that provides various tempos for use as background rhythm for other instruments or vocalists.

RIAA. Recording Industry Association of America.

Royalty. Percentage of money earned from the sale of records or use of a song.

SASE. Abbreviation for self-addressed stamped envelope.

SBSA. Santa Barbara Screenwriters' Association.

SBSG. Santa Barbara Songwriters' Guild.

Scratch track. Rough working tape demonstrating idea for a commercial.

SESAC. Performing rights organization.

Shop. To pitch songs to a number of companies or publishers.

Single. 45 rpm record.

SIRMA. Small Independent Record Manufacturers Association.

Song shark. Person who deals with songwriters deceptively for his own profit.

Songwriter's Guild. Formerly called AGAC.

Soundtrack. The audio, including music and narration, of a film, videotape or audiovisual program.

Split Publishing. To divide publishing rights between two or more publishers.

SRS. Songwriters Resources and Services, now called The National Academy of Songwriters (NAS)..

Staff writer. A salaried songwriter who writes exclusively for one publishing firm.

Standard. A song popular year after year; an evergreen.

Statutory royalty rate. The minimum payment for mechanical rights guaranteed by law that a record company must pay the songwriter and his publisher for each record or tape sold.

Stiff. The first recording of a song that commercially fails.

Subpublishing. Certain rights granted by a US publisher to a foreign publisher in exchange for promoting the US catalog in his territory.

Synchronization. Technique of timing a musical soundtrack to action on film or video.

Synchronization rights. Right to a use composition in time-relation to action on film or video.

TMA. Texas Music Association.

Track. Divisions of a recording tape (e.g., 24-track tape) that can be individually recorded in the studio, then mixed into a finished master.

Trades. Publications that cover the music industry.

U/C. Urban contemporary.

U-matic. 3/4" professional videocassette format.

VHS. 1/2" videocassette format.

Work. To pitch or shop a song.

Late Arrivals

The following is a listing of markets received too late for inclusion in the regular sections of this book. Please refer to the "Using Your Songwriter's Market" section and the individual section introductions for important information concerning these listings.

Music Publishers

APON PUBLISHING CO., Box 3082, Steinway Sta., Long Island City NY 11103. Manager: Don Zemann. Music publisher, record company and record producer. ASCAP. Publishes 250 songs/year. Pays according to special agreements made with individual songwriters.
How to Contact: Call first. Prefers cassette with 1-6 songs and lyric sheet. SASE. Reports in 1 month.
Music: Classical, background music, dance-oriented, easy listening, folk and international. Recently published "Polka Fever," (by Slawko Kunst), recorded by Czech Brass/Apon Records (polkas); "Russian Gypsy Melodies," (by Sandor Lakatos), recorded by Hungarian Gypsy Orchestra/Apon Records (gypsy tunes); and "Czech Songs," (by Alojz Skolka), recorded by Budvarka Ensemble/Apon Records (folk/pop).
Tips: "We are sub-publishers for pop music overseas."

BIG WEDGE MUSIC, Box 25329, Nashville TN 37202. (615) 754-2950. President: Ralph Johnson. BMI. Music publisher. Publishes 75 new songwriters/year. Pays standard royalty.
How to Contact: Prefers cassette and lyric or lead sheet. SASE. Reports in 2 weeks.
Music: Mostly country, pop and rock; also gospel. Recently published "Body Language,"(by Andy Wilson Jr. and Jack Wiggins); "I'd Go Through It All Over Again," (by Ralph Johnson), recorded by R.J. Wiggins on Wedge Records; and "Another Little Piece Of Her Love," written and recorded by Kenny Pierce on Wedge Records.
Tips: "Make sure your demo is clearly recorded and well produced."

CANADIAN CUSTOM RECORDS, Box 369, West Hill, Ontario M1E 4V9, Canada. (416) 283-8827. President: Barbara L. Kroetsch. PRO, CAPAC. Music publisher, record company (Via Records), and record producer (DeBarre Productions).
How to Contact: Prefers cassette with 6 songs and lead sheet. SAE and IRC. Reports in 4 weeks.
Music: Rock, country, gospel, blues, and jazz.

D.S.M. PRODUCERS, Suite 1204, 161 W. 54th St., New York NY 10019. (212) 245-0006. Contact: A&R/Publishing Div. ASCAP. Music publisher and record producer. Publishes 20 + songs/year. Pays standard royalty.
How to Contact: Prefers cassette or videocassette and lyric/lead sheets. SASE. Reports in 4 weeks.
Music: Mostly dance/R&B, dance/rock, and country; also jazz, gosspel, and pop. Recently published

"Hustlin' Time," (by E. Mauge), recorded by American Steel on Silver Screen Records (dance/R&B); "Stay With Me," (by E&M Ross) (pop/rock); and "What We Need Is Love," (by S. Mauge) (rock/dance).

FLIN-FLON MUSIC, 102 Veterans Ave., Mullen NE 69152. (308) 546-2294. General Manager: L.E. Walker. Music publisher. BMI. Pays standard royalty.
How to Contact: Prefers 7½ ips reel to reel or cassette with 1-3 songs and lyric sheet. SASE. Reports in 1 month.
Music: Bluegrass, disco, folk, R&B, country, contemporary, gospel and soft rock. Recently published "Nine Twenty Train," (by Randy Robinson), recorded by WDLJ/Flin-Flon Records (MOR); "All Thru The Night," (by Jeanie Snyder), recorded by WDLJ/Flin-Flon Records (country); and "Hello Ba——by," (by Earl Walker), recorded by Group/Varsity Records (jazz).

GENESIS MUSIC, 7 Jupiter St., Winston Hills NSW 2153, Australia. (02) 686-1194. A&R: Bob Goodfellow. APRA. Music publisher, record company and record producer. Publishes varying number of songs and new songwriters/year. Pays standard royalty. Affiliates include Tempo Music.
How to Contact: Prefers cassette with maximum 3 songs and lyric/lead sheets. Does not return unsolicited material.
Music: Gospel.
Tips: "We're looking for good gospel songs with contemporary feel."

GOTOWN PUBLISHING CO., 706 W. Mechanic St., Leesville LA 71446-3446. (318) 239-7121. President: John E. Kilgore. Music publisher, record company and record producer. BMI. Publishes varying number of songs/year. Pays statutory rate.
How to Contact: Prefers cassette with 4-6 songs and lyric sheet. Reports within 6 months.
Music: Mostly gospel; also church/religious, R&B and soul.

GP MUSIC CORP., Namikibashi Property 407, 1-32-13 Higashi, Shibuya-ku, Tokyo 150, Japan. (03) 499-0270. President: Daniel Nenishkis. Music publisher. Publishes 10,000 songs/year; publishes 5 new songwriters/year. Pays standard royalty.
How to Contact: Prefers cassette with any number songs. Does not return unsolicited material. "Please include your full name and address." Reports in 4 weeks.
Music: Mostly rock, pop, and MOR; also jazz.

HE ROSE PUBLISHING, 1098 Rose, El Centro CA 92243. (619) 352-5774. A&R: Danny Berg. BMI. Music publisher and record company. Publishes 20 songs/year; publishes 10 new songwriters/year. Pays standard royalty.
How to Contact: Prefers cassette with 1-3 songs and lyric sheet. Does not return unsolicited material.
Music: Mostly gospel and contemporary Christian. Recently published "Raised up Again," (by Tom Renard), recorded by The New Jerusalem Band on He Rose Records (contemporary Christian); "Overcomer," (by Brad Messer), recorded by The New Jerusalem Band on He Rose Records (contemporary Christian); and "Reasons," (by Bucky Storm), recorded by Chronicles on He Rose Records (contemporary Christian).
Tips: Looking for music with a "good message and a good melody."

ISLAND MUSIC, 22 St. Peters Square, London W6, England. Senior Professional Executive: Richard Zuckerman. Record company and music publisher.
How to Contact: Prefers cassette with 3 songs and lyric sheet. SAE and IRC.
Music: Mostly pop and rock.

KASPERSIN MUSIC PUBLISHING CO., 2846 Dewey Ave., Rochester NY 14616. (716) 621-6270. President: David R. Kaspersin. BMI. Music publisher and record company (DRC Records). Publishes 10 songs/year; publishes 10 new songwriters/year. Pays standard royalty.
How to Contact: Write or call first and obtain permission to submit. Prefers cassette, 15 ips reel to reel or ¾" U-matic videocassette with 4 songs and lyric sheet. Looking for "clean simple demos with no fancy leads or intros. Get right to the hook of the song." SASE. Reports in 6 weeks.
Music: Mostly country/R&B, rock and gospel. Recently published "Production," written and recorded by Marty Owens on DRC Records (R&B); "You're My Friend Before My Lover," (by Frank Herkimer, Sam Scozzari and Bob Dandrea), recorded by Kelly Roberts on DRC Records (top 40); and "Rising Of The Moon," written and recorded by Prospect Highway on DRC Records (rock).

BUTCH KELLY PRODUCTIONS AND PUBLISHING, 11 Shady Oak Trail, Charlotte NC 28210. (704) 554-1611. Manager: Butch Kelly. Music publisher, record company, record producer, and song-

writer. ASCAP. Publishes 3 songs/year; publishes 2 new songwriters/year. Pays standard royalty.
How to Contact: Write first. Prefers cassette or videocassette with 2-3 songs and lyric sheet. "Include photo, if possible." SASE. Reports in 1 month.
Music: Mostly R&B; also dance oriented, easy listening, gospel, jazz, soul, and top 40/pop. Recently published "Super Star" (R&B single), "13 Years" (R&B single); and "Finger Licking Good," (all by Dennis Jones), recorded by The L.A. Stars on Executive Records and "Fantasy II" (by Butch Kelly), recorded by Melisa Kelly Montgomery on Executive Records (pop).

KENWOOD MUSIC PUBLISHING, 11F Shionogi Shibuya Bldg., 2-17-5 Shibuya, Shibuya-ku, Tokyo 150, Japan. (03) 486-5745. Copyright Manager: Yoichi Maeda. JASRAC. Music publisher. Publishes 20 songs/year. Pays standard royalty.
How to Contact: Submit demo tape. SAE and IRC.

MARK VIII MUSIC, 438 Vallejo, San Francisco CA 94133. (415) 433-2945. Publisher: Henry Ward. BMI. Music publisher, record company (Quantum Records), and record producer. Publishes 30 songs/year; publishes 15 new songwriters/year. Works under co-publishing arrangement.
How to Contact: Prefers cassette, reel to reel, or videocassette with 1-3 songs and lyric or lead sheet. SASE. Reports in 4 weeks.
Music: Rock, pop, blues, and country; also gospel, jazz and new wave. Recently published "Searching On," (by Saldate), recorded by Oliver Jicicco on Quantum Records (fusion); "Burning Giants," (by Kim Nomad), recorded by Tom Jones on Fire Brand Records (pop); and "Diamond John," written and recorded by Villion on Quantum Records (rock).
Tips: "Put everything together clean and clear."

MARMETTE RECORDS, Box 5, Amityville NY 11701. Owner: Richy "Rag" Gordon. ASCAP. Music publisher and record company. Publishes 2 songs/year. Pays standard royalty.
How to Contact: Write first and obtain permission to submit. Prefers cassette with lyric and lead sheets. Does not return unsolicited material. Include SASE for reply. Reports in 8 weeks.
Music: Looking for "upbeat and funny folk, rock, blues, and jazz."

BRIAN MILLAN MUSIC CORP., Suite 1212, 3475 Urbain St., Montreal, Quebec H2X 2N4, Canada. President: Brian Millan. Music publisher and record producer. ASCAP. Publishes 200 songs/year; publishes 15-20 new songwriters/year. Works with lyricists and composers and teams collaborators. Pays standard royalty.
How to Contact: Submit cassette only with 1-4 songs and lead sheet. SAE and IRC. Reports in 2 weeks.
Music: Country, MOR, top 40, rock, new wave, instrumental, soul, dixieland and children's. Recently published "If We Never Call It Love," by Ke Rieme/CBS Records (MOR); "Say Something Nice," by Chiarelli-Spilmon/Ariola Records (country); and "Forever More My Love," by Chiarelli-Spilmon/Rediffusion Records, England (MOR).
Tips: "Mail us your best songs. Only the material itself has any weight——not the artist's name."

OAKWOOD MUSIC, Reed Ave., Canterbury, Kent CT1 1ET, England. 44-01-0227-50033. Contact: Managing Director. Music publisher and record producer. MCPS, PRS. Publishes 30 songs/year. Works with composers. Pays standard royalty; royalties paid directly to US songwriters.
How to Contact: Prefers cassette with 1-4 songs and lyric sheet. SAE and IRC. Reports in 1 month.
Music: Mostly pop; also dance oriented.
Tips: "Songs need good hooks. I prefer working artists."

SAFFRED MUSIC LTD., Hurworth Cottage, Hurworth, Darlington, Durham DL2 2HD, England. (0325) 720792/721143. Managing Director: Elaine Saffer. Music publisher. Publishes 30 songs/year; publishes 2 new songwriters/year. Pays standard royalty.
How to Contact: Prefers cassette or reel to reel with 4 songs and lyric sheet. SAE and IRC. Reports in 4 weeks.
Music: Mostly pop, MOR and rock. Recently published "Noises in the Night," (by Elaine Saffer), recorded by Winston Groovy (pop/reggae); "You're A Mystery," (by Saffer/Wilson/Dyer), recorded by Love Train on Crashed Records (pop); and "A Little Kiss," (by Saffer/Porter), recorded by Julie (pop).
Tips: "Send clear demos only. Do not send music only or lyrics."

SIVATT MUSIC PUBLISHING CO., Box 7172, Greenville SC 29610. (803) 295-3177. President: Jesse B. Evatte. Music publisher and record company. BMI. Publishes 20 songs/year; publishes 5 new songwriters/year. Pays standard royalty.
How to Contract: Prefers cassette with 2-6 songs and lead sheet. SASE. Reports in 1 month.
Music: Mostly gospel; also bluegrass, church/religious, country, easy listening and folk. Recently

published "L-O-V-E" (by Johnnny Halloway), recorded by The Gospel Jubilee (gospel); and "His Bride" (by David Abbott), recorded by Abbott on Mark Five Records (gospel).

SPECTRUM ONE MUSIC, A division of Spectrum 1 Network Inc., Box 7464, Burbank CA 91510. (818) 897-2060. A&R Director/Publisher: Rachel Kae. BMI, ASCAP. Music publisher and record company (Reliance Records). Estab. 1984. Publishes 4-8 songs/year; publishes 2-5 new songwriters/year. Pays standard royalty. Affiliates include Shadow Three Music and Seven Palms Music.
How to Contact: "Submit demo tape by mail. Do not call." Prefers cassette. SASE. Reports in 8-12 weeks.
Music: Mostly funk/dance, soft new wave, and disco/R&B. Recently published "Out of Sight,"written and recorded by Kevin McGettigan on Reliance Records (pop); "Fantasy," (by Kevin McGettigan), recorded by Marisa on Reliance Records (disco); "Rainbows,"(by Marisa/Ken Rose), recorded by Marisa on Reliance Records (new wave).
Tips: "Submit material in our main areas of interest. We see far too much material cross our desks that has no relationship to what we do."

STIFF MUSIC LTD., 22 St. Peters Square, London W6 9NW, England. (01) 741-1511. Professional Manager: Roger Bannister. Music publisher. Publishes 50 songs/year. Pays standard or negotiable royalty.
How to Contact: Prefers cassette with 4 songs and lyric sheet. SAE and IRC. Reports in 3 weeks. Recently published "Boys From The County Hell," (by Shane Macgowan), recorded by The Pogues on Stiff Records (folk Irish "country-billy"); "Find The Love," (by Don Snow), recorded by The Catch on Stiff Records (pop); "Pair Of Brown Eyes," (by Shane Macgowan), recorded by The Catch on Stiff Records (Irish ballad).

SULTAN MUSIC PUBLISHING, Box 461892, Garland TX 75046. (214) 487-8120. Owner/President: Don Ferguson. BMI. Music publisher. Publishes 15 songs/year; publishes varying number of new songwriters/year. Pays standard royalty. Affiliates include HRS Publishing (ASCAP).
How to Contact: Prefers cassette or 7½ips reel to reel with 3 songs and lyric sheet. "Submit a well recorded demo." SASE. Reports in 3 weeks.
Music: Mostly country and MOR. Recently published "Songwritin' Dream," (by T.G. Huddleston), recorded by Jamie Massey on Puzzle Records (country); "Before My Time,"written and recorded by Nolan Wiley on Puzzle Records (country); and "The Devil's An Angel Too," (by Nolan Wiley), recorded by Patricia Carter on Puzzle Records (country).

UNREGULATED MUSIC, Box 81485, Fairbanks AK 99708. (907) 456-3419. President: Michael States. Music publisher, record company and record producer. BMI. Publishes 25 songs/year; publishes 8 new songwriters/year. Pays standard royalty.
How to Contact: Prefers cassette with 2-5 songs and lyric sheet. "Include a statement of your goals." SASE. Reports in 1 month.
Music: Gospel, black gospel, and new wave gospel. Recently published "Swimming The Straits Of Hormuz," recorded by Mike Wedgwood (new wave); "The Faith Of The Little Ones,"by John Lentine (gospel); "Slow Elvis," recorded by Randy Reaves (country rock); and "Balance Of Power," by Robyn Hood (new wave gospel).

VISION DISCS/HEAVEN MUSIC, Box 302, London NW8 2RW, England. (01) 435-0710. Director: Vic Coppersmith. PRS, MCPS. Music publisher, record company and record producer. Publishes 50 songs/year; publishes 2 new songwriters/year. Pays 60% royalty.
How to Contact: Prefers cassette with 1 or 2 songs. Does not return unsolicited material.
Music: Mostly rock, pop, and gospel; also classical.
Tips: "Concentrate on perfecting one song, even if it entails rewriting. Keep the rhythms exciting."

WESTBURY MUSIC LTD., 35 N. Audley St., London W1Y 1WG, England. (01) 409-0766. Managing Director: Caroline Robertson. PRS. Music publisher. Publishes 50-100 songs/year; publishes 5-10 new songwriters/year. Pays varying royalty. Affilitates include Riff-Raff Music and Bosco Music.
How to Contact: Prefers cassette and lyric sheet. Does not return unsolicited material. Reports in 2 weeks.
Music: Mostly soul, jazz and reggae. Recently published "One Love Jamdown," written and recorded by Jahnet Enwright on Island Records (reggae); "She'll Be Mine Tonight," (by Tony Graham), recorded by Tony's Crime of Passion (soul); and the entire catalog by Bootsy Collins (of Bootsy's Rubber Band/Island Records).
Tips: "Regardless of the style of song, it must have a good basic melody."

Record Companies

J. JACOBSEN WAREN KONTOR GMBH, Rahlau 4-6, 2000 Hamburg 70, West Germany. (040) 66-99-81. General Manager: Hans-Jürgen Jacobsen. Labels include Tobacco Road, Platinum and Horizont. Record company and record producer. Works with musicians/artists and songwriters on contract. Pays varying royalty to artists on contract.
How to Contact: Write first and obtain permission to submit or to arrange personal interview. Prefers cassette. SAE and IRC. Reports in 2 weeks.
Music: Mostly rock, jazz, and country; also blues and pop.

JALYN RECORDING CO., 369 Millwood Dr., Nashville TN 37217. (615) 242-2220. President: Jack Lynch. Record company, music publisher (Jaclyn Music) and distributor. Releases 6 singles/year and 6 albums/year. Works with artists on contract. Works with lyricists and composers and teams collaborators. Pays 5-10% royalty to artists on contract; statutory rate to publishers for each record sold.
How to Contact: Write or call first. Prefers cassette with 1-3 songs and lyric sheet. SASE. Reports in 1 week.
Music: Bluegrass, church/religious. country and gospel. Recently released "Gonna Be A Lady." by Cecilia Lee; "The Nashville Wildcat," and "Just One In A Crowd," by Pat Osborne; and "Road To Nowhere," by Trimble Wright (country singles).

OAT WILLIE PRODUCTIONS, 10-03 48th Ave., Long Island City NY 11101. (718) 786-5732. President: Debra Chiusano. Vice President: Jim Carney. Record company and record producer. Works with artists on contract; musicians on salary for in-house studio work. Pays 4½%-8% royalty to artists on contract; statutory rate to publishers for each record sold.
How to Contact: Prefers cassette with 1-3 songs and lyric sheet.
Music: Mostly top 40/pop; also country, dance oriented, easy listening, R&B and rock (all types).

POWDERWORKS RECORDS AND TAPES PTY. LTD., 28 Cross St., Brookvale 2100, Australia. (02) 938-2200. Managing Director: K. Harding. Record company.
How to Contact: Prefers cassette. Does not return unsolicited material.
Music: Mostly MOR, rock, and blues; also country, gospel and jazz.

RED BUS RECORDS (INT.) LTD.,Red Bus House, 48 Broadley Terrace, London NW1, England. (01) 258-0324. Director: Eliot Cohen. Record company and music publisher. Releases 12 singles/year and 3 LPs/year. Works with musicians/artists on contract. Pays 6-10% royalty to artists on contract.
How to Contact: Prefers cassette. SAE and IRC. Reports in 6 weeks.
Music: Mostlky R&B, pop and rock. Other artists include Room 101.

RELIANCE RECORDS, A division of Spectrum 1 Network Inc., Box 7464, Burbank CA 91510. (818) 897-2060. A&R Director: Rachel Kae. Labels include Reliance Records and Lynné Records. Record company and music publisher. Releases 1-5 singles/year and 2-6 albums/year. Works with musicans/artists and songwriters on contract. Pays negotiable royalty.
How to Contact: Prefers cassette. SASE. "Please, no phone inquiries on unsolicited material." Reports in 8-12 weeks.
Music: Mostly funk/dance. soft new wave, and disco/R&B. Recently released "Out of Sight," written and recorded by Kevin McGettigan on Reliance Records (pop); "Fantasy/Rainbows," (by Marisa and Ken Rose), recorded by Marisa on Reliance Records (dance/funk).

SUNSET RECORDS INC., 1577 Redwood Dr., Harvey LA 70058. (504) 367-8501. Labels include Sunburst Records. President: George Leger. Record company, record producer, and music publisher (Country Legs Music and Golden Sunburst Music). Member CMA. Releases 5 singles/year. Works with artists and songwriters on contract. Works with lyricists and teams collaborators. Pays 7% royalty to artists on contract.
How to Contact: Prefers clean, good quality cassette with 3-5 songs and lyric and lead sheets. "Artists——send tape showing vocal abilities." SASE. Reports in 1-2 months.
Music: Mostly country; also gospel, progressive country, R&B, and seasonal (Christmas, Mother's Day, etc.). Recently released "Broken Homes," by Sonny Tears (country single); and "I Don't Care," by Larry Maynard (country single).
Tips: "Write one good, smoothly flowing song rather than 10 songs that aren't."

Record Producers

JACK BIELAN PRODUCTIONS, Suite 102, 2031 Belgrave Ct., Simi Valley CA 93063. Contact: Jack Bielan. Record producer and music publisher (Steamroller Music). Works with lyricists. Produces 4 singles and 1-2 albums/year. Fee derived from sales royalty.
How to Contact: Prefers cassettte with maximum 2 songs and lyric sheet. Does not return unsolicited material. Reports in 1 month.
Music: Mostly top 40; also country, dance oriented and easy listening. Recently produced "Going In For The Kill,"by Steamroller/Motown Records (top 40 single); "40 Miles of Bad Road," by Con-ception/Tapestry Records (top 40 single); and "To All The Girls I've Loved Before," by Bobby Vinton/Tapestry Records (top 40/AC).

CUMMINGS PRODUCTIONS, Suite 303, 14045 S. Main, Houston TX 77035. (713) 870-8422, 641-0793. A&R Director: Robert Jackson. Record producer, music publisher (Sirloin Music Publishing), and record company (Happy Beat and MSB Records). Deals with artists and songwriters. Produces 20 singles and 6 albums/year. Works with 25 new songwriters/year. Works with lyricists and composers and teams collaborators. Fee derived from sales royalty or outright fee from songwriter/artist or record company.
How to Contact: Write first. Prefers cassette or videocassette with 3-6 songs and lyric sheet. "Don't send the master copy of your video. Indicate speed of video sent." SASE. Reports in 1 month.
Music: Mostly rock, soul and dance; also blues, country, gospel, jazz, R&B, and top 40/pop. Recently produced "Drag Lady," by Max (dance/top 40 single); "Gimme The Chance," by Chance/Happy Beat Records (pop single); "I Would Like To Know You," by Carl Stewart/Happy Beat Records (soul single); and "Expectation," by Martha Bryant (pop single). Other artists include Invasion and Friction.

D.S.M. PRODUCERS, Suite 1204, 161 W. 54th St., New York NY 10019. (212) 245-0006. Producer: Suzan Badek. Record producer and music publisher (D.S.M. Producers Enterprises Publishing Co.). Deals with artists and songwriters. Produces 6 singles and 3-4 albums/year. Fee derived from outright fee from songwriter/artist or record company. Requires 50% deposit for studio time 10 days prior to start of session, unless a major label contract.
How to Contact: Write first to arrange personal interview. Prefers cassette or videocassette and lyric/lead sheets. SASE. Reports in 4 weeks.

DOUG MOODY PRODUCTIONS, 6277 Selma Ave., Hollywood CA 90028. President: Doug Moody. Record producer, music publisher (Doug Moody Music/BMI) and music library. Deals with artists, songwriters and record producers. Produces 20 singles and 30 albums/year. Fee derived from sales royalty as negotiated by individual contract.
How to Contact: Prefers cassette with 1-2 songs and lyric sheet.
Music: Hard rock. Recently produced *Sound of Hollywood*, a compilation LP of 12 female groups; *What Happens Next?*, by Ill Repute (punk rock LP); and *Slam-O-Lation*, a compilation LP of 15 slam dance groups. Other artists include Dr. Know, Incognito, Bone Cabla, The Mentors and The Grim.
Tips: "Concentrate on the 'agitated' beat in pop music rather than the 'horsehoof' typebeat."

MICHAEL JAMES PRODUCTIONS, 22030 De La Osa St., Woodland Hills CA 91364. (805) 529-2189. Executive Producer: Michael James. Record producer. Deals with artists and songwriters. Produces 25-50 singles and 5-10 albums/year. Fee derived from sales royalty or outright fee from songwriter/artist (artist preference).
How to Contact: Prefers cassette or videocassette (any format) and lyric sheet. "Please send any other information possible including photo." Does not return unsolicited material. Reports in 4-6 weeks.
Music: Mostly pop/rock, pop/R&B, original top 40; also all other styles. Recently produced "Every Ba-T-Rock," by Who Me?/Sugar Bear Records (pop/funk single); "Look and Learn," by Vine Beau James/Revenge Records (pop/rock single); and "In The Mood," by Magic Knight (pop/R&B single). Other artists include Alien, Nathan Shaffer, Peter Cross, Teleport, A.K.A., Raw Dawg, Nightshift, Elijah, James Bentey, and The Swanson Brothers.
Tips: "Must submit excellent quality recording. We will review lesser quality recording but the better the recording the better your chances of getting a deal."

JEREMY McCLAIN/HAPPY DAYS MUSIC, Box 852, 469 Crescent Dr., Beverly Hills CA 90213. (818) 980-3812. President: Jeremy McClain. Record producer and music publisher (Happy Days Music). Deals with artists and songwriters. Produces 12-20 singles and 1-2 albums/year. Fee derived from sales royalty or outright fee from record company.
How to Contact: Write first to arrange personal interview or submit demo tape. Prefers cassette or VHS

videocassette and lyric/lead sheet. SASE. Reports in 4-6 weeks.
Music: Mostly rock, top 40, and country; also contemporary gospel. Recently produced "Devil With The Blue Dress,"by Pratt & McClain/Warner Brothers Records (rock single); and "The Way Things Used To Be," by Tom Gillan/Brother Love Records (country single). "In addition, we have direct publishing access to Christopher Cross, Donna Summer and Debbie Boone."

MOM AND POP PRODUCTIONS, INC., Box 96, El Cerrito CA 94530. Executive Vice President: James Bronson, Jr. Record producer, record company and music publisher (Toulouse Music/BMI). Deals with artists, songwriters and music publishers. Fee derived from sales royalty.
How to Contact: Prefers cassette with 2-4 songs and lyric sheet. SASE. Reports in 1 month.
Music: Bluegrass, gospel, jazz, R&B and soul. Artists include Les Oublies du Jazz Ensemble.

*MONOTONE RECORDS, 281 E. Kingsbridge Rd., Bronx NY 10458. (212)582-3240. President: Murray Fuller. Record producer and music publisher (Sun Island Music Publishing Co.). Deals with artists and songwriters. Produces 1 single/year. Fee derived from sales royalty.
How to Contact: Prefers cassette with 3-5 songs and lyric sheet. SASE. Reports in 6 weeks.
Music: Blues, dance-oriented, easy listening, jazz, R&B, soul and top 40/pop.

MONTICANA PRODUCTIONS, Box 702, Snowdon Station, Montreal, Quebec H3X 3X8 Canada. Executive Producer: David Leonard. Record producer. Deals with artists, songwriters and artists' managers. Fee derived from sales royalty.
How to Contact: Prefers 7½ or 15 ips reel-to-reel, cassette, phonograph record or VHS videocassette with maximum 10 songs and lyric sheet. "Demos should be as tightly produced as a master." Does not return unsolicited material.
Music: Mostly top 40; also bluegrass, blues, country, dance-oriented, easy listening, folk, gospel, jazz, MOR, progressive, R&B, rock and soul.

MOPRO, INC., 5950 Beech Dell Dr., Cincinnati OH 45238. (513)281-4954. President: Helen Y. Morr. Record producer and record company. Deals with artists, songwriters and arrangers. Produces 3 albums/year. Pays statutory rate to publishers for each record sold.
How to Contact: Write first and obtain permission to submit. Prefers cassette with 2-3 songs. Does not return unsolicited material. Reports in 2 weeks.
Music: "Jazz only." Recently produced *Butterfly*, *Live at Carmelo's* and *The Smooth One*, by Blue Wisp Big Band (jazz LPs, Mopro Records); and *From the Neck Down*, by Tim Hagans (jazz LP, Mopro Records). Other artists include Ron Boustead, Cal Collins and Marshall Vente/Project Nine.

*MOTORCOACH PUBLISHING, Apt. 3, 2401 Golf Rd., Eau Claire WI 54701. (715)832-4812. President: Daniel Korn. Record producer and music publisher. Deals with artists and songwriters. Produces 2 singles/year. Fee derived from outright fee from record company.
How to Contact: Write or call first and obtain permission to submit or to arrange personal interview. Prefers cassette and lyric sheet or lead sheet. "Submit no demos until given permission to do so." SASE. Does not return unsolicited material. Reports in 1 week.
Music: Mostly blues, jazz and rock; also country, classical gospel and short stories. Recently produced "Skin and Bones," by Dan Korn (rock single on Sojourn); and "This Empty Space," and "A Christmas Song," by D. Korn (classical singles on Sojourn).
Tips: "Have instruments intonated, have material well prepared and have idea of how you would like to arrange things."

*MTI RECORDS, 25533 Five Mile, Redford MI 48239. (313)531-5354. President: Nick Canzano. Record producer and music publisher (No-Town Productions). Deals with artists and songwriters. Produces 25 singles/year and 10 albums/year. Fee is negotiable.
How to Contact: Write or call first and obtain permission to submit. Prefers 7½ or 15 ips reel-to-reel with 4-5 songs and lyric sheet and lead sheet. Does not return unsolicited material. Reports in 4 weeks.
Music: Mostly pop, rock and country; also gospel. Recently produced *Times Runnin Out*, by Nucleus (rock LP, MTI); and "Ain't No Stoppin Us Now," by Gino Danelli & The Detroit Tigers (dance single, MTI).

*SANTO MOLLICA, 331 E. 9th St., New York NY 10003. (212)473-7833. Producer: Santo Mollica. Record producer. Deals with artists and songwriters. Produces 2 singles/year and 2 albums/year. Fee derived from outright fee from songwriter/artist or record company; "depends on situation."
How to Contact: Write first and obtain permission to submit. Prefers cassette, 15 ips reel-to-reel or VHS videocassette with 3-5 songs and lyric sheet.

JOHN YOUNG/MODE MUSIC PRODUCTIONS, 130 S. Bonsall St., Philadelphia PA 19103. (215) 557-0388. Record producer, music publisher (W.W.T. Music), and Fairlight CMI programmer. Works with artists and songwriters. Fee derived form sales royalty or outright fee from songwriter/artists or record company.
How to Contact: Prefers cassette and lyric sheet. "Send only your strongest material." SASE. "No phone calls please."
Music: Heavy dance oriented, "supersonic" hip-hop, heavy metal and reggae. "We're looking for anything that has a fresh edge and will scorch the dance floor.
Tips: "Be outrageous and work to achieve some notoriety. Take a few chances. The world can live without mediocrity."

Managers & Booking Agents

HORRICK TALENT AGENCY, RR #15, Onion Lake Rd., Thunder Bay, Ontario P7B 5N1, Canada. (807)345-0101. Owner: Tom Horrick. Management agency, booking agency, record company (Covered Wagon Records), and music publisher (Earthshine Music and Bird Dance Music). Represents groups and songwriters. Deals with artists from anywhere. Currently handles 12 acts. Reviews material for acts.
How to Contact: Prefers cassette and lyric sheet. Does not return unsolicited material. Reports "if interested."
Music: Mostly top 40 and commercial country. Works primarily with vocalists, dance and bar bands. Current acts include Overnight Angels, Boardwalk, and Cimmarron.

T.S.J. PRODUCTIONS INC., 6640 14th Ave. S., Richfield MN 55423. (612) 869-1779. Vice President & Artist Manager: Katherine J. Lange. Management firm and booking agency. Represents artists, groups and songwriters; currently handles 1 act. Receives 10-15% commission. Reviews material for acts.
How to Contact: Write first or submit demo tape. Prefers "any reel to reel or cassette——inquire before sending video——with minimum 2 songs and lyric sheet." SASE. Reports in 2 weeks.
Music: Mostly country rock, symphonic rock, easy listening and MOR; also blues, country, folk, jazz, progressive, R&B and top 40/pop. Works primarily with vocalists. Current acts include Thomas St. James.

Play Producers & Publishers

NEW TUNERS THEATRE, 1225 W. Belmont, Chicago IL 60657. (312) 929-7367. Associate Producer: George H. Gorham. Play producer. Estab. 1984. Produces 3 musicals/year. "The theatre building where we work houses three 148-seat theatres." Pays 6-8% royalty. Query with synopsis, character breakdown and set description, or submit complete manuscript, score and tape of songs. "Either submission method is fine. Score is less necessary than tape." SASE. Reports in 6 months.
Musicals: "We're interested in traditional forms of musical theatre as well as the more innovative styles. We have less interest in operetta and operatic works, but are willing to consider anything. We are far more interested in shows in which the songs move the plot along rather than comment thereon, i.e. musicals more than plays with music. We are also interested in seeing individual songs, primarily comedic, for possible inclusion in a 'new faces' type revue. We can't really consider any show with a cast exceeeding 15. Less is better. Also, we're interested in using younger (35 and under) actors. We have very little wing space and no fly space, so scene shifts should be minimal. Still, we're very imaginative and authors should submit their work. We'll see what we can do."
Recent Productions: *Two*, by Fredricka Weber (growing up); *Babes in Barns*, by John R. Carroll, Charlotte Samples and John Sparks ("Micky and Judy" spoof); and *Toddlin' Town* arranged by Roy Lauderdale and George H. Gorham (revue of Chicago songwriters).
Tips: "I'm surprised by the work I receive as much of it seems to have been written by writers who have never seen a musical play. Go to the theatre!"

Index

A

Use an up-to-date Market Directory!

Make sure you have a current edition of Songwriter's Market

Songwriter's Market has been the songwriter's bible for years. Each edition contains hundreds of changes to give you the most current information to work with. Make sure your copy is the latest edition.

This card will get you the 1987 edition... at 1986 prices! ⬇

Order your 1987 Songwriter's Market NOW!

Z

Other Writer's Digest Books

Music
> **The Craft of Lyric Writing**, by Sheila Davis $16.95
> **Making Money Making Music**, by James Dearing (paper) $12.95
> **The Performing Artist's Handbook**, by Janice Papolos $15.95

Art/Photography
> **Artist's Market**, $16.95
> **Developing the Creative Edge in Photography**, by Bert Eifer (paper) $16.95
> **How to Create and Sell Photo Products**, by Mike and Carol Werner (paper) $14.95
> **How You Can Make $25,000 a Year With Your Camera**, by Larry Cribb (paper) $9.95
> **Photographer's Market**, $16.95
> **Sell & Re-Sell Your Photos**, by Rohn Engh $14.95
> **Starting—And Succeeding In—Your Own Photography Business**, by Jeanne Thwaites $18.95
> **Wildlife & Nature Photographer's Field Guide**, by Michael Freeman $14.95

General Writing
> **The Complete Guide to Writing Nonfiction**, edited by Glen Evans $24.95
> **Getting the Words Right: How to Revise, Edit, and Rewrite**, by Theodore Cheney $13.95
> **How to Get Started in Writing**, by Peggy Teeters $10.95
> **How to Write While You Sleep**, by Elizabeth Irvin Ross $12.95
> **Writer's Encyclopedia**, edited by Kirk Polking $19.95
> **Writer's Market**, $19.95
> **Writer's Resource Guide**, $16.95

Fiction Writing
> **Fiction Is Folks: How to Create Unforgettable Characters**, by Robert Newton Peck $11.95
> **Fiction Writer's Market**, $17.95
> **How to Write a Play**, by Raymond Hull $13.95
> **Storycrafting**, by Paul Darcy Boles $14.95
> **Writing the Novel: From Plot to Print**, by Lawrence Block (paper) $8.95
> **Writing Romance Fiction**, by Helene S. Barnhart $14.95

Special Interest Writing
> **Children's Picture Book: How to Write It, How to Sell It**, by Ellen E.M. Roberts $17.95
> **Complete Book of Scriptwriting**, by J. Michael Straczynski $14.95
> **The Craft of Comedy Writing**, by Sol Saks $14.95
> **How to Make Money Writing Fillers**, by Connie Emerson (paper) $8.95
> **How to Write and Sell Your Personal Experiences**, by Lois Duncan $10.95
> **How to Write and Sell (Your Sense of) Humor**, by Gene Perret $12.95
> **On Being a Poet**, by Judson Jerome $14.95
> **The Poet's Handbook**, by Judson Jerome $11.95
> **Poet's Market**, edited by Judson Jerome $16.95
> **Programmer's Market**, edited by Brad M. McGehee (paper) $16.95
> **Writing for the Soaps**, by Jean Rouverol $14.95

The Writing Business
> **Complete Handbook for Freelance Writers**, by Kay Cassill $14.95
> **How to Be a Successful Housewife/Writer**, by Elaince Fantle Shimberg $10.95
> **How to Understand & Negotiate a Book Contract**, by Richard Balkin $11.95
> **How to Write a Book Proposal**, by Michael Larsen $9.95
> **How to Get Your Book Published: An Insider's Guide**, by Herbert Bell $15.95
> **How You Can Make $20,000 a Year Writing**, by Nancy Hanson (paper) $6.95
> **The 29 Most Common Writing Mistakes & How to Avoid Them**, by Judy Delton $9.95

To order directly from the publisher, include $2.00 postage and handling for 1 book and 50¢ for each additional book. Allow 30 days for delivery.

Writer's Digest Books, Department B
9933 Alliance Road, Cincinnati OH 45242

Prices subject to change without notice.

Notes

Notes

Notes

Notes

Notes

Notes

Notes

Notes